# *Directory of*
# Musicians in Ireland



Featuring 1,600 classical, traditional and jazz musicians and performing groups, in and from Ireland, North and South

**Music Network**

The Coach House, Dublin Castle, Dublin 2

Tel: +353 1 6719429, Fax: +353 1 6719430

email: musicnet@indigo.ie

Directory of Musicians in Ireland

FIRST PUBLISHED IN 1998 BY:
Music Network
The Coach House
Dublin Castle
Dublin 2
Republic of Ireland
Tel: +353 1 6719429
Fax: +353 1 6719430
Email: musicnet@indigo.ie



GRANT AIDED BY:
The Arts Council

SPONSORED BY:
ESB

ISBN: 0-9528783-2-1

DESIGN AND LAYOUT:
Brosna Press Ltd., Church Street, Ferbane, County Offaly.

PRINTED AND BOUND IN THE REPUBLIC OF IRELAND BY:
Colourbooks Ltd., Baldoyle Industrial Estate, Dublin 13.

# Contents

Reference Map of Ireland

# What is Music Network?

Music Network is the national music development organisation, established in 1986 by the Arts Council to develop music nationwide. The organisation aims to make music accessible to everybody, no matter who they are or where they live.

Among the key activities of the organisation are an extensive classical, jazz and traditional music touring scheme and a cross border 'Musicwide' scheme which supports Irish musicians. Concerts from these live music programmes are currently offered to eighty local concert promoters working in their communities throughout the island. A Promoter Forum held by the organisation also provides support for these promoters.

Music Network also provides a national music information service covering all aspects of non-commercial music in Ireland. It has published two information publications - the Irish Music Handbook and this Directory of Musicians in Ireland.

The organisation has innovative pilot projects in a number of counties where it supports a wide range of arts and community based organisations, developing all aspects of music to locally sets agendas.

Music Network is also active in the area of advocacy, and publishes the Boydell Papers - a series of essays on music and music policy in Ireland.

Music Network is core funded by the Arts Council and receives significant sponsorship from ESB.

**Editor**
Michelle Hoctor

**Associate Editor**
Ann Swift

**Assistant Editor**
Gillian Keogan

**Many thanks to Michelle Barnes, Amanda Dunne, David Darcy, Deirdre McCrea, Shona McKenna and in particular, Mahon Carmody, for all their work in relation to administrative aspects of the project.**

# Acknowledgements

**Many people assisted us at various stages of this initiative.**

We are particularly grateful to:

Pat Moore and Dermot McLaughlin of the Arts Council, Pamela Smith, Arts Council of Northern Ireland, David Byers, BBC Northern Ireland, Harry White, Professor of Music at University College, Dublin, Michael Dervan, Fintan Vallely and Ray Comiskey of the Irish Times, Allen Smith and Gerry Godley of the Improvised Music Company, Nicholas Carolan and Harry Bradshaw at the Irish Traditional Music Archive/Taisce Cheol Dúchais Éireann, Eve O'Kelly at the Contemporary Music Centre, Séamus Crimmins and Brian Day in RTÉ, Margaret McConnell from the Irish Chamber Orchestra, John Buckley, Una Johnston, Dearbhla Collins, Benjamin Dwyer and Dave Fleming.

We are also very grateful to the individuals and organisations who assisted in the research process:

A little Night Music Agency, Allegro Music Agency, British Trombone Society, Cairde na Cruite, Castleward Opera, Classical Guitar Society of Northern Ireland, Corn Séan Ó Riada, Cumann Náisiúnta na gCór, Dublin Corporation Music Bursary, Dublin International Organ Competition, EPTA Ireland, ESTA Ireland, Feis Ceoil, Flutewise, Guardian Dublin International Piano Competition, Heinekin Violin Competition, IMRO, International Concert Management, Irish Association of Brass and Concert Bands, Irish Pipe Band Association, John McCormack Golden Voice of Ireland Competition, Lisney Young Pianist Competition, Live Music Now, Music Department, National University of Ireland, Maynooth, Na Piopari Uilleann, North of Ireland Bands Association, O'Carolan Harp Festival, Opera Theatre Company, RTÉ Young Musician of the Future Competition, Sligo International Choral Festival, Ulster Bank Music Foundation, Ulster Orchestra, Veronica Dunne Singing Bursary, West Belfast Classical Bursary, Yamaha Music Foundation, Dr Ita Beausang, Dr Hilary Bracefield, Máire Breatnach, John Brophy, Peter Browne, Brian Carson, Ciaran Carson, Dr David Cox, Barbara Dagg, Liz Doherty, Keith Donald, Maura Eaton, Ian Fox, Amy Garvey, Dr Bernadette Greevy, Ronan Guilfoyle, Lisa Irvine, John Kelly, Mari Kennedy, Anthony Madigan, Sheila Murphy, Ronan Nolan, Dr John O'Conor, Prof Michéal O'Suilleabháin, Simon Taylor, Sam Ellis, Paddy McElwee, Dr Simon Tresize and Ian Woodfield.

# Forewords

I am delighted to commend to you this Directory of Musicians in Ireland. The Directory follows on Music Network's other major publication the Irish Music Handbook which was published in 1996 and which has quickly established itself as a valuable source of information for specialists and the general music public alike.

Music Network seeks to bring music and its audience together. Even a cursory glance through this guide reminds us yet again of the wealth of talent that we have available to us in this country. This Directory will facilitate easier contact between promoters (at home and abroad) and musicians, and will help maximise the opportunities for musicians to perform. It will help to wed our existing degree of musical accomplishment with the ever increasing desire of audiences to experience that wealth at first hand.

Music knows no barriers, and Music Network has worked closely with both Arts Councils to present a comprehensive guide to musicians, North and South. I know that Music Network are committed to ensuring that everyone living on this island will have proper access to music performance and this Directory will, I believe, be an important aid to the achievement of that objective.

I very much welcome the publication of this Directory and I commend it and the work of Music Network to you all.

**Síle de Valera,** *TD,*
*Minister for Arts, Heritage, Gaeltacht and the Islands.*

I am pleased that Music Network has worked closely with the Arts Council of Northern Ireland in the preparation of this Directory in terms of background advice. Both organisations have for many years brought numerous benefits to the musical communities of both parts of this island through a joint approach and co-operative association.

I hope the Directory of Musicians will prove useful to all musicians in Ireland and form the basis of bringing their talents to the attention and appreciation of a wider audience.

**Tony Worthington** *MP,*
*Minister for the Arts in Northern Ireland.*

# Sponsor's Message

An overview of ESB's sponsorship portfolio shows a common thread. All of the initiatives seek to:

- Build audiences
- Increase participation
- Encourage young people to reach their full potential

In approaching our sponsorship activity in this way we are supporting the recommendations of various Arts Council plans as well as those of both the Piano and Forte Reports. Music Network's structure and programmes are recognised as addressing many of the areas of need outlined in these reports.

In each case our involvement encourages community based activity which aims to remove barriers to access, participation and development. It is in ESB's interest, as well as that of the communities we serve, that they are vibrant and dynamic entities, both economically and culturally.

The Directory of Musicians in Ireland is one more building block in the development of music in Ireland - music in the broadest sense. In common with our other initiatives and activities carried out by Music Network, the document has been thoroughly researched, is laid out and designed on the basis of discussions with you, the user. It is meant to be a working reference which will provide a much needed profile for many musicians seeking to achieve their full potential.

**Ken O'Hara,**
*Chief Executive, ESB.*

# Introduction

In a country which has an extraordinary wealth of performing talent and a proud musical tradition, Music Network is very pleased to bring you this one-stop information guide to classical, traditional and jazz musicians in and from the island of Ireland, North and South. This book we hope will complement our first information directory, the Irish Music Handbook, which was published in 1996.

In monitoring the calls which have come through to the Music Network information service in the last number of years, it has become very clear to us that there is a need in this country for a detailed directory giving useful information about musicians. After fifteen months of intensive research, we are pleased to publish this Directory.

The Music Network information service plays an important part in the overall work of Music Network developing music in Ireland. Information provision is an essential tool for the development of music, and by putting together this Directory of Musicians, we hope that we will help to bridge the gap between the enormous wealth of Irish musical talent, and their prospective employers at home and abroad. We are also certain that the Directory will have a broader appeal, and that other musicians, individuals and organisations working at national and local level, and people with a general interest in music will also find it useful.

An extensive consultation process with musicians and organisations was carried out in 1996 prior to the start of the project. Music Network has taken on board many of the differing views expressed by these individuals in an attempt to make the Directory as balanced and useful a document as possible. Like all directories, it cannot perfectly fulfil the needs of everyone but we feel it is a good compromise.

We had many more addresses than questionnaires returned and we apologise for any inevitable omissions. This project however is very much a rolling initiative and we will continue to update existing material and gather new information about artists etc. Care has been taken with every questionnaire and basic parameters based on objective criteria were set to allow for inclusion within the Directory. Many musicians/ ensembles included additional support material such as cv's, repertoire lists etc. with their questionnaire. This extra information is held on file and we will be happy to supply this material on request. We will also offer, as we have done with the Irish Music Handbook, a telephone support service to help with any queries.

Music Network would like to thank once again, those who advised us during our consultation period and those who patiently took our telephone calls during the lengthy research process. We would also like to acknowledge the funding we receive from the Arts Council and the sponsorship from ESB without which, this Directory could not have been published.

I hope you will find this Directory useful and informative.

**Michelle Hoctor,** *Editor*

# Notes for using this Directory

- As many musicians/ensembles play more than one instrument and/or fall into more than one musical genre, there is one main entry for each musician with the duplication of their contact details across other sections. These cross references are marked by the symbol and a page number will direct you to their detailed entry.

- We have ensemble/group categories in the Directory across the different musical genres. Many of the ensemble/group members also submitted individual entries. You will be directed to their entries at the end of their ensemble/group entry.

- Many entries have listed other musicians and groups with whom they regularly perform or conduct. In many cases these other musicians are in the Directory. Refer to the index.

- In detailing telephone and fax numbers in the Directory we have used the standard international access codes to precede the numbers. However, in the case of callers from the Republic of Ireland to Northern Ireland, there is a different code to follow. The international access code for the UK: '+44' should be replaced by '080', followed by the local code. For example, a number in Northern Ireland marked in the Directory as +44 1234 5678910 should be dialled from the Republic of Ireland as 080 1234 5678910. The initial 'a' beside some telephone numbers relate to a contact for an agent.

- You will note in a number of entries that a review list appears under "Selected Reviews since January 1994". Many of these reviews were included by the musicians/ ensembles along with other support materials. These are held on file by Music Network.

- The details provided in the additional information section of the entries have been provided by the musicians themselves.

- Please note that many players of orchestral instruments other than those listed in Section One, are in the Performing Groups section under their respective orchestras i.e. the National Symphony Orchestra of Ireland, the RTÉ Concert Orchestra, the Irish Chamber Orchestra and the Ulster Orchestra.

- The words RTÉ (Radio Telifís Éireann) and CCÉ (Comhaltas Ceoltoirí Éireann) are abbreviated in the text. Many music colleges, orchestras and venues are also abbreviated. For example, when a college is mentioned for the first time in each entry, it will be given its full name. However for any subsequent mentions within that entry, it will be abbreviated, therefore the DIT Conservatory of Music and Drama would become the DIT CMD. If you are unclear about these abbreviations they are listed in both formats in the index.

# Section one

## Classical Instrumentalists



**For names of other players of woodwind, brass, percussion and string instruments, please check the orchestra members lists in the Performing Groups section - National Symphony Orchestra of Ireland, the RTÉ Concert Orchestra, the Irish Chamber Orchestra and the Ulster Orchestra. (This section begins on page 140).**

# CLASSICAL ACCORDION

## Joseph Corbett *Accordion*

**Contact:** Mr Joseph Corbett
50, Goldhurst Terrace
London NW6 3HT
England
**Tel:** +44 171 6246280
*See baritone page 112.*

## Dermot Dunne *Accordion*

**Contact:** Mr Dermot Dunne
57, Ludford Drive
Ballinteer
Dublin 16
**Tel:** +353 1 2985394

*"He confirmed his status as one of our most exciting young musicians in a long time"*

18.8.96 The Sunday Tribune (Ian Fox)

**KEY IRISH PERFORMANCES** (since January 1994):
1996 Galway, promoted by the Galway Arts Festival.
1996 Kilkenny, promoted by Kilkenny Arts Festival.
1996 John Field Room, National Concert Hall, Dublin, appearing with the Glinka Quartet.
1996 Royal Dublin Society, Dublin, promoted by RTÉ/Bank of Ireland Young Proms.
**KEY PERFORMANCES OUTSIDE IRELAND** (since January 1994):
4.96 Irish College, Paris, promoted by Festival L'Imaginaire Irlandais.
7.95 Abruzzo, Italy, promoted by Concorso Internationale di Moro D'Oro
**SELECTED BROADCASTS AND/OR RECORDED WORK:**
1996 'Live at Three' for RTÉ.
1996 'L' Imaginaire Irlandais' for RTÉ.
1996 'Sounds Classical' for RTÉ.
**SELECTED REVIEWS** (since January 1994):
2.4.96 Irish Times.
20.7.96 Irish Independent.
**PRIZES/AWARDS/APPOINTMENTS:**
6.95 West Belfast Classical Bursary from RTÉ.
30.1.96 Winner of the RTÉ Young Musician of the Future.
**TRAINING AND/OR QUALIFICATIONS:**
1994 Moscow, studied with Prof Vyatcheslav Semyonov.
Summer 1995 Belgrade, (teacher Prof Ljiljana Ivanovic).
4.96 Tchaikovsky Conservatory, Kiev (teacher Prof V. Besfamilnoff).
8.96 Waterford Institute of Technology (teacher Elisabeth Moser).
**AVAILABILITY:**
January, June, July, August.

# BASSOON

Also see orchestra members lists on page 140.

## Adrian Hughes *Bassoon*

**Contact:** Mr Adrian Hughes
33, Cúl na Gréine
Old Bawn
Tallaght, Dublin 24
**Tel:** +353 1 4510101
**Other instruments:** Contrabassoon, recorders (SATB), piano

**KEY IRISH PERFORMANCES** (since January 1994):
11.2.97 O'Reilly Hall, University College, Dublin, promoted by RTÉ, appearing with the RTÉ Concert Orchestra.
13.2.97 Town Hall, Cork, promoted by RTÉ, appearing with the RTÉCO
**KEY PERFORMANCES OUTSIDE IRELAND** (since January 1994):
From 22.6.96 to 4.7.96, Aix en Provence Festival, appearing with the Royal Northern College of Music Chamber Orchestra.
7.96 Chester, promoted by Manchester Camerata, appearing with John Wilson.
30.10.96 Royal Northern College of Music, appearing with the RNCM Symphony Orchestra.
27.1.97 RNCM, Manchester, appearing with John Wilson.
**SELECTED BROADCASTS AND/OR RECORDED WORK:**
4.96 'Metropolis' for Doyen.
10.96 'Early English Wind Music' for Naxos.
14-15.12.96 'Granger Wind Orchestra Music' for Chandos.
**PRIZES/AWARDS/APPOINTMENTS:**
3.96 Winner of the McCullough Cup for Woodwind Concerto at the Feis Ceoil, Dublin
**TRAINING AND/OR QUALIFICATIONS:**
Since 9.95, Studying for B Mus (Hons) at the Royal Northern College of Music (teacher Edward Warren).
**REGULARLY PERFORMS WITH:**
Bohemian Wind Octet.
**AVAILABILITY:**
Mid-December to mid-January, July, August.
**ADDITIONAL INFORMATION:**
Specialises in playing the contrabassoon in the RNCM Symphony Orchestra, Wind Orchestra and Wind Ensemble. Has appeared solo with the RTÉ Concert Orchestra and has recorded for radio. Winner of numerous piano competitions.

## Michael Jones *Bassoon*

**Contact:** Mr Michael Jones
11, The Rise, Woodpark
Ballinteer, Dublin 16
**Tel:** +353 1 2988826

**PRIZES/AWARDS/APPOINTMENTS:**
Since 1980, appointed Principal Bassoon of the National Symphony Orchestra of Ireland.
**TRAINING AND/OR QUALIFICATIONS:**
From 1976 to 1979, LRAM, ARCM and ABRSM scholarship from the Royal College of Music, London.
From 1979 to 1980, Dip NCOS from the National Centre for Orchestral Studies, London.
**AVAILABILITY:**
Subject to the NSOI schedule.
**ADDITIONAL INFORMATION:**
Also performs occasionally as a soloist and in chamber groups. Has worked with the BBC Symphony Orchestra Hallé Orchestra, Bournemouth Symphony and Northern Sinfonia.

## Rachel Nolan *Bassoon*

**Contact:** Rachel Nolan
29, Royal Canal Bank
Dublin 7
**Tel/Fax:** +353 1 8308603

**SELECTED BROADCASTS AND/OR RECORDED WORK:**
1993 'Earth to Earth'.
**PRIZES/AWARDS/APPOINTMENTS:**
1997 Aappointed bassoon tutor, at the Royal Irish Academy of Music, Dublin.
**TRAINING AND/OR QUALIFICATIONS:**
From 1987 to 1991, B Mus Ed from Trinity College, Dublin and DIT Conservatory of Music and Drama.
**REGULARLY APPEARS WITH:**
Oboe, piano, clarinet and flute players.
**AVAILABILITY:**
General.

# Ciara Sheehan *Bassoon*

**Contact:** Ms Ciara Sheehan
38, Newlyn Vale
Rochestown Road, Cork
**Tel:** +353 21 894673
*See piano page 50.*

# Peter Whelan *Bassoon*

**Contact:** Mr Peter Whelan
207, The Grove
Celbridge, Co Kildare
**Tel:** +353 1 6271407
**Email:** whelanpp@tcd.ie
**Other instruments:** Contra-bassoon, piano.

**KEY IRISH PERFORMANCES** (since January 1994):
1.97 National Concert Hall, Dublin, appearing with the National Youth Orchestra.
1.97 John Field Room, NCH, 'High Scorers Concert' held in Association with the ABRSM, appearing with Michael Ball.
5.97 Queen's University, Belfast, appearing with the Esposito Wind Quintet.
6.97 NCH, Dublin appearing with the National Children's Choir and Gillian Smith.
**KEY PERFORMANCES OUTSIDE IRELAND** (since January 1994):
8.96 Nice, France, promoted by Nice Conservatoire, appearing with Dublin Youth Orchestra Wind Quintet.
3.97 Caen Conservatoire, France, promoted by DYO appearing with DYO Symphony Orchestra.
3.97 Orlean, France, promoted by DYO appearing with DYOSO.
4.97 Paris Conservatoire, promoted by Musicova - Paris Conservatoire, appearing with Esposito Wind Quintet.
**PRIZES/AWARDS/APPOINTMENTS:**
4.97 1st Prizewinner, Senior Bassoon and Senior Chamber Music Ensemble, awarded by the Feis Ceoil, Dublin.
4.97 3rd Prizewinner, Musicova Chamber Music Competition, awarded by Paris Conservatoire, France.
**TRAINING AND/OR QUALIFICATIONS:**
From 1989 to 1997, Royal Irish Academy of Music (teacher Gillian Smith).
From 1993 to 1997 (teacher Michael Jones).
Since 1996, Trinity College, Dublin
**REGULARLY PERFORMS WITH:**
Riona Ó'Duinnin, Suzanne Brennan, Ann Frain (Exposito Wind Quintet).
**AVAILABILILTY:**
General.
**ADDITIONAL INFORMATION:**
Also a piano accompanist.

## CLARINET

Also see orchestra members lists on page 140.

# Emma Canavan *Clarinet*

**Contact:** Ms Emma Canavan
2, Farley Drive
Seven Kings
London IG3 8LT
England
**Tel:** +44 181 5971659

# Ted Courtney *Clarinet*

**Contact:** Mr Ted Courtney
Kingsford
Newtownsmith
Sandycove
Co Dublin
**Tel/Fax:** +353 1 2804519 / +353 1 2082072
**Other instruments:** Tenor voice, piano.

**SELECTED BROADCASTS AND/OR RECORDED WORK:**
1.94 'Crotchety Christmas' for RTÉ.
9.95 '12 to 1' for RTÉ.
4.96 'Condensed Classics' for RTÉ.
**PRIZES/AWARDS/APPOINTMENTS:**
1994 and 1995, winner of Corn Hardebec at the Feis Ceoil, Dublin.
**TRAINING AND/OR QUALIFICATIONS:**
From 1968 to 1971, BA, B Mus H Dip from London City University.
From 1973 to 1976, ARIAM from the Royal Irish Academy of Music.
From 1983 to 1985, MA from Cleremont, California.
From 1983 to 1985, LTCL from Trinity College, London.
**AVAILABILITY:**
Weekdays except Tuesday and Thursday.

# Celia Donoghue *Clarinet*

**Contact:** Ms Celia Donoghue
4, Pinevalley Drive
Rathfarnham
Dublin 16
**Tel:** +353 1 4947982

# Ronan Dunne *Clarinet*

**Contact:** Mr Ronan Dunne
28, Maywood Park
Raheny
Dublin 5
**Tel:** +353 1 8313973

*See double bass page 9.*

# John Finucane *Clarinet*

**Contact:** Mr John Finucane
23, Belgrave Square
Monkstown
Co Dublin
**Tel/Mobile:** +353 1 2809393 / +353 87 447203

*"The loveliest clarinet player I have ever heard"* Irish Times

**KEY IRISH PERFORMANCES OUTSIDE IRELAND** (since January 1994):
11.95 Wexford Festival with the National Symphony Orchestra of Ireland.
5.96 Royal Hospital, Kilmainham, Dublin.
**AVAILABILITY:**
Subject to NSOI schedule

*See conductors page 170.*

# Cathy Gallagher *Clarinet*

**Contact:** Ms Cathy Gallagher
43, Moyville Estate
Ballyboden Road
Rathfarnham
Dublin 16
**Tel:** +353 1 4944002
**Other instruments:** Eb clarinet, piccolo

**KEY IRISH PERFORMANCES** (since January 1994):
11.96 DIT Conservatory of Music and Drama, Dublin, solo recital, accompanied by Peter Dains.
1.97 Oak Room, Mansion House, Dublin, solo recital, accompanied by Peter Dains.
2.97 Loreto Abbey, Balbriggan, clarinet concerto, appearing with the Dublin Orchestral Players.
3.97 O'Reilly Hall, UCD, Dublin, clarinet concerto, appearing with the Dublin Orchestral Players
**KEY PERFORMANCES OUTSIDE IRELAND** (since January 1994):
9.94 National Concert Hall, Lisbon, appearing with the European Wind Ensemble.
8.95 Orford Arts Centre, Canada.
9.95 Conservatoire of Music, Luxembourg, appearing with the European Wind Ensemble.
9.96 Yale University, USA, appearing with the DIT Conservatory of Music and Drama Wind Band
**SELECTED BROADCASTS AND/OR RECORDED WORK:**
9.94 Recording of European National Anthem with European Wind Ensemble.
3.95 'Lifestyles' for RTÉ.
**PRIZES/AWARDS/APPOINTMENTS:**
2.95 Winner of the Ruaighri Roberts/Aer Rianta Bursary (Irl).
3.96 Winner of the William Shanahan Concerto Cup (Irl).
**TRAINING AND/OR QUALIFICATIONS:**
Since 1994, B Mus Performance course, at DIT CMD.
From 7.95 to 9.95, Masterclasses at Orford Arts Centre, Canada (teacher Andre Moisan).
10.96 Masterclasses with Michael Collins.
From 8.97 to 9.97 Masterclasses at Orford Arts Centre, Canada (teacher Robert Crowley).
**REGULARLY PERFORMS WITH:**
DIT CMD Wind Band, European Youth Wind Ensemble, National Youth Orchestra of Ireland.
**AVAILABILITY:**
Weekends, evenings, Easter and Christmas holidays.

# Ruth Hickey *Clarinet*

**Contact:** Ms Ruth Hickey
12, Orchard Grove
Blanchardstown
Dublin 15
**Tel:** +353 1 8211507
**Email:** clar@indigo.ie
**Other instruments:** Bass and Eb clarinets.

**KEY IRISH PERFORMANCES** (since January 1994):
7.95 John Field Room, National Concert Hall, Dublin, trio recital, promoted by NCH "Platform for Youth".
10.95 Samuel Beckett Theatre, Dublin, promoted by Dublin Theatre Festival, appearing with Coscéim Dance Theatre.
5.96 Bank of Ireland Arts Centre, Dublin, promoted by Vocal Heritage Arts, appearing with Virginia Kerr (soprano).
31.12.96 Town Hall Theatre, Galway, promoted by Galway Arts Festival, appearing with Virginia Kerr.
**SELECTED BROADCASTS AND/OR RECORDED WORK:**
7.96 Music for film by Rhona Clarke. 11.96 RTÉ Young Musician of the Future competition for RTÉ (chamber music finals).
**SELECTED REVIEWS** (since January 1994):
7.95 Irish Times.
**TRAINING AND/OR QUALIFICATIONS:**
From 1991 to 1995, B Mus (Perf) from Trinity College, Dublin.
From 1994 to 1996, masterclasses with Michael Collins.
1997 Masterclasses with Jean-Michel Bertelli, Lyon, France.
**REGULARLY PERFORMS WITH:**
Virginia Kerr, RTÉ Concert Orchestra.
**AVAILABILITY:**
General.

# Amanda Irvine *Clarinet*

**Contact:** Mrs Amanda Irvine
38, Plantation Avenue
Carrickfergus, BT38 9BJ
Northern Ireland
**Tel:** +44 1960 361695
**Other instruments:** Saxophone, voice.

**TRAINING AND/OR QUALIFICATIONS:**
From 1988 to 1991, B Mus awarded by Queen's University, Belfast.
From 1991 to 1993, MA (Perf) awarded by Queen's University, Belfast.
From 1993 to 1994, PGCE, awarded by University of Ulster, Jordanstown.
**REGULARLY PERFORMS WITH:**
Colin Irvine (flute), Castleward Wind Quintet.
**AVAILABILITY:**
General.

# Anthony Long *Clarinet*

**Contact:** Mr Anthony (Anto) Long
**Mobile:** +353 86 8121503

**TRAINING AND/OR QUALIFICATIONS:**
Studied with Brian O'Rourke.
**REGULARLY PERFORMS WITH:**
National Symphony Orchestra of Ireland, RTÉ Concert Orchestra, Harlequin Quintet.
**ADDITIONAL INFORMATION:**
Interested in orchestral playing, chamber music and education. Has also performed with the Irish Chamber Orchestra. Part-time lecturer of clarinet at the Waterford Institute of Technology.

# Gillian McCutcheon *Clarinet*

**Contact:** Ms Gillian McCutcheon
45, Glendarragh
Belfast BT4 2WB
Northern Ireland
**Tel:** +44 1232 760759
**Other instruments:** Piano

*"[her] technique and command of colour was quite outstanding, particularly in the brilliant Fantasia on 'La Traviata' "* 10.1.94 Belfast Telegraph.

**KEY IRISH PERFORMANCES** (since January 1994):
8.1.94 Elmwood Hall, Belfast, promoted by BMS appearing with Elizabeth Bicker (piano).
18.6.96 Ulster Hall, Belfast, as part of the 1996 Proms, appearing with the Ulster Orchestra.

20.7.96 Primate's Chapel, Armagh, promoted by the Armagh Arts Council, appearing with Elizabeth Bicker.
22.11.96 Down Cathedral, promoted by the Bishop of Down, appearing with Elizabeth Bicker.
**KEY PERFORMANCES OUTSIDE IRELAND** (since January 1994):
10.94 and 3.96, Concert Hall, Athens, promoted by Athens Camerata, appearing with Instrumental Ensemble of London.
17.12.94 St Paul's Church, London, promoted by St Paul's Festival Choir, appearing with St Paul's Orchestra.
**SELECTED BROADCASTS AND/OR RECORDED WORK:**
12.9.95 BBC Radio Ulster Lunchtime Recital.
25.10.96 'Songs of Praise' for BBC.
4.3.97 BBC Radio Ulster Lunchtime Recital.
**SELECTED REVIEWS** (since January 1994):
15.8.96 Belfast Telegraph
**PRIZES/AWARDS/APPOINTMENTS:**
1990 Awarded Frazer Scholarship to study at the Royal Academy of Music, London, by Edinburgh University.
1992 Very Highly Commended for the Geoffrey Hawkes Clarinet Prize at the Royal Academy of Music, London.
**TRAINING AND/OR QUALIFICATIONS:**
From 1986 to 1990, B Mus (Hons) from Edinburgh University.
From 1990 to 1992, LRAM and M Mus (Performance and Related Studies) from the Royal Academy of Music, London.
**REGULARLY PERFORMS WITH:**
Instrumental Ensemble of London, Ulster Orchestra.
**AVAILABILITY:**
General.
**ADDITIONAL INFORMATION:**
Has attended masterclasses with Michael Collins at the Purcell Room (chosen to represent the Royal Academy of Music), Karl Leister at Riva del Garda and Harold Wright at Tanglewood. Works regularly with Francis King (piano) and Michael McGuffin (piano).

## Carol McGonnell *Clarinet*

**Contact:** Ms Carol McGonnell
37, Glendoher Drive
Rathfarnham
Dublin 16
or
Willemerstr, 23
60594 - Frankfurt (M)
Germany
**Tel:** +353 1 4931053 / +49 69 96201583

**KEY IRISH PERFORMANCES** (since January 1994):
12.94 Queen's University, Belfast, appearing with the QU Orchestra.
1.96 National Concert Hall, Dublin, appearing with the National Symphony Orchestra of Ireland.
8.96 NCH, Dublin, Dundalk and Waterford, appearing with the Junior National Youth Orchestra.
1.97 Aulu Maxima, University College, Galway, promoted by UCG appearing with Alexandra Lubchansky (piano).
**KEY PERFORMANCES OUTSIDE IRELAND** (since January 1994):
9.95 Weikerskeim Music Festival, appearing with Peter Marino.
1.96 Concert Hall, Schweinfurt appearing with Peter Marino.
3.96 Concert Hall, Würzburg, appearing with Peter Marino.
2.97 Goethe University, Frankfurt, appearing with Alexandra Lubchansky (piano).
**SELECTED BROADCASTS AND/OR RECORDED WORK:**
1.96 RTÉ Young Musician of the Future composition and woodwind finals for RTÉ.
1.96 RTÉ Young Musician of the Future concerto final for RTÉ.
4.97 Ulster Bank Music Foundation competition for RTÉ.
**SELECTED REVIEWS** (since January 1994):
1.96 Irish Times.
8.96 Irish Times
**PRIZES/AWARDS/APPOINTMENTS:**
1.96 Woodwind and composition finalist for the RTÉ Young Musician of the Future competition.
4.97 Wind finalist for the RTÉ Young Musician of the Future competition.
**REGULARLY PERFORMS WITH:**
Alexandra Lubchansky (piano).
**AVAILABILITY:**
Evenings.
**ADDITIONAL INFORMATION:**
Currently a holder of a Deutsche Akademischer Austauschdienst (DAAD) Scholarship to help further performance studies in Germany.

## Patrick O'Keeffe *Clarinet*

**Contact:** Mr Patrick O'Keeffe
126, North Main Street
Youghal
Co Cork
**Tel:** +353 24 92820
**Other instruments:** Piano, saxophone.

**TRAINING AND/OR QUALIFICATIONS:**
From 1.10.83 to 30.6.86, B Mus from University College, Cork.
From 1.9.86 to 30.5.88, Dip CSM from Cork School of Music (teacher Una Hunt).
1989 LTCL clarinet (Perf) from Trinity College, London.
**AVAILABILITY:**
Weekends.
**ADDITIONAL INFORMATION:**
Currently completing an MA in Performance and Interpretation at the National University of Ireland, Maynooth, (thesis title: 'A Survey of Contemporary Irish Music for Clarinet and Piano').

## Andrew Rowan *Clarinet* 

**Contact:** Mr Andrew Rowan
10, Galbraith Gardens
Waringstown BT66 7QN
Northern Ireland
**Tel:** +44 1762 881097
*See flute page 19.*

## Michael Seaver *Clarinet*

**Contact:** Michael Seaver
Cross Cool Harbour, (off Red Lane)
Blessington
Co Wicklow
**Tel:** +353 45 520264

**TRAINING AND/OR QUALIFICATIONS:**
Has studied with John Finucane and John Davies, London.
**REGULARLY PERFORMS WITH:**
Niall O'Loughlin, cello, Réamonn Keary, piano.
**AVAILABILITY:**
General.
**ADDITIONAL INFORMATION:**
Principal Clarinet with the RTÉ Concert Orchestra. Has performed throughout the USA, Mexico, Denmark, Austria. Has performed several premieres of works by Irish composers.
*See composers page 185.*

## Conor Sheil *Clarinet*

**Contact:** Mr Conor Sheil
24, Botanic Avenue
Drumcondra, Dublin 9
**Tel:** +353 1 8375210

## Fintan Sutton *Clarinet*

**Contact:** Mr Fintan Sutton
20, Old Court Manor
Firhouse, Dublin 24
**Tel.:** +353 1 4519089
**Other instruments:** Saxophone.

**TRAINING AND/OR QUALIFICATIONS:**
Royal Academy of Music, London, studied clarinet and saxophone.
**REGULARLY PERFORMS WITH:**
Slí Nua.
**ADDITIONAL INFORMATION:**
Has worked with English National Ballet and Scottish Opera. 1988 appointed clarinet/bass clarinet player with the National Symphony Orchestra of Ireland. Interested in contemporary music and was founder member of Nua Nós. Current director of Slí Nua. Teacher at the Royal Irish Academy of Music, Dublin.

## Rachel Talbot *Clarinet*

**Contact:** Ms Rachel Talbot
117, Templeogue Road
Dublin 6w
**Tel:** +353 1 4907512
**Email:** rtalbot@clubl.ie
*See soprano page 127.*

## Peadar Townsend *Clarinet*

**Contact:** Mr. Peadar Townsend
Flat 2
8, Mayfield Road
Whalley Range
Manchester M16 8FT,
England
**Tel/Mobile:** +44 161 2329315 / +44 421 366376
*See percussion page 31.*

# CONCERT HARP

Also see orchestra members lists on page 140.

## Maria Christina Cleary *Concert Harp*

**Contact:** Ms Maria Christina Cleary
Ryswykseweg 340-9
2516 HM, Den Haag
The Netherlands
**Tel/Fax:** +31 70 3952605
**Other instruments:** Historical harps (triple harp, single action harp).

*"... shows intelligent musicianship, particularly in her small scale shaping of line".*
Irish Times (Michael Dervan).

**KEY IRISH PERFORMANCES** (since January 1994):
4.95 Royal Hospital, Kilmainham, promoted by RHK, appearing solo.
8.96 National Concert Hall, Dublin, promoted by RTÉ, appearing with the RTÉ Concert Orchestra.
11.96 RDS, promoted by the RDS (Young Artist Series), appearing solo.
**KEY PERFORMANCES OUTSIDE IRELAND** (since January 1994):
4.94 Kastal Wittenburg, The Hague, promoted by K.C.
8.94 Trondheim, Norway, promoted by the Trondheim Music Festival, appearing with Mari Giske (viola).
5.95 Diligentia Theatre, The Hague, promoted by K.C. (Mozart Concerto).
8.95 Saarlouis, Germany, promoted by UNESCO, soloist with a baroque orchestra.
**SELECTED BROADCASTS AND/OR RECORDED WORK:**
11.91 Britten's 'Ceremony of Carols' for RTÉ.
8.94 Bax Sonata and Debussy Trio for Norwegian Broadcasting.
4.96 Solo recordings with piano for Dutch Radio, KRO.
**PRIZES/AWARDS/APPOINTMENTS:**
1993,'94,'95 Semifinalist in Ulster Bank Music Foundation.
1996 String finalist, RTÉ Young Musician of the Future.
**TRAINING AND/OR QUALIFICATIONS:**
From 1992 to 1994, Performers Degree from Royal Conservatory Den Haag (UM).
From 1994 to 1996, Historical Harp course from Hochschule für Kunst Bremen.
From 1994 to 1996, Solo Masters Degree from Royal Conservatory Brussels.
From 1994 to 1996, Masters in Chamber Music from Royal Conservatory Den Haag (AKM).
**REGULARLY PERFORMS WITH:**
Annette Cleary (cello), Frescobaldi Ensemble (baroque group), Mari Giske (viola).
**AVAILABILITY:**
General.
**ADDITIONAL INFORMATION:**
Places special emphasis on contemporary music for harp, both solo and in chamber groups. Has performed the music of Berio, Ligeti, Donatoni, Crumb, and Carter. Also interested in historical harps and is a continuo player for music from the 16th to the 18th century. Performs regularly on a single action pedal harp and triple (Monteverdi) harp. Is a participant in the 1997-1999 Early Music Network (Netherlands) touring scheme as a soloist performing on 18th century authentic instruments. Has also worked for the Netherlands Impressiariat.

## Clíona Doris *Concert Harp*

**Contact:** Dr Clíona Doris
53, Saul Road, Downpatrick
Co Down BT30 6PA
Northern Ireland
**Tel:** +44 1396 613856
**Email:** doris@unite.co.uk

**KEY IRISH PERFORMANCES** (since January 1994):
3.97 BBC Studio, Belfast, promoted by the BBC.
3.97 Clotworthy Arts Centre, Antrim, promoted by Norfest and Antrim Borough Council, appearing with Sinikka Langeland (Norway).
**KEY PERFORMANCES OUTSIDE IRELAND** (since January 1994):
11.95 Auer Concert Hall, Indiana University, USA, appearing as soloist with Indiana University Chamber Orchestra.
7.96 Ford Hall, Indiana University, promoted by 'Crossroads of Tradition' Inter-American Twentieth Century Festival, appearing with Ricardo Gallardo (percussion), Ann Yeung (harp).
7.96 Rialto Theatre, Tacoma, Washington, USA, promoted by the World Harp Congress, accompanied by Peter Henderson (piano).
7.96 Theatre on the Square, Tacoma, Washington, promoted by the World Harp Congress, appearing solo.
**SELECTED BROADCASTS AND/OR RECORDED WORK:**
6.96 BBC Studio Recital for BBC.
3.97 BBC Studio Recital for BBC
**PRIZES/AWARDS/APPOINTMENTS:**
1995 Mozart Concerto Competition Winner from Indiana University, Bloomington, USA.
1997 Daphne Boden Prize from the Royal Over-Seas League Music Competition, London.

**TRAINING AND/OR QUALIFICATIONS:**
From 1989 to 1992, B Mus (Hons), LRSM and LTCL Performers Diploma from Queen's University, Belfast.
From 1992 to 1997, DM (Doctor of Music in Harp Performance and Music Literature). MM (Master of Music in Harp Performance) from the School of Music, Indiana University, USA.
**AVAILABILITY:**
General.
**ADDITIONAL INFORMATION:**
Has recently returned to Ireland after four years of study at the School of Music, Indiana University, Bloomington. Has extensive recital, chamber music, orchestral and broadcasting experience.

# Denise Kelly *Concert Harp*

**Contact:** Denise Kelly
66, Dartmouth Square
Ranelagh, Dublin 6
**Tel:** +353 1 6689366
**Other instruments:** Irish Harp, also a composer.

**KEY IRISH PERFORMANCES** (since January 1994):
1997 National Concert Hall, Dublin, concert to honour Dr Brian Boydell, promoted by the Association of Irish Composers.
1997 Bank of Ireland, Arts Centre promoted by The Arts Club and the Bank of Ireland, appearing with Bernadette Greevy.
**KEY PERFORMANCES OUTSIDE IRELAND** (since January 1994):
1996 Australia, three concerts appearing with Bernadette Greevy.
1996 Seattle, USA, composition premiére, promoted by the World Harp Congress.
**SELECTED BROADCASTS AND/OR RECORDED WORK:**
1985 Soloist with the Ulster Orchestra in recording for HARTY.
1995 'Dreams' for Trend.
1996 'Oft in the Stilly Night' for Absolute Music.
**PRIZES/AWARDS/APPOINTMENTS:**
1997 Appointed tutor at the DIT Conservatory of Music and Drama.
**REGULARLY PERFORMS WITH:**
Bernadette Greevy, Moya O'Grady
**AVAILABILITY:**
General.
**ADDITIONAL INFORMATION:**
Harpist, accompanist, composer (specialist in contemporary music for harp), teacher, examiner, adjudicator.

# Jean Kelly *Concert Harp*

**Contact:** Ms Jean Kelly
11, Summerhill South
Cork
**Tel:** +353 21 316088
**Email:** grantkelly@tinet.ie
**Other instruments:** Cello, piano.

**KEY IRISH PERFORMANCES** (since January 1994):
6.96 Cork, promoted by Cork Orchestral Society, appearing with Evelyn Grant.
7.96 Boyle, promoted by Boyle Arts Festival.
12.96 Cork School of Music, promoted by RTÉ.
**PRIZES/AWARDS/APPOINTMENTS:**
9.96 Foundation Scholarship awarded from the Royal College of Music, London.
**REGULARLY PERFORMS WITH:**
Evelyn Grant (flute), Gerard Kelly (cello).
**AVAILABILITY:**
General.
**ADDITIONAL INFORMATION:**
Performs own arrangements as well as the standard concert repertoire.

# Emer Kenny *Concert Harp*

**Contact:** Ms Emer Kenny
c/o Mr John Murphy
48, Balreask Village
Navan
Co Meath
**Tel:** +353 46 71459
*See Irish Harp page 229.*

# Aibhlín McCrann *Concert Harp*

**Contact:** Ms Aibhlín McCrann
50, Wyvern
Killiney
Co Dublin
**Tel/Fax:** +353 1 2856345 / +353 1 6768007
*See Irish harp page 229.*

# Andreja Mali̇ř *Concert Harp*

**Contact:** Andreja Mali̇ř
139, Templeville Drive
Terenure
Dublin 6w
**Tel/Fax:** +353 1 4904439
**Other instruments:** Irish harp.

*"One of the highlights of the West Cork Chamber Music Festival . . . breathtaking performance of the introduction and allegro with magical playing . . ."* 14.7.96 Sunday Tribune.

**KEY IRISH PERFORMANCES** (since January 1994):
1.95 Dublin, Waterford, Limerick, promoted by RTÉ, appearing with the RTÉ Concert Orchestra.
2.96 Castletownbere, promoted by West Cork Music, appearing with Deirdre Brady (flute).
6.96 Bantry, promoted by West Cork Music, appearing with the Parisi Quartet and the RTÉ Vanbrugh Quartet.
11.96 Dublin, Galway, Cork, Wexford, promoted by and appearing with the Athenaeum Chamber Orchestra.
**KEY PERFORMANCES OUTSIDE IRELAND** (since January 1994):
1.94 Paris, promoted by Irish College, appearing with Deirdre Brady.
4.94 Sweden, promoted by Music I Halland, appearing with the String Quartet Hallands Ensemble.
7.96 Seattle Tacoma, USA, promoted by World Harp Congress, appearing with Philip Martin (piano).
6.97 The Hague, Netherlands, appearing with Athenaeum Chamber Orchestra.
**SELECTED BROADCASTS AND/OR RECORDED WORK:**
1995 Philip Martin Harp Concerto for Marco Polo/Naxo.
1996 Solo Harp Music (Independent cassette).
1997 Debussy Danses for harp and orchestra for Siemens Nixdorf.
**SELECTED REVIEWS** (since January 1994):
1.95 Irish Times.
6.96 Irish Times.
11.96 Irish Times
**PRIZES/AWARDS/APPOINTMENTS:**
1.88 Appointed Principal Harp with the National Symphony Orchestra of Ireland.
8.91 1st Prize for interpretation of Spanish Music from Music de Compostela.

**TRAINING AND/OR QUALIFICATIONS:**
From 9.83 to 12.87, OM Performance Degree from Konklijk Conservatory. LLCM Performer's Diploma from the London College of Music (external). FTCL from Trinity College, London (external).
**REGULARLY PERFORMS WITH:**
Deirdre Brady (flute).
**AVAILABILITY:**
General.

## Anne-Marie O'Farrell *Concert Harp*

**Contact:** Ms Anne-Marie O'Farrell
28, Grange Manor Drive
Rathfarnham
Dublin 16
**Tel:** +353 1 4931873
**Other instruments:** Voice, Irish harp.

*"Unfailingly musical"* 10.94 Irish Times.

**KEY IRISH PERFORMANCES** (since January 1994):
10.94 Dublin Castle, appearing with the National Chamber Choir.
12.95 St Patrick's Cathedral, Dublin, appearing with Anúna.
7.96 Coláiste Mhuire, Ennis, promoted by the Ennis/IMRO Summer School appearing with Philippa Davies (flute).
11.96 St Patrick's Cathedral, Dublin promoted by Red Cross, appearing with Brian Kennedy and Stockton's Wing.
**KEY PERFORMANCES OUTSIDE IRELAND** (since January 1994):
10.94 Dreifaltigkeitskirche, Alsfeld, Frankfurt, Germany, promoted by Hans Koppenburg and South German Radio appearing with the Oriol Ensemble, Berlin (Baroque Orchestra).
9.95 De Rode Hoed, Amsterdam promoted by the European Harp Symposium, appearing with Cormac de Barra.
3.96 Pleasance Theatre, Edinburgh promoted by Edinburgh Harp Festival.
6.97 Asilomar Conference Centre Monterey, promoted by the Lyon and Healy Harpfest.
**SELECTED BROADCASTS AND/OR RECORDED WORK:**
1992 'Heads & Harps' for Eagle Productions.
1993 'Harping Bach to Carolan' for Number Twenty Nine.
1997 'Songs of Praise' for BBC.
**SELECTED REVIEWS** (since January 1994):
1.94 Irish Times.
**PRIZES/AWARDS/APPOINTMENTS:**
1986, Awarded a 12 month scholarship from the German Academic Exchange Board, DAAD, to study in Bonn University.
1987 Awarded a 12 month scholarship for study in University College, Dublin.
**TRAINING AND/OR QUALIFICATIONS:**
From 1984 to 1989, BA (Hons) and B Mus (Hons) from University College, Dublin.
From 1987 to 1988, ARIAM (teacher Helen Davies) awarded from the Royal Irish Academy of Music.
From 1980 to 1992, LTCL and ALCM from the DIT Conservatory of Music and Drama.
**REGULARLY PERFORMS WITH:**
Cormac de Barra (harp), Ellen Cranitch (flute), Anúna.
**AVAILABILITY:**
General.
**ADDITIONAL INFORMATION:**
Has a particular interest in the development of the Irish harp as a concert instrument. Own compositions, arrangements and transcriptions contribute to the body of new repertoire for the harp.

## Claire Roche *Concert Harp*

**Contact:** Ms Claire Roche
34, Hampton Crescent
St Helen's Wood
Booterstown
Co Dublin
**Tel:** +353 1 2835135
**Other instruments:** Irish harp, voice

*"Claire Fleming's [née Roche] remarkable voice and harp playing"* 3.90 First Coast Entertainer (Rick Grant).

**KEY IRISH PERFORMANCES** (since January 1994):
8.94 Douglas Hyde Building, Sligo, promoted by the WB Yeats Summer School.
8.95 Tyrone, promoted by the William Carleton Summer School.
8.96 Town Hall, Sligo, promoted by the WB Yeats Summer School.
**KEY PERFORMANCES OUTSIDE IRELAND** (since January 1994):
3.96 West Palm Beach, Florida, promoted by the Irish Cultural Institute.
5.96 Florida Folk Festival, promoted by the Florida State Department of Folk Life.
5.97 Florida Folk Festival, promoted by the FSDFL.
**SELECTED BROADCASTS AND/OR RECORDED WORK:**
1988 'Cursaí Éalaine' for RTÉ.
1988 'Ronan Collins Show' for RTÉ.
1995 'Dancing in the Wind' private CD recording (8 poems by Yeats set to music).
**PRIZES/AWARDS/APPOINTMENTS:**
1986 2nd Prize winner for song and harp at the O'Carolan Harp Festival, Keadue, Co Roscommon.
**AVAILABILITY:**
General.
**ADDITIONAL INFORMATION:**
Has toured Boston and performed in London, Normandy and Paris with poet Séamus Hogan and reader Michael Gradwell.

## Caitríona Yeats *Concert Harp*

**Contact:** Ms Caitríona Yeats
Sophus Bauditzvej 8
DK 2800 Lyngby
Denmark
**Tel:** +45 45871161

*"Her playing sparkled and bubbled like a fine champagne"* Louisville Courier Journal.

**KEY IRISH PERFORMANCES** (since January 1994):
1995 and 1996, Dublin, promoted by Cáirde na Cruite.
**SELECTED BROADCASTS AND/OR RECORDED WORK:**
Many recordings with several orchestras.
**PRIZES/AWARDS/APPOINTMENTS:**
1973 Prizewinner in the Israel International Harp Competition.
**TRAINING AND/OR QUALIFICATIONS:**
From 1967 to 1973, Orchestral Diploma, Solo Diploma and Prize of Excellence from the Hague Conservatory of Music.
**REGULARLY PERFORMS WITH:**
Flute and harp duo.
**AVAILABILITY:**
By arrangement.
**ADDITIONAL INFORMATION:**
Since 1993, Principal Harp with the Danish National Radio Symphony Orchestra.

## COR ANGLAIS

Also see orchestra members lists on page 140.

### David Agnew *Cor Anglais*

**Contact:** Mr David Agnew
Beaufort House
Butterfield Avenue
Rathfarnham
Dublin 14
**Tel/Fax:** +353 1 4945939
**Email:** oboeking@iol.ie
*See oboe page 24.*

### Ms Ruby Ashley *Cor Anglais*

**Contact:** Ms Ruby Ashley
49, Weirview Drive
Stillorgan
Co Dublin
**Tel:** +353 1 2882467
*See oboe page 24.*

### Aisling Casey *Cor Anglais*

**Contact:** Ms Aisling Casey
12, Beverly
Ovens
Co Cork
**Tel:** +353 21 870676
*See oboe page 25.*

### Colin Stark *Cor Anglais*

**Contact:** Mr Colin Stark
41, Somerton Park
Belfast BT15 4DP
Northern Ireland
**Tel/Fax:** +44 1232 772325

**ADDITIONAL INFORMATION:**
Principal Cor Anglais with the Ulster Orchestra. Keen exponent of 20th century music and has given several Northern Ireland premieres, including works by Hellawell, Carter, Berio and Lutoslawski.
*See oboe page 25.*

## DOUBLE BASS

Also see orchestra members lists on page 140.

### David Daly *Double Bass*

**Contact:** Mr David Daly
6, Field View Road
Blandford Forum
Dorset, DT11 7JH
England
**Tel:** +44 1258 455596
**Email:** daly@clara.net

**ADDITIONAL INFORMATION:**
Member of Bournemouth Symphony Orchestra.

### Dominick Dudley *Double Bass*

**Contact:** Mr Dominick Dudley
National Symphony Orchestra of Ireland
c/o National Concert Hall
Earlsfort Terrace
Dublin 2
**Mobile:** +353 87 625931

**PRIZES/AWARDS/APPOINTMENTS:**
1994 Appointed Principal Double Bass of the National Symphony Orchestra of Ireland.
**TRAINING AND/OR QUALIFICATIONS:**
Guildhall School of Music and Drama, London (teachers Thomas Martin and Kevin Rundell).
**REGULARLY PERFORMS WITH:**
Prism and the NSOI.
**AVAILABILITY:**
General.
**ADDITIONAL INFORMATION:**
Started playing the double bass at the age of 13. Has worked with the Philharmonia BBC Symphony Orchestra and the London Symphony Orchestra. Since 1994, has played with the Orchestra of St Cecilia. Performed the Bottesini Concerto with the Hibernia Chamber Orchestra and the 1997 Schubert/Brahms series with Philippe Cassard.

### Ronan Dunne *Double Bass*

**Contact:** Mr Ronan Dunne
28, Maywood Park
Raheny, Dublin 5
**Tel:** +353 1 8313973
**Other instruments:** Clarinet

**KEY IRISH PERFORMANCES** (since January 1994):
From 1993 to 1996, Dublin, Cork, Waterford, appearing with Irish Youth Orchestra.
1995 Trinity College, Dublin, accompanied by Donagh Collins.
5.97 Dublin, Galway, Limerick, appearing with the Irish Chamber Orchestra.
**KEY PERFORMANCES OUTSIDE IRELAND** (since January 1994):
From 1993 to 1997, appearing in Europe and South America with the European Youth Orchestra.
Since 1995, touring Britain with the Rambert Dance Company.
2/6/7.97 London, appearing with the London Symphony Orchestra
**SELECTED BROADCASTS AND/OR RECORDED WORK:**
1995 BBC Proms.

1996 BBC Proms, appearing with the European Youth Orchestra.
11.96 Backing track for dance demo for an independent company.
**PRIZES/AWARDS/APPOINTMENTS:**
1995 Winner of the Hamilton Cup at the Wesley Feis, Dublin.
4.97 Winner of the Eugene Cruft Memorial at the Guildhall School of Music and Drama, London.
**TRAINING AND/OR QUALIFICATIONS:**
1994 Studied with Rodney Slatford at the GSMD.
Since 9.95, studied with Tom Martin at the GSMD.
1996 Studied with Peter Puhn at the Manchester Conservatoire.
1997 Participated in the String Experience Scheme with the London Symphony Orchestra.
**REGULARLY PERFORMS WITH:**
Alicia Bailey (piano), Naomi Samuel (cello), Valeria Nasushkina (violin).
**AVAILABILITY:**
General.
**ADDITIONAL INFORMATION:**
Has worked throughout Europe with the European Youth Orchestra under conductors such as Colin Davis, Bernard Haitink and Carlo Maria Giulini.

## Mike Quellin *Double Bass*

**Contact:** Mr Mike Quellin
11, Primate's Manor
Armagh, BT60 2LP
Northern Ireland
**Tel/Fax:** +44 1861 526304 / +44 1850 247582
*See jazz double bass page 270.*

## Malachy Robinson *Double Bass*

**Contact:** Mr Malachy Robinson
81c, Monkstown Road
Blackrock
Co Dublin
**Tel/Fax:** +353 1 2805730 / +353 61 202617
**Other instruments:** Bass guitar.

*"Gripping from start to finish"*
18.7.97 London Independent.

**KEY IRISH PERFORMANCES** (since January 1994):
Regular performances all over Ireland including University of Limerick Concert Hall, National Concert Hall, Dublin and smaller venues from Schull to Ballyshannon.
**KEY PERFORMANCES OUTSIDE IRELAND** (since January 1994):
7.95 With André Bernard, Gressony Music Festival, Italy.
11.96 Concertgebouw, Amsterdam.
4.97 Barbican Irish Festival, London with Mícheál Ó Súilleabháin.
7.97 Wigmore Hall, London appearing with Franco Gulli (violin).
**SELECTED BROADCASTS AND/OR RECORDED WORK:**
1996 'Sult' for RTÉ.
7.97 Irish Chamber Orchestra 'Romantic Irish Music' for ASV Records, London.
1997 CD with Mícheál Ó Súilleabháin.
**SELECTED REVIEWS** (since January 1994):
Irish Times.
**AVAILABILITY:**
General.
**ADDITIONAL INFORMATION:**
Principal Double Bass with the Irish Chamber Orchestra. Also works regularly with other orchestras (NSOI and RTÉCO), small ensembles and other recording groups.

## Michele Strong *Double Bass*

**Contact:** Ms Michele Strong
73, Ballygowan Road
Belfast BT5 7TP
Northern Ireland
**Tel:** +44 1232 402901

**KEY IRISH PERFORMANCES** (since January 1994):
15.11.94 and 9.11.95 Harty Room, Belfast, promoted by Belfast Festival at Queen's, appearing with Quintessence.
21.11.94 Elmwood Hall, Belfast, promoted by Belfast Festival at Queen's, appearing with the Ulster Camerata.
16.5.97 Harty Rooms, Belfast, promoted by Queen's University Music Society, appearing with the Singing Wardrobes.
**SELECTED BROADCASTS AND/OR RECORDED WORK:**
6.5.94 Kelly Show with Big Bad Bass for UTV.
16.5.97 Séan Rafferty Show for BBC Radio Ulster.
**SELECTED REVIEWS** (since January 1994):
16.11.94 Belfast Newsletter.
**PRIZES/AWARDS/APPOINTMENTS:**
Since 1985, Sub Principal Double Bass with the Ulster Orchestra.
**TRAINING AND/OR QUALIFICATIONS:**
From 1970 to 1976, Diploma from New South Wales State Conservatorium of Music, Sydney, Australia.
From 1977 to 1980, NSWSCM, Sydney, (teacher John Gray).
From 1980 to 1991, NCOS Diploma from the National Centre for Orchestral Studies, Goldsmith's College, London.
**REGULARLY PERFORMS WITH:**
Ulster Orchestra, Big Bad Bass, The Singing Wardrobes, Quintessence.
**AVAILABILITY:**
General.

# FLUTE AND PICCOLO

Also see orchestra members lists on page 140.

## Gary Arbuthnot *Flute*

**Contact:** Mr Gary Arbuthnot
20, Brook Avenue
Wembley
Middlesex, HA9 8PH
England
**Tel/Fax:** +44 181 9084484
**Email:** g.arbuthnot@ram.ac.uk
**Other instruments:** Piccolo, alto flute, bass flute.

*"One of the most exciting musical prospects ever seen in Ireland"* 1991 Belfast Telegraph.

**KEY IRISH PERFORMANCES** (since January 1994):
1994 Harty Room, Belfast, promoted by Belfast Festival at Queen's, appearing with Sophia Rahman (piano).
1994 Clotworthy Arts Centre, Antrim, appearing with Sophia Rahman.
1997 St Mathais, Killiney, Dublin, promoted by Dún Laoghaire/ Rathdown County Council, appearing with Eleanor Meynell (piano).
1997 Harty Room, Belfast, promoted by 39th Old Boys Flute Ensemble, appearing with Eleanor Meynell.
**KEY PERFORMANCES OUTSIDE IRELAND** (since January 1994):
1994 Pollack Hall, Montreal, promoted by McGill Arts Society, appearing with Olga Gross (piano).
1996 Margaret Greenham Theatre, promoted by Banff Festival for the Arts, appearing with Eleanor Meynell.
1996 Town Hall, Stratford-Upon-Avon, appearing with Eleanor Meynell.
1997 Post Graduate Medical Centre, Isle of Man, promoted by Music in Minature Society, appearing with Mark Ashford (guitar).

**SELECTED BROADCASTS AND/OR RECORDED WORK:**
1996 Music from Strathgarry, for BBC Radio Scotland.
1997 Lunchtime recital, for BBC Radio Ulster.
1997 Friday Night 'Platform Live', for Classic FM.
**SELECTED REVIEWS** (since January 1994):
1997 Belfast Telegraph.
**PRIZES/AWARDS/APPOINTMENTS:**
1995 1st Prize, awarded by Albert Cooper Flute Competition, Stratford-Upon-Avon.
1997 Semi-finalist, Concert Artist Guild competition, New York.
**TRAINING AND/OR QUALIFICATIONS:**
From 1991 to 1995 LRAM and B Mus (Perf), London.
From 1993 to 1994 Exchange programme to McGill University, Montreal.
From 1995 to 1996, Diploma of Advanced Studies, from the Royal Academy of Music, London.
1997 Private tuition with James Galway
**REGULARLY PERFORMS WITH:**
Mark Ashford (guitar), Emma Ramsdale (harp), Sophia Rahman (piano).
**AVAILABILITY:**
General.
**ADDITIONAL INFORMATION:**
Other awards include the 1996 English Speaking Union Menuhin Banff Scholarship, Wind finalist in the 1996 RTÉ Young Musician of the Future Competition, 1996 Finalist in the John Tonnel Chamber Music Competition, Hattori Foundation Grant recipient, Foundation for Sport and the Arts, grant recipient, Countess of Munster Musical Trust, grant recipient. Also part of the Menuhins 'Live Music Now' Scheme.

# Elizabeth Bennett *Flute*

**Contact:** Elizabeth Bennett
23, Middle Braniel Road
Belfast BT5 7TU
Northern Ireland
**Tel/Fax:** +44 1232 791937
**Other instruments:** Piccolo.

**PRIZES/AWARDS/APPOINTMENTS:**
Eve Kirsch Prize, Royal College of Music.
**TRAINING AND/OR QUALIFICATIONS:**
Flute at the Royal College of Music.
**REGULARLY PERFORMS WITH:**
Ulster Orchestra, The Belfast Wind Quintet, Phoenix Flute and Harp duo.
**AVAILABILITY:**
Subject to orchestra schedule.
**ADDITIONAL INFORMATION:**
1974 Appointed Principal Flute of the BBC Northern Ireland Orchestra, doubling as Principal Piccolo. Has performed throughout the United Kingdom as a soloist.

# Angela Bradley *Flute*

**Contact:** Ms Angela Bradley
14, Bridgewater
Caw
Derry City, BT47 1YA
Northern Ireland
**Tel/Fax:** +44 1504 311938 / +44 1504 48595
**Other instruments:** Piccolo, violin.

**KEY IRISH PERFORMANCES** (since January 1994):
2.94 John Field Room, Trinity College and The Royal Dublin Society, Dublin, Young Performers Platform, appearing with Evelyn Grant (piano).
7.95 Foyle Summer School, Derry, promoted by Ray McGinley, appearing with Ruth McGinley (piano).
7.95 Triskel Arts Centre, Cork, promoted by Cork School of Music, appearing with Evelyn Grant.
**SELECTED BROADCASTS AND/OR RECORDED WORK:**
4.93 'Day Out With Dana', for Scottish Television.
**PRIZES/AWARDS/APPOINTMENTS:**
9.95 Stevenson Scholarship, awarded by Royal Scottish Academy of Music and Drama, Glasgow for most outstanding entrant in woodwind section.
**TRAINING AND/OR QUALIFICATIONS:**
From 9.93 to 6.95, Diploma in Teaching, (Dip CSM) from Cork School of Music.
**AVAILABILITY:**
General.
**ADDITIONAL INFORMATION:**
Currently studying at RSAMD. Has had the opportunity of training with the National Youth Orchestra and Ulster Youth Orchestra. Received tuition from Marzio Conti and Göran Marcussan.

# Deirdre Brady *Flute*

**Contact:** Deirdre Brady
32, Danesfort
Castle Avenue
Clontarf
Dublin 3
**Tel:** +353 1 8335829

**KEY IRISH PERFORMANCES** (since January 1994):
10.94 BOI Arts Centre, appearing with Andrea Malir̆ (harp).
1.95 Dublin, Limerick, Waterford, appearing with the RTÉ Concert Orchestra and Andrea Malir̆.
2.96 Castletownbere, Co Cork, promoted by West Cork Music appearing with Andrea Malir̆.
**KEY PERFORMANCES OUTSIDE IRELAND** (since January 1994):
5.94 Derngate, North Hampton, promoted by Nene University, appearing with John Cranmer (piano).
6.97 Copenhagen, promoted by MTV Europe, appearing with musicians of the Danish Radio Orchestras (playing a new commission by Palle Mikkelborg.
**PRIZES/AWARDS/APPOINTMENTS:**
1.77 Appointed Flautist to the National Symphony Orchestra of Ireland.
10.92 Appointed Flautist to the RTÉ Concert Orchestra.
**TRAINING AND/OR QUALIFICATIONS:**
Senior Scholarship from the Royal Irish Academy of Music (teacher Doris Keogh). LRSM Diploma from the Royal Irish Academy of Music. Also studied with Jean Pierre Rampal in Nice.
**REGULARLY PERFORMS WITH:**
Entracte Duo (flute and harp).
**AVAILABILITY:**
Evenings.

# Marie Comiskey *Flute*

**Contact:** Ms Marie Comiskey
26, Sandyford Downs
Sandyford
Dublin 18
**Tel:** +353 1 2958742
**Email:** breilly@tinet.ie
**Other instruments:** Piccolo, alto flute.

**KEY IRISH PERFORMANCES** (since January 1994):
5.95 John Field Room, National Concert Hall, Dublin, appearing with Thérèse Fahy.
2.96 Royal Dublin Society, appearing with Thérèse Fahy.
3.97 John Field Room, NCH, Dublin, appearing with the Irish String Trio.
**REGULARLY PERFORMS WITH:**
Leslie Cassidy (guitar), Thérèse Fahy (piano).

**AVAILABILITY:**
General.
**ADDITIONAL INFORMATION:**
Studied flute with Doris Keogh at the Royal Irish Academy of Music and with Edward Beckett in London. Has given solo and chamber recitals in Dublin and plays regularly with the National Symphony Orchestra of Ireland, RTÉ Concert Orchestra and the Irish Chamber Orchestra.

## Anita Conway *Flute*

**Contact:** Anita Conway
62, Oakington Drive
Sunbury-on-Thames
Middlesex, TW16 5NW
England
**Mobile:** +44 958 200836
**Other instruments:** Piccolo.

**SELECTED BROADCASTS AND/OR RECORDED WORK:**
1990 'Maureen Hegarty show' for BBC Northern Ireland.
1993 Orford Festival de Jeunesses Musicales, for Orford Arts Centre, Quebec, Canada.
1994 Reigate Summer Music Festival, for Radio Mercury (live broadcast).
**PRIZES/AWARDS/APPOINTMENTS:**
1992 Music award from the Arts Council of Northern Ireland.
1992 Hamilton Harty award, from Queen's University, Belfast.
**TRAINING AND/OR QUALIFICATIONS:**
From 1990 to 1993, B Mus (Hons) from Queen's University, Belfast. Since 1993, Masterclasses with James Galway, William Bennett, Trevor Wye, David Butt. Private study with Kenneth Smith.
**AVAILABILITY:**
July, August.
**ADDITIONAL INFORMATION:**
Has performed at several international music festivals including Belfast Festival at Queen's and Edinburgh Festival. Available for orchestral and solo work and chamber music ensembles.

## Emma Coulthard *Flute*

**Contact:** Ms Emma Coulthard
8, Alexandra Terrace
Novara Avenue
Bray
Co Wicklow
**Tel:** +353 1 2867168
**Email:** mgmccart@indigo.ie
*See period flutes page 121.*

## Ellen Cranitch *Flute*

**Contact:** Ms Ellen Cranitch
33, Westfield Road
Harold's Cross
Dublin 6w
**Tel/Fax:** +353 1 4923486
**Other instruments:** Alto flute.
*See jazz flute page 271.*

## Eleanor Dawson *Flute*

**Contact:** Ms Eleanor Dawson
7a, Martello Avenue
Sandycove
Co Dublin
**Tel:** +353 1 2803870
*See baroque and renaissance flutes page 121.*

## Louisa Dennehy *Flute*

**Contact:** Miss Louisa Dennehy
37, Glenwood
Carrigaline
Co Cork
**Tel:** +353 21 372498
**Other instruments:** Piccolo, piano.

*"... Great technical assurance ... a particularly good range of dynamics ... the best performance of Bach's 'Badinerie' I've ever heard"*
2.97 The Examiner.

**KEY IRISH PERFORMANCES** (since January 1994):
9.95 Royal Irish Academy of Music, Dublin, promoted by William Halpin and Bríd Grant, solo flute concert.
12.96 City Hall, Cork, appearing with the Cork Youth Orchestra.
4.97 Bantry House, Co Cork, promoted by the West Cork Arts Festival, appearing with Evelyn Grant (piano).
5.97 BOI Arts Centre, Dublin, promoted by William Halpin and Bríd Grant, appearing with Evelyn Grant.
**KEY PERFORMANCES OUTSIDE IRELAND** (since January 1994):
7.95 Valencia, Spain, promoted by the International Festival for Youth Orchestras, appearing with the Cork School of Music Symphony Orchestra.
8.95 Hutton-le-Hole, North Yorkshire, promoted by Anna Noakes, appearing with Kathron Sturrock (piano).
8.96 Hutton-le-Hole, North Yorkshire, promoted by Anna Noakes, appearing with Kathron Sturrock and Gillian Tingay (harp).
**SELECTED BROADCASTS AND/OR RECORDED WORK:**
5.96 'Young Musicians of Cork' for Campus Radio.
12.96 'Young Musicians in Concert' for RTÉ Cork.
12.96 Appearing with the National Youth Orchestra of Ireland at the National Concert Hall, Dublin for RTÉ.
**PRIZES/AWARDS/APPOINTMENTS:**
1.97 1st Prize in Senior Recital Competition and Casey Cup for highest placed woodwind/brass entry by the Cork School of Music.
3.97 1st Prize Solo medal at the Feis Ceoil, Dublin, (senior flute).
**TRAINING AND/OR QUALIFICATIONS:**
Since 1990, all grades from the Cork School of Music (First Class honours obtained for first year of B Mus (Perf)).
From 1.8 to 8.8 in 1994, 1995 and 1996, and in 9.95 and 5.97 invited to perform at masterclasses with Marzio Conti and Anna Noakes
**REGULARLY PERFORMS WITH:**
Patrick Zuk (piano), Evelyn Grant (piano), Cork School of Music Flute Ensemble.
**AVAILABILITY:**
Weekends, evenings and any time during college holiday periods.
**ADDITIONAL INFORMATION:**
Has won 1st Prize at many national competitions. Experienced as Principal/First Flute with the National Youth Orchestra and local orchestras.

# William Dowdall *Flute*

**Contact:** Mr William Dowdall
13, Effra Road
Rathmines, Dublin 6
**Tel/Fax:** +353 1 4973381 / +353 1 8725292

*"... [Varese's 'Density 21.5' for solo flute, now over half a century old], is always a pleasure to encounter, especially in as persuasive a performance as it was given by William Dowdall ..."*

Irish Times.

**KEY IRISH PERFORMANCES** (since January 1994):
22.3.95 Dublin Castle, appearing with the Irish Chamber Orchestra.
6.96 West Cork Chamber Music Festival.
12.9.97 National Concert Hall, Dublin, appearing with the National Symphony Orchestra of Ireland.
16.9.97 NCH, appearing with Birgit Katzarofski (piano).
**KEY PERFORMANCES OUTSIDE IRELAND** (since January 1994):
10-12.4.95 Cleveland and Kent, Ohio, promoted by Kent State University and Cleveland Schools, appearing with Yoko Yamada.
12-17.12.95 Auckland, New Zealand, promoted by the New Zealand Flute Society, appearing with Ingrid Wahlberg.
**SELECTED BROADCASTS AND/OR RECORDED WORK:**
11.93 Soloist with the Shanghai Symphony Orchestra in the Shanghai Radio Music Festival.
6.95 'Nua Nós' and 'Density 21.5' for RTÉ.
4.96 Hamilton Harty, in Ireland, for Naxos/Marco Polo.
**SELECTED REVIEWS** (since January 1994):
23.5.94 Irish Times.
**PRIZES/AWARDS/APPOINTMENTS:**
9.79 Appointed Principal Flute of the NSOI by RTÉ.
9.95 Appointed Professor of Flute at the Royal Irish Academy of Music, Dublin.
**TRAINING AND/OR QUALIFICATIONS:**
From 9.65 to 6.68, studied at the Cleveland Music School Settlement (scholarships).
From 9.68 to 6.73, Graduate Diploma from the Cleveland Institute of Music (teacher Maurice Sharp).
**REGULARLY PERFORMS WITH:**
John Feeley (guitar), Birgit Katzarofski (piano), Réamonn Keary (piano).
**AVAILABILITY:**
General.
**ADDITIONAL INFORMATION:**
Returned to Ireland from Cleveland at the age of twenty one to become Principal Flute of the RTÉ Concert Orchestra. Since 1979, has held the position of Principal Flute with the NSOI. Has performed extensively as a soloist abroad, including appearances in USA, Hungary and China, as well as appearances on both national and international radio and television. Keen interest in contemporary music and future commissions include a sonata by Patrick Zuk and a concerto (to be commissioned by RTÉ).

# Susan Doyle *Flute*

**Contact:** Ms Susan Doyle
11, Springfield Drive
Templeogue, Dublin 6W
**Tel:** +353 1 4900316
**Other instruments:** Piccolo, alto flute.

*"... Her tone was rich and rounded ... and her phrasing was as natural and uncontrived"*

29.5.92 Irish Times, Douglas Sealy.

**KEY IRISH PERFORMANCES** (since January 1994):
15 - 30.10.96 Wexford Festival Opera, appearing with the National Symphony Orchestra of Ireland.
31.10.96 Bank Of Ireland Arts Centre, Dublin, appearing with Patrick Zuk.
22.2.97 John Field Room, National Concert Hall, promoted by Dublin Guitar Festival, appearing with Ben Dwyer.
**KEY PERFORMACES OUTSIDE IRELAND** (since January 1994):
4.94 Lucca, Italy, promoted by Istituto L. Boccherini, appearing with Giulia Dori.
2.9.94 Moulin d'Ande, France, promoted by Academi d'Eté, appearing with Satoko Matsumoto.
27.7.95 Cloître de Cimiez, Nice, France, promoted by Academie International d'Eté de Nice, appearing with Michele Innocenti.
15.7.96 Austrian Embassy, London, promoted by Eugene Feild, appearing with the London Wind Quintet.
**SELECTED BROADCASTS AND/OR RECORDED WORK:**
10.95 Pacini's 'Saffo', for Naxos, Wexford Opera Festival with NSOI.
15 - 30.10.96 Meyerbeer 'l'Etoile Du Nord', for Naxos, Wexford Opera festival with NSOI.
28.1.97 Benjamin Dwyer Sonata for flute and guitar, 3rd movement, on Cursaí Ealaine for RTÉ.
**SELECTED REVIEWS** (since January 1994):
4.95 Irish Times, (Douglas Sealy on the Irish Chamber Orchestra).
11.96 Irish Times, (Martin Adams on Mostly Modern Series).
2.97 Irish Times, (Martin Adams on final recitals of Dublin Guitar Week).
**PRIZES/AWARDS/APPOINTMENTS:**
5.95 Appointed flute teacher, at the Royal Irish Academy of Music, Dublin.
**TRAINING AND/OR QUALIFICATIONS:**
From 9.87 to 6.91 B Mus (Perf), from Trinity College, Dublin, (teacher William Halpin).
12.88 LTCL, from Trinity College London.
12.90 FTCL, from Trinity College, London.
10.93 to 10.94 Performance Diploma, from Istituto L. Boccherini, Italy, (teacher Marzio Conti)
**REGULARLY PERFORMS WITH:**
Duo with Benjamin Dwyer (guitar), Patrick Zuk (piano) and the London Wind Quintet.
**AVAILABILITY:**
General.

# Sabine Ducrot-MacNamara *Flute*

**Contact:** Sabine Ducrot-MacNamara
9, The Heights
Broadale
Co Cork
**Tel:** +353 21 895017

**SELECTED BROADCASTS AND/OR RECORDED WORK:**
RTÉ, France Musique and French television.
**PRIZES/AWARDS/APPOINTMENTS:**
1987 Prizewinner at the Maria Canals International Flute Competition.
1992 Prizewinner in the French International Sonata Competition (Vierzon).
**REGULARLY PERFORMS WITH:**
Brian McNamara (piano)
**AVAILABILITY:**
General
**ADDITIONAL INFORMATION:**
Graduated from the Conservatoire National de Region D'Aubervillers La Courneuie with Five Premier Prix at the age of fourteen. Further prizes were won during studies at the Conservatoire National Supérieur de Musique de Paris. Was First Flautist in the Paris Conservatoire Orchestra and was subsequently appointed First Flautist in the French Philharmonic Orchestra. Has performed a number of concertos with the Philharmonic Orchestra of Radio France and The Orchestra d'Ile de France.

## Brian Dunning *Flute*

**Contact:** Mr Brian Dunning
72, Moyglare Village
Maynooth
Co Kildare
**Tel/Fax:** +353 1 6285678
**Other instruments:** Alto flute.
*See jazz flute page 271.*

## Colin Fleming *Flute*

**Contact:** Mr Colin Fleming
37, Green Road
Ballyclare
Co Antrim, BT39 9AP
Northern Ireland
**Tel/Fax:** +44 1960 322958 or +44 1960 354529 / +44 1960 354529
**Email:** pyramid@iol.ie

**PRIZES/AWARDS/APPOINTMENTS:**
Appointed Principal Flute with Ulster Orchestra.
**REGULARLY PERFORMS WITH:**
Michael McGuffin (piano) and The Elmwood Trio (flute, oboe, piano).
**AVAILABILITY:**
General.

## Cathy Gallagher *Piccolo*

**Contact:** Ms Cathy Gallagher
43, Moyville Estate
Ballyboden Road
Rathfarnham
Dublin 16
**Tel:** +353 1 4944002
*See clarinet page 4.*

## James Galway *Flute*

**Contact:** Mr James Galway
c/o Kathryn Enticott
IMG Artists
Media House
3, Burlington Lane
Chiswick
London W4 2TH
England
**Tel/Fax:** +44 181 2335800 / +44 181 2335801
**Other instruments:** Penny whistle, conductor.

*"Galway, of course, is a flautist in a class of his own ..."* 21.5.97 Irish Times.

**ADDITIONAL INFORMATION:**
In 1969, was appointed Principal Flute with the Berlin Philharmonic. Since beginning a solo career in 1975, has played world-wide and his recordings (several of which have gone platinum), have won many prizes including the Grand Prix du Disque and Record of the Year Award (Billboard and Cash Box magazines). Has been awarded an OBE for his services to music.

## Evelyn Grant *Flute*

**Contact:** Ms Evelyn Grant
11, Summerhill South
Cork
**Tel:** +353 21 316088
**Email:** grantkelly@tinet.ie
**Other instruments:** Piano.

**KEY IRISH PERFORMANCES** (since January 1994):
5.96 Duncathel House, Cork, promoted by University College Cork 150, appearing with Jean Kelly and the d'Amici Ensemble.
3.97 Everyman Theatre, Cork, promoted by Childrens' Music Hour, appearing with Cork Pops Orchestra.
5.97 City Hall, Cork, appearing with the Cork Festival Orchestra.
**KEY PERFORMANCES OUTSIDE IRELAND** (since January 1994):
4.94 Conservatoire, Nice, France, appearing with Eleanor Malone.
8.96 Helmsley, Yorkshire, promoted by Ryedale Arts festival, appearing with Anna Noakes.
1.97 St Martin-in-the-Fields, London, promoted by J Pearson, appearing with Lochrian Chamber Orchestra.
3.97 St Martin-in-the-Fields, promoted by J Pearson, appearing with Lochrian Chamber Orchestra.
**SELECTED BROADCASTS AND/OR RECORDED WORK:**
Weekly broadcast on 'Evelyn Grant's Music Hour', recorded by RTÉ Radio, Cork.
12.96 'Calling The Tune' for RTÉ FM3.
**PRIZES/AWARDS/APPOINTMENTS:**
Lecturer with Cork School of Music.
**TRAINING AND/OR QUALIFICATIONS:**
From 1975 to 1979, Grad Dip, from Hochschule für Musik, Essen, Germany.
1975 LRSM (piano).
1975 LRSM (flute).
1979 FTCL (flute).
**REGULARLY PERFORMS WITH:**
d'Amici Quartet, Eleanor Malone, Jean Kelly.
**AVAILABILITY:**
General
**ADDITIONAL INFORMATION:**
Works in a wide range of musical activity. Lectures and gives regular flute and chamber music recitals. Conducts the Cork Pops Orchestra. Involved in school music projects, playing to over 10,000 children annually.

## Katy Griffiths *Flute*

**Contact:** Ms Katy Griffiths
21, Kipkarren Park
Newtownards
Co Down BT23 7AQ
Northern Ireland
**Tel/Fax:** +44 1247 810820
**Email:** lyttle@unite.co.uk
**Other instruments:** Piano (accompaniment).

**KEY IRISH PERFORMANCES** (since January 1994):
10.10.94 Whiteabbey Music Club, Belfast, appearing with Billy McCay.
1.5.96 Town Hall, Limavady as part of the Jane Ross Festival, appearing with Stephanie Hughes.
15.11.96 Elmwood Hall, Belfast, promoted by Belfast Festival at Queen's, appearing with the City of Belfast Sinfonia.
23.11.96 Town Hall, Portadown, promoted by Music Network, appearing with Stephanie Hughes
**KEY PERFORMANCES OUTSIDE IRELAND** (since January 1994):
14.7.94 Parish Church, Grimsby, as part of the Grimsby Festival, appearing with Andrew Cantrill.
19.7.94 Stag Theatre, Sevenoaks, Kent, appearing with the Lydian Orchestra.

1.10.95 Sutton Valence School, Kent, promoted by the Sutton Valence Music Club, appearing with the Sorella Trio.
7.10.95 Newton-Stewart School, promoted by Newton-Stewart Music Club, appearing with the Sorella Trio.
**SELECTED RECORDED WORK:**
31.1.95 Lunchtime concert for BBC Northern Ireland.
**PRIZES/AWARDS/APPOINTMENTS:**
1991 Awarded Bursary for Instrument Purchase by the Countess of Munster Musical Trust, London.
**TRAINING AND/OR QUALIFICATIONS:**
From 9.87 to 6.91, GRNCM (Graduate Diploma) and PPRNCM (Performance Diploma) from the Royal Northern College of Music, Manchester.
**REGULARLY PERFORMS WITH:**
Sorella Trio (flute, violin, harpsichord).
**AVAILABILITY:**
General.

## Aedín Halpin *Flute*

**Contact:** Ms Aedín Halpin
28, Simmonscourt Road
Ballsbridge
Dublin 4 (h)
c/o Royal Irish Academy of Music
36-38 Westland Row
Dublin 2 (w)
**Tel:** +353 1 6608146 (h) / +353 1 6764412 (w)
*See recorder page 122.*

## Cormac Henry *Flute*

**Contact:** Mr Cormac Henry
Flat 36
Sundial Court
38-42, Chiswell Street
London EC17 4XR
England
**Tel/Fax:** +44 171 3740495 / +44 171 6382662
**Other instruments:** Piccolo.

**KEY IRISH PERFORMANCES** (since January 1994):
5.95 John Field Room, National Concert Hall, Dublin, accompanied by Clarke Canavan.
1.96 JFR, NCH, Dublin, appearing with Anne-Marie O'Farrell and Niamh Nelson (RTÉ Musician of the Future Competition).
4.96 University of Limerick Concert Hall, appearing with UL Chamber Orchestra.
5.96 JFR, NCH, accompanied by Peter Dains.
**KEY PERFORMANCES OUTSIDE IRELAND** (since January 1994):
9.95 Luxembourg Conservatoire, appearing with the Symphonic Band of the European Union.
9.96 Felio Petrocc Theatre, Spain, appearing with the SBEU.
1.97 Barbican Centre, London, promoted by BBC Radio 3, appearing with the Guildhall Chamber Group.
**SELECTED BROADCASTS AND/OR RECORDED WORK:**
1.96 RTÉ Young Musician of the Future.
3.97 'Black Box', for RTÉ.
**PRIZES/AWARDS/APPOINTMENTS:**
4.94 Advanced Performance Certificate, awarded by Associated Board of the Royal School of Music.
**TRAINING AND/OR QUALIFICATIONS:**
From 9.94 to 6.96, DIT Conservatory of music and Drama (teacher William Halpin).
1.95 Boccerini Conservatoire, Lucca, Italy (teacher Marzio Conti).
Since September 1996, Guildhall School of Music and Drama, London, (teacher Avril Williams).
**AVAILABILITY:** General.

**ADDITIONAL INFORMATION:**
Has performance experience, both solo and orchestral, from the Irish Youth Orchestra, the European Union Youth Orchestra and in the orchestras of the GSMD.

## Philip Horan *Flute*

**Contact:** Mr Philip Horan
17, Elm Mount Park
Beaumont
Dublin 9
**Tel:** +353 1 8316096
**Other instruments:** Piccolo, recorder, shakuhachi.

**KEY IRISH PERFORMANCES** (since January 1994):
2.95 The National University of Ireland, Maynooth, appearing with John Murphy and Jonathan Healy.
12.95 Boydell Room, Trinity College, Dublin, appearing with Jonathan Healy.
3.96 University College, Cork, and The Ark, Dublin appearing with Melanie Brown and Viv Long.
5.96 Bank of Ireland Arts Centre, Dublin, promoted by UNICEF, appearing with Jonathan Healy and Raymond Deane
**KEY PERFORMANCES OUTSIDE IRELAND** (since January 1994):
9.96 Royal Albert Hall, London, promoted by promenade concerts, appearing with 'Promers' Orchestra.
11.96 Conservatoire de Saint Maur, Paris, promoted by Association Française de La Flûte, appearing with Convention Orchestra.
**TRAINING AND/OR QUALIFICATIONS:**
From 1990 to 1994, B Mus from The National University of Ireland, Maynooth.
1995 Diploma of Licentiate (flute), from Royal Irish Academy of Music, Dublin.
**REGULARLY PERFORMS WITH:**
'Flutes En Vacances', Jonathan Healy (piano), John Murphy (clarinet).
**AVAILABILITY:**
General.
**ADDITIONAL INFORMATION:**
Programme can be adapted to incorporate the following: works by Irish composers; neglected Czech and Slovak repertoire; contemporary works with extended techniques; world music (performed on the traditional instruments of Japan, China, India); crossover music (mixtures of classical, jazz, world music).

## Colin Irvine *Flute*

**Contact:** Mr Colin Irvine
38, Plantation Avenue
Carrickfergus
Co Antrim BT38 9BJ
Northern Ireland
**Tel/Fax:** +44 1960 361695

**KEY IRISH PERFORMANCES** (since January 1994):
9.95 and 9.96, BBC Belfast appearing with Michael McGuffin.
**SELECTED BROADCASTS AND/OR RECORDED WORK:**
9.95 and 9.96 Lunchtime recitals for BBC.
**TRAINING AND/OR QUALIFICATIONS:**
From 1985 to 1986, Certificate completed in Foundation Studies in Music from the University of Ulster at Jordanstown.
1986 to 1989, B Mus (Hons) from the University of Ulster at Jordanstown.
**REGULARLY PERFORMS WITH:**
Castleward Wind Quintet, Amanda Irvine (clarinet).

# Jonathan Johnston *Flute*

**Contact:** Mr Jonathan Johnston
70, Knockany Road
Carr, Lisburn
Co Down, BT27 6YB
Northern Ireland
**Tel/Mobile:** +44 1846 638546 / +44 402 477232

**KEY IRISH PERFORMANCES** (since January 1994):
25.11.94 Down Cathedral, Downpatrick, Northern Ireland a 'Celebration for the Gift of Music' by Dr Edgar Boucher, appearing with Elizabeth Bicker.
27.4.95 Government House, Hillsborough, promoted by Riding for the Disabled, appearing with Gertrude Jamison.
9.2.96 Methodist College, Belfast, appearing with Denis Totton.
23.2.96 Belfast City Hall, Belfast, promoted by Combat Cancer, appearing with Gertrude Jamison.
**KEY PERFORMANCES OUTSIDE IRELAND** (since January 1994):
25.7.95 Guild Chapel, Stratford International Flute Festival, Stratford-Upon-Avon, England, appearing with Judith Keaney.
31.7.96 Town Hall, Stratford-Upon-Avon, appearing with Corrine Auger.
22.3.97 Doncaster, Melbourne, Australia, promoted by Doncaster Charity Committee appearing with Joseph Rutherford.
**PRIZES/AWARDS/APPOINTMENTS:**
3.95 Winner of Northern Ireland Young Musician of the Year competition organised by Comber Rotary, Co Down.
10.96 Appointed Principal Flute player with the Northern Irish Chamber Orchestra.
**TRAINING AND/OR QUALIFICATIONS:**
From 1990 to 1995, studied with Mr W Dunwoody.
8.94 Masterclass with James Galway in Switzerland.
7.96 Masterclass with Jaques Zoon (Principal Flute in Boston Symphony Orchestra).
Since 9.96, Studying at Royal Northern College of Music, Manchester with Richard Davis and Peter Lloyd.
**AVAILABILITY:**
Subject to college commitments.

# Andrea Kuypers *Flute*

**Contact:** Ms Andrea Kuypers
c/o Ms Barbara Devlin
3, Abbotsford Crescent
Strathaven, ML10 6EQ
Scotland
**Tel:** +44 1357 21234

**TRAINING AND/OR QUALIFICATIONS:**
External Diploma LGSM, from Royal Northern College of Music.
**REGULARLY PERFORMS WITH:**
Cadenza.
**AVAILABILITY:**
General.
**ADDITIONAL INFORMATION:**
Has been freelancing for 10 years with orchestras. Has worked with the Royal Scottish National Orchestra, the Orchestras of Scottish Opera, Scottish Chamber Orchestra, Scottish Ballet Orchestra, BBC Scottish Symphony Orchestra and Northern Symphonia. Also is a part-time flute lecturer at Napier University in Edinburgh.

# Emer McDonough *Flute*

**Contact:** Ms Emer McDonough
3, Greenlawns
Sandyford Road
Dublin 16
**Tel:** +353 1 2956754

**Other instruments:** Recorder, piano.

*"A star was surely born ... her spirited solo work in [Kurt] Schwertsik's Instant Music was quite outstanding"* 22.2.97 Manchester Evening News (Tom Waghorn).

**KEY IRISH PERFORMANCES** (since January 1994):
7.94 National Concert Hall, Dublin, Principal Flute, Irish Youth Orchestras, conducted by Robert Houlihan.
11.95 House of Lords, Dublin, appearing with John Wilson, promoted by Classical Choice, Bank of Ireland.
**KEY PERFORMANCES OUTSIDE IRELAND** (since January 1994):
10.94 Queen's Hall, Edinburgh, Ibert Concerto, appearing with Meadows Orchestra.
10.95 South of England tour, performing the William Alwyn Concerto, appearing with Royal Northern College of Music Manchester Wind Ensemble.
7.96 Derby Cathedral, England, performing the Mozart Concerto in G Major, appearing with Derby Concert Orchestra.
2.97 Manchester RNCM, appearing with RNCM Wind Orchestra, performing Schwertsik's 'Concerto for flute'.
**SELECTED BROADCASTS AND/OR RECORDED WORK:**
4.89 Pergolesi's, 'Flute Concerto in G', for EBU Young Musicians Concert, Belgium.
11.92 Minuet and Badinaire, Suite No. 2, by J.S. Bach, for RTÉ.
2.93 Ballade for Flute, strings and piano by Martin for RTÉ.
**PRIZES/AWARDS/APPOINTMENTS:**
1990 Rose Bowl and McCullough prize, awarded by Feis Ceoil.
1993/94/95 Awards from the Arts Council and the Doris Keogh Trust.
**TRAINING AND/OR QUALIFICATIONS:**
From 1984 to 1993, Studied flute and recorder at the Royal Irish Academy of Music, Dublin (teacher Doris Keogh).
From 1981 to 1993, Studied piano, Leinster School of Music (teacher Mabel Swainson).
From 1993 to 1997 B Mus, RNCM, Manchester, (teacher Peter Lloyd).
**AVAILABILITY:**
Subject to college commitments
**ADDITIONAL INFORMATION:**
Reached semi-finals of Shell London Symphony Orchestra wind scholarship in 1997. Has worked with BBC Philharmonic and Hallé Orchestras. Since 9.97 studying for a Postgrd. Dip. for advanced performers at RNCM.

# Ann Macken *Flute*

**Contact:** Ann Macken
1, Eatonwood Court
Shankill, Co Dublin
**Tel:** +353 1 2823352
**Other instruments:** Piccolo, alto flute.

**KEY IRISH PERFORMANCES** (since January 1994):
Since 1994, Tour of Ireland with the Opera Theatre Company as part of the orchestra/ensemble.
Since 1994, concerts with the RTÉ Concert Orchestra.
**PRIZES/AWARDS/APPOINTMENTS:**
From 1987 to 1988, Appointed to RTÉ Concert Orchestra as Sub-Principal Flute.
1990 Awarded scholarship for post-graduate study at the Guildhall School of Music and Drama, London.
**TRAINING AND/OR QUALIFICATIONS:**
From 1983 to 1987, BA Mod in Music from Trinity College, Dublin.
From 1989 to 1990, Certificate of Advanced Studies in Orchestral Training from the Guildhall School of Music and Drama, London.
**REGULARLY PERFORMS WITH:**
Piacevole Wind Quintet.
**AVAILABILITY:**
General.

**ADDITIONAL INFORMATION:**
Has worked as Principal Flute with the Irish Chamber Orchestra, Opera Theatre Company, RTÉ Concert Orchestra, Irish Youth Wind Ensemble and, in 1989, was Principal Flute with the European Community Wind Ensemble during their concert tour of France, Belgium and Luxembourg. Wind finalist in both the RTÉ Young Musician of the Future Competition and twice in the Lombard and Ulster Music Foundation Competition.

# Eimear Mangan *Flute*

**Contact:** Ms Eimear Mangan
16, Glenageary Woods
Glenageary
Co Dublin
**Tel:** +353 1 2842086
*See mezzo soprano, page 104.*

# Kieran Moynihan *Flute*

**Contact:** Mr Kieran Moynihan
65, The Rise
Bishopstown
Cork
**Tel:** +353 21 542958
**Email:** kieran-m@gsmd1.demon.co.uk
**Other instruments:** Piccolo.

**KEY IRISH PERFORMANCES** (since January 1994):
1995 Triskel Arts Centre, Cork, appearing with Evelyn Grant.
1995 John Field Room, National Concert Hall, Dublin, appearing with various students of the Cork School of Music.
**KEY PERFORMANCES OUTSIDE IRELAND** (since January 1994):
1996 Montalcino, Tuscany, Italy, appearing with a wind quintet.
1996 Valencia, Spain, appearing with the European Symphonic Band.
1997 Italian Institute, London, promoted by the Guildhall School of Music and Drama, London.
**SELECTED RECORDED WORK:**
1995 and 1996 for RTÉ.
1997 Missa Solemnis, appearing with the Guildhall School of Music and Drama for BBC.
**PRIZES/AWARDS/APPOINTMENTS:**
1995 1st Prize for Senior Flute at Feis Ceoil, Dublin.
1995 Winner of fellowship scholarship from the Royal College of Music, London.
**TRAINING AND/OR QUALIFICATIONS:**
From 1985 to 1995, studied with Evelyn Grant at the Cork School of Music.
From 1995 to 1997, studied with Avril Williams at the GSMD.
**AVAILABILITY:**
Christmas, Easter and summer holiday periods.

# Mary Nugent *Flute*

**Contact:** Ms Mary Nugent
9, Gledswood Park
Clonskeagh
Dublin 14
**Tel:** +353 1 2693956
*See traditional flute page 218.*

# Ríona Ó Duinnín *Flute*

**Contact:** Ríona Ó Duinnín
Old Road
Carlingford
Co Louth
**Tel:** +353 42 73331
**Other instruments:** Piano, recorder.

*"A wonderful player ... a bit above the generally towering standards of excellence around her even"* 8.8.94 Guardian.

**KEY IRISH PERFORMANCES** (since January 1994):
2.95 Royal Dublin Society, promoted by the 'Spotlight on Youth' series, accompanied by Owen Lorigan.
3.96 National Concert Hall, Dublin, appearing with the RIAM Symphony Orchestra.
8.96 St Canice's Church, promoted by the Kilkenny Arts Festival, appearing with the RIAM Baroque Ensemble.
11.96 Pepper Canister Church, Dublin, appearing with the Hibernian Chamber Orchestra.
**KEY PERFORMANCES OUTSIDE IRELAND** (since January 1994):
8.94 Albert Hall, London, as part of the Proms series, appearing with the National Youth Orchestra of Great Britain.
5.95 The Netherlands, promoted by the Royal Irish Academy of Music, accompanied by Owen Lorigan.
7.97 Lake Placid Arts Centre, New York, as part of the Lake Placid Flute seminar, accompanied by Juliette Allen.
**SELECTED REVIEWS** (since January 1994):
7.96 Irish Times (National Youth Orchestra of Ireland).
3.97 Sunday Tribune (RDS recital with Finghin Collins).
**PRIZES/AWARDS/APPOINTMENTS:**
2.97 Awarded Woodwind Scholarship from the Yamaha Music Foundation.
4.97 Awarded West Belfast Classical Music Bursary and Audience Prize.
**TRAINING AND/OR QUALIFICATIONS:**
Since 9.94, BA in Music Performance at the Royal Irish Academy of Music, Dublin.
**REGULARLY PERFORMS WITH:**
Duo with Finghin Collins (piano), Presburg Trio, Esposito Wind Quintet.
**AVAILABILITY:**
General (prepared to travel any distance).
**ADDITIONAL INFORMATION:**
1990 - concerto performance as part of EBU Young Soloists concert in Istanbul. From 1992 to 1994, Principal Flute of the National Youth Orchestra of Great Britain. Currently a deputy with the NSOI. Has attended masterclasses with Geoffrey Gilbert, Andras Adorjan, Peter Lukas Graf, Aurele Nicolet and Julius Baker in USA.

# Eilís O'Sullivan *Flute*

**Contact:** Ms Eilís O'Sullivan
Ivy Bridge
Ballyhillogue
Mourne Abbey
Mallow, Co Cork
**Tel:** +353 22 29159
**Other instruments:** Piccolo, guitar, piano.

*"Unfazed by her formidable task ... negotiated every obstacle. Especially impressive were her expressive phrasing and rock-solid rhythmic sense"* 4.3.97 Tacoma News Tribune, Seattle, USA.

**KEY IRISH PERFORMANCES** (since January 1994):
6.96 Crawford Art Gallery, lunchtime series, appearing with Evelyn Grant (piano).
2.97 National Concert Hall, Dublin, promoted by Dublin Guitar Week, appearing with G Creedon and M Mulcahy (voice and guitars).
5.97 Triskel Arts Centre, Cork, appearing with Gerry Creedon.
5.97 Ursuline Convent, Thurles, appearing with Pat O'Keeffe (piano).
**KEY PERFORMANCES OUTSIDE IRELAND** (since January 1994):
4.95 Merchants' Hall, Glasgow, appearing with Colin Stone.
6.95 Royal Scottish Academy of Music and Drama, Glasgow, appearing with RSAMD Symphony Orchestra.
6.95 RSAMD Glasgow, promoted by Academy Now! - (contemporary music festival).
3.97 Federal Way and Auburn, Seattle, USA, appearing with Federal Way Philharmonic.
**SELECTED BROADCASTS AND/OR RECORDED WORK:**
7.94 For RTÉ, Cork.
1.95 Celtic Connections Festival, 'Mr Anderson's Fine Tunes', for BBC Scotland.
1.97 'Live At 3' for RTÉ.
**PRIZES/AWARDS/APPOINTMENTS:**
12.94 Silver medal awarded by Worshipful Company of Musicians, London.
6.94 Ist Prize, awarded by Governors Recital competition, Glasgow.
**TRAINING AND/OR QUALIFICATIONS:**
From 10.89 to 7.91, Dip CSM, LRSM, LTCL and ALCM, from Cork School of Music, Cork.
10.91 to 7.94 BA Musical studies, RSADM Glasgow.
From 10.94 to 7.95 M Mus from RSADM, Glasgow.
**REGULARLY PERFORMS WITH:**
Judith Keaney (piano), Evelyn Grant (piano), Gerry Creedon (guitar).
**ADDITIONAL INFORMATION:**
Awarded scholarships including the VEC scholarship, the Associated Board scholarship and several Arts Council awards and scholarships at the Cork School of Music. Has attended masterclasses given by James Galway, William Bennett and Andreas Brau. Broadcast and toured in Britain with the Academy Wind Quintet. Played solo flute with the European Union Wind Orchestra. Has also performed with the National Symphony Orchestra of Ireland, the RTÉ Concert Orchestra and the BBC National Orchestra of Wales.

# Ruth O'Sullivan *Flute*

**Contact:** Ms Ruth O'Sullivan
6, Clarinda Park East
Dún Laoghaire
Co Dublin
**Tel/Fax:** +353 1 2804501 or +353 1 2807268 / +353 1 2301406
**Other instruments:** Baroque flute.

**PRIZES/AWARDS/APPOINTMENTS:**
1979 Senior Flute medal at the Feis Ceoil, Dublin.
1982 Woodwind Concerto Cup at the Feis Ceoil, Dublin.
**TRAINING AND/OR QUALIFICATIONS:**
From 1979 to 1983, BA Mod (Mus) from Trinity College, Dublin.
1983 LTCL from Trinity College of Music, London.
**REGULARLY PERFORMS WITH:**
David Adams (harpsichord), Abey Donovan (guitar), Andreja Mali ř (harp), Áine Ní Dhúill (harp), Luke Tobin (guitar).
**AVAILABILITY:**
Weekends, evenings.

# Kathleen Raymond *Flute*

**Contact:** Ms Kathleen Raymond
72, Stack's Villas
Tralee
Co Kerry
**Tel:** +353 66 26973
**Other instruments:** Piano, recorder, tin whistle.

**KEY IRISH PERFORMANCES** (since January 1994):
9.96 Tralee, promoted by the Kerry School of Music, appearing with Audrey O'Carroll.
5.97 GP Conference, Killarney, promoted by the Kerry School of Music, appearing with Aidan O'Carroll.
5.97 Kenmare, appearing with Josie Le Gultrei.
**SELECTED BROADCASTS AND/OR RECORDED WORK:**
1992 'Kerry the Kingdom' a broadcasting company production of Tralee Visitor Attractions.
**TRAINING AND/OR QUALIFICATIONS:**
From 1990 to 1994, BA (Music) from the Waterford Institute of Technology.
From 1994 to 1995, Higher Diploma in Education from Trinity College, Dublin.
**REGULARLY PERFORMS WITH:**
St Brendan's Folk Choir, Siamsa Tire group, Tralee.
**AVAILABILITY:**
General.
**ADDITIONAL INFORMATION:**
Flexible repertoire. Welcomes all performance opportunities in the Kerry region.

# Emma Roche *Flute*

**Contact:** Ms Emma Roche
Cruachan
Sarsfields Court
Glanmire
Co Cork
**Tel:** +353 21 866198
**Other instruments:** Piccolo, alto flute, baroque flute.

**KEY IRISH PERFORMANCES** (since January 1994):
1.95 National Concert Hall, Dublin, appearing with Cork School of Music Flute Trio.
7.95 Triskel Arts Centre, Cork, appearing with Evelyn Grant (piano).
**KEY PERFORMANCES OUTSIDE IRELAND** (since January 1994):
12.96 Edinburgh, appearing with Magic Flutes.
3.97 Royal Scottish Academy of Music and Drama, Glasgow, appearing with Magic Flutes.
**REGULARLY PERFORMS WITH:**
Magic Flutes (flute quartet).
**PRIZES/AWARDS/APPOINTMENTS:**
1995 McCullough-Pigott trophy for senior wind section, awarded by Cork School of Music.
1996 Senior Flute, awarded by Feis Ceoil, Dublin.
**TRAINING AND/OR QUALIFICATIONS:**
From 9.86 to 6.95, Cork School of Music, (teacher Evelyn Grant).
Since 9.95 Royal Scottish Academy of Music, (teacher David Nicholson).
**AVAILABILITY:**
General.

## Andrew Rowan *Flute*

**Contact:** Mr Andrew Rowan
10, Galbraith Gardens
Waringstown BT66 7QN
Northern Ireland
**Tel:** +44 1762 881097
**Other instruments:** Tin whistle, clarinet, saxophone.

**TRAINING AND/OR QUALIFICATIONS:**
FLCM, LLCM, ALCM.
**AVAILABILITY:**
Weekends, evenings from July to August.
**ADDITIONAL INFORMATION:**
Has worked for the last 25 years as a soloist. Adjudicator at the Carrickfergus and Portadown Music Festivals. Also adjudicates brass/woodwind/accordion, bands and groups, in Northern Ireland and Donegal. Lecturer on part-flute bands and their development. Has been involved in broadcasts with Radio Ulster/BBC World Service since 1974.

# CLASSICAL GUITAR

## Johanna Byrne *Classical Guitar*

**Contact:** Ms Johanna Byrne
36, Shannon Drive
Corbally
Limerick
**Tel:** +353 61 342829
*See mezzo soprano page 100.*

## Leslie Cassidy *Classical Guitar*

**Contact:** Mr Leslie Cassidy
38, The Thatch Road
Whitehall
Dublin 9
**Tel:** +353 1 8377076
**Other instruments:** Flamenco guitar, electric guitar, banjo, mandolin.

*"Leslie Cassidy played with admirable skill and smoothness ... "* 5.94 Irish Times.

**KEY IRISH PERFORMANCES** (since January 1994):
5.94 National Concert Hall, Dublin, solo performance.
9.94 NCH Dublin, appearing with Mary Sheridan de Bruin.
9.95 and 5.97 NCH, Dublin, solo performance.
**SELECTED BROADCASTS AND/OR RECORDED WORK:**
10.88 'Classics from the Romantic Repertoire' own cassette.
10.92 Arts Channel.
9.95 'Live at 3' for RTÉ.
**SELECTED REVIEWS** (since January 1994):
9.95 Irish Times.
**PRIZES/AWARDS/APPOINTMENTS:**
12.79 Awarded Senior Scholarship by the Royal Irish Academy of Music, Dublin.
**TRAINING AND/OR QUALIFICATIONS:**
From 1977 to 1981, LTCL from the Royal Irish Academy of Music.
From 1980 to 1986, Masterclasses with Gabrielle Estarellas, Timothy Kain, Elliot Fisk and Paul Gregory.
From 1981 to 1985, FTCL from the DIT Conservatory of Music and Drama.
**REGULARLY PERFORMS WITH:**
Goyescas Duo with Patricia Higgins (violin) and duo with Marie Comiskey (flute).
**AVAILABILITY:**
General, during summer months.
**ADDITIONAL INFORMATION:**
Offers a recital programme featuring both flamenco and classical guitar(s). Teacher at the DIT CMD, Newpark Music Centre and the Leinster School of Music. Has also taught at the Waterford Institute of Technology.

## Barbara Connolly *Classical Guitar*

**Contact:** Ms Barbara Connolly
c/o Ms Barbara Devlin
3, Abbotsford Crescent
Strathaven, ML10 6EQ
Scotland
**Tel:** +44 1357 21234

*"Strong, colourful, incisive and confident ... played to perfection"* 1992 Classical Guitar Magazine.

**PRIZES/AWARDS/APPOINTMENTS:**
1983 RTÉ Young Musician of the Future.
1983 Seven year scholarship to study in England, awarded by Ericsson.
1991 Govenor's Prize for strings (2nd), awarded by Royal Scottish Academy of Music and Drama.
**TRAINING AND/OR QUALIFICATIONS:**
From 9.86 to 7.90, GRNCM from Royal Northern College of Music, Manchester.
From 9.90 to 7.91, Postgraduate Degree, from Royal Scottish Academy of Music and Drama.
**REGULARLY PERFORMS WITH:**
Cadenza (flute and guitar).
**AVAILABILITY:**
General.

## Jerry Creedon *Classical Guitar*

**Contact:** Mr Jerry Creedon
25, Melbourn Court
Model Farm Road, Cork
**Tel:** +353 21 341826
**Other instruments:** Jazz guitar.

*"I was much impressed by what I perceive as a Jerry Creedon who has upped his performing skills by an untold number of percentage points! congratulations!"* 12.11.90 The Examiner.

**KEY IRISH PERFORMANCES** (since January 1994):
15.2.92 National Concert Hall, Dublin, promoted by Dublin Guitar Week, appearing with Eilís O'Sullivan (flute) and Mary Mulcahy (soprano).
28.7.94 St Barrahane's Festival of Church Music, Castletownshend, Co Cork, appearing with Patricia Moynihan (flute).
19.5.95 NCH, Dublin.
14.5.96 NCH, Dublin, appearing with Mel Mercier (percussion).
**KEY PERFORMANCES OUTSIDE IRELAND** (since January 1994):
6.95 Skopelos Festival, Greece.
6.97 Cannes, France, appearing with Eilís O'Sullivan (flute).
**SELECTED BROADCASTS AND/OR RECORDED WORK:**
3.91 'Kenny Live' for RTÉ.
10.93 'Bibi' for RTÉ.
1.97 'Live at 3' for RTÉ.

**SELECTED REVIEWS** (since January 1994):
5.94 The Examiner.
5.96 Irish Times.
2.97 Irish Times.
**PRIZES/AWARDS/APPOINTMENTS:**
1982 Awarded scholarship to study Spanish Music by the Spanish Government.
1990 Appointed Director of Guitar Studies by Cork County VEC.
**TRAINING AND/OR QUALIFICATIONS:**
From 1971 to 1975, BA from University College, Cork.
From 1981 to 1982, Studied privately in Germany (teacher Professor Siegfried Behrend).
1982, Diploma in Spanish Music from University of Santiago de Compostela, Spain.
From 1983 to 1995, Cordoba, Spain, attended masterclasses with John Williams.
**REGULARLY PERFORMS WITH:**
Eilís O'Sullivan (flute), Jerry Creedon Jazz Ensemble, Orpheus Trio (flute, guitar, cello).
**AVAILABILITY:**
General.
**ADDITIONAL INFORMATION:**
Experienced in performing, both as a soloist and a member of various ensembles. Specialises in crossover music (classical and jazz).

## Benjamin Dwyer *Classical Guitar*

**Contact:** Mr Benjamin Dwyer,
90, The Steeples
Chapelizod, Dublin 20
**Tel/Fax/Mobile:** +353 1 6234397 / +353 1 6234397 / +353 87 616391
**Email:** bdwyer@indigo.ie

*" Command of the necessary subtleties was one of this recital's many rewards ... subtle, provocative, highly artistic ... very rewarding"* Irish Times.

**KEY IRISH PERFORMANCES** (Since January 1994):
8.96 Dublin performing the Villa-Lobos Guitar Concerto with the RTÉ Concert Orchestra.
7.97 National Concert Hall, Dublin, Schubert Bi-Centenary Concert Series (devised by B Dwyer) and appearing with John Elwes (tenor) and Hugh Tinney (piano).
1.97 Hugh Lane Municipal Gallery of Modern Art, in a performance of own compositions.
**PRIZES/AWARDS/APPOINTMENTS:**
Awarded MacNamara Gold Medal for Excellence. Awarded Villa Lobos Centenary Medal by the Brazillian Government. Awarded scholarship to study composition at Doctorate level at Queen's University, Belfast.
**TRAINING AND/OR QUALIFICATIONS:**
Degree in Music (First Class Hons) from Trinity College Dublin and DIT Conservatory of Music and Drama. Has studied composition with John Buckley.
**REGULARLY PERFORMS WITH:**
Kenneth Edge (saxophone), Trio Cervantes.
**ADDITIONAL INFORMATION:**
Has given several performances in Europe and the USA. Was featured in the ISCM Festival in Moldova in 1995. Output includes works for choir, chamber orchestra and chamber music combinations. Director and Artistic Director of the Bank of Ireland Mostly Modern series.
*See composers page 181.*

## John Feeley *Classical Guitar*

**Contact:** John Feeley
14, Wesley Road
Rathgar, Dublin 6
**Tel/Fax:** +353 1 4905495

**Other instruments:** Vihuela, lute, baroque guitar.

*"He is bolder, more imaginative interpreter than most of the young guitarists with an especially appealing ability to impart a gently fluid momentum to the line"* New York Times (Joseph Horowitz).

**KEY IRISH PERFORMANCES** (since January 1994):
Has performed extensively: Ulster Hall with Ulster Orchestra and the National Concert Hall, Dublin, O'Reilly Hall, University College, Dublin, appearing with the RTÉ Concert Orchestra
**KEY PERFORMANCES OUTSIDE IRELAND** (since January 1994):
Has performed extensively: Sydney Opera House, Old Opera House, Frankfurt, Bath International Guitar Festival, Scottish Royal Conservatory, Glasgow, Carnegie Hall New York, etc.
**SELECTED BROADCASTS AND/OR RECORDED WORK:**
1985 'John Feeley' for Gael Linn.
1990 'Spanish Guitar Classics' for CBA Classics.
1996 'Contemporary Irish Guitar Music' for BGS Classics.
**SELECTED REVIEWS** (since January 1994):
Classical Guitar Magazine, Guitar Review.
**PRIZES/AWARDS/APPOINTMENTS:**
1984 Special Award for Interpretation at the Mauro Giuliani Competition, Italy. Lecturer in guitar at the DIT Conservatory of Music and Drama.
**TRAINING AND/OR QUALIFICATIONS:**
MA from City University, New York. B Mus, FTCL LTCL.
**REGULARLY PERFORMS WITH:**
William Dowdall (flute).
**AVAILABILITY:**
General.
**ADDITIONAL INFORMATION:**
Has studied in the USA with a number of guitarists including Oscar Ghiglia, Angel Romero and David Russell.
Compositions written for him include: A guitar concerto, by Jerome de Bromhead; a quintet for guitar and string quartet, by Andrew Shiels. 'Four Pieces' by Jane O'Leary; two concertos by Brent Parker and an extended work for solo guitar by the American Composer, Robert Newell. Has performed with jazz guitarist Louis Stewart, the Alice Artzt Trio, Ray Burley, Simon Dinnigan, Alan Neave. Currently compiling a CD of contemporary Irish music for international release.

## Alan Grundy *Classical Guitar*

**Contact:** Alan Grundy
c/o The Dublin School of Guitar
26/27, Drury Street
Dublin 2
**Tel/Fax:** +353 1 6714732 or +353 1 6249199 / +353 1 6796049

*". . . An excellent guitarist"*
Classical Guitar International (Colin Cooper).

**KEY IRISH PERFORMANCES** (since January 1994):
25.10.96 National Concert Hall, Dublin, appearing with RTÉ Concert Orchestra.
**KEY PERFORMANCES OUTSIDE IRELAND** (since January 1994):
4.97 Three performances in Budapest.
**SELECTED BROADCASTS AND/OR RECORDED WORK:**
8.94 'Guitar Moods' (own tape).
2.95 'Cursaí' for RTÉ.
25.10.96 Vivaldi - Concerto in D for RTÉ plus other recordings for RTÉ FM3.
**PRIZES/AWARDS/APPOINTMENTS:**
1981 Appointed classical guitar teacher at the DIT Conservatory of Music and Drama.

**TRAINING AND/OR QUALIFICATIONS:**
ALCM from London College of Music, LRSM from the Associated Board of the Royal Schools of Music.
**REGULARLY PERFORMS WITH:**
Trio Cervantes.
**AVAILABILITY:**
General.
**ADDITIONAL INFORMATION:**
Has given numerous recitals throughout Ireland and Europe. Performed the 1993 world premiere at the Hugh Lane Municipal Gallery of Modern Art, Dublin of 'Homage to Segovia' by Donal Hurley. Also performed the Italian and Hungarian premiers of this work, in Rome and Budapest respectively.

## Shayron Hobbs *Classical Guitar*

**Contact:** Ms Shayron Hobbs
110, Earlwood Estate
The Lough
Cork
**Tel:** +353 21 962370

*See soprano page 89.*

## Michael Howard *Classical Guitar*

**Contact:** Mr Michael Howard
53, Balkill Park
Howth
Co Dublin
**Tel:** +353 1 8323475
**Email:** howmac@indigo.ie
**Other instruments:** Mandolin, bouzouki, bodhrán.

**KEY IRISH PERFORMANCES** (since January 1994):
9.94 Clifden Community Arts Week, Co Galway promoted by Brendan Flynn.
11.96 St Patrick's Cathedral, Dublin, promoted by Sutton Park School in a premier of work for guitar and strings.
5.97 Instituto Cervantes Dublin, promoted by the IC.
**KEY PERFORMANCES OUTSIDE IRELAND** (since January 1994):
7.95 Skein, Norway, ensemble performance.
**SELECTED BROADCASTS AND/OR RECORDED WORK:**
1989 'In our own time' for by Harmac Records.
**PRIZES/AWARDS/APPOINTMENTS:**
1967 1st Prize, awarded by Feis Ceoil, Dublin.
**TRAINING AND/OR QUALIFICATIONS:**
From 1969 to 1972, Studied with Julian Byzantine.
From 1973 to 1974, Masterclasses with Oscar Ghiglia in Italy and John Williams in London.
**REGULARLY PERFORMS WITH:**
Aisling Drury Byrne (cello), John Sheahan (fiddle) Máire Breathnach (violin and viola).
**AVAILABILITY:**
General.
**ADDITIONAL INFORMATION:**
Variety of experiences as a solo performer and composer in different media and as an ensemble performer in duo, trio, quartet and orchestral settings. Also works in recording and has a experience in television and radio.

## Michael McCartney *Classical Guitar*

**Contact:** Mr Michael McCartney
8, Alexandra Terrace
Novara Avenue
Bray
Co Wicklow
**Tel/Fax:** +353 1 2867168
**Email:** mgmccart@indigo.ie
**Other instruments:** 19th Century guitars.

**KEY IRISH PERFORMANCES** (since January 1994):
10.94 St Finian's Church, Dublin, appearing with Emma Coulthard.
12.94 Coláiste Ráithín, Bray, promoted by Bray VEC, appearing with Emma Coulthard.
6.95 St Ann's Church, Dawson Street, Dublin, appearing with Emma Coulthard.
**KEY PERFORMANCES OUTSIDE IRELAND** (since January 1994):
10.94 State University of New York at Purchase.
9.95 Snug Harbour Cultural Center, Staten Island, New York, promoted by Snug Harbour Cultural Center, and the Department of Foreign Affairs, appearing with Emma Coulthard.
**SELECTED BROADCASTS AND/OR RECORDED WORK:**
1993 'Pat Kenny Show' for RTÉ.
1993 Anna Livia Radio.
1994 Opera Interval Talk (Wexford Festival) for RTÉ.
**PRIZES/AWARDS/APPOINTMENTS:**
From 1989 to 1990, appointed assistant to David Starobin, Head of Guitar at the State University of New York at Purchase.
**TRAINING AND/OR QUALIFICATIONS:**
From 1984 to 1988, Bachelor of Fine Arts (cum laude) from State University of New York.
From 1989 to 1990, studied at State University of New York with David Starobin.
Since 1993 studies for PhD at Queen's University, Belfast.
**REGULARLY PERFORMS WITH:**
Emma Coulthard (flute).
**AVAILABILITY:**
General.

## Jim McCullagh *Classical Guitar*

**Contact:** Mr Jim McCullagh
c/o Ulster College of Music
13, Windsor Avenue
Belfast BT9
Northern Ireland
**Tel:** +44 1232 381314
**Other instruments:** Classical and jazz piano, jazz guitar.

**KEY IRISH PERFORMANCES** (since January 1994):
1995 Europa Hotel, Belfast.
10.96 Hillsborough Castle, promoted by the Ulster College of Music.
3.97 Belfast City Hall, promoted by the Ulster College of Music.
12.97 Culloden Hotel, Hollywood, Co Down promoted by Ted Palmer.
**KEY PERFORMANCES OUTSIDE IRELAND** (since January 1994):
8.96 The Guildhall, Bath, England, promoted by the International Guitar Festival appearing with other students.
**PRIZES/AWARDS/APPOINTMENTS:**
6.96 Award from the Arts Council of Northern Ireland to attend the Guitar Summer School in Bath.
**TRAINING AND/OR QUALIFICATIONS:**
From 1988 to 1989, Certificate in Music from the University of Ulster at Jordanstown.
From 1988 to 1990, Queen's University, Belfast, Certificate in Music History.
From 1984 to 1990, Belfast School of Music, Grade 8 theory and Grade 8 guitar.

1994/1996, Attended the International Jazz Summer School in the University of Ulster at Jordanstown.
**REGULARLY PERFORMS WITH:**
The Classical Guitar Society of Northern Ireland and occasionally with jazz ensembles.
**AVAILABILITY:**
General.

## Margo McGeeney *Classical Guitar*

**Contact:** Ms Margo McGeeney
Geeha South
Kinvara
Co Galway
**Tel:** +353 91 637505
*See harpsichord page 125.*

## Mark O'Leary *Classical Guitar*

**Contact:** Mr Mark O'Leary
59, Greenhills Court
South Douglas Road
Cork
**Tel:** +353 21 361808
*See jazz guitar page 274.*

## Eilís O'Sullivan *Classical Guitar*

**Contact:** Ms Eilís O'Sullivan
Ivy Bridge
Ballyhillogue
Mourne Abbey
Mallow
Co Cork
**Tel:** +353 22 29159
*See flute page 17.*

## Michael O'Toole *Classical Guitar*

**Contact:** Mr Michael O'Toole
49, Great Southern
Newbridge
Co Kildare
**Tel:** +353 45 434163

**KEY IRISH PERFORMANCES** (since January 1994):
1995/96 National Concert Hall, Dublin.
1995 Irish Museum of Modern Art, Dublin.
1996 Belfast Arts Centre.
1996/97 Wexford Arts Centre.
**KEY PERFORMANCES OUTSIDE IRELAND** (since January 1994):
1995/96/97 Bath Guitar Festival.
**PRIZES/AWARDS/APPOINTMENTS:**
9.95 M Mus Scholarship and appointed Guitar Tutor by DIT Conservatory of Music and Drama, Dublin.
**TRAINING AND/OR QUALIFICATIONS:**
From 9.91 to 6.95 B Mus (Perf), Grad Dip Mus from DIT CMD (teacher John Feeley).
From 9.95 to 9.97 M Mus from University College, Cork and DIT CMD.
**AVAILABILITY:**
General.
**ADDITIONAL INFORMATION:**
Winner of Feis Ceoil Solo Guitar and George Lowder Cup for Bach on Guitar. String finalist in 1995/96 Ulster Bank Foundation Music Competition.

## Sebastien Petiet *Classical Guitar*

**Contact:** c/o Marie Petiet
23, Park Crescent House
Blackhorse Avenue
Dublin 7
**Tel:** +353 1 8681210
*See violin page 65.*

## Philip Richardson *Classical Guitar*

**Contact:** Mr. Philip Richardson
16, Aberdelghy Park
Lisburn
Co Antrim
BT27 4QF Northern Ireland
**Tel:** +44 1846 664953

**KEY IRISH PERFORMANCES** (since January 1994):
7.96 Foyle Arts Centre, Derry City, promoted by Foyle Summer School of Music and Drama.
11.96 Belfast Festival at Queen's.
2.97 Queen's University Belfast, promoted by Northern Ireland Guitar Society.
4.97 Triskel Arts Centre, Cork.
**SELECTED REVIEWS** (since January 1994):
2.95 Irish News.
15.11.95 Lisburn Echo.
11.96 Belfast Newsletter.
**TRAINING AND/OR QUALIFICATIONS:**
From 10.88 to 6.91, B Mus (Hons), awarded by University of Ulster, Jordanstown.
From 9.92 to 6.93, Certificate of Advanced Performance, awarded by the Guildhall School of Music and Drama, London.
From 1993 to 1994, Certificate of Advanced Performance, awarded by Royal Scottish Academy of Music and Drama.
**REGULARLY PERFORMS WITH:**
Quodlibet.
**AVAILABILITY:**
General.

## Simon Taylor *Classical Guitar*

**Contact:** Mr Simon Taylor
17, The Rise
Parc Na Silla
Loughlinstown
Co Dublin
**Tel:** +353 1 2820193

**SELECTED BROADCASTS AND/OR RECORDED WORK:**
1987 'The Irish Guitar', for Ossian, Cork.
**TRAINING AND/OR QUALIFICATIONS:**
1979 ALCM, LLCM and FLCM from the London College of Music.
**AVAILABILITY:**
General.
**ADDITIONAL INFORMATION:**
Has performed in Madrid, Iceland and the USA.

## Hilary Travers *Classical Guitar*

**Contact:** Ms Hilary Travers
39, Brook Court
Monkstown, Co Dublin
**Tel:** +353 1 2809699
*See violin page 67.*

## Bernard Traynor *Classical Guitar*

**Contact:** Mr Bernard Traynor
26/27, Drury Street
Dublin 2
**Tel/Mobile:** +353 1 4518527 (h) / +353 87 2345736
**Other instruments:** Piano.

**RECORDED WORK:**
1997 Anna Livia Radio recording.
**PRIZES/AWARDS/APPOINTMENTS:**
Winner of numerous classical guitar competitions.
**TRAINING AND/OR QUALIFICATIONS:**
FLCM, LTCL, LLCM.
**REGULARLY PERFORMS WITH:**
Classical Fusion and Blue Guitar Quartet.
**AVAILABILITY:**
General.

# FRENCH HORN

Also see orchestra members lists on page 140.

## David Carmody *French Horn*

**Contact:** David Carmody
33, Westfield Road
Harold's Cross
Dublin 6w
**Tel:** +353 1 4923486
**Other instruments:** Hand horn, cornetto.

**AVAILABILITY:**
Subject to RTÉ Concert Orchestra schedules.
**ADDITIONAL INFORMATION:**
Principal Horn and soloist with the RTÉ Concert Orchestra. Has also performed solo on hand horn and would welcome more opportunity to do so. Enjoys choral conducting as a past time, and has conducted the Cameron Singers for some years.

## Andre Cavanagh *French Horn*

**Contact:** Mr Andre Cavanagh
37, Slieve Bloom Park
Drimnagh
Dublin 12
**Tel:** +353 1 4521282

**PRIZES/AWARDS/APPOINTMENTS:**
6.95 Walton Cup winner at the Feis Ceoil, Dublin.
1.96 Honourable mention at the RTÉ Young Musician of the Future Competition.
**REGULARLY PERFORMS WITH:**
Royal Irish Academy of Music Horn Quintet.
**AVAILABILITY:**
General.

## Mary Curran *French Horn*

**Contact:** Mary Curran
Derryribbeen
Clogher
Westport
Co Mayo
**Tel:** +353 98 41983

**SELECTED BROADCASTS AND/OR RECORDED WORK:**
Performances with the RTÉ Concert Orchestra.
**PRIZES/AWARDS/APPOINTMENTS:**
From 1992 to 1996, full-time freelance with the RTÉ Concert Orchestra.
**REGULARLY PERFORMS WITH:**
RTÉCO, The Five Bells Wind Quintet, Westport Ensemble.
**AVAILABILITY:**
General.

## Eoin Gillen *French Horn*

**Contact:** Eoin Gillen
1, Southwood Park
Blackrock
Co Dublin
**Tel:** +353 1 2880880
**Email:** ggillen@homenet.ie

**KEY IRISH PERFORMANCES** (since January 1994):
1.94/95/96 National Concert Hall, Dublin appearing with the National Youth Orchestra.
7.95 Boyle Arts Festival, Methodist Church, Boyle appearing with 'Just 4 Horns'.
21.9.96 Clifden Community Arts Week, Church of Ireland, Clifden, appearing with Cambridge Winds.
20.9.96 Instituto Cervantes, Dublin.
**KEY PERFORMANCES OUTSIDE IRELAND** (since January 1994):
7.94 Tour of Hungary, appearing with the NYO.
11.94 Cambridge Elgar Festival, Corn Exchange, Cambridge appearing with Cambridge University Chamber Orchestra.
8.95 Threshold Theatre Company, Edinburgh Fringe Festival, Southside Theatre, Edinburgh.
3.97 Emmanuel College Music Society, appearing with the Emmanuel College Orchestra, Queen's Building, Cambridge.
**SELECTED REVIEWS** (since January 1994):
9.8.94 Irish Times.
11.8.95 Roscommon Herald.
**PRIZES/AWARDS/APPOINTMENTS:**
9.94 Instrumental Award from Cambridge University.
9.96 Deputy member of the National Symphony Orchestra of Ireland.
**TRAINING AND/OR QUALIFICATIONS:**
From 10.94 to 6.97, BA Mus (Ist Hons) awarded by Cambridge University.
**AVAILABILITY:**
General.
**REGULARLY PERFORMS WITH:**
Cambridge Winds.
**ADDITIONAL INFORMATION:**
Experienced as a soloist and chamber musician. Has performed with Trinity Brass Quintet in the young performers platform at the National Concert Hall and has attended regular wind quintet masterclasses with oboist, Douglas Boyd.

## Paul Goodman *French Horn*

**Contact:** Mr Paul Goodman
Ballyminogue
Scariff
Co Clare
**Other instruments:** Piano.

**KEY IRISH PERFORMANCES** (since January 1994):
1996 Ulster Hall, appearing with Ulster Orchestra.
1996 National Concert Hall, Dublin, appearing with National Symphony Orchestra of Ireland.
1997 Guildhall, Derry, promoted by the Classical Music Society, appearing with Francis King.
**PRIZES/AWARDS/APPOINTMENTS:**
1985 Entrance Scholarship to the Royal College of Music, London.
**TRAINING AND/OR QUALIFICATIONS:**
From 1982 to 1985, Chetham's School of Music, Manchester.
From 1985 to 1989, Dip RCM and ARCM from the Royal College of Music, London.
**AVAILABILITY:**
General.
**ADDITIONAL INFORMATION:**
Always interested in speaking to other musicians wanting to form new groups. Has taught brass for the library music services in Northern Ireland.

## Aidan Lynch *French Horn*

**Contact:** Mr Aidan Lynch
15, Hawthorn Avenue
Ballycasheen
Killarney
Co Kerry
**Tel/Fax/Mobile:** +353 64 33749 / +353 87 2202382
*See trumpet page 54.*

## Fearghal Ó Ceallacháin *French Horn*

**Contact:** Mr Fearghal Ó Ceallacháin
7, Laurel Hill
Upper Glenageary Road
Dún Laoghaire
Co Dublin
**Tel:** +353 1 2800270

## John Killian Ryan *French Horn*

**Contact:** Mr John Killian Ryan
27, Whitecliff
Rathfarnham
Dublin 16
**Tel:** +353 1 4943902
**Other instruments:** Piano.

**KEY IRISH PERFORMANCES** (since January 1994):
1995 Armoury Arts, Dublin, promoted by the Bank of Ireland, appearing with D Kelleher.
**KEY PERFORMANCES OUTSIDE IRELAND** (since January 1994):
4.97 Conservatoire, Caen, France Concerto no 1, by Strauss, appearing with the Dublin Youth Symphony Orchestra.
**SELECTED BROADCASTS AND/OR RECORDED WORK:**
12.94 'Late Late Show' for RTÉ, appearing with Frank McNamara.
6.97 RTÉ FM3, appearing with D Kelleher.
**PRIZES/AWARDS/APPOINTMENTS:**
3.94 Senior French Horn winner at the RDS, Dublin.
3.97 Guinness Brass Bursary winner at the Feis Ceoil, Dublin.
**TRAINING AND/OR QUALIFICATIONS:**
Masterclasses with Julian Baker and Jeff Bryant.
6.95 Associated Board Advanced Certificate (distinction).
8.96 Wind Quintet masterclasses at the Nice Academy, France (teacher Marzio Conti).
**REGULARLY PERFORMS WITH:**
National Youth Orchestra, European Youth Orchestra.
**AVAILABILITY:**
Subject to college schedule.

# OBOE

Also see orchestra members lists on page 140.

## David Agnew *Oboe*

**Contact:** Mr David Agnew
Beaufort House
Butterfield Avenue
Rathfarnham, Dublin 14
**Tel/Fax:** +353 1 4945939
**Email:** oboeking@iol.ie
**Other instruments:** Cor anglais, recorders.

**KEY IRISH PERFORMANCES** (since January 1994):
8.94 National Concert Hall Dublin, promoted by RTÉ, appearing with RTÉ Concert Orchestra.
8.95 St Michael's, Dún Laoghaire, Co Dublin, promoted by Dún Laoghaire Organ Festival, appearing with Peter Sweeney (organ).
9.95 NCH Dublin, appearing at Lord Mayor's Gala with the RTÉCO.
8.96 NCH promoted by RTÉ, appearing with the RTÉCO.
**KEY PERFORMANCES OUTSIDE IRELAND** (since January 1994):
10.94 Munich Concert Hall, promoted by Munich Festival Committee, appearing with RTÉCO.
11.94 Hammermet Tunisia, promoted by London/Tunisia office.
3.97 New York, promoted by Mayor's Office, appearing with Phil Coulter.
1997 Roy Theatre, Toronto, promoted by RTÉ and Gamma Productions, appearing with RTÉCO.
**SELECTED BROADCASTS AND/OR RECORDED WORK:**
6.89 'Music of the Night' for KTel.
12.92 'The Way I Feel' for KTel.
11.96 'Celtic Moods' for KTel.
**TRAINING AND/OR QUALIFICATIONS:**
1981, LTCL (teaching) from the DIT Conservatory of Music and Drama, Dublin.
**REGULARLY PERFORMS WITH:**
RTÉCO, Frank McNamara (piano).
**AVAILABILITY:**
General.
**ADDITIONAL INFORMATION:**
Recitals range from strictly classical, to popular oboe and organ repertoire with Peter Sweeney, to an evening of talk and light classical music.

## Ruby Ashley *Oboe*

**Contact:** Ms Ruby Ashley
49, Weirview Drive
Stillorgan
Co Dublin
**Tel:** +353 1 2882467
**Other instruments:** Oboe d'amore, cor anglais.

*"A most memorable performance of 'Swan of Tuonela' - beautifully spacious"* 3.91 Irish Times.

**KEY IRISH PERFORMANCES** (since January 1994):
5.93 National Gallery of Ireland, Dublin, promoted by RTÉ, appearing with The Degani Ensemble.
1/2.94 National Concert Hall, Dublin, promoted by RTÉ, appearing with The Degani Ensemble.
6.94 Hugh Lane Municipal Gallery of Modern Art, Dublin, promoted by the Arts Council, appearing with Concorde.
11.94 NCH, appearing with The Degani Ensemble.
**SELECTED BROADCASTS AND/OR RECORDED WORK:**
1991 Bach's Oboe d'Amore Concerto in D minor for RTÉ.
1992 Donizetti's Cor Anglais Concerto, for RTÉ.
1993 Love sonata for Oboe d'Amore, recorded by RTÉ.
**PRIZES/AWARDS/APPOINTMENTS:**
1979 Awarded Concerto Prize by The Royal Northern College of Music, Manchester.
1979 DAAD scholarship, awarded by Deutsche Academischer Austauschdienst.
1981 Scholarship, awarded by the Rotary Club.
**TRAINING AND/OR QUALIFICATIONS:**
From 1976 to 1980, GRNCM, from the RNCM.
From 1980 to 1982, Attended Nordwestdeutsche Musicadademie, West Germany.
From 1982 to 1983, Diploma in Orchestral Studies, awarded by Goldsmiths University, London.
**REGULARLY PERFORMS WITH:**
Degani Ensemble (wind quintet, string quartet and piano where necessary), Concorde.
**AVAILABILITY:**
Subject to schedule.
**ADDITIONAL INFORMATION:**
Freelances in Ireland. Has an interest in contemporary music for oboe, oboe d'amore and cor anglais. Also conducts a children's orchestra, arranging music for all instruments. Coach for the oboe section of the National Youth Orchestra of Ireland.

# Aisling Casey *Oboe*

**Contact:** Ms Aisling Casey
12, Beverly, Ovens
Co Cork
**Tel:** +353 21 870676
**Other instruments:** Cor anglais, oboe d'amore.

**KEY IRISH PERFORMANCES** (since January 1994):
1.94 Bank of Ireland, Dublin, promoted by RTÉ Young Musician of the Future, appearing with Darina Gibson.
3.94 Cork School of Music, promoted by Cork Orchestral Society, appearing with the RTÉ Vanbrugh Quartet.
2.96 Cork School of Music, promoted by Cork Orchestral Society, appearing with the Chameleon Trio.
**KEY PERFORMANCES OUTSIDE IRELAND** (since January 1994):
5.95 Nine concerts in South Africa, promoted by CAPAB, appearing with the Chameleon Trio.
2.96 Kanapée, Hannover, appearing with the Chameleon Trio.
12.96 Hochschule, Hannover, appearing with Catherine Roycroft.
5.97 Würzburg Hochschule, appearing with Catherine Roycroft.
**SELECTED BROADCASTS AND/OR RECORDED WORK:**
1.94 For RTÉ.
5.95 For SABC.
5.96 For RTÉ.
**SELECTED REVIEWS** (since January 1994):
5.95 East London Herald (South Africa).
**PRIZES/AWARDS/APPOINTMENTS:**
1.94 1st Prize in the Yamaha Scholarship, Germany.
13.5.97 3rd Prize winner in the Hochschule Competition, Germany.
**TRAINING AND/OR QUALIFICATIONS:**
From 1990 to 1993, BA in Music and Psychology, from University College, Cork.
1992 LTCL From Trinity College, London.
From 1993 to 1997, KA from the Hochschule für Musik (teacher Prof Klaus Becker).
**REGULARLY PERFORMS WITH:**
Chameleon Trio (oboe bassoon, piano), Viala Trio (2 oboes, cor anglais).
**AVAILABILITY:**
Subject to orchestra schedule - see below*.
**ADDITIONAL INFORMATION:**
Since August 1997, Co Principal oboe* with the Nederlands Philharmonic Orchestra.

# Brenda McCarthy *Oboe*

**Contact:** Ms Brenda McCarthy
90, Trees Road
Mount Merrion
Co Dublin
**Tel:** +353 1 2889758
*See piano page 42.*

# Cecilia Madden *Oboe*

**Contact:** Ms Cecilia Madden
44, Downey Street
Killalee
Limerick
Co Limerick
**Tel:** +353 61 400820
**Other instruments:** Piano, recorder.

*"... some lovely oboe playing ..."*
1996 Adjudication commentary at Feis Ceoil, Dublin.

**KEY IRISH PERFORMANCES** (since January 1994):
4.6.97 University of Limerick, promoted by Cór na nÓg, appearing with Moira Grey.
**PRIZES/AWARDS/APPOINTMENTS:**
1995 2nd Prize winner of piano duet, U-17, Feis Ceoil, Dublin.
1995 Gerard Shanahan Cup winner, Feile Luimni, Limerick.
1996 Winner of the Dorothy Meyer Cup at Feis Ceoil, Dublin.
**REGULARLY PERFORMS WITH:**
Early Music Consort at the Limerick School of Music, Limerick Baroque Players, University of Limerick Orchestra, Clare and Galway Youth Orchestras.
**AVAILABILITY:**
General.

# Colin Stark *Oboe*

**Contact:** Mr Colin Stark
41, Somerton Park
Belfast BT15 4DP
Northern Ireland
**Tel/Fax:** +44 1232 772325

**OTHER INSTRUMENTS:**
Cor Anglais.
**PRIZES/AWARDS/APPOINTMENTS:**
Ashby Prize and Hamilton Harty Scholarship.
**TRAINING AND/OR QUALIFICATIONS:**
B Mus with English (Hons) from Queen's University, Belfast.
**REGULARLY PERFORMS WITH:**
Ulster Orchestra, Belfast Wind Quintet.
**AVAILABILITY:**
Subject to orchestra schedule.
*See Cor Anglais page 9.*

# ORGAN

## David Adams *Organ*

**Contact:** Mr David Adams
3, Belgrave Place
Rathmines
Dublin 6
**Tel:** +353 1 4962079
*See harpischord page 124.*

## Timothy Allen *Organ*

**Contact:** Timothy Allen
2, St Columb's Court
Londonderry, BT48 6PT
Northern Ireland
**Tel/Fax:** +44 1504 262412
**Other instruments:** Piano.

**KEY IRISH PERFORMANCES** (since January 1994):
7.95 Guildhall, Derry, promoted by Derry City Council.
7.96 Guildhall, Derry, promoted by Derry City Council.
6.97 St Anne's Cathedral, Belfast.
**KEY PERFORMANCES OUTSIDE IRELAND** (since January 1994):
11.95 Chelmsford Cathedral.
1.96 St Michael's, Cornhill, London.
**PRIZES/AWARDS/APPOINTMENTS:**
6.91 Appointed Organist and Master of the Choristers at St Columb's Cathedral, Derry.
7.92 Appointed City Organist of Derry City Council.
**TRAINING AND/OR QUALIFICATIONS:**
From 1981 to 1984, MA from Cambridge University.
1991 FRCO from Royal College of Organists.
**AVAILABILITY:**
General.
**ADDITIONAL INFORMATION:** President of the Ulster Society of Organists and Choirmasters. Teacher in the Music Department of Queen's University, Belfast. A member of the Music Panel for the Arts Council of Northern Ireland. Examiner for the Associated Board of the Royal Schools of Music. Regularly conducts with St Columb's Cathedral Choir and the Two Cathedrals Festival Chorus, Derry.

## Antoinette Baker *Organ*

**Contact:** Ms Antoinette Baker
'Kinalea'
Killeen
Innishannon
Co Cork
**Tel:** +353 21 775655
**Other instruments:** Piano.

**KEY IRISH PERFORMANCES** (since January 1994):
10.7.94 St Michael's Church, Dún Laoghaire.
16.8.95 St Iberius' Church, Wexford, promoted by Music for Wexford.
21.4.96 St Fin Barre's Cathedral, Cork.
6.6.97 National Concert Hall, Dublin.
**SELECTED BROADCASTS AND/OR RECORDED WORK:**
29.5.88 'Sunday Mass' for RTÉ.
25.4.93 'Morning Worship' for RTÉ.
8.10.95 'Harvest Thanksgiving' for RTÉ.
**SELECTED REVIEWS** (since January 1994):
11.7.94 Irish Times.
21.8.95 The Guardian (Wexford).
**PRIZES/AWARDS/APPOINTMENTS:**
18.3.97 Winner of the Fitzgerald Trophy for Advanced Organ Playing from the Feis Ceoil.
**TRAINING AND/OR QUALIFICATIONS:**
From 1985 to 1989, BA Mod (Music and Irish) from Trinity College, Dublin.
From 1985 to 1992, DIT Conservatory of Music and Drama, (teacher Brent Parker).
From 1986 to 1997, DIT CMD, LTCL and FTCL (teacher Peter Sweeney).
From 1991 to 1993, MA in Performance and Interpretation from the National University of Ireland, Maynooth.
**REGULARLY PERFORMS WITH:**
Glaslinn Choir, Robert Beare (voice), Marina Cassidy (voice, harp), Colette Kidney (voice).
**AVAILABILITY:**
General.
**ADDITIONAL INFORMATION:**
Regular accompanist for teacher, Robert Beare. Also accompanist for the Glaslinn Choir, Bandon.

## Conor Biggs *Organ*

**Contact:** Mr Conor Biggs
Ardvinkaai 33
1000 Brussels
Belgium
**Tel/Fax:** +32 2 223 11 89 / +32 2 223 42 22
*See bass baritone page 111.*

## John Wolf Brennan *Organ*

**Contact:** Mr John Wolf Brennan
Luzernerstr 8
CH 6353
Weggis, Switzerland
**Tel/Fax:** +41 41 3902777 / +41 41 3902761
*See piano page 32.*

## Shane Brennan *Organ*

**Contact:** Mr Shane Brennan
Director
Schola Cantorum
St Finian's College
Mullingar, Co Westmeath
**Tel/Mobile:** +353 44 42906 or +353 44 44957 / +353 88 528029
**Other instruments:** Baritone.

*"His approach guarantees that works like Bach's Fugue, the Magnificat, can be delivered as it were in one long sustained breath"*
7.90 Irish Times (Michael Dervan)

**KEY IRISH PERFORMANCES** (since January 1994):
8.96 Dún Laoghaire Organ Festival.
10.96 Guildhall, Derry promoted by the Two Cathedrals Festival.
3.97 St Audeon's Church, Dublin at the inaurgural concert for Prolofonia Choir.
5.97 National Concert Hall, Dublin.

**KEY PERFORMANCES OUTSIDE IRELAND** (since January 1994):
Has toured throughout England and Sweden.
**SELECTED BROADCASTS AND/OR RECORDED WORK:**
5.96 Multifarnham, Cork, Good Friday Service recording.
5.96 Sunday Mass recording for RTÉ.
1997 Recording of organ music for CDG.
**PRIZES/AWARDS/APPOINTMENTS:**
From 1984 to 1997, Appointed main acccompanist at Mullingar Cathedral, Co Westmeath. Since 1984, Director of the Schola Cantorum, Mullingar, Co Westmeath.
**TRAINING AND/OR QUALIFICATIONS:**
BA B Mus in Musicology (Ist Hons). Has attended masterclasses with Gerard Gillen, David Sanger, Tom Koopman and Ewald Kooiman.
**AVAILABILITY:**
Weekdays, weekends during the summer.
**ADDITIONAL INFORMATION:**
Main interest is in the interpretation and performance of early choral and organ repertoire particularly J.S. Bach, Sweelinck and Buxtehude. Has also collaborated frequently as an accompanist with the National Youth Choir and its conductor Dr Geoffrey Spratt. Has given the first Irish performances of modern choral works, including the premiere (in Britain and Ireland) of the 'Prague' Te Deum by Pter Eben.

# Emer Buckley *Organ*

**Contact:** Ms Emer Buckley
23, Rue de Rungis
75013, Paris, France
**Tel:** +33 1 45895858
*See harpsichord page 124.*

# Colm Carey *Organ*

**Contact:** Mr Colm Carey
78a, Herga Court
Harrow-on-the-Hill
London HA1 3RT
England
**Tel:** +44 181 426 5961

**KEY IRISH PERFORMANCES** (since January 1994):
8.95 St Michael's Church, Dún Laoghaire, Dublin.
**KEY PERFORMANCES OUTSIDE IRELAND** (since January 1994):
1994 Westminister Cathedral, London.
1995 Markuskirche, Munich, Germany.
1996 St John's Smith Square, London.
1997 St Pierre Cathedral, Geneva, Switzerland.
**SELECTED BROADCASTS AND/OR RECORDED WORK:**
1993 'Fauré Requiem' for Naxos.
1997 Music for cornett and Sackbut for Meridian.
**PRIZES/AWARDS/APPOINTMENTS:**
1994 Awarded student fellowship by Royal Academy of Music, London.
1995 Awarded Julius Isserlis scholarship, by Royal Philharmonic Society, London.
**TRAINING AND/OR QUALIFICATIONS:**
From 1989 to 1995, B Mus, LRAM and Dip RAM, awarded by Royal Academy of Music, London.
From 1995 to 1997, Premier Prix de Virtuosité avec distinction, awarded by Conservatoire de Musique de Genéve.
**REGULARLY PERFORMS WITH:**
Carys Lane (soprano), Jonathan Freeman-Attwood (trumpet). QuintEssential (cornett and sackbut ensemble).
**AVAILABILITY:**
General.
**ADDITIONAL INFORMATION:**
About to embark on a solo organ career, having finished studies in London and Geneva. Has performed in the UK, Germany, France, Switzerland and the Channel Islands. Regularly plays continuo and give concerts with other instrumentalists.

# Declan Daly *Organ*

**Contact:** Mr Declan Daly
Tossey
Loughmourne
Castleblayney
Co Monaghan
**Tel:** +353 42 45041
*See violin page 60.*

# Eoin Gillen *Organ*

**Contact:** Mr Eoin Gillen
1, Southwood Park
Blackrock, Co Dublin
**Tel:** +353 1 2880880
*See French Horn page 23.*

# Gerard Gillen *Organ*

**Contact:** Professor Gerard Gillen
Department of Music
National University of Ireland
Maynooth
Co Kildare
**Tel/Fax:** +353 1 7083768 or +353 1 2880880 /
+353 1 6289432

*"His handling of the vast organ showed complete control - we look forward to his return"*
16.3.92 Evening Star, Washington.

**KEY IRISH PERFORMANCES** (since January 1994):
1994 National Concert Hall, organ series.
1994 St Michael's Church, Dún Laoghaire, Co Dublin, appearing with Emmanuel Lawler.
1995 Cathedral Church, Tullamore, Co Offaly, appearing with Mark O'Keeffe.
1995 NCH, Bach concert.
**KEY PERFORMANCES OUTSIDE IRELAND** (since January 1994):
1995 Copenhagen Cathedral.
1995 Como, Italy, promoted by Como Organ Festival.
1995 Frederiksburg Castle, Denmark.
1995 Reading School, UK.
**SELECTED BROADCASTS AND/OR RECORDED WORK:**
1993 'Baroque Splendour' CD recorded for SDG.
1994 NCH, concert recorded by RTÉ.
1995 Inaugural organ concert, Tullamore, recorded for RTÉ.
**PRIZES/AWARDS/APPOINTMENTS:**
1958 Winner of Advanced Organ, awarded by the Feis Ceoil, Dublin.
1960 Awarded the Lorcan Sherlock medal, by the DIT Conservatory of Music and Drama.
1964 Appointed Laureat, by Bruges International Organ Competition.
**TRAINING AND/OR QUALIFICATIONS:**
From 1960 to 1965, B Mus and MA from University College, Dublin.
From 1965 to 1967 B Litt, The Queen's College, Oxford.
From 1967 to 1970 Premier Prix and Prix d'Excellence from the Royal Antwerp Conservatoire.
**REGULARLY PERFORMS WITH:**
Emmanuel Lawler (tenor), Mark O'Keeffe (trumpet).
**AVAILABILITY:**
General.
**ADDITIONAL INFORMATION:**
Plays a wide repertory of music, from the earliest period right up to the most contemporary music. Bach is a speciality interest. Irish

composers Gerald Barry, John Buckley, Raymond Deane, James Wilson, and foreign composers Kenneth Leighton and Flor Peeters have dedicated works to him.

# Beatrix Hermann *Organ*

**Contact:** Mrs Beatrix Hermann
139, Richmond Park
Bray
Co Wicklow
**Tel:** +353 1 2867488
**Other instruments:** Piano.

*"... Gives the composition a youthful swing ... highly interesting music selection"*

30.7.95 Schwarzwälder Bofe.

**KEY IRISH PERFORMANCES** (since January 1994):
17.11.94 and 16.11.95 Bray Organ Festival, promoted by Frank Hayes, appearing with Róisín O'Toole.
27.9.96 Delgany, Co Wicklow, promoted by Delgany Parish, appearing with Róisín O'Toole and children's choir.
30.8.97 Galway Cathedral, promoted by Raymond O'Donnell of Galway Cathedral.
**KEY PERFORMANCES OUTSIDE IRELAND** (since January 1994):
'94, '95, '96, '97 Johanneskirche, Villingen, Germany, promoted by Evang Bezirkskarforat, VS-Villingen.
**SELECTED BROADCASTS AND/OR RECORDED WORK:**
17.11.94 Contemporary Night at Bray Organ Festival.
23.8.96 'Akzerte' own live tape.
15.11.97 'Trumpa agus Orgel' (contemporary organ and trumpet) for RTÉ.
**SELECTED REVIEWS** (since January 1994):
25.7.94, 26.8.96 Südkurier, Badische Zeitung, Stadtanzeiger.
**PRIZES/AWARDS/APPOINTMENTS:**
1995 2nd Prize at the Feis Ceoil, Dublin.
**TRAINING AND/OR QUALIFICATIONS:**
From 1984 to 1989, Studied with Bernd Böse.
From 1989 to 1995, LTCL for Organ Performance from the DIT Conservatory of Music and Drama (teacher Peter Sweeney).
1997 Studied with John Scott in London.
**REGULARLY PERFORMS WITH:**
'Trumpa agus Orgel' with Eoin Daly (trumpet).
**AVAILABILITY:**
General.
**ADDITIONAL INFORMATION:**
Musical repertoire: pre-baroque up to contemporary music - (contemporary German, American, French). Specialises in contemporary Irish organ music.

# Edward Holly *Organ* 

**Contact:** Mr Edward Holly
40, Glenmore Drive
Drogheda
Co Louth
**Tel:** +353 41 38000
*See piano page 39.*

# Desmond Hunter *Organ*

**Contact:** Dr Desmond Hunter
16, The Hermitage
Drumbeg Road
Belfast BT17 9NH
Northern Ireland
**Tel/Fax:** +44 1232 622696 / +44 1232 366870
**Email:** d.hunter1@ulst.ac.uk
**Other instruments:** Harpsichord.

*"Strong, no-nonsense performances, high on technical skill and musical intelligence"*

9.94 Gramophone.

**KEY IRISH PERFORMANCES** (since January 1994):
2.2.96 National Concert hall, Dublin.
21.3.94 Guildhall, Derry.
**KEY PERFORMANCES OUTSIDE IRELAND** (since January 1994):
2.5.95 Indiana University, South Bend.
21.7.95 Chiesa S. Carlo, Brescia, Italy, appearing with Christopher Stembridge.
25.7.95 Chiesa, S. Sigismondo, Cremona, Italy, appearing with Christopher Stembridge.
**SELECTED BROADCASTS AND/OR RECORDED WORK:**
1994 Stanford Complete Organ Sonatas for Priory.
**SELECTED REVIEWS** (since January 1994):
17.7.94 Giornale Di Brescia.
2.96 Irish Times.
**PRIZES/AWARDS/APPOINTMENTS:**
1970 1st Prize, National Organ Competition (England).
1973 Appointed Associate, Royal Academy of Music, London.
1975 2nd Prize, St Alban's International Organ Festival, England.
**TRAINING AND/OR QUALIFICATIONS:**
1966 FRCO from the Royal College of Organists.
1968 Premier Prix from Antwerp Conservatoire.
1982 MA from University College, Cork.
1989 PhD from University College, Cork
**AVAILABILITY:**
General.
**ADDITIONAL INFORMATION:**
Authority on the performance of virginalist music. Regularly conducts masterclasses in Italy.
*See harpischord page 124.*

# Andrew Johnstone *Organ*

**Contact:** Mr Andrew Johnstone
37, Sandford Road
Ranelagh
Dublin 6
**Tel:** +353 1 4973145

# David Lee *Organ*

**Contact:** Mr David Lee
10, Corbawn Drive
Shankill, Dublin 18
**Tel:** +353 1 2821303
**Other instruments:** Harpsichord, piano.

**KEY IRISH PERFORMANCES** (since January 1994):
10.95 St Patrick's Cathedral, Dundalk.

11.95 Greystones Parish Church.
9.96 St Michael's Church, Dún Laoghaire.
10.96 National Concert Hall, Dublin.
**SELECTED REVIEWS** (since January 1994):
1994 Irish Times (Martin Adams).
3.10.96 Irish Times (Michael Dervan).
29.10.96 Irish Times (Martin Adams).
**PRIZES/AWARDS/APPOINTMENTS:**
1953 Bernard Hale (open) Scholarship, awarded by Peterhouse College, Cambridge. Professor of organ at the Royal Irish Academy of Music, Dublin.
**TRAINING AND/OR QUALIFICATIONS:**
From 1953 to 1957, BA, MA, B Mus, awarded by Cambridge University (teachers Boris Ord, Thurston Dart).
From 1969 to 1970, Freiburg Musik Hochscule (teachers Walter Kraft, Stanislav Heller).
**AVAILABILITY:**
General.

# Brenda McCarthy *Organ*

**Contact:** Ms Brenda McCarthy
90, Trees Road
Mount Merrion
Co Dublin
**Tel:** +353 1 2889758
*See piano page 42.*

# Paul McKeever *Organ*

**Contact:** Paul McKeever
10, Prospect Road
Glasnevin
Dublin 9
**Mobile/Fax:** +353 87 2311031 / +353 1 6771000 (w)
**Other instruments:** Piano.

*"Paul McKeever gave a vigorous, well registered ... performance of Dupré's Prelude and Fugue in B"* 6.97 Irish Times (Martin Adams).

**KEY IRISH PERFORMANCES** (since January 1994):
5.97 National Concert Hall, Dublin.
**KEY PERFORMANCES OUTSIDE IRELAND** (since January 1994):
1994 Strasbourg, France and Tübingen, Germany.
**SELECTED BROADCASTS AND/OR RECORDED WORK:**
Various recordings for RTÉ.
**PRIZES/AWARDS/APPOINTMENTS:**
1995 Prizewinner in Feis Ceoil, Dublin.
1995 Appointed Director of Music at the Franciscan Friary, Church of Adam and Eve, Merchants' Quay, Dublin 8
**TRAINING AND/OR QUALIFICATIONS:**
LGSM, from the Guildhall School of Music and Drama, London.
FTCL, from Trinity College, London.
LRSM, from the Associated Board of the Royal Schools of Music
**AVAILABILITY:**
General.
**ADDITIONAL INFORMATION:**
Has an interest in improvisation. Accentor in St Columba's College, Rathfarnham. Also a consultant in organ building.

# Colin Nicholls *Organ*

**Contact:** Mr Colin Nicholls
8, Dean Street
Cork
**Tel:** +353 21 963433
**Other instruments:** Piano, also choral conductor.

*"There was Baylero with accompanist Colin Nicholls' splendidly ringing right hand evoking rural France"* 10.3.97 The Examiner.

**KEY IRISH PERFORMANCES** (since January 1994):
6.94 Chapel, Trinity College, Dublin, promoted by Madrigal '75.
4.95 City Hall, Cork, promoted by the Cork International Choral Festival, appearing with Festival Choirs performing 'Petite Messe Solenelle'.
3.97 City Hall, Cork promoted by Barra O'Tuama.
5.97 Cork Cathedral and Tralee, appearing with Cantairí Mhuscraí performing Fauré's Requiem and Vivaldi's 'Gloria'.
**KEY PERFORMANCES OUTSIDE IRELAND** (since January 1994):
5.95 Corfu, appearing with Cantairí Mhuscraí.
8.95 Hereford Cathedral, appearing with St Fin Barre's Cathedral Choir.
5.97 Mozarthalle, Vienna, promoted by the International Schubert Festival, appearing with Cantairí Mhuscraí.
**SELECTED BROADCASTS AND/OR RECORDED WORK:**
7.82 Choral Music from St Fin Barre's for Abbey Recordings.
4.95 Rossini Mass Cork International Choral Festival for RTÉ.
4.95 Broadcast from Bandon for RTÉ.
**PRIZES/AWARDS/APPOINTMENTS:**
1984 Appointed Organist and Choirmaster for St Fin Barre's Cathedral Choir, Cork.
1992 Appointed official accompanist for strings and wind at Feis Maithiú.
**TRAINING AND/OR QUALIFICATIONS:**
From 1962 to 1965, GTCL and LTCL Mus Ed from Trinity College, London.
1969 LRAM (piano) from the Royal Academy of Music.
1978 FRCO from the Royal College of Organists, London.
1979 Choimaster Diploma from the Royal College of Organists, London.
**REGULARLY PERFORMS WITH:**
St Fin Barre's Cathedral Choir, Cork.
**AVAILABILITY:**
General.
**ADDITIONAL INFORMATION:**
Organ tutor for Cork School of Music. Part-time lecturer in Harmony, University College, Cork. Available as organist, conductor, and accompanist on piano/ organ.
*See conductor page 172.*

# Malcolm Proud *Organ*

**Contact:** Mr Malcolm Proud
St Canice's Cottage
St Canice's Cathedral, Kilkenny
**Tel/Fax:** +353 56 61497
*See harpischord page 125.*

# Una Russell *Organ*

**Contact:** Ms Una Russell
6, Kincora Terrace
Dundalk, Co Louth
**Tel/Fax:** +353 1 6603979 / +353 1 4023584 (w)
**Other instruments:** Piano.

*"... And went on to provide playing of real sparkle in Walther's 'Concerto del Sigr. Vivaldi'... "* 8.92 Irish Times.

**KEY IRISH PERFORMANCES** (since January 1994):
2.7.95 St Michael's Church, Dún Laoghaire, promoted by Dún Laoghaire-Rathdown Co Council.
1.5.96 Christchurch Cathedral, Dublin, promoted by DIT Conservatory of Music and Drama, Choral Society. (Bernstein, Chichester Psalms)
20.6.96 Christchurch Cathedral, Dublin, promoted by Dublin International Organ Festival, appearing with John Feeley (guitar).
14.12.96 National Concert Hall, Dublin, promoted by Dublin Choral Foundation, appearing with the Lassus Scholars.
**SELECTED BROADCASTS AND/OR RECORDED WORK:**
4.78 'Organ Gallery' from the Willis Organ, Dundalk for RTÉ.
8.87 Modern Organ Music from Whitefriar Street, Dublin, including Eibhlis Farrell's 'Play' for BBC Northern Ireland.
**PRIZES/AWARDS/APPOINTMENTS:**
1975 Special Diploma, Eerste Prijs, J Callaerts and Firmin Swinnen Prizes from the Royal Flemish Conservatory of Music, Antwerp (teacher Prof Stanislas Deriemaeker.
1990 Appointed lecturer in keyboard at the DIT CMD.
**TRAINING AND/OR QUALIFICATIONS:**
From 1968 to 1972, DIT CMD (teacher Sidney Greig).
1976 Summer school at Santiago de Compostela, Spain with Montserrat Torrent.
**REGULARLY PERFORMS WITH:**
John Feeley (guitar).
**AVAILABILITY:**
General.
**ADDITIONAL INFORMATION:**
Both soloist and accompanist. Has played abroad and at numerous Irish venues including the National Concert Hall, St. Michael's, Dún Laoghaire and in Ghent and Bruges Cathedrals. Has travelled to Antwerp, Moscow and Italy (Sora Cathedral and Alvito Handel Festival). Repertoire spans the entire range of organ styles. Has special interest in early French and Spanish schools.

## Peter Sweeney *Organ*

**Contact:** Mr Peter Sweeney
4, Orwell Park
Rathgar
Dublin 6
**Tel:** +353 1 4966740

*"colourful and flamboyant player . . . can turn the simplest of runs or embellishments into an attention grabbing flourish"*
1.9.97 Irish Times (Michael Dervan)

**KEY IRISH PERFORMANCES** (since January 1994):
6.96 National Concert Hall, Dublin premiere of a organ concerto by Ian Wilson appearing with the National Symphony Orchestra of Ireland.
6.97 NCH, performance of contemporary Irish music.
8.97 Kilkenny Arts Festival appearing with David Agnew.
30.8.97 Finale solo concert in the Organ Series at St Michael's Church, Dún Laoghaire, Co Dublin.
**KEY PERFORMANCES OUTSIDE IRELAND** (since January 1994):
St Patrick's Basilica, Montreal, Canada in a performance of contemporary Irish music to celebrate the 150th anniversary of the Basilica.
Christchurch Cathedral, Montreal, playing contemporary music by Philip Hammond.
**SELECTED BROADCASTS AND/OR RECORDED WORK:**
4.7.97 Contemporary American music at the NCH, recorded for RTÉ.
**SELECTED REVIEWS** (since January 1994):
7.7.97 Irish Times (Martin Adams).
**PRIZES/AWARDS/APPOINTMENTS:**
1970 Lorcan Sherlock Gold medal, awarded by the DIT Conservatory of Music and Drama.
1974 Fitzgerald Trophy, awarded by Feis Ceoil, Dublin.
1975 Prix Rochette awarded by the Geneva Conservatoire.
1975 Geneva Conservatoire, awarded by Prix Otto Barblan.
**TRAINING AND/OR QUALIFICATIONS:**
Two years at the Conservatoire de Musique, Geneva. Private tuition with Gillian Weir, London.
**REGULARLY PERFORMS WITH:**
David Agnew (oboe), Helen Roycroft (soprano).
**AVAILABILITY:**
General.
**ADDITIONAL INFORMATION:**
Available for recitals, masterclasses, lectures, private engagements, and as a compère.

## Andrew Synnott *Organ*

**Contact:** Andrew Synnott
98, Wilfield Road
Sandymount
Dublin 4
**Tel:** +353 1 2696023
*See piano page 50.*

## Rachel Talbot *Organ*

**Contact:** Ms Rachel Talbot
117, Templeogue Road
Dublin 6w
**Tel:** +353 1 4907512
**Email:** rtalbot@clubi.ie
*See soprano page 127.*

# PERCUSSION

See also orchestra members lists on page 140.

## Lloyd Byrne *Percussion*

**Contact:** Mr Lloyd Byrne
c/o 46, Loreto Avenue
Rathfarnham
Dublin 14
**Tel/Mobile:** +353 1 4950103 / +353 87 2390961

**AVAILABILITY:** General.

## Edward Holly *Percussion*

**Contact:** Mr Edward Holly
40, Glenmore Drive
Drogheda
Co Louth
**Tel:** +353 41 38000
*See piano page 39.*

## Andrew Lavery *Percussion*

**Contact:** Mr Andrew Lavery
37, Glengoland Gardens
Dunmurry
Belfast BT17 OJE
Northern Ireland
**Tel:** +44 1232 621505
*See drums/other percussion page 296.*

## Marney O'Sullivan
### *Timpani and other Percussion*

**Contact:** Mr Marney O'Sullivan
4 Pasture Crescent
Chapel Allerton
Leeds LS7 4QS
England
**Tel:** +44 113 2697936

**REGULARLY PERFORMS WITH:**
Opera North, English Northern Philharmonia.
**AVAILABILITY:**
Subject to orchestra schedule.

## Bernard Reilly *Percussion*

**Contact:** Mr Bernard Reilly
26, Sandyford Downs
Dublin 13
**Tel:** +353 1 2958742
**Email:** breilly@tinet.ie

**OTHER INSTRUMENTS:**
Vibraphone (jazz).

## Peadar Townsend
### *Timpani and other Percussion*

**Contact:** Mr Peadar Townsend
Flat 2
8, Mayfield Road
Whalley Range
Manchester M16 8FT
England
**Tel/Mobile:** +44 161 2329315 / +44 421 366376
**Other instruments:** Violin, clarinet.

*"...He had the élan for the music and the physical presence for a performance of this physical work"* 5.8.96 Irish Times.

**KEY PERFORMANCES OUTSIDE IRELAND** (since January 1994):
Various performances at the Royal Northern College of Music, Manchester.
**SELECTED BROADCASTS AND/OR RECORDED WORK:**
8.96 'Lunchtime Summer Sounds' for RTÉ.
**SELECTED REVIEWS** (since January 1994):
10.96 Irish Times (critique of solo concerto with RTÉ Concert Orchestra).
**TRAINING AND/OR QUALIFICATIONS:**
From 1980 to 1992, Distinction in violin Grade 8 from Cork School of Music (teacher C Zanidache).
From 1989 to 1992, clarinet Grade 5 from Cork School of Music (teacher B Casey).
1993, Distinction in percussion Grade 8 from Cork School of Music (teacher P Rennicks).
From 1993 to 1997, B Mus Hons in percussion from the Royal Northern College of Music, Manchester (teacher I Wright).
**AVAILABILITY:**
General.
**ADDITIONAL INFORMATION:**
Has covered all techniques and styles of percussion music, from orchestral to Latin/jazz and solo which are all part of the curriculum offered in the RNCM, Manchester.

# PIANO

## David Adams *Piano*

**Contact:** Mr David Adams
3, Belgrave Place
Rathmines
Dublin 6
**Tel:** +353 1 4962079
*See harpischord page 124.*

## Timothy Allen *Piano*

**Contact:** Timothy Allen
2, St Columb's Court
Londonderry
BT48 6PT, Northern Ireland
**Tel/Fax:** +44 1504 262412
*See organ page 26.*

## Antoinette Baker *Piano*

**Contact:** Ms Antoinette Baker
'Kinalea'
Killeen
Innishannon
Co Cork
**Tel:** +353 21 775655
*See organ page 26.*

## Dorothy Bergin *Piano*

**Contact:** Ms Dorothy Bergin
35, Mount Eagle Drive
Leopardstown Heights
Sandyford
Dublin 18
**Tel:** +353 1 2957096
*See soprano page 85.*

## Elizabeth Bicker *Piano*

**Contact:** Elizabeth Bicker
Echo Hall
Spa, Ballinahinch
Co Down BT24 8PT
Northern Ireland
**Tel/Fax:** +44 1238 565187

*"Fine technical finish and sensitivity"*
21.10.96 Belfast Telegraph.

**KEY IRISH PERFORMANCES** (since January 1994):
1994, National Concert Hall, Dublin, appearing with the Northern Ireland Symphony Orchestra.
1996 Kilkenny Arts Festival, appearing with Cliodhna Ryan (violin).
1996 Elmwood Hall, Belfast, appearing with the Studio Symphony Orchestra.
1997 Belfast Studio, Belfast Waterfront Hall, promoted by SSAFA appearing with the Choir of St George's, Catherine Harper and Niall Keatley.
**KEY PERFORMANCES OUTSIDE IRELAND** (since January 1994):
1994 Hereford, Ayr, Frazerburgh appearing with George Zukerman.
1995 Wales, West Scotland, appearing with George Zukerman.
**SELECTED BROADCASTS AND/OR RECORDED WORK:**
1984 'Irish Fancies' for Sutton Sound, London.
1990 'I Love a Piano' for BBC Northern Ireland.
1997 Lunchtime recitals for BBC Northern Ireland.
**SELECTED REVIEWS** (since January 1994):
1994 Fortnight Review (Belfast).
1996 Belfast Telegraph.
1997 Belfast Telegraph.
**PRIZES/AWARDS/APPOINTMENTS:**
1992 Honourary ARAM awarded by the Royal Academy of Music, London.
**TRAINING AND/OR QUALIFICATIONS:**
From 1960 to 1964, LRAM from the Royal Academy of Music, London (teacher Harry Isaacs).
**AVAILABILITY:**
General.
**ADDITIONAL INFORMATION:**
Varied career as a solo pianist and accompanist has taken her to all parts of Ireland, Britain and to Europe. Has appeared several times in Belfast, and in the NCH, Dublin, as concerto soloist. Has broadcast for over twenty-five years on radio and television. Has also worked as an adjudicator. Owner of a rare Pleyel double piano, which was the subject of BBC documentary which told the story of discovery and restoration of the instrument.

## Conor Biggs *Piano*

**Contact:** Mr Conor Biggs
Arduinkaai 33
1000 Brussel
Belgium
**Tel/Fax:** +32 2 223 11 89 / +32 2 223 42 22
*See bass baritone page 111.*

## John Wolf Brennan *Piano*

**Contact:** Mr John Wolf Brennan
Luzernerstr 8
CH 6353
Weggis
Switzerland
**Tel/Fax:** +41 41 3902777 / +41 41 3902761
**Other instruments:** Organ, composer.

*"Born in Ireland, now a Swiss resident . . . balances the romanticism of the one with the watchmaker exactness of the other ...*
7.90 The Wire, Issue 77 (Brian Morton).

**KEY PERFORMANCES OUTSIDE IRELAND** (since January 1994):
5.95, St Petersburg, Russia, promoted by Pro Helvetia, appearing with Slava Gaironsky (trumpet).
5.95 Moscow, Russia, promoted by Groupe Lacroix, appearing with Marianne Schroeder (piano).
15.95 Cortona, Italy, promoted by ETH, Zurich, appearing with Tony Majdalani (percussion).
21.10.95 Basel, Switzerland, promoted by Contrapunkt, appearing with Hans Kennel (trumpet).
**SELECTED BROADCASTS AND/OR RECORDED WORK:**
1989/1995 'Henceforward' recorded for Leo records, London.
1995 'Shooting Stars and Traffic lights', recorded for Bellaphon, Frankfurt.
1994 'Text, Context, Co-Text and Co-Co-Text' recorded for Creative works, Lucerne, Switzerland.
**SELECTED REVIEWS SINCE** (January 1994):
21.5.95 Sunday Times.
1994 'The Penguin Guide to Jazz'.
**PRIZES/AWARDS/APPOINTMENTS:**
1989 Awarded Werkjahr scholarship, by the City of Lucerne.
1993 Awarded scholarship, by Tyrone Guthrie Centre.
1994 Awarded Kulturpreis, by the Union Bank of Switzerland.
1996 'Album of the Year' for CD 'Pago Libre', awarded from 'Jazzthetik', (German magazine) Munich.
1997 London-Fellowship awarded by the Zuger Kulturstiftung Landis and Gyr.
**TRAINING AND/OR QUALIFICATIONS:**
From 9.75 to 9.79, BA from the University of Fribourg.
From 10.79 to 2.84, PhD in Piano, from The Conservatory of Music, Lucerne.
From 5.84 to 9.84, Studied at the Creative Music Studio, New York.
From 10.85 to 7.87, PhD in Composition, Conducting, Singing and Organ, from the Akademie für Kirchenmusik, Lucerne.
**REGULARLY PERFORMS WITH:**
The Pago Libre Quartet (Tscho Theissing (violin), Daniele Patumi (double bass) and Arkady Shilkloper (french horn and alphorn), Trio Aurealis and Organic voices.
**AVAILABILITY:**
General.
**ADDITIONAL INFORMATION:**
Performer, composer and improviser. Has toured in Russia, Japan, USA, Ukraine and many European cities. Regularly appears on TV and radio. Has recorded over 20 CD's. Works with Gabriele Hasler, Lindsay Cooper, Robert Dick, Tscho Theissing, Alex Cline, Daniele Patumi, Arkady Shilkloper, Hans Kennel. Member of the Association of Irish Composers, STV,The Swiss Composers Association and Groupe Lacroix.

## Colma Brioscú *Piano*

**Contact:** Ms Colma Brioscú
Apt. 6, Riverbank
Dodder Park Road
Rathfarnham
Dublin 14
**Tel:** +353 1 4904279

**KEY IRISH PERFORMANCES** (since January 1994):
22.11.95 Royal Irish Academy of Music, Dublin.
12.5.96 Hermitage Golf Club charity concert.
8.11.96 John Field Room, National Concert Hall, Dublin.
25.4.97 JFR, NCH, Dublin.
**SELECTED BROADCASTS AND/OR RECORDED WORK:**
1984 Short recital programmes for RTÉ (Liszt 'Consolations', Op.3 pieces by Rachmaninov and group of Debussy preludes).

**PRIZES/AWARDS/APPOINTMENTS:**
3.83, 2nd Prize winner at Concours International Artists Musiciennes, Paris.
**TRAINING AND/OR QUALIFICATIONS:**
From 1977 to 1980, BA Degree in Irish and Music from University College, Dublin.
From 1981 to 1983, French Government scholarship to École Normale de Musique de Paris.
5.95 FTCL (Perf) Fellowship of Trinity College, London.
**AVAILABILITY:**
Weekdays, evenings, and during summer months.
**ADDITIONAL INFORMATION:**
Teaching for 21 years, and staff member at the Royal Irish Academy of Music since 1986. Also a music examiner for the local centre examinations system since 1993. Performs annually in Dublin and has participated in summer courses in Morges, Switzerland and Conservatoire de Region de Nice, France. Certificate with 1st Hons in Radio Broadcasting/Production from Newman College, Dublin.

# Dearbhla Brosnan *Piano*

**Contact:** Ms Dearbhla Brosnan
48, Ballytore Road
Rathfarnham
Dublin 14
**Tel/Mobile/Fax:** +353 1 4908495 / +353 87 2310238 / +353 1 4926806
**Email:** brsn@iol.ie

**PRIZES/AWARDS/APPOINTMENTS:**
9.95 Appointed Resident Accompanist at the Royal Irish Academy of Music.
12.95 Winner of Major van Someron Godfrey Prize for Piano Accompaniment of English Song at the Royal Academy of Music, London.
**TRAINING AND/OR QUALIFICATIONS:**
From 9.80 to 6.94, Studied with Dr John O'Conor at the Royal Irish Academy of Music, Dublin.
From 9.88 to 6.92, BA (Mod) in Music from Trinity College, Dublin.
From 9.94 to 6.96, Advanced Certificate in Piano Accompaniment from the Royal Academy of Music, London (teacher John Streets).
**REGULARLY PERFORMS WITH:**
Chalemeau Trio with Paul Roe (clarinet) and William Butt (cello).
**AVAILABILITY:**
General.
**ADDITIONAL INFORMATION:**
Regular performer in chamber music ensembles and as an accompanist. Has worked as repetiteur with Opera Theatre Company and Lyric Opera. Is a regular official accompanist for masterclasses and auditions in Ireland, London and New York.

# Anthony Byrne *Piano*

**Contact:** Mr Anthony Byrne
190, Dunluce Road
Clontarf
Dublin 3
**Tel/Mobile:** +353 1 8335085 / +353 87 618706
**Email:** byrne@indigo.ie

*"In Debussy's 'L'Isle Joyeuse', Byrne triumphed. He played the work in one vast paragraph and his fingers never faltered under the storm of notes entrusted to them"* 3.91 Musical Opinion.

**KEY IRISH PERFORMANCES** (since January 1994):
2.3.97 Inaugural recital at Boyle Arts Festival.
13.5.97 Piano recital at Bank of Ireland Arts Centre, Dublin.
15.6.97 Dublin, First Irish performance of the Piano Concerto by Leroy Anderson with Colman Pearce.
10.11.97 Piano recital at the R.D.S., Dublin.
**KEY PERFORMANCES OUTSIDE IRELAND** (since January 1994):
29/30.11.96 Geneva and Lucerne Switzerland appearing with Geraldine O'Grady and Oonagh Keogh.
**SELECTED BROADCASTS AND/OR RECORDED WORK:**
1992 Concert for the Environment for Unicef.
95/96 The complete piano music of John Buckley, for Naxos-Marco Polo and RTÉ.
6.6.97 Performance of 'Quaternion' for piano and orchestra by Raymond Deane, appearing with the NSOI under Colman Pearce for Naxos-Marco Polo and RTÉ.
**SELECTED REVIEWS** (since January 1994):
19.3.96, 26.5.97, 21.6.97 Irish Times.
**PRIZES/AWARDS/APPOINTMENTS:**
1979 Awarded Gold Medal from the DIT Conservatory of Music and Drama, Dublin.
1993 Awarded Ishibashi-Zogoro Memorial Scholarship from Ueno Gakuen, Tokyo.
**TRAINING AND/OR QUALIFICATIONS:**
From 1970 to 1980, Studied at DIT CMD (teacher Marie Jones).
From 1980 to 1981, Studied at the RIAM (teacher Dr John O'Conor).
From 1981 to 1982, Studied at the University of Western Ontario (teacher Peter Katin).
From 1982 to 1984, New York (teacher Adele Marcus), London (teacher Alexander Kelly).
**REGULARLY PERFORMS WITH:**
Alan Smale, Kenneth Edge.
**ADDITIONAL INFORMATION:**
Regular soloist with the NSOI and RTÉCO. Works extensively in contemporary music having commissioned many new works and is recording for the Naxos-Marco Polo Label.

# Johanna Byrne *Piano*

**Contact:** Ms Johanna Byrne
36, Shannon Drive
Corbally
Limerick
**Tel:** +353 61 342829
*See mezzo soprano page 100.*

# Jan Càp *Piano*

**Contact:** Mr Jan Càp,
Cork School of Music
Union Quay
Cork
**Tel/Fax:** +353 21 270076 / +353 21 276595

**KEY IRISH PERFORMANCES** (since January 1994):
1.97 Theatre Royal, Waterford, promoted by Waterford Music Club, appearing with Catherine Leonard.
2.97 Cork School of Music, promoted by Cork Orchestral Society.
1-5.97 Crawford Art Gallery, Cork, 3 concerts in a Brahms/Schubert series, appearing with the Crawford Piano Trio.
**KEY PERFORMANCES OUTSIDE IRELAND** (since January 1994):
3.94 Chagal Museum/Nice Conservatoire, appearing solo and with J Petcu and Aisling Casey.
6.96 Town Hall, Guilford, UK, promoted by the City of Guilford, appearing with the Crawford Piano Trio.
11.96 City Library, Köln, Germany, promoted by the City of Köln, appearing with C Leonard.
4.97 Music Institut, Erlangen, Germany, appearing with the Marleau Ensemble.
**SELECTED BROADCASTS AND/OR RECORDED WORK:**
7.95 Reger, Messiaen, Klemmstein violin/piano works for Bavarian Radio.

11.95 'Serendipity' P.Trio No. 1 for Altarus Record Company.
4.97 Brahms Horn Trio for Bavarian Radio.
**SELECTED REVIEWS** (since January 1994):
12.96 Gramophone.
2.97 The Examiner.
**PRIZES/AWARDS/APPOINTMENTS:**
1974 3rd Prize winner at the Monza International Piano Competition.
1978 3rd Prize at Florenze International Chamber Music Competition.
**TRAINING AND/OR QUALIFICATIONS:**
From 1961 to 1966, Graduate Diploma from Prague Conservatoire.
From 1966 to 1968, Postgraduate studies at Moscow Conservatoire.
1969 ARCM.
1970 FTCL.
**REGULARLY PERFORMS WITH:**
C. Leonard, J. Petcu, Evzen Rattay, Crawford Piano Trio, Marteau Ensemble.
**AVAILABILITY:**
General.
**ADDITIONAL INFORMATION:**
Apart from concerts, is frequently engaged in workshops and master-classes in Ireland and abroad. Also works as Examiner for County Cork VEC, DIT Conservatory of Music and Drama, Dublin, and the National University of Ireland, Maynooth. Specialist interest is Czech music.

## Elaine Clark *Piano*

**Contact:** Miss Elaine Clark
3, Belgrave Road
Monkstown
Co Dublin
**Tel:** +353 1 2808883
*See violin page 58.*

## Aidan Coleman *Piano*

**Contact:** Mr Aidan Coleman
28, Lisalea
Frascati Park
Blackrock, Co Dublin
**Tel:** +353 1 2835117
*See bass baritone page 112.*

## Dearbhla Collins *Piano*

**Contact:** Ms Dearbhla Collins
54, The Waterside
Charlotte Quay
Dublin 4
**Tel/Mobile/Fax:** +353 1 6672546 / +353 87 459458 / +353 1 2985402

*" Fine keyboard work was outstanding ... an Irish musician whose name you should note"*

22.5.95 The Examiner.

**KEY IRISH PERFORMANCES** (since January 1994):
6.96 National Concert Hall, Dublin in a performance of Prokoviev Concerto No. 1 appearing with the National Symphony Orchestra of Ireland.
9-10.96 Pianist for the nationwide tour of 'Katja Kabanova' promoted by Opera Theatre Company.
5.97 Siamsa Tíre,Tralee, promoted by Music Network and Martin Whelan appearing with Colette McGahon and Kathleen Tynan.
6.97 John Field Room, NCH, solo recital.
**KEY PERFORMANCES OUTSIDE IRELAND** (since January 1994):
4.94 Kalamazoo, Michigan, USA, appearing at the Irving S. Gilmore International Keyboard Festival.
14.9.95 St Cyprian's Church, London, masterclasses.
5.97 St Cyprian's Church, London, appearing at the master classes international showcase.
**SELECTED BROADCASTS AND/OR RECORDED WORK:**
9.93 Gershwin 'Rhapsody in Blue' in 'Off the Record' programme for RTÉ.
**SELECTED REVIEWS** (since January 1994):
7.3.95 Irish Times.
21.09.95 Irish Times.
**PRIZES/AWARDS/APPOINTMENTS:**
5.91 Awarded the Charles Brennan prize for the highest placed Irish competitor at the GPA Dublin International Piano Competition.
4.93 Awarded special prize, at the Palm Beach Invitational International Piano Competition.
5.94 Awarded the John Field prize, at the GPA Dublin IPC.
5.94 Awarded the Irish Business Woman's Prize, at the GPA Dublin International Piano Competition.
**TRAINING AND/OR QUALIFICATIONS:**
From 1974 to 1989, Studied at the Royal Irish Academy of Music.
From 1989 to 1993, Diploma, awarded by the Hochschule für Musik und darstellende Kunst, Vienna.
1986 ARCM (Hons), awarded by the Royal College of Music, London
**REGULARLY PERFORMS WITH:**
Irish Piano Trio Kathleen Tynan and Colette McGahon. Also with Aileen Dullaghan (violin and piano duo).
**AVAILABILITY:**
General.
**ADDITIONAL INFORMATION:**
Regular soloist with the NSOI and the RTÉCO and is a frequent recitalist abroad. Currently the teaching assistant for Dr John O'Conor at the Royal Irish Academy of Music, Dublin.

## Finghin Collins *Piano*

**Contact:** Mr Finghin Collins
56, Mount Carmel Road
Goatstown, Dublin 14
**Tel/Fax:** +353 1 2985402

*"He can create magic, heartbreak, exultation, tension, relief, anything. Wherever he plays, go hear him."* 4.10.96 Evening Herald.

**KEY IRISH PERFORMANCES** (since January 1994):
7.94 National Concert Hall, Dublin, promoted by RTÉ, appearing with the National Symphony Orchestra of Ireland.
11.94 RDS, Dublin, promoted by Royal Dublin Society.
5.96 National Concert Hall, Dublin, promoted by RP (Ireland), appearing with the RTÉ Concert Orchestra.
3.97 John Field Room, National Concert Hall, Dublin, promoted by the Guardian Dublin International Piano Competition.
**KEY PERFORMANCES OUTSIDE IRELAND** (since January 1994):
1995 Korschenbroich, Germany, promoted by Erica Wuslich.
1996 Toronto, Canada, promoted by and appearing with Dublin Youth Orchestra.
1996 Pedara, Sicily, promoted by Carmelo Pappalarod.
1997 Town Hall, Leeds, promoted by Leeds International Concert Season, appearing with City of Leeds Youth Orchestra.
**SELECTED BROADCASTS AND/OR RECORDED WORK:**
1994 Tchaikowsky Piano Concerto for RTÉ.
1996 'Success in Leeds' for RTÉ.
1997 Lisney Piano Competition for RTÉ.
**SELECTED REVIEWS** (since January 1994):
17.1.95 Irish Times.
29.8.96 Belfast Telegraph.
23.3.97 Sunday Tribune.
**PRIZES/AWARDS/APPOINTMENTS:**
1992 3rd Prize, Ettlingen International Piano Competition. First prize

EMCY Junior piano competition, Antwerp.
1994 Overall winner of the RTÉ Young Musician of the Future Competition. Dublin, 96, 2nd Prize EMCY Senior Piano Competition.
1996 Semi Final Prize at the Leeds International Piano Competition.
**TRAINING AND/OR QUALIFICATIONS:**
From 1983 to 1995, Royal Irish Academy of Music with Dr John O'Conor. Since 1995, BA (Performance) from the Royal Irish Academy of Music with Dr John O' Conor. ARCM, Performer's diploma in piano, Royal College of Music, London. Teacher's diploma, Harmony and Counterpoint, ARIAM.
**FREQUENTLY PERFORMS WITH:**
Catherine Leonard (violin) and Hanno Strydom (cello) as a trio, Riona Ó Dúinnin (flute), Robin Tritschler (tenor).
**AVAILABILITY:**
General.
**ADDITIONAL INFORMATION:**
Ireland's representative at EBU's concert for Young Soloists in Valencia, Spain (1992) and at Eurovision Competition, Warsaw (1994). Has played with all major Irish orchestras and has also performed in the UK, France, Germany, Belgium, Holland, Canada, Norway and the Czech Republic. Semi-finalist and winner of the Brennan Prize for highest placed Irish competitor at the Guardian Dublin International Piano Competition.

# Neil Cooney *Piano*

**Contact:** Mr Neil Cooney
15, Pinewood Avenue
Glasnevin
Dublin 11
**Tel/Fax:** +353 1 8422475 / +44 181 8835844

*"Exemplary touch, fluent and with that all important clarity"* 5.89. Channel Island Press.

**KEY IRISH PERFORMANCES:**
7.2.94 National Concert Hall, Dublin, promoted by RTÉ, appearing with RTÉ Chamber Orchestra.
1.3.95 Town Hall, Dundalk, promoted by Dundalk UDC, recital.
10.3.95 Royal Dublin Society (RDS), recital.
28.6.96 NCH, Dublin, appearing with the National Symphony Orchestra of Ireland.
**KEY PERFORMANCES OUTSIDE IRELAND** (since Janaury 1994):
21.4.95 Conway Hall, London, promoted by Edge and Ellison.
25.10.96 Leighton House, London, promoted by Irish Heritage.
10.5.97 Northampton Arts Centre, promoted by the Rotary Club.
9.7.97 St Martin-In-Ludgate, recital.
**SELECTED BROADCASTS AND/OR RECORDED WORK:**
5.4.94 Solo Recital, recorded for Peugeot, Ireland.
2.3.95 Recital at the Hugh Lane Municipal Gallery of Modern Art, Dublin for RTÉ.
26.6.96 RTÉ broadcast from NCH.
**SELECTED REVIEWS** (since January 1994):
Irish Times.
**PRIZES/AWARDS/APPOINTMENTS:**
1989 Winner of the Lombard and Ulster Music Foundation Award.
1991 Anna Instone Award winner, from the British Conservatories.
**TRAINING AND/OR QUALIFICATIONS:**
From 1981 to 1987, studied at the DIT Conservatory of Music and Drama. From 1988 to 1991, Dip RAM from the Royal Academy of Music, London. Since 1992, (teacher Maria Curcio).
**REGULARLY PERFORMS WITH:**
Emmanuel Lawler (tenor).
**AVAILABILITY:**
General.

# Joseph Corbett *Piano*

**Contact:** Mr Joseph Corbett
50, Goldhurst Terrace
London NW6 3HT
England
**Tel:** +44 171 624 6280
*See baritone page 112.*

# Ted Courtney *Piano*

**Contact:** Mr Ted Courtney
Kingsford
Newtownsmith
Sandycove
Co Dublin
**Tel/Fax:** +353 1 2804519 / +353 1 2082072
*See clarinet page 3.*

# Niamh Crowley *Piano*

**Contact:** Ms Niamh Crowley
Rosses Point
County Sligo
**Tel:** +353 71 77178
*See violin page 59.*

# Donald Cullington *Piano*

**Contact:** Dr Donald Cullington
113, Station Road
Greenisland
Carrickfergus
Co Antrim BT38 8UW
Northern Ireland
**Tel:** +44 1232 863852

**KEY IRISH PERFORMANCES** (since January 1994):
17.10.95 Dalriada House, Jordanstown, promoted by Music Division of the University of Ulster.
4.10.96 Town Hall, Ballymena, promoted by Ballymena Borough Council.
24.10.96 Harty Room, Queen's University, Belfast, promoted by the Queen's University Music Society, appearing with Shaun Ryan (piano).
14.2.97 Courtyard Theatre, Ballycool, promoted by the Newtownabbey Borough Council, appearing with various younger artists.
**SELECTED BROADCASTS AND/OR RECORDED WORK:**
11.91 and 11.92 'The Classical Show' for BBC Radio Ulster.
**TRAINING AND/OR QUALIFICATIONS:**
1965 LRAM (piano teacher), ARCM (performance).
1974 D Mus from the University of Edinburgh. (All musical qualifications taken externally).
**AVAILABILITY:**
General.
**ADDITIONAL INFORMATION:**
Career as performer and teacher has taken him from England to Scotland, New Zealand and, finally, Northern Ireland. Has been Head of Music at the University of Ulster, and since 1971, appears regularly, as piano soloist and accompanist. Broad repertoire including jazz-based pieces of the 1920's and 1930's and classics, both celebrated and neglected.

## Peter Dains *Piano*

**Contact:** Mr Peter Dains
The Sheiling
Kilmore Avenue
Killiney
Co Dublin
or
DIT Conservatory of Music and Drama
Chatham Row
Dublin 2
**Tel:** +353 1 2851536

**KEY IRISH PERFORMANCES** (since January 1994):
5.1.97 Hugh Lane Municipal Gallery of Modern Art, Dublin, promoted by Gavin O'Sullivan and the Goethe Institute, appearing with Annette Cleary (cello).
2.2.97 HLMGMA, Dublin, appearing with Annette Cleary (cello), performing the complete cello and piano works of Beethoven.
9.3.97 HLMGMA, Dublin, promoted by Gavin O'Sullivan and Alliance Française, appearing with Gillian Williams (violin).
**KEY PERFORMANCES OUTSIDE IRELAND** (since January 1994):
1995 Luxembourg, appearing with Ioana Petcu (violin)
**PRIZES/AWARDS/APPOINTMENTS:**
From 1978 to 1992, Appointed Senior Lecturer in Piano and Course Tutor for B Mus Ed Course (with Trinity College) by the Royal Irish Academy of Music, Dublin.
Since 1992, Appointed accompanist for B Mus Perf Course at the DIT CMD.
**TRAINING AND/OR QUALIFICATIONS:**
From 1968 to 1972, FTCL, ARCM, LRAM from Trinity College, London.
**REGULARLY PERFORMS WITH:**
Annette Cleary (cello), Gillian Williams (violin).
**AVAILABILITY:**
General.

## Declan Daly *Piano*

**Contact:** Mr Declan Daly
Tossey
Loughmourne
Castleblayney
Co Monaghan
**Tel:** +353 42 45041
*See violin page 60.*

## Diane Daly *Piano*

**Contact:** Ms Diane Daly
Tossey
Loughmourne
Castleblayney
Co Monaghan
**Tel:** +353 42 45041
*See violin page 60.*

## Raymond Deane *Piano*

**Contact:** Mr Raymond Deane
c/o Contemporary Music Centre
95, Lower Baggot Street
Dublin 2
**Tel/Fax:** +353 1 6612105 / +353 1 6762639
**Email:** info@cmc.ie

**KEY IRISH PERFORMANCES** (since January 1994):
23.9.94 John Field Room, National Concert Hall, solo recital.
4.5.95 Harty Room Belfast, solo recital.
9.6.96 Bank of Ireland Arts Centre, Dublin, solo recital.
**KEY PERFORMANCES OUTSIDE IRELAND** (since January 1994):
6.4.95 Kishinev, Moldova, appearing with Kenneth Edge (saxophone).
21.10.96 La Friche, Marseille.
**PRIZES/AWARDS/APPOINTMENTS:**
1972 Winner of the Nordell Cup (sonata playing) at the Feis Ceoil, Dublin.
**AVAILABILITY:**
General.
**ADDITIONAL INFORMATION:**
Composer and performs mainly own compositions. Repertoire also includes works by a number of living Irish composers, as well as some compositions from contemporary composers abroad.

## Louisa Dennehy *Piano*

**Contact:** Miss Louisa Dennehy
37, Glenwood
Carrigaline
Co Cork
**Tel:** +353 21 372498
*See flute page 12.*

## Barry Douglas *Piano*

**Contact:** Mr Barry Douglas
c/o IMG Artists
Media House
3, Burlington Lane
London W4 2TH
**Tel/Fax:** +44 181 2335800 / +44 181 2335801

*"... Douglas displayed his galvanising energy, animation and emphasis in a towering interpretation of distinctive authority"* 4.95 Daily Telegraph.

**KEY IRISH PERFORMANCES** (since January 1994):
1.97 Waterfront Hall, Belfast, performing Beethoven's 'Emperor' Concerto with the Ulster Orchestra at the opening Gala Concert of the Waterfront Hall.
2.97 National Concert Hall, Dublin, appearing with the RTÉ Symphony Orchestra.
**KEY PERFORMANCES OUTSIDE IRELAND** (since January 1994):
11.95 Carnegie Hall, New York, USA, appearing with the Moscow Philharmonic Orchestra.
12.96 Munich, Germany, promoted by Bayrische Rundfunk.
4.97 London, appearing with the London Symphony Orchestra.
**SELECTED BROADCASTS AND/OR RECORDED WORK:**
Many recordings for RCA, most recently the Britten 'Piano Concerto' and Debussy 'Fantasie' with the Orchestre Philharmonique de Radio, France.
**PRIZES/AWARDS/APPOINTMENTS:**
1986 Gold Medal winner at Tchaikowsky International Piano Competition, Moscow.
Awarded Hon D Mus from Queen's University, Belfast.
From 1992 to 1993, Visiting Fellow, Oriel College, Oxford.

# Mary Dullea *Piano*

**Contact:** Ms Mary Dullea
Killountain
Bandon
Co Cork
**Tel:** +353 23 41951

*"She made us see Philip Martin's composition as sparkling, exciting and imaginative"*
6.92 The Examiner.

**KEY IRISH PERFORMANCES** (since January 1994):
8.94 Boathouse, Castletownsend, promoted by Margaret Warren, appearing with Darragh Morgan (violin).
8.94 Drumcliffe Church, Sligo, promoted by the Model Arts Centre, appearing with Darragh Morgan.
4.96 Cork School of Music, promoted by Cork Orchestral Society.
5.97 Crawford Gallery, Cork, summer lunchtime series.
**KEY PERFORMANCES OUTSIDE IRELAND** (since January 1994):
11.94 Palais des Beaux Arts, Brussels, promoted by 12 Pianos pour La Recherche Médicale.
11.95 Conservatoire Luxembourg and Salle Pleyel, Paris, promoted by '15 Pianos pour L'Europe'.
7.96 Lichfield, England, promoted by Lichfield Festival, appearing with Hilary Parsons (soprano).
**SELECTED BROADCASTS AND/OR RECORDED WORK:**
5.97 With the Fidelio Trio, for Hong Kong Radio Four.
3.94 For BBC Radio Ulster.
**SELECTED REVIEWS** (since January 1994):
11.95 Hamstead and Highgate Express.
**PRIZES/AWARDS/APPOINTMENTS:**
3.91 Edith Best Scholarship Award from the Feis Ceoil, Dublin.
2.97 Award from the Martin Scholarship Fund, London.
**TRAINING AND/OR QUALIFICATIONS:**
From 9.87 To 7.91, Cork School of Music (teacher Mary Beattie).
From 9.91 to 7.95, B Mus (Hons), ARCM (PG), Dip RCM (Hons) from the Royal College of Music, London.
Since 2.96 (teacher Paul Roberts).
**AVAILABILITY:**
General, school holidays (including half term weeks).
**REGULARLY PERFORMS WITH:**
Fidelio Trio. Michael Atkinson (cello), Katie Samways (saxophone).
**ADDITIONAL INFORMATION:**
Performs regularly throughout London as soloist and has had master-classes with David Dolan, Jorge Luis Prats, Vladimir Tropp and Peter Frankel. Intends to spend more time in Ireland.

# Thérèse Fahy *Piano*

**Contact:** Ms Thérèse Fahy
12, Malachi Road
Dublin 7
**Tel:** +353 1 6771508

*"A musician of great style with a deep understanding [of the musical aspects] of the works she played"* 4.88 Sunday Tribune.

**KEY IRISH PERFORMANCES** (since January 1994):
89/90/97 John Field Room, National Concert Hall, Dublin.
89/92 NCH promoted by RTÉ, appearing with the National Symphony Orchestra of Ireland.
1994 Alliance Francaise, Dublin.
22.6.97 Hugh Lane Municipal Gallery of Modern Art, Dublin, promoted by Gavin O'Sullivan and the Instituto Cervantes.
**KEY PERFORMANCES OUTSIDE IRELAND** (since January 1994):
1994 Tel Aviv, Israel, promoted by the New Israeli Opera appearing with the Israel Symphony Orchestra and the Israeli Opera Chorus.
1995 Amsterdam, the Netherlands.
**SELECTED BROADCASTS AND/OR RECORDED WORK:**
9.94 Lunchtime recital series, for BBC Belfast.
**PRIZES/AWARDS/APPOINTMENTS:**
1985 Awarded Fulbright Scholarship, by the Department of Foreign Affairs and the US Government.
1987 1st Prize winner at the St Louis Concerto Competition, awarded by St Louis Conservatory of Music, USA.
**TRAINING AND/OR QUALIFICATIONS:**
From 1972 to 1984, LRIAM, from the Royal Irish Academy of Music (teachers Dina Copeman and Dr John O'Conor).
From 1980 to 1984, B Mus, from Trinity College, Dublin.
From 1984 to 1985, tuition with Monique Deschaussées, Paris (French Governement Scholarship).
From 1985 to 1987, MM in Piano Performance from St Louis Conservatory of Music (teacher Joseph Kalichstein).
**REGULARLY PERFORMS WITH:**
Prism, Marie Comiskey (flute).
**AVAILABILITY:**
General.
**ADDITIONAL INFORMATION:**
Entrance scholar to the RIAM. Has given recitals in France, America, Holland and the UK. Has played at many arts festivals throughout Ireland and has performed with both BBC and RTÉ. Concerto Soloist with the NSOI. Lecturer in piano at RIAM and gives master classes and seminars throughout Ireland. Celebrated return to the concert platform on 22.6.97 with a performance of 'Goyescas' by Granados at the HLMGMA, Dublin.

# Kevin Fitzpatrick *Piano*

**Contact:** Mr Kevin Fitzpatrick
Patch
Glenamaddy
Galway
Ireland
**Tel:** +353 907 59619

*"... Delighted his audience ... dexterity of the highest order"* 6.92 Goole Chronicle, Yorkshire.

**KEY IRISH PERFORMANCES** (since January 1994):
16.5.97 Glenamaddy Town Hall, Galway, promoted by Glenamaddy Musical Society.
**KEY PERFORMANCES OUTSIDE IRELAND** (since January 1994):
9.94 Leeds Music Club.
11.94 Leeds Music Club.
1.95 Selby Abbey, Yorkshire.
3.95 Goole Concert Society, Yorkshire.
**SELECTED REVIEWS** (since January 1994):
24.5.97 Tuam Herald.
**TRAINING AND/OR QUALIFICATIONS:**
4.85 ALCM (Perf) from London College of Music.
7.85 LLCM (Perf) from London College of Music.
7.87 LTCL (Perf) from Trinity College of Music, London.
**REGULARLY PERFORMS WITH:**
Dulciana.
**AVAILABILITY:**
General.
**ADDITIONAL INFORMATION:**
Studied piano in London with Sidney Harrison. Has performed extensively in the North of England. Taught at the Leeds College of Music, the Yorkshire College of Music and St Peter's School, York.

## Patrick Fitzpatrick *Piano*

**Contact:** Patrick Fitzpatrick
IFSC, 96, Custom House Harbour
Dublin 1
**Tel:** +353 1 6701949 / +353 1 8326172 (a)
*See piano page 295.*

## John Gibson *Piano*

**Contact:** Mr John Gibson
41, Cloverhill Estate
Blackrock
Cork
**Tel:** +353 21 357676

*"Shapely and responsive playing."* 2.2.97 Irish Times.

**KEY IRISH PERFORMANCES** (since January 1994):
6.6.96 Lismore Castle, promoted by the AIB Festival of Music in Great Irish Houses, appearing with Alan Smale (violin).
1.12.96 Town Hall, Galway, promoted by Music for Galway, appearing with Alan Smale.
2.2.97 National Concert Hall, Dublin, promoted by RTÉ, appearing with Robert Cohen.
4.2.97 NCH, Dublin, promoted by RTÉ, appearing with the National Symphony Orchestra of Ireland.
**SELECTED BROADCASTS AND/OR RECORDED WORK:**
1980s, 'Contemporary Piano Music', CMC recording.
1993 'Aislingi Ceoil' for Gael Linn.
11.94 'Reflections in the Water', own label DC and Cassette.
**SELECTED REVIEWS** (since January 1994):
11.94 The Examiner.
5.2.97 The Examiner.
**PRIZES/AWARDS/APPOINTMENTS:**
9.82 Lectureship in Piano (CSM), appointed by City of Cork VEC.
2.97 Nijinsky Medal, awarded by the Polish Ministry of Arts.
**TRAINING AND/OR QUALIFICATIONS:**
From 1961 To 1971, LRAM, ARCM, from the Royal Irish Academy of Music (teacher Rhona Marshall).
From 1971 to 1973, and from 1975 to 1976, Diploma in Mus Ed from University College, Dublin.
1975, Masterclass in Siena, Italy (teacher Guido Agosti).
1994, Masterclass in Moscow (teacher Prof V. Schubinskaya)
**REGULARLY PERFORMS WITH:**
Philip Thomas, Alan Smale.
**AVAILABILITY:**
General.
**ADDITIONAL INFORMATION:**
Has been active as a pianist and composer since the 1970s - (over thirty concerti in repertoire and has composed of over forty works). Performs widely as a soloist with various Irish orchestras and as recitalist, chamber musician and accompanist. Has worked with all major conductors and guest conductors visiting Ireland including Stockhausen, Lutoslawski etc.

## Owen Gilhooly *Piano*

**Contact:** Owen Gilhooly
c/o Royal College of Music
Prince Consort Road
London SW7 2BS
**Mobile:** +44 973 673760
*See baritone page 113.*

## Deirdre Gilsenan *Piano*

**Contact:** Ms Deirdre Gilsenan
Loughan
Kells, Co Meath
**Mobile:** +353 88 2756326
*See soprano page 88.*

## Paul Goodman *Piano*

**Contact:** Mr Paul Goodman
Ballyminogue
Scariff, Co Clare
*See French Horn page 24.*

## Evelyn Grant *Piano*

**Contact:** Ms Evelyn Grant
11, Summerhill South
Cork
**Tel:** +353 21 316088
**Email:** grantkelly @tinet.ie
*See flute page 14.*

## Katy Griffiths *Piano*

**Contact:** Ms Katy Griffiths
21, Kipkarren Park
Newtownards
Co Down BT23 7AQ
Northern Ireland
**Tel/Fax:** +44 1247 810820
**Email:** lyttle@unite.co.uk
*See flute page 14.*

## Patrick Healy *Piano*

**Contact:** Mr Patrick Healy
1, Cavendish Mansions
Hazelbourne Road
London SW12 4NX, England
**Tel/Fax:** +44 181 6752086 / +44 1332 740 423
**Other instruments:** Voice.

**KEY IRISH PERFORMANCES** (since January 1994):
Regular appearances at the National Concert Hall, Dublin.
**KEY PERFORMANCES OUTSIDE IRELAND** (since January 1994):
London Festival Hall, promoted by the Stephanie Williams Association appearing with Richard Barker. Fangulich Hall, London, promoted by Martin McEvoy, appearing with David Guests. London, promoted by Martin McEvoy, appearing with Richard Barker.
**SELECTED BROADCASTS AND/OR RECORDED WORK:**
Recording of Benjamin Britten's 'Curlew River' with English National Opera.
**REGULARLY PERFORMS WITH:**
English National Opera.
**AVAILABILITY:**
General.
**ADDITIONAL INFORMATION:**
Opera coach, repetiteur and accompanist of musical events. Has been the musical director for Richard Barker music show 'Grand Tour'.

## Louise Higgins *Piano*

**Contact:** Ms Louise Higgins
257, Malahide Marina Village
Co Dublin
**Tel:** +353 1 8450802
*See violin page 61.*

## Shayron Hobbs *Piano*

**Contact:** Ms Shayron Hobbs
110, Earlwood Estate
The Lough
Cork
**Tel:** +353 21 962370
*See soprano page 89.*

## Edward Holly *Piano*

**Contact:** Mr Edward Holly
40, Glenmore Drive
Drogheda
Co Louth
**Tel:** +353 41 38000
**Other instruments:** Organ, keyboards, percussion.

**KEY IRISH PERFORMANCES** (since January 1994):
10.94 BOI Arts Centre, Dublin, 'Classical Choice', appearing with Doreen Curran (mezzo soprano).
4.95 Royal Hospital, Kilmainham, Dublin, as part of the Lombard and Ulster Music Foundation Award.
12.95 Droichead Arts Centre, Drogheda, Co Louth promoted by the Arts Centre.
**KEY PERFORMANCES OUTSIDE IRELAND** (since January 1994):
1994 Performance at the Moscow State University as part an exchange programme with DIT Conservatory of Music and Drama, Dublin.
1996 Performance at the IBLA Ragusa, Sicily, Italy.
**SELECTED BROADCASTS AND/OR RECORDED WORK:**
1990, 'Theatre Nights' for RTÉ (performance of Gershwin's 'Rhapsody in Blue').
1993 'Late Late Show' for RTÉ.
**PRIZES/AWARDS/APPOINTMENTS:**
1988 Winner of Esposito Cup and Larchet Memorial Cup at the Feis Ceoil, Dublin.
1992 Winner of the Senior Piano Rosebowl at the Feis Ceoil, Dublin.
**TRAINING AND/OR QUALIFICATIONS:**
From 1988 to 1992, Grad Dip Mus and B Mus (Perf) from the DIT CMD.
Since 1994, following Masters Degree programme at the National University of Ireland, Maynooth.
**AVAILABILITY:**
General.
**ADDITIONAL INFORMATION:**
Experience in solo recitals and accompanying. Has 5 years experience in choral conducting. Involved with numerous styles of music - classical, swing/ jazz, light entertainment, Irish and popular music

## Una Hunt *Piano*

**Contact:** Ms Una Hunt
13, Mountainview Road
Ranelagh
Dublin 6
**Tel/Fax:** +353 1 4962503 / +353 1 6775109

**KEY IRISH PERFORMANCES** (since January 1994):
1.6.97 Irish Museum of Modern Art, Dublin, performing Spring/Summer Chamber Music with Fionnuala Hunt (violin).
4.6.97 Carton House, Kildare, AIB Festival of Music in Great Houses, performing with Dublin Piano Trio with Bruno Giuranna (viola).
20.1.97 City Hall, Belfast, 75th Anniversary Concert, with Belfast Music Society.
**KEY PERFORMANCES OUTSIDE IRELAND** (since January 1994):
14.10.95 Centre for the Arts, Portland, Indiana, USA, performing with Fionnuala Hunt (violin).
21.10.95 Boston, USA, Nakamichi Concert Series.
21.7.96 Givet, Brussels, Belgium, to mark Ireland's EU Presidency performing with the Dublin Piano Trio.
**SELECTED BROADCASTS AND/OR RECORDED WORK:**
'Irish Fantasy', works by Irish composers, with Fionnuala Hunt (violin), for Continuum CCD 1051.
1993 and 1994, RTÉ Proms, performing Beethoven Piano Concerto No. 5 'Emperor'.
**TRAINING AND/OR QUALIFICATIONS:**
Queens University, Belfast, B Mus (Hons).
Konzertfach Diploma, Hochschule for Musik, Vienna.
**AVAILABILITY:**
General.
**ADDITIONAL INFORMATION:**
Particularly interested in music by Irish, Spanish and American composers. Interests span the romantic period up to selected 20th century music. Studied with Rhona Marshall, Dieter Weber, Noel Flores, Vlado Perlemuter, Menahim Pressler, Andre Tchaikovsky and Tamas Vasary. Has worked with James Galway, William Bennett, Marzio Conti and Patricia Bardon.

## Mairéad Hurley *Piano*

**Contact:** Ms Mairéad Hurley
20, Church Avenue
South Circular Road, Dublin 8
**Tel:** +353 1 4549500

**KEY IRISH PERFORMANCES** (since January 1994):
10.94 National Concert Hall, Dublin, promoted by Ashley Pringle, appearing with Louise Walsh and Giuseppe Morino.
5.95 Galway Arts Festival, Galway, appearing with Orla Boylan.
5.95 RTÉ Proms, Dublin, repetiteur for 'Don Pasquale'.
6.95 Trinity College, Dublin, promoted by Swift Productions, repetiteur for New Opera.
**KEY PERFORMANCES OUTSIDE IRELAND** (since January 1994):
1.94 Belfast, promoted by Opera Northern Ireland, repetiteur for 'Il Barbiere Di Siviglia'.
5.95 Antrim, promoted by ONI, workshop with ONI Chorus.
8.95 Belfast, promoted by ONI, repetiteur for 'Don Giovanni'.
**SELECTED BROADCASTS AND/OR RECORDED WORK:**
1993/94 'Live at 3' for RTÉ.
1995 'Late Late Show' for RTÉ.
1995 Recital with Órla Boylan for RTÉ.
**PRIZES/AWARDS/APPOINTMENTS:**
74/82 Royal Irish Academy of Music, annual scholarship.
1983 Winner of Morris Grant Bursary at the Feis Ceoil, Dublin.
1991 Awarded 1 year scholarship to the National Opera Studio, London.
1992 Awarded a Bursary to study in London by the Arts Council.
**TRAINING AND/OR QUALIFICATIONS:**
From 1971 to 1985, LRIAM awarded by RIAM.
1980 to 1984, B Mus from University College, Dublin.
From 1985 to 1986, H Dip Ed from UCD.
1991 to 1992, Repetiteur with the National Opera Studio, London.
**REGULARLY PERFORMS WITH:**
Dublin Grand Opera Society and Opera Ireland as repetiteur and tutor to chorus.
**AVAILABILITY:**
General.
**ADDITIONAL INFORMATION:**
Performs regularly as accompanist for public concerts, e.g. operatic evenings at National Concert Hall, the Royal Dublin Society Platform series and the Bank of Ireland Arts Centre concert series. Repetiteur and Director of the Opera Ensemble at the DIT Conservatory of Music and Drama. Official accompanist for the RTÉ Young Musician of the Future competition.

# Michael Joyce *Piano*

**Contact:** Mr Michael Joyce
Richard Wagner - Str. 42
50674 Köln
Germany
**Tel:** +49 221 2579801

**KEY IRISH PERFORMANCES** (since January 1994):
2.94 City Hall, Cork, appearing with Cork School of Music Symphony Orchestra.
5.95 Dunkatnel House, Cork, promoted by Cork Orchestral Society.
5.96 Crawford Gallery, Cork, promoted by Cork Orchestral Society.
11.96 Killorglin Arts Festival, Co Kerry, promoted by Killorglin Festival 1996, appearing with Christina Sirbu (violin).
**KEY PERFORMANCES OUTSIDE IRELAND** (since January 1994):
4.96 VHS Lemgu, Germany.
2.97 Chateau De Chambesy, Geneva, appearing with Aube Wagnière, Viola Orchestra and Ars Nova.
4.97 Besançon, France.
**SELECTED BROADCASTS AND/OR RECORDED WORK:**
5.96 Performance for RTÉ.
**SELECTED REVIEWS** (since January 1994):
2.94 The Examiner.
5.95 The Examiner.
6.96 The Examiner.
**PRIZES/AWARDS/APPOINTMENTS:**
1994 Hamilton Harty Cup winner at the Feis Ceoil, Dublin.
1996 Heneghan Cup from the Feis Ceoil, Dublin.
**TRAINING AND/OR QUALIFICATIONS:**
From 1988 to 1990, Dip CSM from the Cork School of Music (teachers Dr Bridget Doolan and Jan Càp).
From 1991 to 1996, Künstlerische Reifeprüfung from the Hochschule für Musik, Germany (teacher Prof Nerine Barrett).
**REGULARLY PERFORMS WITH:**
Naoko Shimizu (viola), Christina Sirbu (violin).
**AVAILABILITY:**
General.

# Réamonn Keary *Piano*

**Contact:** Mr Réamonn Keary
c/o The Royal Irish Academy of Music
Westland Row
Dublin 2
**Tel/Fax:** +353 1 6764412 / +353 1 6622798

**PRIZES/AWARDS/APPOINTMENTS:**
Professor at the Royal Irish Academy of Music, Dublin.
**TRAINING AND/OR QUALIFICATIONS:**
Masters Degree (Hons) in Performance and Interpretation from the National University of Ireland, Maynooth.
**REGULARLY PERFORMS WITH:**
Haenjo Trio, Goudarzi-Tobin Keary Piano duet.
**ADDITIONAL INFORMATION:**
Studied with Dr John O'Conor in Dublin and Leonid Brumberg in Vienna. Has recorded for RTÉ and performs frequently as a chamber musician and accompanist. Has appeared as a soloist with the RTÉ Concert Orchestra.

# Elizabeth Keighary *Piano*

**Contact:** Ms Elizabeth Keighary
27, Temple Manor Way
Dublin 12
**Tel:** +353 1 4565586

**KEY IRISH PERFORMANCES** (since January 1994):
1994 St Clare's Church, Carlow, appearing with Colette McGahon (mezzo-soprano) and the Carlow Choral Society.
1995 Church of Ireland College of Education, promoted by the Kodály Society of Ireland, appearing with Audrey McAllister (violin) cellos and voice.
1995 and 1996, Scoil Mobhi, Dublin, appearing with Adele O'Dwyer and the Scoil Mobhi Strings.
1996 and 1997, Castlebar, Co Mayo and John Field Room, National Concert Hall, promoted by the Italian Cultural Institute, appearing with Doreen Curran (mezzo-soprano) and the Choir of the Italian Cultural Institute.
**KEY PERFORMANCES OUTSIDE IRELAND** (since January 1994):
1995 Institute Kodály, Keckskemèt, Hungary, final concert of the Kodály Institute Summer Course, appearing with other participants.
**PRIZES/AWARDS/APPOINTMENTS:**
From 1974 to 1976, Awarded continuation scholarships and prizes from the DIT Conservatory of Music and Drama, Dublin.
1979 Winner of the Edith Best Scholarship to the Royal College of Music, London at the Feis Ceoil, Dublin.
**TRAINING AND/OR QUALIFICATIONS:**
From 1976 to 1979 (teacher Mabel Swainson) in Dublin, and attended masterclasses at Dartington, England (teacher Sequiera Costa).
From 1979 to 1981, ARCM and LRAM (Performer's and Teacher's), from the Royal College of Music, London, (teacher Peter Wallfisch).
From 1981 to 1982, Guildhall School of Music and Drama, London, participated in chamber music masterclasses and recitals (with Gordon Bach).
From 1982 to 1984, participated in chamber music masterclasses, with members of the National Symphony Orchestra of Ireland, given by Bruce Dukov in Dublin.
**REGULARLY PERFORMS WITH:**
Colette McGahon (mezzo-soprano), Doreen Curran (mezzo-soprano), Audrey McAllister (violin).
**AVAILABILITY:**
Evenings and June, July, August, Christmas, Easter and October break.
**ADDITIONAL INFORMATION:**
Enjoys singing in chamber choirs - Gaudete Singers, Musica Sacra; and large choirs - RTÉ Philharmonic, London Philharmonic and accompanying when necessary. Has been musical director of Carlow Choral Society (from 1989 to 1993). Enjoys giving recitals with singers, instrumentalists and choral groups.

# Deborah Kelleher *Piano*

**Contact:** Deborah Kelleher
36, Anna Villa
Ranelagh
Dublin 6
**Mobile/Tel:** +353 88 698409 / +353 1 4960260

**PRIZES/AWARDS/APPOINTMENTS:**
1996 Finalist in the chamber music section at the RTÉ Young Musician of the Future competition. Morris Grant Cup and Bursary-senior piano cup winner at the Feis Ceoil, Dublin.
**TRAINING AND/OR QUALIFICATIONS:**
BA (Mod) Pure Music, from Trinity College, Dublin. Studied piano with Frank and Ann Heneghan. Studied harpsicord with Aisling Heneghan at the DIT Conservatory of Music and Drama. MM from University College, Dublin, where she is a junior tutor.
**REGULARLY PERFORMS WITH:**
Geraldine O'Grady and Oonagh Keogh.
**ADDITIONAL INFORMATION:**
Piano teacher in DIT CMD, and is répétiteur for vocal and orchestral departments. Has given numerous recitals and broadcasts for radio and television in Ireland, England and Russia.

## Frances Kelleher *Piano*

**Contact:** Ms Frances Kelleher
90, High Street
Hampton
London TW12 2SW
England
**Tel:** +44 181 9795864

**KEY IRISH PERFORMANCES** (since January 1994):
5.94 Waterford City Hall, promoted by Waterford Music Society, appearing Bridget Knowles.
6.94 Cork City Hall, promoted by Kinsale Opera Society, appearing with Cara O'Sullivan and Majella Cullagh.
12.94 Triskel Art Centre, Cork promoted by the Centre, appearing with Fiona O'Reilly.
7.95 Clonmel, Co Tipperary appearing with Maeve Carey.
**KEY PERFORMANCES OUTSIDE IRELAND** (since January 1994):
6.96 St John Smiths Square, London, promoted by Graham Johnson Almanak, appearing with Finnur Bjarnason.
10.96 Guildhall School of Music and Drama, London, promoted by GSMD appearing with Finnur Bjarnason.
1.97 St Martins, London, promoted by the Academy of St Martin's-in-the-Field, appearing with Finnur Bjarnason and Natalie Christie.
6.97 Holy Trinity Church, London, appearing with the 'Singers of London'.
**PRIZES/AWARDS/APPOINTMENTS:**
From 1995 to 1997, Two-year scholarship, awarded by the Guildhall School of Music and Drama, London.
4.96 Memorial Accompaniment Prize, awarded by Sir Anthony Lewis.
**TRAINING AND/OR QUALIFICATIONS:**
From 1985 to 1988, B Mus awarded by University College, Cork.
From 1989 to 1991, Dip CSM, awarded by Cork School of Music.
1991, LTCL, (performers) awarded by Trinity College, London.
From 1995 to 1997, Postgrad in Accompaniment, awarded by GSMD.
**AVAILABILITY:**
General.

## Jean Kelly *Piano*

**Contact:** Ms Jean Kelly
11, Summerhill South
Cork
**Tel:** +353 21 316088
**Email:** grantkelly@tinet.ie
*See concert harp page 7.*

## Claire Keville *Piano*

**Contact:** Ms Claire Keville
Claran
Ower
Co Galway
**Tel:** +353 93 35952
*See concertina page 202.*

## Frances King *Piano*

**Contact:** Mr Frances King
2, Chippendale Vale
Bangor
Co Down, BT20 4QJ
Northern Ireland
**Tel:** +44 1247 459336

*"Ensemble playing of a high order ... recording companies should take note"* 17.11.94 Belfast Newsletter.

**KEY IRISH PERFORMANCES** (since January 1994):
6.94 Hugh Lane Municipal Gallery of Modern Art, Dublin, appearing with John O'Kane.
11.94 Project Arts Centre, Dublin, appearing with Sequenza.
6.95 Castlereagh, Belfast, promoted by Castlereagh Borough Council, appearing with Quintessence.
9.95 BBC Northern Ireland, appearing with Gillian McCutcheon.
**SELECTED BROADCASTS AND/OR RECORDED WORK:**
1993 Ibert 'Divertissement' with the Ulster Orchestra, conducted by Tortelier for Chandos.
9.95 Lunchtime recital, for BBC.
**TRAINING AND/OR QUALIFICATIONS:**
From 1970 to 1974, B Mus (Hons) from University of Edinburgh.
From 1974 to 1976, MA from Queen's University, Belfast.
1971 LRAM from Royal Academy of Music.
1974 FTCL from Trinity College, London.
**REGULARLY PERFORMS WITH:**
Sequenza, Quinessence.
**AVAILABILITY:**
General.
**ADDITIONAL INFORMATION:**
Soloist, accompanist, vocal and instrumental coach, repetiteur (Opera Northern Ireland and Castleward Opera), orchestral pianist (Ulster Orchestra). Founder-member of 20th Century group Sequenza.

## David Lee *Piano*

**Contact:** Mr David Lee
10, Corbawn Drive
Shankill
Dublin 18
**Tel:** +353 1 2821303
*See organ page 28.*

## Catherine Leonard *Piano*

**Contact:** Catherine Leonard
4 Willowmere
Rochestown
Cork
**Tel/Fax:** +353 21 894366 / +353 21 272879
*See violin page 62.*

## Conor Linehan *Piano*

**Contact:** Mr Conor Linehan
19, Anglesea Avenue
Blackrock
Co Dublin
**Tel:** +353 1 2881956

## Denise Long *Piano*

**Contact:** Denise Long
26/27, Drury Street
Dublin 2
**Tel:** +353 87 2345736
*See soprano page 91.*

## Vyvienne Long *Piano*

**Contact:** Ms Vyvienne Long
'Haddington'
32, Lower Mounttown Road
Dún Laoghaire
Co Dublin
**Tel:** +353 1 2800505
*See cello page 69.*

## Owen Lorigan *Piano*

**Contact:** Mr Owen Lorigan
13, Merville Avenue
Stillorgan, Co Dublin
**Tel/Fax:** +353 1 2880113 / +353 1 2827710

**KEY IRISH PERFORMANCES** (since January 1994):
2.3.97 University of Limerick Concert Hall, promoted by Limerick Music Association.
10.4.97 Waterford Music Club, promoted by the Club, solo recital.
29.4.97 National Concert Hall Dublin, promoted by Royal Irish Academy of Music, appearing at a graduation concert.
19.6.97 National Concert Hall and the Royal Irish Academy of Music, appearing at a graduation recital.
**KEY PERFORMANCES OUTSIDE IRELAND** (since January 1994):
17.4.95 Tel Aviv, Israel, promoted by Ramat Hasharon.
20.5.95 Grote Kirk, De Rijp, Nlderijp Festival, The Netherlands, appearing with R. Ó Duinnín.
13.7.95 Tarrytown, New York, promoted by Summit Music festival.
21.7.95 Tarrytown, New York, promoted by Summit Music Festival appearing with Scott Brady.
**SELECTED BROADCASTS AND/OR RECORDED WORK:**
25.1.96 RTÉ Musician of the Future, selected ensemble, recorded by RTÉ FM3.
16.4.97 Solo recital, recorded by RTÉ.
4.6.96 Concerto performance with the National Symphony Orchestra of Ireland, recorded by RTÉ.
**PRIZES/AWARDS/APPOINTMENTS:**
2.97 Briscoe Cup winner for most outstanding student of 1996, awarded by The Royal Irish Academy, Dublin.
7.94 Runner-up in Festival Concerto Competition, awarded by the Summit Music Festival, New York.
**TRAINING AND/OR QUALIFICATIONS:**
From 1993 to 1997, BA Mus (Per) Royal Irish Academy of Music (teacher Deirdre Doyle).
1991 ARIAM (in teaching and performance) from the RIAM (teacher Deirdre Doyle).
1994 LRIAM (in performance) from the RIAM (teacher Deirdre Doyle).
**REGULARLY PERFORMS WITH:**
Presburg Trio (flute, cello, piano), Scott Brady (cello), Linda Gryffudd (contralto).
**AVAILABILITY:**
General.
**ADDITIONAL INFORMATION:**
One of the five Irish competitors in 1997 Guardian Dublin International Piano Competition. Has performed Gershwin's 'Rhapsody in Blue' with Hibernian Chamber Orchestra (conducted by John Finucane).

## Aidan Lynch *Piano*

**Contact:** Mr Aidan Lynch
15, Hawthorn Avenue
Ballycasheen, Killarney
**Tel/Fax:** +353 64 33749 / +353 64 33749 / +353 87 2202382
*See trumpet page 54.*

## Brenda McCarthy *Piano*

**Contact:** Ms Brenda McCarthy
90, Trees Road
Mount Merrion
Co Dublin
**Tel:** +353 1 2889758
**Other instruments:** Organ, oboe.

**TRAINING AND/OR QUALIFICATIONS:**
From 9.93 to 6.97, B Mus Ed and Dip Mus Ed from Trinity College, Dublin and the DIT Conservatory of Music and Drama.
From 9.94 to 6.95, ARIAM (piano) from the Royal Irish Academy of Music, Dublin.

## Jim McCullagh *Piano*

**Contact:** Mr Jim McCullagh
c/o Ulster College of Music
13, Windsor Avenue
Belfast BT19
Northern Ireland
**Tel:** +44 1232 381314
*See classical guitar page 21.*

## Gillian McCutcheon *Piano*

**Contact:** Ms Gillian McCutcheon
45, Glendarragh
Belfast BT4 2WB
Northern Ireland
**Tel:** +44 1232 760759
*See clarinet page 4.*

## Emer McDonough *Piano*

**Contact:** Ms Emer McDonough
3, Greenlawns
Sandyford Road
Dublin 16
**Tel:** +353 1 2956754
*See flute page 16.*

## Catriona McElhinney Grimes *Piano*

**Contact:** Catriona McElhinney Grimes
264, Marina Village
Malahide
Co Dublin

**KEY IRISH PERFORMANCES** (since January 1994):
4.95 and 9.95 National Concert Hall, Dublin, solo recitals.
**KEY PERFORMANCES OUTSIDE IRELAND** (since January 1994):
7.94 Hinde Street Church promoted by Trinity College, London.
1.96 Purcell Room, London, promoted by Park Lane Group PLC.
1.96 South Bank Centre, London.
**TRAINING AND/OR QUALIFICATIONS:**
1988 ALCM from the Royal Irish Academy of Music.

1990 LTCL from the RIAM.
From 1990 to 1994, GTCL from Trinity College of Music, London.
**AVAILABILITY:**
General.
**ADDITIONAL INFORMATION:**
Specialises in contemporary music and performs the works of Ligeti, Stockhausen, Berio, Schnittke. Repertoire also includes the complete 'Vingt Regards' by Messiaen. Has a keen interest in Irish contemporary music and included a piece by Irish composer John Buckley, in debut recital in London's South Bank Centre.

# Maria McGarry *Piano*

**Contact:** Ms Maria McGarry
'Devlis'
Ballyhaunis
Co Mayo
**Tel/Fax:** +353 907 30170 / +353 907 30679

*"A passionate intelligence and ambition were evident in Maria McGarry's playing"*

14.3.97 Irish Times (Martin Adams)

**KEY IRISH PERFORMANCES** (since January 1994):
26.7.96 St Nicholas Cathedral, Galway, promoted by Music for Galway.
4.2.97 Royal Dublin Society, Dublin, promoted by Sinéad Ó Duinnín.
10.3.97 John Field Room, National Concert Hall, Dublin, promoted by Guardian Dublin International Piano Competition.
23.8.97 St Canice's Cathedral, Kilkenny, promoted by Kilkenny Arts Week.
**SELECTED BROADCASTS AND/OR RECORDED WORK:**
26.2.97 'Focus on Youth', Lisney Young Pianist Awards, for RTÉ FM3.
4.97 Guardian Dublin International Piano Competition, for RTÉ FM3.
**SELECTED REVIEWS** (since January 1994):
7.5.97 Irish Times (Michael Dervan).
30.7.96 Irish Times (Michael Dervan).
**PRIZES/AWARDS/APPOINTMENTS:**
11.4.97 Ulster Bank Bursary, awarded by Ulster Bank Music Foundation.
15.5.97 John Field Prize, awarded by Guardian Dublin International Piano Competition.
**TRAINING AND/OR QUALIFICATIONS:**
From 9.88 to 11.96, Royal Irish Academy of Music (teacher Thérese Fahy).
Since 11.96, RIAM, Dublin (teacher Dr John O'Conor).
From 12.4.97 to 18.4.97 (teacher Christopher Elton).
**ADDITIONAL INFORMATION:**
1996 Winner of Morris-Grant Bursary at the Feis Ceoil, Dublin. Also awarded the 1996 Fitzwilton Exceptional Talent Search prize and is the winner of other scholarships at the Royal Irish Academy, Dublin. Other recitals during 1996 and 1997 included Clifden Community Arts Week and Boyle Arts Festival 1997.

# David McGrory *Piano*

**Contact:** Mr David McGrory
Flat 2/2
2 Skirving Street
Shawlands
Glasgow G41 3AA
Scotland
**Tel:** +44 410 483467

**KEY IRISH PERFORMANCES** (since January 1994):
10.95 Harty Room, Queen's University, Belfast, promoted by Queen's University Music Society.
6.96 Harty Room, Queen's University, Belfast, promoted by City of Belfast School of Music.
6.96 Ulster Hall, Belfast, promoted by Duke of Edinburgh Award Scheme, appearing with City of Belfast Youth Orchestra.
**KEY PERFORMANCES OUTSIDE IRELAND** (since January 1994):
11.96 and 2.97 Stevenson Hall, Royal Scottish Academy of Music and Drama, Glasgow, promoted by the Royal Scottish Academy of Music and Drama.
2.97 RSAMD Glasgow, promoted by RSAMD.
**SELECTED BROADCASTS AND/OR RECORDED WORK:**
4.94 Downtown Radio, Co Down.
2.97 BBC Radio Ulster.
**PRIZES/AWARDS/APPOINTMENTS:**
4.97 Awarded the 'Making Belfast Work Award' from West Belfast Classical Bursary.
**TRAINING AND/OR QUALIFICATIONS:**
From 9.82 to 6.89, (teacher Doreen Brownlee).
9.89 to 6.96, City of Belfast School of Music (teacher Joan Smyth).
Since 9.96, RSAMD (teacher Vanessa Latarche).
**AVAILABILITY:**
Subject to College schedule.
**ADDITIONAL INFORMATION:**
Has competed in the Irish preliminary round of the Guardian Dublin International Piano Competition, the King House Piano Awards, Co Roscommon (finalist) and the 1997 Ulster Bank Music Foundation (semi-finalist).

# Brian MacKay *Piano*

**Contact:** Mr Brian MacKay
Front Flat
8, Kenilworth Road
Dublin 6
**Tel/Fax:** +353 1 4974812 / +353 1 4902822
**Other instruments:** Harpsichord, oboe.

**KEY IRISH PERFORMANCES** (since January 1994):
6.96 Bank of Ireland, Arts Centre, Dublin, appearing with the Douglas Gunn Ensemble.
1.97 National University of Ireland, Maynooth appearing with Adèle O'Dwyer.
3.97 Carlow, appearing with the Orchestra of St Cecilia.
7.97 John Field Room, National Concert Hall, Dublin, appearing with Anthony Norton (tenor).
**KEY PERFORMANCES OUTSIDE IRELAND** (since January 1994):
5.97 Prague and Moravia, promoted by the Czech Handel Society, appearing with Alastair Bamford and Judith Fleet.
6.97 Purcell Room, London, appearing with Alastair Bamford.
**SELECTED BROADCASTS AND/OR RECORDED WORK:**
1995 Radio programme for RTÉ.
7.96 'Music by the Roseingrave Family' for Melrose Music.
10.97 Live recording for BBC Radio Ulster appearing with Peter Wells.
**PRIZES/AWARDS/APPOINTMENTS:**
1984 Winner of the Latham Koenig Chamber Music Prize.
1985 Purcell Room Recital arranged by the Park Lane Group.
**TRAINING AND/OR QUALIFICATIONS:**
From 1980 to 1984, GRSM (Hons) ARCM from the Royal College of Music, London.
From 1990 to 1992, Honours Certificate from the Institute Kodály.
**REGULARLY PERFORMS WITH:**
Alastair Bamford (baritone), Anthony Norton (tenor), Julia Canavan (soprano).
**AVAILABILITY:**
General.
**ADDITIONAL INFORMATION:**
Since moving to Dublin in 1993, has worked as a pianist, conductor, harpsichordist and vocal coach. Performs, conducts and teaches in England, Europe and Africa, countries, which he visits regularly, with many Irish/British singers and instrumentalists.
*See conductor page 171.*

## Paul McKeever *Piano*

**Contact:** Paul McKeever
10, Prospect Road
Glasnevin
Dublin 9
**Mobile/Fax:** +353 87 2311031 / +353 1 6771000 (w)
*See organ page 29.*

## Brian McNamara *Piano*

**Contact:** Brian McNamara
9, The Heights
Broadale
Douglas, Co Cork
**Tel:** +353 21 895017

**PRIZES/AWARDS/APPOINTMENTS:**
1981 Overall winner of the RTÉ Young Musician of the Future Competition. Received the Premier Prix in both piano and chamber music from the Conservatoire National Supérieur de Musique de Paris (only Irish pianist to receive this award). Recipient of many awards and distinctions including the Fitzwilliam Trust Bursary, an IBM scholarship, as well as Arts Council and French Government scholarships. 1992 Prize winner in the French International Sonata Competition.
**REGULARLY PERFORMS WITH:**
Sabine Ducrot-MacNamara (flute).
**AVAILABILITY:**
General.
**ADDITIONAL INFORMATION:**
Has given concerto performances with the RTÉ Concert Orchestra and the National Symphony Orchestra of Ireland. Experienced recitalist having performed and recorded many times in Ireland and France. Currently lecturing in piano at the Cork School of Music.

## David McNulty *Piano*

**Contact:** Mr David McNulty
23, Adelaide Park
Malone Road
Belfast BT9 6FX
Northern Ireland
**Tel/Fax:** +44 1232 667300 / +44 1232 681418

**KEY IRISH PERFORMANCES** (since January 1994):
10.94 Rupert Stanley Building, Belfast appearing with the Belfast Youth Orchestra.
2.96 Comber appearing with a piano trio.
3.96 Harty Room, Queen's University Belfast public recital performing Chopin, Liszt, Shostakovich, Brahms and Gershwin.
**KEY PERFORMANCES OUTSIDE IRELAND** (since January 1994):
8.97 Concerts in Bergen, promoted by Holland music sessions.
**PRIZES/AWARDS/APPOINTMENTS:**
1997 1st Prize Huban Cup, 2nd Prize Hamilton Harty Cup at the Feis Ceoil, Dublin.
3.97 2nd Prize, King House Boyle Piano Awards, Co Roscommon.
**TRAINING AND/OR QUALIFICATIONS:**
From 1990 to 1993, Studied at the City of Belfast School of Music (teacher Tom Davidson).
From 1990 to 1992, and from 1993 to 1996, Royal Irish Academy of Music (teacher Réamonn Keary).
1995 Masterclasses in Mozarteum, Salzburg, Austria.
**AVAILABILITY:**
Weekends, summer months.
**ADDITIONAL INFORMATION:**
Has attended masterclasses with Phillipe Cassard, Pavel Nersessian, Joseph Paratore, Christopher Elton and John Yorke.

## Veronica McSwiney *Piano*

**Contact:** Veronica McSwiney
Glencree Cottage
Ballywaltrim Lane
Bray
Co Wicklow
**Tel/Fax:** +353 1 2828740

**KEY PERFORMANCES OUTSIDE IRELAND** (since January 1994):
1995, Manchester, appearing with the BBC Philharmonic Orchestra.
1996, Grieg Concert Hall, Bergen, Norway (recital).
1996, Canterbury, England ('Grieg Story').
1996, Sydney, Australia (recital).
**TRAINING AND/OR QUALIFICATIONS:**
Studied with Dr O'Reilly (DIT Conservatory of Music and Drama, Dublin), Dennis Mathews (London), Bruno Seidlhofer (Salzburg) and Ilona Kabos (London).
**REGULARLY PERFORMS WITH:**
Geraldine O'Grady (violin).
**AVAILABILITY:**
General.

## Cecilia Madden *Piano*

**Contact:** Ms Cecilia Madden
44, Downey Street
Killalee
Limerick
Co Limerick
**Tel:** +353 61 400820
*See oboe page 25.*

## Eimear Mangan *Piano*

**Contact:** Ms Eimear Mangan
16, Glenageary Woods
Glenageary
Co Dublin
**Tel:** +353 1 2842086
*See mezzo soprano page 104.*

## Philip Martin *Piano*

**Contact:** Mr Philip Martin
Chapel House
Theobald's Green
Calstone
Calne Wilts SN11 8QE
England
**Tel/Fax:** +44 1249 812508

*"Philip Martin has a really ravishing pianissimo and lacks nothing in his transcendental virtuosity. He is the pre-eminent Gottschalk interpreter of the 80's and 90's."* Gramophone.

**KEY IRISH PERFORMANCES** (since January 1994):
1995 National Concert Hall, Dublin, promoted by RTÉ, appearing with the National Symphony Orchestra of Ireland.
1996 Royal Dublin Society, promoted by RTÉ, appearing with the RTÉ

Concert Orchestra.
1996 John Field Room, National Concert Hall, Dublin, promoted by RTÉ, appearing with Penelope Price Jones.
**KEY PERFORMANCES OUTSIDE IRELAND** (since January 1994):
2.97 Blackburn, UK, appearing with the Hallé Orchestra.
5.97 Bradford, UK, appearing with the Hallé Orchestra.
7.97 Kenwood, London, promoted by English Heritage.
**SELECTED RECORDED WORK:**
1996 Gottschalk (Vol 3 of piano music) for Hyperion Records.
7.97 Gottschalk (piano and orchestra) for BBC.
8.15.97 Barber/Menotti Festival for BBC Northern Ireland.
**SELECTED REVIEWS** (since January 1994):
1997 Gramophone Magazine. Fanfare Magazine. USA, Birmingham Post.
**PRIZES/AWARDS/APPOINTMENTS:**
1973 Awarded Gulbenkian Fellowship.
1980 Awarded UK/US Bicentennial Arts Fellowship.
1987 Fellow of the Royal Academy of Music, London.
**REGULARLY PERFORMS WITH:**
Penelope Price Jones (soprano).
**AVAILABILITY:**
General.
**ADDITIONAL INFORMATION:**
(Of duo with Penelope Price Jones) "Your splendid New York Recital was an outstanding success. Penelope has such a beautiful voice, equally effective in the works of Purcell and Martin and the 'Barber Sonata' - such drive - such energy!" Louise Talma.
*Also a composer.*

# Geraldine Montague *Piano*

**Contact:** Ms Geraldine Montague
c/o 40, Innismore
Crumlin Village
Dublin 12
**Tel:** +353 1 4560551
*See soprano page 93.*

# Juliet Montague *Piano*

**Contact:** Juliet Montague
c/o 40, Innismore
Crumlin Village
Dublin 12
**Tel:** +353 1 4560551

**KEY PERFORMANCES OUTSIDE IRELAND** (since January 1994):
1996 Stockholm, appearing with Nacka Group (Chopin - Busoni recital).
1997 Stockholm, appearing with the Stockholm Academic Orchestra (Chopin Concerto No.1)
**SELECTED RECORDED WORK:**
1992 Schumann's 'Kreisieriana' Op 16 for Svensk Radio, Sweden.
**PRIZES/AWARDS/APPOINTMENTS:**
1990 Entrance Exhibition and Scholarship to the Royal Academy of Music, London.
1990 British Council Award.
**TRAINING AND/OR QUALIFICATIONS:**
From 1983 to 1986, Royal Irish Academy of Music, Dublin (teacher Dr John O'Conor).
From 1986 to 1990, Studied at the Stockholm Conservatoire, Sweden.
1989 Attended masterclasses at Moneglia, Italy.
From 1990 to 1993, Postgrad Diploma in Advanced Studies at the Royal Academy of Music, London.

# Fionnuala Moynihan *Piano*

**Contact:** Fionnuala Moynihan
65, The Rise
Bishopstown
Cork
**Tel:** +353 21 542958

**KEY IRISH PERFORMANCES** (since January 1994):
1994 John Field Room, National Concert Hall, Dublin, promoted by the Cork School of Music.
1995 Bantry House, Cork, promoted by the Cork School of Music.
1996 Royal Dublin Society, Dublin, promoted by Constantin Zani Dache, appearing as part of a piano trio.
1997 Belfast as part of a lunchtime series.
**KEY PERFORMANCES OUTSIDE IRELAND** (since January 1994):
1994 and 1996, Wiltshire, England, masterclass concert with Philip Martin.
1996 Holland, Chamber Music competition, appearing as part of a piano trio.
**SELECTED RECORDED WORK:**
1994 'Hullabullu' (piano trio) for RTÉ.
From 1995 to 1997, 'Evelyn Grant's Music Hour' for RTÉ (Cork).
1995 'Focus on Youth' for RTÉ.
**PRIZES/AWARDS/APPOINTMENTS:**
1996 Winner of Caroline Elizabeth O'Reilly Cup for Senior Piano Solo at the Feis Ceoil, Dublin.
**TRAINING AND/OR QUALIFICATIONS:**
From 1987 to 1995, Scholarship for Grades 1 to 8 at Cork School of Music.
1994 and 1996, Attended masterclasses with Philip Martin.
1996, Attended masterclass with Barry Douglas.
1997, Attended masterclass with Christopher Elton.
Since 1997 B Mus (Perf) at Birmingham Conservatoire.
**AVAILABILITY:**
General.

# Barbara Murray *Piano*

**Contact:** Barbara Murray
10, Barnhill Park
Dalkey, Co Dublin
**Tel:** +353 1 2852066

**KEY PERFORMANCES OUTSIDE IRELAND** (since January 1994):
1997 Regent Hall, London.
1997 Hinde Street Church, London.
1997 Burgh House, London.
1997 Arts Centre, North France and Switzerland.
**PRIZES/AWARDS/APPOINTMENTS:**
1989 1st Prize in Petrof Cup Competition, awarded by the DIT Conservatory of Music and Drama, Dublin.
1995 Winner of Senior Baroque Section, awarded by Feis Maithiú.
**TRAINING AND/OR QUALIFICATIONS:**
From 1987 to 1991, BA (Hons) Music and Italian.
1995 LTCL, Trinity College, London.
1995 LGSM from the Guildhall School of Music and Drama, London and private studies with Philip Martin.
From 1985 to 1996, MA in Performance, from University of London.
**AVAILABILITY:**
General.

# Frances Nesbitt *Piano*

**Contact:** Frances Nesbitt
Victoria Ville
Victoria Road, Cork
**Tel:** +353 21 963086
*See fiddle page 210.*

# Colin Nicholls *Piano*

**Contact:** Mr Colin Nicholls
8, Dean Street
Cork
**Tel:** +353 21 963433
*See organ page 29.*

# Colm "Stride" O'Brien *Piano*

**Contact:** Mr Colm "Stride" O'Brien
2, Cleveragh Park
Listowel
Co Kerry
**Tel/Fax:** +353 68 21407 / +353 68 21434
*See jazz piano page 281.*

# Marie O'Byrne *Piano*

**Contact:** Marie O'Byrne
Shanaway Road
Ennis
Co Clare
**Tel:** +353 65 41602
*See violin page 64.*

# Isabelle O'Connell *Piano*

**Contact:** Ms Isabelle O' Connell
9, Templemore Avenue
Rathgar
Dublin 6
**Tel:** +353 1 4976302

**KEY IRISH PERFORMANCES** (since January 1994):
17.8.94 Dublin, promoted by Alliance Francaise, appearing with Sarah McMahon.
10.4.95 Dublin, promoted by Trinity College Music Society.
12.10.95 Dublin, promoted by UCD Music Society.
30.9.96 Dublin, promoted by Goethe Institut.
**KEY PERFORMANCES OUTSIDE IRELAND** (since January 1994):
8.97 Düsseldorf, Germany, promoted by Andreas Kern.
**SELECTED BROADCASTS AND/OR RECORDED WORK:**
1995 'Young Performers of the RIAM' for Anna Livia Radio, Dublin.
**PRIZES/AWARDS/APPOINTMENTS:**
4.95 Senior Piano Rosebowl and Jameson Bursary from the Feis Maitiú.
12.96 Weaving Cup and Tibor Medal from the Royal Irish Academy of Music, Dublin.
1996 Scholarship to the Dartington International Summer School, England (teacher Stephen Kovacevich).
**TRAINING AND/OR QUALIFICATIONS:**
4.96 Masterclass with Philippe Cassard.
10.96 Masterclass with Pnina Salzman.
Since 9.96, BA in Music Performance from the RIAM (teacher Réamonn Keary).
**AVAILABILITY:**
General.
**ADDITIONAL INFORMATION:**
Performs as a soloist, accompanist and as a member of various chamber groups.

# John O'Conor *Piano*

**Contact:** Dr John O'Conor
36, Garville Avenue
Dublin 6
**Tel/Fax:** +353 1 4977914 / +353 1 4966894
**Email:** joc@riam.iol.ie

*" This artist has the kind of flawless touch that makes an audience gasp"* Washington Post.

**SELECTED BROADCASTS AND/OR RECORDED WORK:**
Has made over 25 CDs for the American label Telarc including the complete Sonatas and Bagatelles of Beethoven, Mozart and Field Piano Concertos, the complete Nocturnes and Sonatas of John Field, Schubert Impromptus, Moments Musicals, Waltzes and Sonatas and the Trout Quintet (with the Cleveland Quartet). He also recorded the complete Concertos of John Field with the Irish Chamber Orchestra.
**PRIZES/AWARDS/APPOINTMENTS:**
1973 Ist Prize winner at the International Beethoven Competition in Vienna.
1975 Ist Prize winner at the Bösendorfer Competition.
**AVAILABILITY:**
Subject to schedule.
**ADDITIONAL INFORMATION:**
After initial studies in native Dublin, spent five years in Vienna studying with pedagogue Dieter Weber at the Hochschule für Musik and made a special study of Beethoven with German pianist Wilheim Kempff. Has performed with the Czech Philharmonic, Vienna Symphony, Royal Philharmonic, Scottish Chamber, Stuttgart Chamber, Orchestre National de France, Philharmonia Hungarica and, in Japan, with the NHK, Yomiuri, Sapporo and Kyushu Symphonies. In the United States and Canada has appeared with over 20 orchestras including the symphonies of Cleveland, Dallas, Detroit, Montreal and Washington DC. Co-founder and Artistic Director of the Guardian Dublin International Piano Competition. Director of the Royal Irish Academy of Music, Dublin. Awarded an Honorary Doctorate by the National University of Ireland, and Honorary Fellowship by the RIAM for services to music. Has been decorated by the French, Italian and Polish Governments.

# Dearbhaile O'Donnell *Piano*

**Contact:** Dearbhaile O'Donnell
16, Chanel Grove
Dublin 5
**Tel:** +353 1 8480211

**KEY IRISH PERFORMANCES** (since January 1994):
5.94 Sutton Park School, Co Dublin.
**KEY PERFORMANCES OUTSIDE IRELAND** (since January 1994):
7.94 Ruinekerk, Bergen an der zee, promoted by Holland Music Sessions.
11.94 Parktheater, Iserlohn, Germany, promoted by Herbstage für Musik, Iserlohn.
**SELECTED BROADCASTS AND/OR RECORDED WORK:**
8.90 Works by Chopin and Beethoven recorded for RTÉ FM3.
9.90 Brahms Op. 118, for BBC Northern Ireland.
6.91 Mendelssohn recital broadcast, for BBC Northern Ireland.
**PRIZES/AWARDS/APPOINTMENTS:**
11.85 Winner of the RTÉ Young Musician of The Future competition.
5.88 Charles Brennan prize, awarded by the GPA Dublin International Piano Competition.
**TRAINING AND/OR QUALIFICATIONS:**
From 1982 to 1991, ARCM (Perf) and LRSM from Royal Irish Academy of Music.
7/8.85/86/87 studies at the Sommerakademie Der Hochschule Mozarteum, Salzburg.
**AVAILABILITY:**
General.

**ADDITIONAL INFORMATION:**
Has performed in the National Concert Hall, Dublin and recorded concerto performances with both the NSOI and the RTÉCO. Has given recitals in many Irish venues including centres in Waterford, Dundalk and Galway.

# Ríona Ó Duinnín *Piano*

**Contact:** Ríona Ó Duinnín
Old Road
Carlingford
Co Louth
**Tel:** +353 42 73331
*See flute page 17.*

# Eily O'Grady *Piano*

**Contact:** Dr Eily O'Grady
c/o Frank Murphy
3, Bethel Terrace
Trafalgar Road
Greystones
Co Wicklow
**Tel:** +353 1 2082766 (w) / +353 1 2876370 (h)

**KEY IRISH PERFORMANCES** (since January 1994):
National Concert Hall, Dublin appearing with Frank Patterson.
**KEY PERFORMANCES OUTSIDE IRELAND** (since January 1994):
Various, including Carnegie Hall, New York, Boston Hall, Boston, MA, The White House, Washington DC and the Roy Thompson Hall, Toronto, Canada, all appearing with Frank Patterson.
**TRAINING AND/OR QUALIFICATIONS:**
Studied piano with Carlo Zecchi (Rome), Elizabeth Hoban (Dublin), Harold Craxton (London). Doctorate in Music from the Salve Regina University, Rhode Island. Doctorate in Fine Arts from Manhattan College, New York.
**REGULARLY PERFORMS WITH:**
Frank Patterson, Geraldine O'Grady.

# Nicholas O'Halloran *Piano*

**Contact:** Mr Nicholas O'Halloran
'Pinewood'
Shanakiel
Co Cork
**Tel:** +353 21 308307

*"The reviewer is obliged to tell it like it was - and it was great!"*
30.5.94 The Examiner (Ref: recital at Crawford Art Gallery, Cork).

**KEY IRISH PERFORMANCES** (since January 1994):
27.4.95 University College Cork, promoted by Cork International Choral Festival.
2.12.95 City Hall, Cork, promoted by and appearing with Cork Youth Orchestra.
3.7.96 Foyle Arts Centre, Derry, promoted by Foyle Summer School of Music.
25.4.97 Cork School of Music, promoted by the school.
**SELECTED BROADCASTS AND/OR RECORDED WORK:**
1985 'New Piano Music from Ireland', recorded by Goasco xx in association with Irish Committee for European Music Year (tape).
1986 Mozart Concertos, appearing with the RTÉ Concert Orchestra.
**REVIEWS** (since January 1994):
10.95 The Examiner.
12.12.95 The Examiner.
**PRIZES/AWARDS/APPOINTMENTS:**
1978 Morris Grant Bursary, awarded by Feis Ceoil, Dublin.
1981 Scholarship to USA, awarded by Fulbright Commission.
**TRAINING AND/OR QUALIFICATIONS:**
From 1968 to 1980, LTCL and FTCL from Cork School of Music, (teacher Jan Càp).
From 1980 to 1981, Performers Diploma from Accademie Chigiana Siena, (teacher Guido Agosti).
From 1981 to 1983, Master of Music, from University of Cincinnati, (teacher Béla Siki). Also many masterclasses in Ireland, Italy, Canada and USA.
**REGULARLY PERFORMS WITH:**
Séamas Conroy (violin).
**AVAILABILITY:**
General.
**ADDITIONAL INFORMATION:**
Has many years experience lecturing on repertoire for piano and a regular feature of recitals is a verbal introduction to the music presented.

# Honor O'Hea *Piano*

**Contact:** Honor O'Hea
Mount Grellan House
Kilbrogan
Bandon
Co Cork
**Tel/Fax:** +353 23 41569
**Email:** honor.o.hea@mail.telepac.pt

*"Based her interpretation on the refinement of tonal culture, creating an oasis of ethereal and transcendental sound"* 10.1.96 Jornal de Madeira.

**KEY IRISH PERFORMANCES** (since January 1994):
5.95 Bank of Ireland Arts Centre, Dublin.
6.95 Triskel Arts Centre, Cork.
7.95 Boyle Arts Festival, Co Roscommon.
8.95 St Barrahane's Festival of Church Music, Castletownshend, Co Cork.
**KEY PERFORMANCES OUTSIDE IRELAND** (since January 1994):
11.95 University of Kansas, Lawrence, Kansas.
10.96 Madeira Theatre, Portugal, promoted by Classical Orchestra of Madeira, appearing with Robert Andres (2 pianos).
5.97 Madeira Theatre, Portugal, promoted by the Classical Orchestra of Madeira.
**SELECTED BROADCASTS AND/OR RECORDED WORK:**
4.93 'Poulenc' for RTÉ.
3.94 'Poulenc / Fleischmann' for RTÉ.
4.94 'Debussy' for RTÉ.
**SELECTED REVIEWS** (since January 1994):
6.95 The Examiner.
**PRIZES/AWARDS/APPOINTMENTS:**
1993 Awarded Yamaha Music Foundation of Europe Scholarship.
1994 Awarded Fulbright Scholarship by the Ireland - US Commission for Educational Exchange.
**TRAINING AND/OR QUALIFICATIONS:**
From 9.90 to 6.94, FTCL and LRSM, (teacher Mabel Swainson).
From 8.93 to 5.96, B Mus (Hons) from University of London.
From 8.94 to 5.96, M Mus in Piano Performance at the University of Kansas (teacher Sequiera Costa).
From 9.96 to 5.97, Studied with Dominique Merlet.
**REGULARLY PERFORMS WITH:**
Robert Andres (4 hands/2 pianos).
**AVAILABILITY:**
By arrangement (living abroad).
**ADDITIONAL INFORMATION:**
First non-American to receive the Adell-Hancock Scholarship from the US Institute of International Education. Member of Phi Kappa Phi Honour Society in recognition of being in top 10% of all US post-graduate students. Performs regularly in Ireland, France, Italy, US, Portugal and Croatia. Has a special interest in French and 20th Century Music.

## Patrick O'Keeffe *Piano*

**Contact:** Mr Patrick O'Keeffe
126, North Main Street
Youghal
Co Cork
**Tel:** +353 24 92820
*See clarinet page 5.*

## Míceál O'Rourke *Piano*

**Contact:** Mr Míceál O'Rourke
3, Rue Jules Ferry
91300 Massy
France
**Tel/Fax:** +33 1 60111921 / +33 1 60133258

*"Chopin worth waiting for ... a master pianist"* 8.95 BBC Music Magazine.

**KEY IRISH PERFORMANCES** (since January 1994):
2.94 National Concert Hall, Dublin, and the Ulster Hall, Belfast, in a performance of Lutoslawsky's Piano Concerto appearing with the National Symphony Orchestra of Ireland.
3.95 National Concert Hall, Dublin, Limerick and Waterford, in a performance of the Prokofiev's Concerto No. 3 with the NSOI.
5.96 NCH, in the Rachmaninov Concerto No. 3, appearing with the NSOI.
**KEY PERFORMANCES OUTSIDE IRELAND** (since January 1994):
1.96, Appearing with the St Petersburg Philharmonic in a performance of Field's 'Concerto No 4' .
10.96 British tour, appearing with the London Mozart Players in a performance of Field's 'Concerto No 4'.
11.96 Appearing with the St Petersburg Philharmonic in a performance of Chopin's Piano 'Concerto No 2'.
**SELECTED BROADCASTS AND/OR RECORDED WORK:**
John Field Eight CD set 1995 Schumann - 'Carnaval' and 'Kreisleriana'.
1995 Chopin - Four Ballades etc, all for Chandos.
**SELECTED REVIEWS** (since January 1994):
3.6.95 The Times.
3/4.95 American Record Guide.
**PRIZES/AWARDS/APPOINTMENTS:**
6.94 Frederic Chopin Medal from the Polish Artists' Guild, Warsaw.
**AVAILABILITY:**
General.
**ADDITIONAL INFORMATION:**
Guest soloist with leading orchestras including Leningrad Philharmonic, Boston Pops, Royal Philharmonic, National Symphony Orchestra of Ireland, Irish Chamber Orchestra, Ulster Orchestra, Ukraine and Lithuanian State Symphonies, Marseille Opera, Mississippi Symphony, London Mozart Players, Bilbao Symphony. Concerto repertoire exceeds fifty works. Has held masterclasses in Warsaw, Beijing, Cork, Dublin. Chandos recording artist since 1988. Recordings also on Carère.

## Danusia Oslizlok *Piano*

**Contact:** Danusia Oslizlok
4, Thornhill Road
Mount Merrion
Co Dublin
**Tel:** +353 1 2888075

**TRAINING AND/OR QUALIFICATIONS:**
Studied at the Royal Irish Academy of Music, the Brussels Conservatoire, the University of Bristol and the Royal Northern College of Music, Manchester.
**REGULARLY PERFORMS WITH:**
Nicola Cleary.
**AVAILABILITY:**
General.

## Mícheál Ó Súilleabháin *Piano*

**Contact:** Prof Mícheál Ó Súilleabháin
Irish World Music Centre
University of Limerick
Co Limerick
**Tel:** +353 61 202065
*See traditional piano page 234.*

## Eilís O'Sullivan *Piano*

**Contact:** Ms Eilis O'Sullivan
Ivy Bridge
Ballyhillogue
Mourne Abbey
Mallow
Co. Cork
**Tel:** +353 22 29159
*See flute page 17.*

## Stuart O'Sullivan *Piano*

**Contact:** Mr Stuart O'Sullivan
54, Saval Park Road
Dalkey
Co Dublin
**Tel:** +353 1 2840781

*"An auspicious appearance by a player who is sure to provide much pleasure in the years ahead"* 30.7.95 Sunday Tribune.

**KEY IRISH PERFORMANCES** (since January 1994):
13.11.94 National Concert Hall, Dublin. During 1995, various venues throughout Dublin, appearing with Dublin Symphony Orchestra.
21.7.95 NCH appearing with the National Symphony Orchestra of Ireland.
28.11.95 Bank of Ireland Arts Centre, Dublin, solo performance.
**KEY PERFORMANCES OUTSIDE IRELAND** (since January 1994):
27.3.94 Butzbach, Germany, promoted by Hessischer Rundfunk.
7.94/95 Ruinekirk, Bergen, The Netherlands, promoted by Holland Music Sesssions.
8/9/95 Bückeburg Castle, Germany, promoted by IMAS, solo performance.
**SELECTED BROADCASTS AND/OR RECORDED WORK:**
27.3.94 Recording from Butzbach, Germany with 'Anna Livia Trio', recorded by Hessdcher, Rundfunk.
16.7.95 Recording from concert Gebouw, Amsterdam, for Dutch National Radio.
28.7.95 'Teatime Summer Sounds' for RTÉ.
**SELECTED REVIEWS** (since January 1994):
17.10.94 Irish Press.
**PRIZES/AWARDS/APPOINTMENTS:**
1993 Winner of RTÉ Young Musician of the Future competition.
1994 Awarded the Brennan prize, GPA Dublin International Piano Competition.
**TRAINING AND/OR QUALIFICATIONS:**
ARIAM, LRIAM from the Royal Irish Academy of Music.
LRAM from the Royal Academy of Music, London.
From 1992 to 1996, BA Music, from the RIAM.

**REGULARLY PERFORMS WITH:**
Anna Livia Trio (soprano, clarinet, piano) and Julia Canavan (soprano).
**AVAILABILITY:**
General.
**ADDITIONAL INFORMATION:**
Regular performer at home and abroad.

## Charles Stephen Lawrence Parker *Piano*

**Contact:** Mr Stephen Parker
19, Raglan House
Ballsbridge Court
Ballsbridge
Dublin 4
**Tel:** +353 1 6603557

**KEY PERFORMANCES OUTSIDE IRELAND** (since January 1994):
British Music Information Centre, South Bank, London. Royal College of Music, London. Edinburgh Festival.
**SELECTED BROADCASTS AND/OR RECORDED WORK:**
6.97 'Sinfonietta' (own composition) with the Philharmonic Orchestra Moravian (conductor Jiri Mikula) for Vienna Modern Masters.
**SELECTED REVIEWS** (since January 1994):
The Examiner. Nationalist Clonmel. Irish Times.
**PRIZES/AWARDS/APPOINTMENTS:**
1974 2 year scholarship (piano) to the Northamptonshire Music School.
1979 4 year scholarship (composition) to the Royal College of Music, London.
**TRAINING AND/OR QUALIFICATIONS:**
From 1979 to 1982, studied at the Royal College of Music, London.
1986 Licentiate Diploma from the Leinster School of Music.
**REGULARLY PERFORMS WITH:**
Finbar Wright, Deirdre Crowley.
**AVAILABILITY:**
General.
**ADDITIONAL INFORMATION:**
Has given a number of solo classical and contemporary music performances nationwide including concerts in Cahir Castle, University College Cork, Waterford Institute of Technology, Trinity College, Dublin, The Belltable Arts Centre Limerick, Kilkenny Arts Week, Black Abbey and the Hugh Lane Municipal Gallery of Modern Art. Also a composer.

## Malcolm Proud *Piano*

**Contact:** Mr Malcolm Proud
St Canice's Cottage
St Canice's Cathedral
Kilkenny
**Tel/Fax:** +353 56 61497
*See harpischord page 125.*

## Niamh Quigley *Piano*

**Contact:** Ms Niamh Quigley
14, Meadowgrove
Blackrock
Cork
**Tel:** +353 21 357399
*See viola page 56.*

## Rachel Quinn *Piano*

**Contact:** Rachel Quinn
**Tel/Fax:** +353 1 2894818

*"An artistically serious young woman ... intense ... but relaxed with full command of what she wanted to achieve."* 2.97 Oslo International Forum Newsletter.

**KEY IRISH PERFORMANCES** (since January 1994):
3.4.97 and 20.4.97 National Concert Hall, Dublin, appearing with Irish Chamber Orchestra, performing Mozart Concerto K414.
12.6.97 Taney Hall, Dublin promoted by Dún Laoghaire Rathdown, Co Council, solo recital.
1.7.97 NCH appearing with the National Symphony Orchestra of Ireland, performing Todtentanz by Liszt.
**KEY PERFORMANCES OUTSIDE IRELAND** (since January 1994):
8.95 Czech Republic, promoted by the International Chopin Festival, performing Chopin Concerto No. 1.
1.97 Oslo, Norway, promoted by the Oslo International Forum and the British Embassy.
12.97 Performances in Japan, promoted by Int. Federation of Artists Management.
**SELECTED BROADCASTS AND/OR RECORDED WORK:**
30.12.96 'Debussy Preludes Book One' for RTÉ, FM3. 5.97 'Live at 3' for RTÉ.
**PRIZES/AWARDS/APPOINTMENTS:**
Morris Grant Bursary, from Feis Ceoil, Dublin.
1986 IBM Instrument Award. Lombard and Ulster Foundation Award.
**TRAINING AND/OR QUALIFICATIONS:**
From 1985, ARCM from the Royal College of Music, London.
1986 LGSM and FTCL from the Guildhall School of Music and Drama, London and Trinity College, London.
1995, MA, Trinity College, Dublin.
**AVAILABILITY:**
General.
**ADDITIONAL INFORMATION:**
Received the Fulbright Scholarship for Professsional Postgrad Studies at the Peabody Institute of the John Hopkins University in Baltimore, Maryland, USA.

## Kathleen Raymond *Piano* 

**Contact:** Ms Kathleen Raymond
72, Stack's Villas
Tralee
Co Kerry
**Tel/Fax:** +353 66 26973
*See flute page 18.*

## Jeannie Reddin *Piano*

**Contact:** Jeannie Reddin
Hadleigh
42E Palmerstown Road
Rathmines
Dublin 6
**Tel/Fax:** +353 1 4977465

## John Killian Ryan *Piano*

**Contact:** Mr John Killian Ryan
27, Whitecliff
Rathfarnham
Dublin 16
**Tel:** +353 1 4943902
*See French horn page 24.*

## Carol Ann Scott *Piano*

**Contact:** Mrs Carol Ann Scott
10, Bloomfield Avenue
Portobello
Dublin 8
**Tel:** +353 1 4535700

**PRIZES/AWARDS/APPOINTMENTS:**
7.94 Masterclasses with Pascal Rosé in Nice, funded by the Royal Irish Academy of Music.
7.97 Masterclasses with Michel Beroff in Nice, funded by the RIAM.
**TRAINING AND/OR QUALIFICATIONS:**
1954, ARIAM from the RIAM.
1963, LRIAM from the RIAM.
1965, LRAM from the Royal Academy of Music, London.
**ADDITIONAL INFORMATION:**
Associate Professor of Piano at the Royal Irish Academy of Music. Diploma Examiner and Examiner to Local Centre exams. Current staff representative on the Board of Governors of the RIAM and has sat on the Board of Studies for several years. Member of European Piano Teachers Association Committee.

## Ciara Sheehan *Piano*

**Contact:** Ms Ciara Sheehan
38, Newlyn Vale
Rochestown Road
Cork
**Tel:** +353 21 894673
**Other instruments:** Bassoon.

**KEY IRISH PERFORMANCES** (since January 1994):
4.96 Curtis Auditorium, Cork School of Music, appearing with Elizabeth Cooney and John McLoughlin.
3.97 Triskel Arts Centre, Cork, appearing with the Degree Class, Cork School of Music.
**KEY PERFORMANCES OUTSIDE IRELAND** (since January 1994):
4.96 Conservatory of Music, Nice, appearing with Elizabeth Cooney and John McLoughlin.
**PRIZES/AWARDS/APPOINTMENTS:**
1.96 Third prize awarded from the Yamaha Music Foundation.
5.96 Finalist for the Lisney Young Pianist Award.
**TRAINING AND/OR QUALIFICATIONS:**
From 9.93 to 6.95, Dip CSM from Cork School of Music.
**AVAILABILITY:**
Weekends, summer months.

## Fergus Sheil *Piano*

**Contact:** Fergus Sheil (senior)
15, Blackheath Park
Clontarf, Dublin 3
**Tel:** +353 1 8336496
*See jazz piano page 282.*

## Andrew Synnott *Piano*

**Contact:** Andrew Synnott
98, Wilfield Road
Sandymount
Dublin 4
**Tel:** +353 1 2696023
**Other instruments:** Organ, harpsichord, voice, also conductor.

*"Andrew Synnott's accompaniments were pointed and stylish."* 10.96 Irish Times.

**KEY IRISH PERFORMANCES** (since January 1994):
1994 Kilkenny Arts Festival, appearing with Gavin Roche.
1995 Kilkenny Arts Festival, appearing with Conor Shiel.
1996 Wexford Festival Opera, appearing with Czech Chamber Choir.
**AVAILABILITY:**
Unlimited.
**ADDITIONAL INFORMATION:**
Trinity College, Dublin graduate. Former organ scholar of the pro-cathedral and the Christchurch Cathedral, Dublin. Active composer, conductor and repetiteur. Keyboard player with the National Symphony Orchestra of Ireland and RTÉ Concert Orchestra. Repetiteur with Opera Northern Ireland and Opera Ireland.
*See conductors page 175.*

## Louise Thomas *Piano*

**Contact:** c/o Ms Alison Thomas
17, Old Ballymun Road
Glasnevin
Dublin 9
**Tel:** +353 1 8374353

*"... Carried off with energy and conviction ... Schumann, tailormade for her sensibility ... exquisite [Schubert] ... a sharp perception of style"* 19.10.91 Irish Times.

**KEY IRISH PERFORMANCES** (since January 1994):
1994 National Concert Hall, appearing with the National Symphony Orchestra of Ireland.
**KEY PERFORMANCES OUTSIDE IRELAND** (since January 1994):
1994 Stefaniensaal, Austria, concerto performance.
1995 Hannover, Germany.
**SELECTED BROADCASTS AND/OR RECORDED WORK:**
1992 For Moscow Radio.
1993 With Gerald Barry Ensemble for NMC.
1994 'Letzte Nacht in Rokokotheater' for Südwestdeutsche Rundfunk.
**SELECTED REVIEWS** (since January 1994):
1994 Irish Times.
1995 Landeszeitung (Germany).
**PRIZES/AWARDS/APPOINTMENTS:**
1987 3rd Prize winner, awarded by Senigallia International Piano Competition.
1991 Winner of the Lombard and Ulster Music Foundation Award.
1993 2nd Prize winner and Bela Bartók award winner, in the Ibla - Ragusa International Piano Competition.
**TRAINING AND/OR QUALIFICATIONS:**
From 1974 to 1990, awarded Gold Medal, from the DIT Conservatory of Music and Drama.
From 1985 to 1989 awarded four performance and teaching diplomas.
From 1986 to 1990, BA Mod, from Trinity College, Dublin.
From 1990 to 1995, KonzertDiplom and Post Graduate Performance Degree, awarded by Hannover Hochschule für Musik.
**AVAILABILITY:**
General.

**ADDITIONAL INFORMATION:**
Winner of awards in Ireland and Britain, including the 1986 IBM Musical Instrument Award, the 1988 Morris Grant Bursary at the Feis Ceoil, Dublin, the 1989 Fitzwilton Bursary and in 1990, a German Government scholarship. Keen chamber music pianist and also involved in contemporary music. Extensive television and radio recordings both for RTÉ and for German Media. From 1986 to 1990, teacher at the DIT Conservatory of Music and Drama.

## Hugh Tinney *Piano*

**Contact:** Mr Hugh Tinney
62, Cherrywood
Loughlinstown
Co Dublin
**Tel/Fax:** +353 1 2825050

*"The [Mozart Concerto] series has all the possibilities of becoming one of the great Irish musical events of the decade"* 1.12.96 Sunday Tribune.

**KEY IRISH PERFORMANCES** (since January 1994):
1995 Irish Museum of Modern Art, Dublin in a Schubert/Beethoven series promoted by IMMA.
1995 Ulster Hall, Belfast, promoted by BBC and appearing with the Ulster Orchestra.
1997 National Concert Hall, Dublin in the Mozart Concerto Series.
1997 Dublin, Cork, Limerick, appearing with the National Symphony Orchestra of Ireland, performing Rhapsody on a theme of Paganini by Rachmaninov.
**KEY PERFORMANCES OUTSIDE IRELAND** (since January 1994):
1994 Barcelona, promoted by Caja de Madrid.
1994 Budapest, promoted by the Spring Festival.
1996 Paris and Caen, promoted by L'Imaginaire Irlandais Festival.
1996 Festival Hall, London, appearing with the London Philharmonic Orchestra.
**SELECTED BROADCASTS AND/OR RECORDED WORK:**
1986 Liszt 'Dante Sonata' for Decca.
1993 Liszt 'Harmonies Poetiques' for Meridian.
1997 Mendelssohn, 'Concertos' (two pianos) for Naxos.
**SELECTED REVIEWS** (since January 1994):
5/6/95 Irish Times.
11.96 Irish Times.
2.97 Gramophone Magazine.
**PRIZES/AWARDS/APPOINTMENTS:**
1983 Ist Prize at the Pozzoli Competition, Seregno, Italy.
1984 1st prize at the O'Shea Competition, Santander, Spain
**AVAILABILITY:**
General.
**REGULARLY PERFORMS WITH:**
RTÉ Vanbrugh Quartet.

## Hilary Travers *Piano*

**Contact:** Ms Hilary Travers
39, Brook Court
Monkstown
Co Dublin
**Tel:** +353 1 2809699
*See violin page 67.*

## Bernard Traynor *Piano*

**Contact:** Mr Bernard Traynor
26/27, Drury Street
Dublin 2
**Tel:** +353 1 4518527 (h)
*See classical guitar page 23.*

## Peter Tuite *Piano*

**Contact:** Peter Tuite
'Tir na nÓg'
Church Road
Malahide
Co Dublin
**Tel:** +353 1 8450922

**KEY IRISH PERFORMANCES** (since January 1994):
11.95 Galway, Feis Ceoil prizewinner's concert.
3.96 Trinity College, Dublin.
**KEY PERFORMANCES OUTSIDE IRELAND** (since January 1994):
7.97 Bundesalle, Berlin.
7.97 Hochschule Der Künste, Berlin three workshop concerts.
**SELECTED BROADCASTS AND/OR RECORDED WORK:**
96/97 Private recordings by Aidán O'Dubhaill.
7.97 Bundesalle Concert, Berlin for Local Radio.
**PRIZES/AWARDS/APPOINTMENTS:**
3.95 Winner of Esposito Cup, at the Feis Ceoil, Dublin.
2.97 Senior Rosebowl Bursary winner at the Feis Maitiú, Dublin.
**TRAINING AND/OR QUALIFICATIONS:**
3.94 Masterclass with Hugh Tinney.
3.96 Masterclass with Davel Nersessiaen.
11.96 Masterclass with Pnina Salzmann.
7.97 Masterclass with Klaus Hellwig.
**AVAILABILITY:**
Weekends from June to October.

## Jimmy Vaughan *Piano*

**Contact:** Mr Jimmy Vaughan
114, Ennafort Road
Raheny
Dublin 5
**Tel:** +353 1 8313631

## Peter Whelan *Piano*

**Contact:** Mr Peter Whelan
207, The Grove
Celbridge
Co Kildare
**Tel:** +353 1 6271407
**Email:** whelanpp@tcd.ie
*See bassoon page 3.*

## Marie Whyte *Piano*

**Contact:** Ms Marie Whyte
36, Offington Manor
Sutton
Dublin 13
**Tel:** +353 1 8393557

**PRIZES/AWARDS/APPOINTMENTS:**
Piano teacher and examiner at the Royal Irish Academy of Music, Dublin.
**ADDITIONAL INFORMATION:**
Has given short piano recitals (mainly broadcasts for RTÉ). Occasional guest artist at RTÉ concerts (orchestral) piano solos. Has a lunchtime recital programme of fifty minutes duration.

## David Wray *Piano*

**Contact:** Mr David Wray
c/o Friends of the Vocal Arts
11, Dawson House
Patrick Street
Dublin 8
**Tel/Mobile:** +353 1 4547971 / +353 87 429482

## Patrick Zuk *Piano*

**Contact:** Mr Patrick Zuk
Cork School of Music
Union Quay
Cork
**Tel/Fax:** +353 21 270076 / +353 21 276595

**ADDITIONAL INFORMATION:**
Repetiteur and accompanist for singers and instrumentalists. Lecturer in orchestration in the Cork School of Music and a lecturer of degree students in the Royal Irish Academy of Music, Dublin. Also a composer and has had works performed by both the national orchestras and the Cork Symphony Orchestra.

# SAXOPHONES

## Kenneth Edge *Saxophone*

**Contact:** Mr Kenneth Edge
c/o 41, Kilmore Drive
Artane
Dublin 5
**Mobile:** +353 87 504568

**SELECTED BROADCASTS AND/OR RECORDED WORK:**
Ronald Binge's Concerto and Eric Coates 'Saxo-Rhapsody' with the Czech-Slovak Symphony Orchestra for Naxos.
**PRIZES/AWARDS/APPOINTMENTS:**
Principal saxophonist with the National Symphony Orchestra of Ireland.
**REGULARLY PERFORMS WITH:**
Anthony Byrne (piano), Benjamin Dwyer (guitar).
**AVAILABILITY:**
General.
**ADDITIONAL INFORMATION:**
Gives regular recital and concert performances and has won numerous awards at home and abroad. Frequently records with the film composer Elmer Bernstein, and his playing is featured on the soundtrack of 'The Grifters' and 'A Rage in Harlem'. Recorded and toured with 'Riverdance the Show' and performs regularly in Mícheál Ó Súilleabháin's, Missa Gadelica.

## John Hogan *Saxophone*

**Contact:** Mr John Hogan
47, Hermitage Drive
Rathfarnham
Dublin 16
**Tel:** +353 1 4947412
*See saxophone page 296.*

## Amanda Irvine *Saxophone*

**Contact:** Mrs Amanda Irvine
38, Plantation Avenue
Carrickfergus
Northern Ireland, BT38 9BJ
**Tel:** +44 1960 361695
*See clarinet page 4.*

## Nicholas Kiely *Saxophone*

**Contact:** Mr Nicholas Kiely
Flat 1
1 Kenilworth Park
Harold's Cross, Dublin 6
**Tel:** +353 1 4922205 or +353 61 419281
*See jazz saxophone page 283.*

## Gerard McChrystal
### *Saxophone (Soprano)*

**Contact:** Mr Gerard McChrystal
24, Leas Close
Totteridge
High Wycombe
Bucks HP13 7UW
England
**Tel/Fax:** +44 1494 464831
**Email:** saxsaxsax@aol.com

*"A performer of such striking personality that he could become the James Galway of the saxophone"* 1989 The Guardian.

**KEY IRISH PERFORMANCES** (since January 1994):
1.96 Ulster Hall, Belfast, appearing with the Ulster Orchestra.
9.96 National Concert Hall, Dublin,appearing with the RTÉ Concert Orchestra.
11.96 St Patrick's Cathedral, Dublin, promoted by the Red Cross, appearing with Anúna.
5.97 RDS, Dublin, promoted by RTÉ, appearing with the National Symphony Orchestra of Ireland.
**KEY PERFORMANCES OUTSIDE IRELAND** (since January 1994):
8.94 Royal Albert Hall, London, promoted by the BBC Proms, appearing with the City of London Sinfonia.
5.95 San Francisco Opera House, promoted by the United Nations, appearing with the Orchestra of San Francisco Ballet.
7.96 London Colliseum, promoted by the Ramberg Dance Company, appearing with London Music.
1.5.97 Newbury, UK, promoted by BBC Radio, appearing with the BBC Concert Orchestra.
**SELECTED BROADCASTS AND/OR RECORDED WORK:**
5.92 'Relief of Derry Symphony'.

5.93 Debussy 'Saxophone Rhapsody' for Chandos.
3.96 'Meeting Point' for Silva Classics.
**SELECTED REVIEWS** (since January 1994):
6.95 New York Times.
6.95 Scotsman.
10.96 Irish Times.
**PRIZES/AWARDS/APPOINTMENTS:**
1988 Winner of the £15,000 bursary from the Lombard and Ulster Music Foundation.
1988 Winner of wind section, Royal Overseas League Music Competition, London.
**TRAINING AND/OR QUALIFICATIONS:**
From 1983 to 1987, PPRNCM (Dist) B Mus both from the Royal Northern College of Music, Manchester.
From 1987 to 1988, Advanced Solo Studies Dip from the Guildhall School of Music and Drama, London.
From 1988 to 1989, MA from Northwestern University, Chicago
**REGULARLY PERFORMS WITH:**
Craig Ogden (guitar), Kathryn Page (piano), Joseph Petric (accordion).
**AVAILABILITY:**
General.
**ADDITIONAL INFORMATION:**
Currently working with Shaun Davey, Andy Irvine, Joanna McGregor, Ensemble Bash and the Canadian accordion player, Joseph Petric. Concerts feature works by many of Ireland's young composers.

## Claire McGlinchey *Saxophone (Alto)*

**Contact:** Ms Claire McGlinchey
235, Moyville
Ballyboden
Dublin 16
**Tel:** +353 1 4945521
**Other instruments:** Soprano saxophone.

**SELECTED BROADCASTS AND/OR RECORDED WORK:**
1996 'Forty Shades of Blue' for IBC.
**PRIZES/AWARDS/APPOINTMENTS:**
1993 Senior Saxophone winner at the Feis Ceoil, Dublin.
1994 McCullough Cup winner at the Feis Ceoil, Dublin.
1997 Finalist of the Yamaha Brass and Woodwind Bursary.
**TRAINING AND/OR QUALIFICATIONS:**
From 1993 to 1997, B Mus (Perf) from the DIT Conservatory of Music and Drama, Dublin.
**AVAILABILITY:**
General.
**ADDITIONAL INFORMATION:**
A classical saxophonist, is equally at home with blues, swing and concert band repertoire. As part of B Mus has completed a thesis entitled 'Women's Contribution to Saxophone Repertoire and Performance in the Twentieth Century'.

## Patrick O'Keeffe *Saxophone*

**Contact:** Mr Patrick O'Keeffe
126, North Main Street
Youghal
Co Cork
**Tel:** +353 24 92820
*See clarinet page 5.*

## Andrew Rowan *Saxophone* 

**Contact:** Mr Andrew Rowan
10, Galbraith Gardens
Waringstown BT66 7QN
Northern Ireland
**Tel:** +44 1762 881097
*See flute page 19.*

# TROMBONE

Also see the orchestra members lists on page 140.

## Niall McCarthy *Trombone*

**Contact:** Niall McCarthy
'Inchamore'
Bellevue Park
St Luke's
Cork
**Tel:** +353 21 503134
**Other instruments:** Violin.

**KEY IRISH PERFORMANCES** (since January 1994):
9.5.96 Curtis Auditorium, Cork, promoted by Cork School of Music, appearing with Cork School of Music Symphony Orchestra
**SELECTED BROADCASTS AND/OR RECORDED WORK:**
12.95 and 12.96 Rimsky-Korsakov Trombone Concerto, 2nd mov. for RTÉ. Bach's 'Arioso' for RTÉ.
**PRIZES/AWARDS/APPOINTMENTS:**
9.96 McCullough Pigott Trophy for Most Outstanding Wind Player from Cork School of Music.
**TRAINING AND/OR QUALIFICATIONS:**
From 1985 to 1993, violin studies at the Cork School of Music.
From 1991 to 1997, trombone studies at the Cork School of Music
**REGULARLY PERFORMS WITH:**
Cork School of Music Symphony Orchestra, National Youth Orchestra.
**AVAILABILITY:** General.

# TRUMPET

Also see the orchestra members lists on page 140.

## Killyan Bannister *Trumpet*

**Contact:** Mr Killyan Bannister
65, Larkfield Gardens
Harold's Cross
Dublin 6
**Tel:** +353 1 4922893

**PRIZES/AWARDS/APPOINTMENTS:**
1994 Appointed to National Symphony Orchestra of Ireland.
**REGULARLY PERFORMS WITH:**
NSOI and Prelude Brass.
**AVAILABILITY:**
Subject to NSOI schedule.

## Vincent Kennedy *Trumpet*

**Contact:** Mr Vincent Kennedy
18, Carriglea Drive
Firhouse, Dublin 24
**Tel:** +353 1 4525580
*See conductors page 176.*

## Aidan Lynch *Trumpet*

**Contact:** Mr Aidan Lynch
15, Hawthorn Avenue
Ballycasheen
Killarney
**Tel/Fax/Mobile:** +353 64 33749 / +353 64 337491
+353 87 2202382
**Other instruments:** Piano, horn, euphonium, tuba, also conductor.

**PRIZES/AWARDS/APPOINTMENTS:**
1987 Fleishmann Prize, awarded by Unveristy College, Cork.
1988 Certificate of Merit, awarded by Killarney Urban District Council.
**TRAINING AND/OR QUALIFICATIONS:**
From 1977 to 1980, B Mus, awarded by University College, Cork.
From 1982 to 1983, H Dip, awarded by University College, Cork
**REGULARLY PERFORMS WITH:**
Brasso, Opus '96 and Killarney Concert Band.
**AVAILABILITY:**
General.
**ADDITIONAL INFORMATION:**
Former member of the Cork Youth Orchestra, Irish Youth Orchestra, UCC Choir, Cork School of Music Orchestra, UCC Orchestra, Cork Symphony Orchestra and founder-member of the Irish Youth Choir.
*See conductors page 166.*

# TUBA (and Euphonium)

Also see the orchestra members lists on page 140.

## Ewan Easton *Tuba*

**Contact:** Ewan Easton
39, Ballyholme Road
Bangor, Co Down, BT20 5JR
Northern Ireland
**Tel/Fax:** +44 1247 452344

**KEY IRISH PERFORMANCES** (since January 1994):
Current solo tuba repertoire with Ulster Orchestra, Belfast.
**KEY PERFORMANCES OUTSIDE IRELAND** (since January 1994):
Salford University Band, Manchester.
**TRAINING AND/OR QUALIFICATIONS:**
Studied at the Royal National College of Music, Manchester.
**PRIZES/AWARDS/APPOINTMENTS:**
Since 1983, Principal Tuba Player with the Ulster Orchestra.
**SELECTED BROADCASTS AND/OR RECORDED WORK:**
Recital programmes for BBC Belfast.
**REGULARLY PERFORMS WITH:**
Ulster Orchestra, Ulster Brass, Tuba Tapestry.
**AVAILABILITY:**
Subject to Ulster Orchestra schedule.
**ADDITIONAL INFORMATION:**
Solo career started professionally with the Ulster Orchestra playing Edward Gregson's 'Tuba Concerto' which was arranged by the composer for the Orchestra, and, the European performance, of John Williams 'Tuba Concerto', for Radio Three. The UO has included Vaughan Williams 'Tuba Concerto' and Steve Picket's 'Concerto for Tuba' (Ulster Orchestra commission funded by the ACNI) in its season. Has worked with numerous other orchestras including the London Symphony Orchestra, the Orchestra of the Academy of St Martin-in-the-Fields, the Chamber Orchestra of Europe, Scottish Chamber Orchestra, Bournemouth Symphony Orchestra, BBC Symphony Orchestra, Liverpool Philharmonic, Hallé Orchestra and the BBC Philharmonic Orchestra.

## Stephen Irvine *Tuba*

**Contact:** Mr Stephen Irvine
10, Devenish Crescent
Silverhill
Enniskillen
Co Fermanagh, BT74 5JP
Northern Ireland
**Tel:** +44 1365 323873

*"The adjudicators, which included ... Angela Feeney, Stephen Barlow, and Martin Barret, were very impressed with the high standard of tuba playing."* 4.97 Impartial Reporter, Co Fermanagh.

**KEY IRISH PERFORMANCES** (since January 1994):
1994 Grand Opera House, Belfast, performing Mahler's 1st Symphony, appearing with the Ulster Youth Orchestra.
1994 Arts Council, Belfast, performing the Stephen Barrett 'Fanfare' appearing with the Ulster Youth Brass Quintet.
1995 National Concert Hall, Dublin, performing the Strauss 'Alpine Symphony' appearing with the Irish National Youth Orchestra.
1996 Ulster Hall, Belfast, performing the Rachmaninov 2nd Symphony appearing with the UYO.
**KEY PERFORMANCES OUTSIDE IRELAND** (since January 1994):
1995 Glasgow and Edinburgh, appearing with the UYO.
1996 Lichfield Cathedral and Albert Hall, Nottingham, appearing with the National Wind Orchestra of Great Britain.
1996 Colchester, appearing with The George Reynolds Brass Ten-Piece Band, performing works by Gershwin, Copland and Gabrielli.
1996 Royal College of Music, London, appearing with the RCM Symphony Orchestra, performing Tchaikovsky's 6th Symphony.
**PRIZES/AWARDS/APPOINTMENTS:**
1996 Awarded four-year Foundation Scholarship to the Royal College of Music, London.
1997 Awarded 3rd West Belfast Classical Bursary. Ireland Fund award winner.
**TRAINING AND/OR QUALIFICATIONS:**
From 1987 to 1992, to Grade 6 singing with Andrew Batchelor, Omagh.
From 1987 to 1996, to Grade 8 piano with Cheryl McCullagh.
From 1993 to 1996, to Grade 8 tuba with Ewan Easton.
Since 1996, BA Degree at the Royal College of Music, London.
**AVAILABILITY:**
December to January, March to April, June to September.
**ADDITIONAL INFORMATION:**
Has also won the following awards/prizes:
From 1995 to 1997, winner of the Roland Betty Memorial Award, and overall bursary winner at Enniskillen Feis.
1996 Arts Council of Northern Ireland Bursary.
1996 Ian Gow Memorial Award.

# James J. Kavanagh *Tuba*

**Contact:** Mr James J. Kavanagh
72, Killester Avenue
Dublin 5
**Tel/Mobile:** +353 1 8312443 or +44 181 5780266 / +44 860 940007

**PRIZES/AWARDS/APPOINTMENTS:**
1991 Gold Medal from the Senior Feis Ceoil.
From 1992 to 1993, Gold Brass Prize from the London College of Music.
**AVAILABILITY:**
General.

# Aidan Lynch *Tuba and Euphonium*

**Contact:** Mr Aidan Lynch
15 Hawthorn Avenue
Ballycasheen
Killarney, Co Kerry
**Tel/Fax:** +353 64 33747
*See Trumpet page 54.*

# Conor O'Riordan *Tuba and Euphonium*

**Contact:** Mr Conor O'Riordan
3, Butterfield Grove
Rathfarnham
Dublin 14
**Tel/Mobile:** +353 1 4933547 / +353 87 2330228

*"... The feats of agility performed by Conor O'Riordan"* Irish Times (Douglas Sealy).

**KEY IRISH PERFORMANCES** (since January 1994):
3.95 Irish Museum of Modern Art, Dublin promoted by DIT Conservatory of Music and Drama, appearing with DIT CMD Wind Ensemble.
3.96 RTÉ, promoted by Ulster Bank Music Foundation competition, appearing with D. Brosnan.
7.96 National Concert Hall, Dublin, promoted by RTÉ, appearing in the children's education programme 'Tubby the Tuba' with the National Symphony Orchestra of Ireland.
**KEY PERFORMANCES OUTSIDE IRELAND** (since January 1994):
3.96 Guildhall School of Music and Drama, London, appearing with the GSMD Wind Ensemble conducted by Peter Gane.
6.96 GSMD, London, appearing with Neil Sissons (piano).
**SELECTED BROADCASTS AND/OR RECORDED WORK:**
1.96-2.96 Semi-final and final competitions of the RTÉ Young Musician of the Future competition recorded live for RTÉ.
3.96 Recordings for GSMD.
**REVIEWS** (since January 1994):
2.96 Irish Times.
**PRIZES/AWARDS/APPOINTMENTS:**
3.95 Awarded the Guinness Brass Bursary.
9.95 Winner of a SIPTU scholarship to study in London.
**TRAINING AND/OR QUALIFICATIONS:**
From 1991 to 1995, DIT CMD, B Mus (Perf) with (Hons) awarded by Trinity College, Dublin.
From 1991 to 1995, Graduate Diploma in music from DIT CMD.
1995 to 1997, Performance Certificate in Advanced Instrumental Studies from GSMD, London.
**REGULARLY PERFORMS WITH:**
Athem Brass.

## VIOLA

Also see the orchestra members lists on page 140.

# Simon Aspell *Viola*

**Contact:** Mr Simon Aspell
October House
Ballyorban
Monkstown
Co Cork
**Tel/Fax:** +353 21 373363

**REGULARLY PERFORMS WITH:**
RTÉ Vanbrugh Quartet.

# Joy Beatty *Viola*

**Contact:** Ms Joy Beatty
6, Upper Celtic Park
Enniskillen
Co Fermanagh, BT74 6JA
Northern Ireland
**Tel:** +44 1365 322753

**SELECTED BROADCASTS AND/OR RECORDED WORK:**
1.97 profile and performance for BBC Radio Ulster.
**TRAINING AND/OR QUALIFICATIONS:**
From 1991 to 1995, B Mus from Queen's University, Belfast.
Since 1991 Royal Scottish Academy of Music and Drama.
1993, LTCL from Trinity College, London.
**AVAILABILITY:**
General.
**ADDITIONAL INFORMATION:**
Experienced performer with a large repertoire of solo, chamber and orchestral music. Has worked under internationally recognised conductors, such as Leon Spierer, En Shao and Jerzy Maksimiuk. Has a particular interest is the performance of chamber and contemporary music.

# Ruth Bebb *Viola*

**Contact:** Ms Ruth Bebb
13, Old Seahill Road
Craigavad
Co Down, BT18 ODA
Northern Ireland
**Tel:** +44 1232 424675

**REGULARLY PERFORMS WITH:**
Bebb Mason Duo.

# Adèle Govier *Viola*

**Contact:** Adèle Govier
11, Earlsfort Park
Lucan, Co Dublin
**Tel/Fax:** +353 1 6211971

**PRIZES/AWARDS/APPOINTMENTS:**
Awarded the Rotary International Scholarship.

Appointed Principal Viola, with the National Symphony Orchestra of Ireland.
**TRAINING AND/OR QUALIFICATIONS:**
BA Mus from the Royal Northern College of Music, Manchester. Studied at the Eastman School of Music, New York.
**REGULARLY PERFORMS WITH:**
Prism, NSOI.
**AVAILABILITY:**
General.

## Noel Lamont *Viola*

**Contact:** Mr Noel Lamont
60, Jordanstown Road
Newtownabbey
Co Antrim, BT37 0QG
Northern Ireland
**Tel:** +44 1232 862371

**TRAINING AND/OR QUALIFICATIONS:**
From 1974 to 1977, Studied at the University of Ulster, Jordanstown, LRSM, LTCL, Dip in Ed with Glyn Parfitt.
**REGULARLY PERFORMS WITH:**
Lowry String Quartet.

## David McCreadie *Viola*

**Contact:** David McCreadie
23, Park Road
Belfast BT7 2FW
Northern Ireland
**Tel/Fax:** +44 1232 692724

**TRAINING AND/OR QUALIFICATIONS:**
Studied at the Guildhall School of Music and Drama, London and University of Michigan, USA.
**REGULARLY PERFORMS WITH:**
Ulster Orchestra, Dennison String Quartet.
**ADDITIONAL INFORMATION:**
Has freelanced with most orchestras in the UK and Ireland.

## Ronald Masin *Viola*

**Contact:** Prof Ronald Masin
21, The Close
Cypress Downs
Templeogue
Dublin 6w
**Tel/Fax:** +353 1 4905263 / +353 1 4920355
*See violin page 63.*

## Ashley Mason *Viola*

**Contact:** c/o Ms Ruth Bebb
13, Old Seahill Road
Craigavad
Co Down, BT18 OEG,
Northern Ireland
**Tel:** +44 1232 424675

**REGULARLY PERFORMS WITH:**
Bebb-Mason Duo.

## Róisín Ní Dhúill *Viola*

**Contact:** Róisín Ní Dhúill
30, Summerstown Grove
Wilton, Cork
**Tel:** +353 21 546779

**KEY IRISH PERFORMANCES** (since January 1994):
6.94 Crawford Art Gallery, Cork, summer lunchtime series appearing with Mary Beatty (piano).
3.95 St Fin Barre's Cathedral, Cork, appearing with the Heidelburg Chamber Orchestra.
10.96 National Concert Hall, Dublin, appearing with the European Union Chamber Orchestra.
**KEY PERFORMANCES OUTSIDE IRELAND** (since January 1994):
Has given many recitals with orchestras and chamber groups in Germany.
**PRIZES/AWARDS/APPOINTMENTS:**
1990 Winner of the Fitzwilton Trust Exceptional Talent Award.
1990 Sligo Feis Ceoil, most outstanding instrumentalist award.

## Cian Ó Dúill *Viola*

**Contact:** Mr Cian Ó Dúill
30, Summerstown Grove
Wilton, Cork
**Tel:** +353 21 546779

*"[Players of quality have emerged from Cork School of Music] who can rival the best young players in Europe ... Cian Ó Dúill is such a player"* 6.97 The Examiner.

**KEY IRISH PERFORMANCES** (since January 1994):
5.95 Cork City Hall, appearing with the Cork School of Music Symphony Orchestra.
7.95 John Field Room, National Concert Hall, Dublin, appearing with the Primavera Quartet.
2-3.97 Irish tour (including NCH, Dublin), appearing with the RTÉ Vanbrugh Quartet.
6.97 Crawford Art Gallery, Cork, appearing with Robin Michael (piano).
**KEY PERFORMANCES OUTSIDE IRELAND** (since January 1994):
5.95 Heerlen, Holland, appearing with the Primavera String Quartet.
7.95 Spain, appearing with the Cork School of Music Symphony Orchestra.
10.96 Notting Hill Gate, London, promoted by the Schubert Society of Great Britain, appearing with the Regent String Quartet.
6.97 Jubilee Hall, Aldeburgh, promoted by the Aldeburgh Festival, appearing with Madeleine Matta (piano).
**SELECTED BROADCASTS AND/OR RECORDED WORK:**
4.93 Beethoven Piano Quartet in C major for RTÉ.
12.96 Albeniz Tango for Viola and Piano for RTÉ.
3.97 Brahms Sextet in B flat major for RTÉ.
**PRIZES/AWARDS/APPOINTMENTS:**
1993, 1994 and 1996 winner of Senior Viola Prize at the Feis Ceoil, Dublin.
1996 Winner of the Fitzwilton Trust Exceptional Talent Award.

## Niamh Quigley *Viola*

**Contact:** Ms Niamh Quigley
14, Meadowgrove
Blackrock,
**Tel:** +353 21 357399
**Other instruments:** Piano.

*"Philip Martin's 'Aria for Viola and Piano' is a modern work that Ms Quigley's viola sang out most sensitively"* 1994 The Examiner.

**KEY IRISH PERFORMANCES** (since January 1994):
1.94 Bank of Ireland Arts Centre, Dublin, promoted by RTÉ, appearing with Mary Beatty.
2.94 Triskel Arts Centre, Cork, appearing with Mary Beatty.
6.96 Cork School of Music, appearing with the Cork School of Music Chamber Orchestra.
3.97 Aula Maxima, Univerity College, Cork, promoted by Suzuki Parents, appearing with the CSM CO.
**SELECTED BROADCASTS AND/OR RECORDED WORK:**
1.94 Recital for RTÉ FM3.
4.97 'Talented Students from the Cork School of Music' for Cork Local Radio.
6.97 'Millstreet, Famine Gathering' for RTÉ.
**SELECTED REVIEWS** (since January 1994):
3.97 The Examiner.
**PRIZES/AWARDS/APPOINTMENTS:**
1.94 String Finalist in RTÉ Young Musician of the Future Competition.
3.97 Winner of senior viola in Feis Ceoil, Dublin.
**TRAINING AND/OR QUALIFICATIONS:**
From 1994 to 1997, Dip CSM from the Cork School of Music.
7-13.7.97 Masterclasses with Sion Jean Sulem.
14-28.7.97 'Jeunes Musicales de Suisse' in Switzerland.
22.8.97-1.9.97 Masterclasses and workshops on the Isle of Man.
**AVAILABILITY:**
General.

## Deirdre Ward *Viola*

**Contact:** Deirdre Ward
Apartment 5
113, Strand Road
Sandymount, Dublin 4
**Tel:** +353 1 2600774
*See violin page 67.*

# VIOLIN

Also see orchestra members lists on page 140.

## Ruth Bebb *Violin*

**Contact:** Ms Ruth Bebb
13, Old Seahill Road
Craigavad
Co Down, BT18 OEG
Northern Ireland
**Tel:** +44 1232 424675

**REGULARLY PERFORMS WITH:** Bebb Mason Duo.

## Angela Bradley *Violin*

**Contact:** Ms Angela Bradley
14, Bridgewater
Caw, Derry City, BT47 1YA
Northern Ireland
**Tel/Fax:** +44 1504 311938 / +44 1504 48595
*See flute page 11.*

## Bróna Cahill *Violin*

**Contact:** Ms Bróna Cahill
Clonkeen House
Churchtown
Ardee, Co Louth
**Tel/Fax/Mobile:** +353 41 55127 / +353 41 55294 / +353 86 2647714

**KEY IRISH PERFORMANCES** (since January 1994):
1996 National Concert Hall, Dublin, appearing with Roy Holmes.
1996 Galway Arts Festival, appearing with Roy Holmes and Joachim Roewer.
1997 Royal Dublin Society, Dublin, appearing with Benjamin Frith and the Hibernia String Trio.
1997 National Gallery of Ireland, Dublin, promoted by the AIB Festival of Music in Great Irish Houses, appearing with Hugh Tinney and the Hibernia String Trio.
**KEY PERFORMANCES OUTSIDE IRELAND** (since January 1994):
7.96 Festival des Arcs, France, appearing with the Hibernian String Trio and Francois Lulu.
**SELECTED BROADCASTS AND/OR RECORDED WORK:**
1993 For RAI Television Network, Italy.
1994 For Illinois Television.
**PRIZES/AWARDS/APPOINTMENTS:**
1994 String finalist in the Ulster Bank Music Foundation Competition.
**TRAINING AND/OR QUALIFICATIONS:**
From 1989 to 1993, Guildhall School of Music and Drama, London (teacher David Takeno), awarded AGSM.
From 1993 to 1995, M Mus, University of Illinois (teacher Professor Sherban Lupu).
1993 Attended an International musicians seminar, Prussia Cove.
1992 Aldeburgh Music Festival.
**REGULARLY PERFORMS WITH:**
Hibernia String Trio, Irish Chamber Orchestra, Roy Holmes (piano).
**AVAILABILITY:**
General.

## Noeleen Carslaw *Violin*

**Contact:** Noeleen Carslaw
13, Sycamore Park
Jordanstown
Newtownabbey, BT39 0NR
Northern Ireland
**Tel:** +44 1232 867980

**KEY IRISH PERFORMANCES** (since January 1994):
Television appearances with Phil Coulter's Orchestra.
BBC programmes and UTV 'Kelly Show'.
Performed with the Ulster Orchestra.
**SELECTED BROADCASTS AND/OR RECORDED WORK:**
'Kelly Show', for UTV.
RTÉ Concert Orchestra recordings, Ulster Orchestra recordings (until 1984).
'Anderson on the Box', for UTV.
**PRIZES/AWARDS/APPOINTMENTS:**
From 1977 to 1984, full-time member of Ulster Orchestra.
**TRAINING AND/OR QUALIFICATIONS:**
From 1974 to 1977, DRSAM from the Royal Scottish Academy of Music.
**REGULARLY PERFORMS WITH:**
Ulster Orchestra. 1st violin with Lowry String Quartet and String Fever Palm Court Trio.
**ADDITIONAL INFORMATION:**
Freelance violinist with both symphony and light orchestras.

# Jane Charles *Violin*

**Contact:** Jane Charles
Bedford Lodge
Mount Prospect Avenue
Clontarf, Dublin 3
**Tel/Fax:** +353 1 8332202

**KEY IRISH PERFORMANCES** (since January 1994):
5.95 St Stephen's Church, Dublin, appearing with Blanaid Murphy.
1.97 Cork and Dublin, appearing as leader with the National Youth Orchestra.
18.2.97 and 15.4.97 Irish Museum of Modern Art appearing as leader with the NYO.
**KEY PERFORMANCES OUTSIDE IRELAND** (since January 1994):
8.94 Toronto, appearing with Carol Birtch.
12.95 Doncaster, appearing with Royal Northern College of Music Chamber Orchestra.
**PRIZES/AWARDS/APPOINTMENTS:**
Frederic Harris Music Grant (for four years study) from the Royal Conservatory of Music, Toronto.
**TRAINING AND/OR QUALIFICATIONS:**
1994, ARCT from the Royal Conservatory of Music, Toronto. From 1995 to 1996, Royal Northern College of Music, Manchester. Since 1996 DIT Conservatory of Music and Drama, (teacher with Brian McNamara), and also at regular intervals with Lydia Mordrovitch.
**ADDITIONAL INFORMATION:**
From 1988 to 1992, was a First Violin in Toronto Symphony Youth Orchestra for four seasons. Has undertaken several masterclasses in Toronto.

# Elizabeth Charleson *Violin*

**Contact:** Ms Elizabeth Charleson
October House
Ballyorban
Monkstown
Co Cork
**Tel/Fax:** +353 21 373363

**REGULARLY PERFORMS WITH:**
RTÉ Vanbrugh Quartet.

# Elaine Clark *Violin*

**Contact:** Miss Elaine Clark
3, Belgrave Road
Monkstown
Co Dublin
**Tel:** +353 1 2808883
**Other instruments:** Piano.

**KEY IRISH PERFORMANCES** (since January 1994):
7.97 National Concert Hall, Dublin, promoted by RTÉ, appearing with the National Symphony Orchestra of Ireland.
**KEY PERFORMANCES OUTSIDE IRELAND** (since January 1994):
5.95 Town Hall, Jersey, promoted by the Guildhall School of Music and Drama, London appearing with the GSMD Chamber Orchestra.
7.95 GSMD London, appearing witht the GSMD Symphony Orchestra.
12.96 Killearn, Scotland, appearing with the Scottish Baroque Orchestra.
**SELECTED BROADCASTS AND/OR RECORDED WORK:**
1991 'Young Musician of the Year' performance for BBC.
1992 Debussy String Quartet for BBC Scotland.
**PRIZES/AWARDS/APPOINTMENTS:**
9.96 Appointed Co-leader of the National Symphony Orchestra of Ireland by RTÉ.
10.96 Inclusion in the recital scheme as part of the Countess of Munster Scholarship.
**TRAINING AND/OR QUALIFICATIONS:**
From 1991 to 1995, B Mus (1st Class Hons) from GSMD (teacher David Takeno).
From 1995 to 1996, Studies with Viktor Liberman at Utrecht Conservatoire.
**REGULARLY PERFORMS WITH:**
David Clark (piano), William Butt and C. Allum (in a string trio).
**AVAILABILITY:**
Weekends.
**ADDITIONAL INFORMATION:**
Co-Leader of the NSOI. Also performs regularly thoughout the UK as a result of scholarship received with the Countess of Munster Recital Scheme.

# Nicola Cleary *Violin*

**Contact:** Nicola Cleary
c/o 110, Custom House Harbour
IFSC, Dublin 1
**Tel/Fax:** +353 1 6701965

**KEY PERFORMANCES OUTSIDE IRELAND** (since January 1994):
2.95 Royal Albert Hall, London, appearing with Wissam Boustamy.
Since 1.94 concerts throughout Europe, appearing with the German Chamber Orchestra.
**PRIZES/AWARDS/APPOINTMENTS:**
Since 1994, Appointed 1st Violin Tutti at the Deutsche Kammerakademie, Germany.
**TRAINING AND/OR QUALIFICATIONS:**
From 1989 to 1993, Performance Diploma from the Royal College, London.
Since 1996, Soloist Diploma at the Hochschule für Musik, Würzburg.
**REGULARLY PERFORMS WITH:**
Danusia Oslizlok (piano).
**AVAILABILITY:**
General.

# Ruxandra Colan *Violin*

**Contact:** Mrs Ruxandra Colan
7, Grosvenor Place
Wellington Road
Cork
**Tel/Fax:** +353 21 505153

*"Splendid interaction of piano and violin"*
25.11.94 The Examiner (performance with Philip Martin).

**KEY IRISH PERFORMANCES** (since January 1994):
1994 Cork, promoted by the Cork Orchestral Society, appearing with Philip Martin.
1995 Cork, promoted by the Triskel Arts Centre, appearing with Philip Martin.
1995 Waterford, promoted by the Waterford Music Club, appearing with Philip Martin.
**SELECTED BROADCASTS AND/OR RECORDED WORK:**
1995 'Two Elegies for Violin and Piano' (CD) with Philip Martin for Altarus Records Incorporated.
1996 'Volume' (CD) playing one of the Elegies, for Crawford Art Gallery.
1996 Granville Sonata for violin and piano for BBC Radio 3.
**SELECTED REVIEWS** (since January 1994):
25.11.94 The Examiner.
6.11.95 The Examiner.
**REGULARLY PERFORMS WITH:**
Philip Martin (piano).
**AVAILABILITY:**
General.

## Elizabeth Cooney *Violin*

**Contact:** Elizabeth Cooney
'Heather'
Brookfield
Rochestown Road
Cork
**Tel:** +353 21 362095

**KEY PERFORMANCES OUTSIDE IRELAND** (since January 1994):
28.6.94 Växjö, Sweden, promoted by the European Broadcasting Union, appearing with the Musica Vitae Orchestra.
6.96 Conservatoire, Nice, France promoted by the Cork School of Music, appearing with Ciara Sheehan.
**SELECTED REVIEWS** (since January 1994):
13.11.95 The Examiner.
6.5.94 The Examiner.
**ADDITIONAL INFORMATION:**
Awarded McCullough-Pigott Scholarship by the Cork School of Music (for achievements at consistently high level).
1995 Awarded McCullough Cup in the Cork School of Music.
1994 Performed Saint-Saens Violin Concerto No. 3 with the Cork School of Music Orchestra. Has appeared on RTÉ television and radio. Leader of the National Youth Orchestra of Ireland.

## Eilís Cranitch *Violin*

**Contact:** Eilís Cranitch
Lungo Po
Antonelli 17
10153 Turin, Italy
**Tel/Fax:** +39 11 8122430 / +39 11 503361

*"She possesses an incredibly expressive and intense sense of phrasing"*

5.5.92 Tiroler Tageszeitung, Innsbruch.

**KEY PERFORMANCES OUTSIDE IRELAND** (since January 1994):
7.1.95 Turin, Italy, promoted by Piemonte in Musica, accompanied by a trombone and string trio.
10.6.95 Turin, Italy, promoted by Tastar de Corda, accompanied by harpsichord.
15.6.96 Vittoriale, Garda, Italy, promoted by D'Annunzio Foundation, accompanied by piano.
6.7.97 Ravenna International Festival, Italy, accompanied by Xenia Ensemble.
**RECORDED WORK:**
24.3.90 'Rare Works of Mercadante/Rossini' for Nuova Era.
26.4.94 Live recording of concert on Swiss radio.
15.11.96 'Cosmic Tangents' art video, for Euphon/Edison.
**SELECTED REVIEWS** (since January 1994):
24.2.94 La Stampa, Italy.
7.9.95 La Republica, Italy.
18.6.96 Il Giornale di Brescia, Italy.
**PRIZES/AWARDS/APPOINTMENTS:**
1974 Arthur Catterall Concerto Cup, awarded by Feis Ceoil, Dublin.
From 1974 to 1977, Scholarship to Santa Cecilia Conservatorio, Rome, awarded by the Italian Government.
**TRAINING AND/OR QUALIFICATIONS:**
From 1970 to 1973, B Mus, from University College, Cork.
From 1973 to 1974, MA awarded by University College, Cork.
From 1974 to 1977 Post-grad Diploma, awarded by Conservatorio Saint Cecilia, Rome (teachers Riccardo Brengola and Arrigo Pelliccia).
From 1994 to 1994, LRSM (performance), awarded by the Associated Board of the Royal Schools of Music, London.
**REGULARLY PERFORMS WITH:**
Piano duo, Xenia Ensemble, Lir Ensemble, I Solisti Aquilani.
**AVAILABILITY:**
General.

**ADDITIONAL INFORMATION:**
Has researched into lesser known 17th and 18th Century composers. Also has a particular interested in 20th Century music, performing works by Italian and Irish composers (Petrassi, Berio, Pizzetti, Barry, Farrell and Wilson). Active as a teacher and recitalist.

## Terry Crehan *Violin*

**Contact:** Terry Crehan
Liffey Bank Promotions
21, Colthurst Close
Huntington Glen
Lucan
Co Dublin
**Tel:** +353 1 621 0090
*See fiddle page 206.*

## Ciaran Crilly *Violin*

**Contact:** Mr Ciaran Crilly
5 Gransha Park
Belfast BT11 8AT
Northern Ireland
**Tel:** +44 1232 613937

*"... A very talented violinist ..."*

1995 Guildhall School of Music and Drama (Gerhard Schmidt).

**PRIZES/AWARDS/APPOINTMENTS:**
1995 Travel award for Szombathely, awarded by the Arts Council of Northern Ireland.
1996 Travel award for Hilversum, awarded by the ACNI.
**TRAINING AND/OR QUALIFICATIONS:**
From 1980 to 1988, School of Music, Belfast, (orchestra, violin and music theory).
From 1989 to 1993, King's College, London, B Mus (Hons).
From 1989 to 1993, Guildhall School of Music, London, violin.
From 1.96 to 6.96, DIT Conservatory of Music and Drama, Dublin (piano).
**ADDITIONAL INFORMATION:**
Has performed with King's College London Orchestras, Queen's Belfast Orchestra, Northern Ireland Symphony and the Irish National Youth Orchestra.
*See conductors page 170.*

## Niamh Crowley *Violin*

**Contact:** Ms Niamh Crowley
Rosses Point
County Sligo
**Tel:** +353 71 77178
**Other instruments:** Piano.

*"Her playing of delicacy, strength in phrasing, her sure-flowing conveying of the melodic poetry of Saint-Saens, bound us to her "*

12.4.94 The Examiner (performance of Saint Saens Concerto No. 3 at the NCH, Dublin).

**KEY IRISH PERFORMANCES** (since January 1994):
10.11.95 Sligo Regional Technical College, appearing with RTÉ Concert Orchestra performing Bruch's Violin Concerto.

8.96 Dublin, finals of Heineken Violin Competition, appearing with Gillian Smith.
**KEY PERFORMANCES OUTSIDE IRELAND** (since January 1994):
20.9.96 Irish Club, Eaton Square, London, appearing with Bláithín Murphy.
**SELECTED BROADCASTS AND/OR RECORDED WORK:**
14.1.96 'Sunday Worship' for RTÉ.
**PRIZES/AWARDS/APPOINTMENTS:**
1994 Arts Council Bursary.
6.96 Highest Leaving Certificate marks in the Country.
**TRAINING AND/OR QUALIFICATIONS:**
From 9.84 to 6.94 Studied at the Royal Irish Academy of Music. Since September 1994, Studies for Perf. Degree at the Royal College of Music, London. Attends annual masterclasses in Salzburg, Budapest, New York, Italy
**AVAILABILITY:**
June to September, December, Easter and all weekends.

## Leonie Curtin *Violin*

**Contact:** Leonie Curtin
St Clare's
Barrington's Avenue
Ballintemple
Cork
**Tel/Fax:** +353 21 294482 / +353 21 291149

**KEY IRISH PERFORMANCES** (since January 1994):
4.94 Triskel Arts Centre, Cork, appearing with John Gibson (piano).
5.94 Crawford Art Gallery, Cork, appearing as soloist with Cork Chamber Orchestra.
7.94 John Field Room, National Concert Hall, Dublin, appearing with Darina Gibson (piano).
4.97 Aula Maxima, University College, Cork, promoted by Suzuki International, appearing as soloist with Cork School of Music Chamber Orchestra.
**KEY PERFORMANCES OUTSIDE IRELAND** (since January 1994):
5.96 Irish Club, London.
**PRIZES/AWARDS/APPOINTMENTS:**
9.95 Arts Council Bursary.
1.97 Gregory Salzman Award from the Worshipful Company of Tobacco Pipe Makers, London.
**TRAINING AND/OR QUALIFICATIONS:**
From 1976 to 1988, Studied Suzuki method with Philippa Lees.
From 1988 to 1994, Cork School of Music (teacher Cornelia Zanidachi).
From 1994 to 1995, (teacher Prof Yfrah Neaman).
Since 1995, with John Glickman at the Guildhall School of Music and Drama, London.
**REGULARLY PERFORMS WITH:**
Patricia Treacy (violin)
**AVAILABILITY:**
July to August and December.

## Declan Daly *Violin*

**Contact:** Mr Declan Daly
Tossey, Loughmourne
Castleblayney
Co Monaghan
**Tel:** +353 42 45041
**Other instruments:** Piano, organ.

*"Declan overcame the difficulties with lovely polish, a delight in phrasing, and lovely tone which made it sound easy - and enjoyable"*

19.7.93 Irish Press (John Brophy).

**KEY IRISH PERFORMANCES** (since January 1994):
1994 National Concert Hall, Dublin, promoted by RTÉ, appearing with National Symphony Orchestra of Ireland.
1995 City Hall, Cork, promoted by Irish Times and RTÉ, appearing with NSOI.
1996 O'Reilly Hall, University College Dublin, promoted by the Dublin Orchestral Players.
**KEY PERFORMANCES OUTSIDE IRELAND** (since January 1994):
7.97 Concert Hall, Utrecht University, promoted by Utrecht International Summer Academy, appearing with a string quartet.
10.96 Mozarteum, Salzburg, appearing with Salzburg Chamber Soloists.
4.97 St John's, Smith Square, London, promoted by Connaught Artists, appearing with Dante String Quartet.
2.5.97 Vredenburg Concert Hall, Utrecht, appearing with a piano trio.
**SELECTED BROADCASTS AND/OR RECORDED WORK:**
1994 Works by Edward Dudley Hughes for Orchid 777 and Nimbus.
1995 'Pat Kenny Show' for RTÉ.
1996 'Late Late Show' for RTÉ.
**SELECTED REVIEWS** (since January 1994):
7.94 Irish Times.
3.95 The Examiner.
2.97 Westmoreland Herald.
**PRIZES/AWARDS/APPOINTMENTS:**
1991 Ist Prize winner of the Heineken Violin Competition.
1993 String winner in the BBC Young Musician Competition.
**TRAINING AND/OR QUALIFICATIONS:**
From 1975 to 1989, ARIAM (Diploma in Performance) from the Royal Irish Academy of Music.
From 1989 to 1993, AGSM (Perf) from Guildhall School of Music and Drama, London.
From 1993 to 1995, Diploma in Professional Performance from the Royal Northern College of Music, Manchester in affiliation with Manchester University.
Diploma of Advanced Studies in Performance from the RNCM.
**REGULARLY PERFORMS WITH:**
Piano and violin duo, piano trio, chamber groups, Irish Chamber Orchestra.
**AVAILABILITY:**
General.
**ADDITIONAL INFORMATION:**
Lives and works in London and Amsterdam. Performs and prepares programmes for concerts with many European ensembles, in Europe and the USA.

## Diane Daly *Violin*

**Contact:** Ms Diane Daly
Tossey
Loughmourne
Castleblayney, Co Monaghan
**Tel:** +353 42 45041
**Other instruments:** Piano.

**KEY IRISH PERFORMANCES** (since January 1994):
1995 Convent, Castleblayney, appearing with family.
1995 Boyle Town Church, promoted by Boyle Arts Festival, appearing with Peter Dains.
1995 Annaghmakerrig, promoted by Cavan Arts Festival, appearing with Peter Dains.
**KEY PERFORMANCES OUTSIDE IRELAND** (since January 1994):
1995 Hampstead Performing Arts Centre, appearing with John York (piano).
1997 Sema Group Concert Hall, Royal Northern College of Music, Manchester appearing with David Jones (piano).
1997 Emmanuel Church, Didsbury, appearing with Johnson Quartet.
**PRIZES/AWARDS/APPOINTMENTS:**
1988 Terry O'Connor Trophy and String Rose Bowl from Feis Ceoil, Dublin.
**TRAINING AND/OR QUALIFICATIONS:**
From 1977 to 1991, Royal Irish Academy of Music (teacher Maeve Broderick).
From 1991 to 1995, B Mus (Hons) Performance Degree from the

Guildhall School of Music and Drama, London (teacher John Glickman).
1993 Masterclasses with Sylvia Rosenberg.
From 1995 to 1997, Postgraduate Diploma in Advanced Performance from the RNCM with Wen Zhou Li.
**AVAILABILITY:**
General.
**ADDITIONAL INFORMATION:**
Soloist and chamber musician. Available also as piano accompanist.

# Michael d'Arcy *Violin*

**Contact:** Mr Michael d'Arcy
16, Viking Harbour
Usher's Island
Dublin 8
**Tel/Fax:** +353 1 6776051

*"Copperplate pure intonation ... a brilliant virtuoso performance ... exquisite musical spirit..."* 7.94 Rhewpfalz Kultur.

**KEY IRISH PERFORMANCES** (since January 1994):
10.94 Bank of Ireland Arts Centre, Dublin, appearing with Nigel Hutchison (piano).
10.95 National Concert Hall, Dublin appearing with the RTÉ Concert Orchestra playing Vivadi's 'Four Seasons'.
1995/96/97 Soloist with RTÉCO in NCH/Cork/Limerick.
**KEY PERFORMANCES OUTSIDE IRELAND** (since January 1994):
7.94 Paris and Wissembourg, playing Mendelssohn's Violin Concerto in E minor, appearing with the Orchestra de la Guarde Republicane.
3.95 London, Leeds and Northampton, appearing with Nigel Hutchison. Guest leader of Bournemouth Symphony Orchestra in the UK/France.
**SELECTED BROADCASTS AND/OR RECORDED WORK:**
7.93 Solo and chamber works of Gerald Barry, CD for NMC plus Ronan Guilfoyle Sonata for CMC.
7.95 and 7.97 RTÉ Proms for RTÉ.
7.95 and 7.97 Solo performance.
10.95 With Nigel Hutchison (piano) for Slovak Radio.
**SELECTED REVIEWS** (since January 1994):
7.94 Dernières Nouvelles D'Alsace.
7.95 Irish Times.
10.94 The Scotsman.
**PRIZES/AWARDS/APPOINTMENTS:**
From 1986 to 1990, Six awards and scholarships from the Royal National College of Music, Manchester.
From 1987 1st Prize winner, RTÉ Young Musician of the Future Competition.
1987 Bass Ireland Arts Award.
1989/1990 Lombard and Ulster Foundation String Award.
**TRAINING AND/OR QUALIFICATIONS:**
From 1986 to 1990, Scholarship to study and GRNCM received, from The Royal Northern College of Music, Manchester.
From 1991 to 1992, Studied in Montreal.
**AVAILABILITY:**
Subject to RTÉCO schedule.
**REGULARLY PERFORMS WITH:**
RTÉ Concert Orchestra, Nigel Hutchison (piano), Irish Piano Trio.
**ADDITIONAL INFORMATION:**
Concerto soloist, recitalist and chamber musician at home and abroad. Leader of the RTÉ Concert Orchestra. Repertoire of over 40 sonatas and more than 25 concerti. Guest leader to many orchestras and has performed throughout Europe.

# Gregory Ellis *Violin*

**Contact:** Mr Gregory Ellis
c/o October House
Ballyorban
Monkstown
Co Cork
**Tel/Fax:** +353 21 891604

**REGULARLY PERFORMS WITH:**
RTÉ Vanbrugh String Quartet.

# Camilla Gunzl *Violin*

**Contact:** Ms Camilla Gunzl
7, Larchfield Park
Roebuck
Dublin 14
**Tel:** +353 1 2982731
**Other instruments:** Baroque violin, viola.

**PRIZES/AWARDS/APPOINTMENTS:**
From 1970 to 1975, Prizes and scholarships from the Royal Academy of Music, London.
**TRAINING AND/OR QUALIFICATIONS:**
From 1970 to 1975, Royal Academy of Music, London (teachers M Hurwitz and S Griller).
From 1972 to 1975, Studied viola with G Edwards.
1984/85/86, Masterclasses with Marie Leonhardt.
1982/83/87/88/90 Masterclasses for baroque violin with José Vazquez.
**AVAILABILITY:**
General.
**ADDITIONAL INFORMATION:**
Principally trained as a string quartet player having studied intensively for 5 years under Sidney Griller.

# Lesley Heron *Violin*

**Contact:** Mrs Lesley Heron
25, Indiana Avenue
Belfast BT15 5BZ
Northern Ireland
**Tel:** +44 1232 371255

**TRAINING AND/OR QUALIFICATIONS:**
Studied at Trinity College of Music, London.
**REGULARLY PERFORMS WITH:**
Dennison String Quartet

# Louise Higgins *Violin*

**Contact:** Ms Louise Higgins
257, Malahide Marina Village
Co Dublin
**Tel:** +353 1 8450802
**Other instruments:** Piano.

**REGULARLY PERFORMS WITH:**
Trio with Mairéad English (flute) David Brophy (piano).

# Fionnuala Hunt *Violin*

**Contact:** c/o The Office of the Irish Chamber Orchestra
Foundation Building
University of Limerick
Limerick
**Tel/Fax:** +353 61 202620 or +353 61 202659 or
+353 61 202583 / +353 61 202617
**Email:** ico@ul.ie

*"As guest leader had plenty to do alone and alongside the principal cello Moray Welsh; the results were relaxed and profoundly spiritual"*
3.4.94 Independent on Sunday (Tom Sutcliffe).

**AVAILABILITY:**
Subject to schedule.
**ADDITIONAL INFORMATION:**
Born in Belfast. Is rapidly becoming known throughout Europe as the the Leader and Artistic Director of the Irish Chamber Orchestra. Has made many solo appearances with the National Symphony Orchestra of Ireland, the RTÉ Concert Orchestra and the Ulster Orchestra. Performances of contemporary works for violin include Lutoslawski's 'Paritia' with Jerzy Maksymluk at Snape Concert Hall and Bernstein's 'Serenade' in Finland conducted by William Boughton. Has played with the Vienna Chamber Orchestra as Leader and spent two years with the Bavarian State Opera Orchestra in Munich. Has been a guest Leader of the London Symphony Orchestra, Hallé Orchestra, and the Bournemouth Symphony Orchestra. In 1995 performed at the Ojai Festival in California as Leader of the Orchestra of Opéra de Lyon conducted by Kent Nagano and on 2.97, led the BBC Philharmonic conducted by Sir Georg Solti. Regularly performs with her sister, Una Hunt (piano) and is also a member of the Dublin Piano Trio. Artistic Director of the 1997 series of chamber music recitals at the Irish Museum of Modern Art, Dublin.

# Oonagh Keogh *Violin*

**Contact:** Ms Oonagh Keogh
'La Pietra'
12, Highfield Park, Dundrum
Dublin 14
**Tel:** +353 1 2986001

**SELECTED BROADCASTS AND/OR RECORDED WORK:**
'Heartstrings in Harmony' CD with Geraldine O'Grady. 'The Lark in the Clear Air' CD with Geraldine O'Grady. Regular broadcasts for RTÉ.
**PRIZES/AWARDS/APPOINTMENTS:**
Awarded prizes in the Leopold Bellan International Competition, J.S. Bach International Competition and the Lombard and Ulster Music Foundation Competition. Since 1995, Principal 2nd Violin with the Irish Chamber Orchestra.
**TRAINING AND/OR QUALIFICATIONS:**
Studied with Jean Fournier in Paris. Attended the Guildhall School of Music and Drama (teachers Yfrah Neaman and David Takeno).
**REGULARLY PERFORMS WITH:**
Irish Chamber Orchestra, Geraldine O'Grady.
**AVAILABILITY:**
General.
**ADDITIONAL INFORMATION:**
Has performed throughout Ireland as a soloist and in 1997 performed the Wieniawski Concerto No. 2 at the University Concert Hall, Limerick and the Mozart Concerto in D with the Orchestra of St. Cecilia. Has toured with her mother Geraldine O'Grady as a violin duo in America and Europe. Has also collaborated with jazz pianist 'Prof' Peter O'Brien.

# Catherine Leonard *Violin*

**Contact:** Catherine Leonard
4 Willowmere
Rochestown
Cork
**Tel/Fax:** +353 21 894366 / +353 21 272879
**Other instruments:** Piano.

*"She seems poised on the brink of international stardom ... places her amongst our leading musicians"* 18.2.96 Sunday Tribune (Ian Fox).

**KEY IRISH PERFORMANCES** (since January 1994):
10.95 National Concert Hall, Dublin, appearing with Maria Kulakowsa (piano).
2.96 RDS, promoted by Royal Dublin Society, appearing with Jan Càp.
1.97 City Hall, Waterford, promoted by Bridget Doolin, appearing with Jan Càp.
6.97 City Hall, Cork, promoted by Gerry Kelly (playing Vivaldi's 'Four Seasons').
**KEY PERFORMANCES OUTSIDE IRELAND** (since January 1994):
10.94 Cologne Philharmonic Hall, appearing with Maria Kulakowska.
7.96 and 7.97 Concertgebouw, Amsterdam, promoted by Holland Music Sessions, appearing with Maria Kalakowska.
7.96 Irish College, Paris, promoted by Department of Foreign Affairs, appearing with Stuart O'Sullivan.
3.97 Herne, Bochum, Germany, promoted by Jan Thürmer, appearing with Maria Kalakowsa.
**SELECTED BROADCASTS AND/OR RECORDED WORK:**
4.94 'Late Late Show' for RTÉ.
3.97 recital from Bank of Ireland Arts Centre, Dublin for RTÉ.
**SELECTED REVIEWS** (since January 1994):
10.95 Irish Times (Douglas Sealy).
2.96 Irish Times (Michael Dervan).
2.97 Ausgabe Herne.
**PRIZES/AWARDS/APPOINTMENTS:**
10.94 Third prize at Kulenkampff International Violin Competition.
3.96 Third prize Scheveningen Violin Competition, The Netherlands.
**TRAINING AND/OR QUALIFICATIONS:**
From 1992 to 1995, Artist Diploma at Southern Methodist University, Dallas, Texas (teacher Dr. Eduard Schmieder).
From 1995 to 1997, Performance Degree from Mozarteum, Salzburg (teacher Ruggiero Ricci).
Since 1997, Sweelinck Conservatory, Amsterdam (teacher Herman Krebbers).
**REGULARLY PERFORMS WITH:**
Piano Trio with Finghin Collins (piano) and Hanno Strijdom (cello).
**AVAILABILITY:**
General.
**ADDITIONAL INFORMATION:**
Winner of Ulster Bank Music Bursary (1994) and Heineken Violin and Bow.

# Niall McCarthy *Violin*

**Contact:** Niall McCarthy
'Inchamore'
Bellevue Park
St Luke's
Cork
**Tel:** +353 21 503134
*See trombone page 53.*

# Anne-Marie McGowan *Violin*

**Contact:** Anne-Marie McGowan
The Stables
Waterloo Lane
Dublin 4
**Tel:** +353 1 6689845

**REGULARLY PEFORMS WITH:**
Dublin Symphony Orchestra, CCÉ.
**AVAILABILITY:**
General.

# Gwendolyn Masin *Violin*

**Contact:** Ms Gwendolyn Masin
21, The Close
Cypress Downs
Templeogue
Dublin 6w
**Tel/Fax:** +353 1 4905263 / +353 1 4920355
**Email:** yes@iol.ie

*"I got great pleasure from Gwendolyn Masin's playing ... winning purity of tone, impeccable taste"* 23.2.95 Irish Times.

**KEY IRISH PERFORMANCES** (since January 1994):
1996 National Concert Hall, Dublin, Waterford, Tralee, Limerick, promoted by Hungarian Embassy, conducted by Robert Houlihan with visiting Hungarian Orchestra.
**KEY PERFORMANCES OUTSIDE IRELAND** (since January 1994):
1995 City Hall, Budapest, promoted by Young European Strings.
1996 Academy Franz Liszt, Budapest promoted by YES.
**SELECTED BROADCASTS AND/OR RECORDED WORK:**
1996 Radio Broadcast for Hungarian Broadcasting.
**SELECTED REVIEWS** (since January 1994):
1996 Irish Times (available from YES Promotion).
**PRIZES/AWARDS/APPOINTMENTS:**
From 1987 to 1996, Junior and Senior Cups from Feis Ceoil, Dublin and Feis Sligo.
From 1996 to 1997, Swiss Government Scholarship.
Since 1997, Austrian Government Scholarship.
**TRAINING AND/OR QUALIFICATIONS:**
From 1987 to 1996, Studied at the DIT Conservatory of Music and Drama.
Since 1996, Studying for a Performance Diploma from Music Conservatory of Bern, Switzerland.
**AVAILABILITY:**
General.
**ADDITIONAL INFORMATION:**
Available for solo performances, recitals and solo appearances with orchestra. Repertoire available on request from YES Promotion Tel: +353 1 4905263.

# Ronald Masin *Violin*

**Contact:** Prof Ronald Masin
21, The Close
Cypress Downs
Templeogue
Dublin 6w
**Tel/Fax:** +353 1 4905263 / +353 1 4920355
**Other instruments:** Viola.

*"He has shown himself to be technically, musically and stylistically an all-round interpreter of music"* Le Matin, Antwerp.

**PRIZES/AWARDS/APPOINTMENTS:**
1965 to 1984, Appointed leader of the Amsterdam Philharmonic Orchestra.
From 1984 to 1986, appointed to Associate Professorship at the University of Cape Town, South Africa.
Since 1997, Senior Lecturer at the DIT Conservatory of Music and Drama, Dublin.
**TRAINING AND/OR QUALIFICATIONS:**
1962 Received Violin and Chamber Music Diplomas from the Royal Music Conservatory of Brussels.
**SELECTED REVIEWS** (since January 1994):
La Metropole, Brussels. The Times, London. Rand Daily Mail, Johanesburg S.A.
**AVAILABILITY:**
General.
**ADDITIONAL INFORMATION:**
Born in Rotterdam of Czech-Dutch Parentage. Began violin studies at the age of five at the Rotterdam Music Conservatory. Made his debut at the age of fourteen with the Johannesburg Symphony Orchestra playing the Bruch violin Concerto. In 1967 formed the chamber music group the Amsterdam Kern* Ensemble, which during the eleven years of existence performed over six hundred concerts in twenty two countries and recorded for EMI. Besides orchestra and chamber music, has pursued a solo career both in recitals and as a soloist with orchestras. Co-author of 'Violin Technique the Natural Way' (1982). Instigator of the ESTA/IRL (European String Teachers Association - Irish Chapter). Founder and Artistic Director of the Music Instrument Fund for Ireland. Frequent guest teacher at national and international masterclasses. (Kern * is Dutch for nucleus).

# Sarah Moffatt *Violin*

**Contact:** Ms Sarah Moffatt
29, Hazelwood
Shankill
Co Dublin
**Tel:** +353 1 2822587
**Email:** mmoffatt@tinet.ie

**KEY IRISH PERFORMANCES** (since January 1994):
15.5.96 National Concert Hall, Dublin, appearing as a soloist with the Royal Irish Academy of Music Baroque Ensemble.
18.11.96 Goethe Institute, Dublin, appearing with Dearbhla Brosnan (piano).
29.4.97 NCH, appearing with the RIAM Baroque Ensemble.
16.6.97 RIAM, appearing with Dearbhla Brosnan.
**KEY PERFORMANCES OUTSIDE IRELAND** (since January 1994):
20.7.96 Kubus, Weimar, Germany, appearing with a clarinet quintet as part of the Weimar International Summer Music Course.
**TRAINING AND/OR QUALIFICATIONS:**
From 9.93 to 9.97, awarded 1st Class Honours in Diploma in Music Teaching and Performance with Deirdre Ward at the RIAM, Dublin.
Since 6.97, BA in Music Performance with Maeve Broderick at the RIAM, Dublin.
**AVAILABILITY:**
General.
**ADDITIONAL INFORMATION:**
A third year student on the BA (Music Performance) course at the RIAM. Having performed in recitals throughout Dublin, and in concerto appearances at the NCH and the Kilkenny Arts Festival, is keen to further broaden performance experience.

## Geraldine Montague *Violin*

**Contact:** Ms Geraldine Montague
40, Innismore
Crumlin Village
Dublin 12
**Tel:** +353 1 4560551
*See soprano page 93.*

## Darragh Morgan *Violin*

**Contact:** Mr Darragh Morgan
The Cottage
Drinaghan
Ballintrillick
Co Sligo
or
37 Ashgrove Park
Belfast BT14 6NE
Northern Ireland
**Tel:** +353 71 66420 / +44 1232 745177
**Email:** darraghm@hotmail.com

**KEY IRISH PERFORMANCES** (since January 1994):
Castletownshend, promoted by Castletownshend Music Society, appearing with Maria Fitzgerald. Hillsborough Castle, promoted by the Duke of Edinburgh Awards, appearing with Elizabeth Bicker. Drumcliff Church, Sligo, promoted by Model Arts Centre, Sligo, appearing with Mary Dullea.
**KEY PERFORMANCES OUTSIDE IRELAND** (since January 1994):
1996 Nelahzeves Castle, Prague, promoted by Nelahzevel Castle Concerts, appearing with Ian Coleman.
1996 Yverdon Festival, Switzerland, appearing with Ian Coleman.
1997 HK Academy, Hong Kong, promoted by Academy String Department, appearing with Woo Zun-Hin.
1997 Hong Kong Academy, promoted by Hong Kong Government, Urban Council and British Council, appearing with Woo Zun Hin.
**PRIZES/AWARDS/APPOINTMENTS:**
1996 Rachel and Allen Percival Memorial Scholarship.
1997 Grant towards purchase of a musical instrument from Skinners Company, London.
**TRAINING AND/OR QUALIFICATIONS:**
From 9.92 to 9.96, B Mus (Hons) and LGSM from the Guildhall School of Music and Drama, London (teacher Professor Detlef Hann).
From 1996 to 1997, Professional Diploma from the Hong Kong Academy of Performing Arts (teacher Professor Michael Ma, Curtis Institute).
**REGULARLY PERFORMS WITH:**
Mary Dullea (piano), Fidelio Trio.
**AVAILABILITY:**
General.

## Frances Nesbitt *Violin*

**Contact:** Frances Nesbitt
Victoria Ville
Victoria Road
Cork
**Tel:** +353 21 963086
*See fiddle page 210.*

## Kate O'Brien *Violin*

**Contact:** Ms Kate O'Brien
9, Station Road
Magherafelt
Co Derry BT45 5DN
Northern Ireland
**Tel:** +44 1648 31995
*See fiddle page 211.*

## Marie O'Byrne *Violin*

**Contact:** Marie O'Byrne
Shanaway Road
Ennis, Co Clare
**Tel:** +353 65 41602
**Other instruments:** Fiddle, piano.

*"Exceptionally sweet tone and technical excellence of the highest standard."*

2.96 Féile Luimní Adjudication.

**KEY IRISH PERFORMANCES** (since January 1994):
2.95 Danlann an Chláir, promoted by Coláiste Mhuire appearing with orchestras for musicals.
2.96 National Concert Hall, Dublin, promoted by Festival of Youth Orchestras, appearing with the Clare Youth Orchestra.
10.96 Old Ground Hotel, Ennis, promoted by Maoin Cheoil an Chláir, appearing with several members of the Irish Chamber Orchestra and the Johann Strauss Orchestra.
1996 University of Limerick Concert Hall, promoted by Féile Luimní.
**KEY PERFORMANCES OUTSIDE IRELAND** (since January 1994):
7.94 Town Hall, Cape Cod, Boston, promoted by A Stone.
10.94 Manchester Cathedral, promoted by Colaiste Mhuire, accompanying choirs.
4.96 Finland, promoted by Coláiste Mhuire, appearing with classical Finnish quartet.
**SELECTED BROADCASTS AND/OR RECORDED WORK:**
4.95 Two appearances for Raidió na Gaeltachta.
4.96 Appeared for BBC radio.
4.96 Finnish Radio.
**SELECTED REVIEWS** (since January 1994):
2.96 Féile Luimní adjudication.
**PRIZES/AWARDS/APPOINTMENTS:**
4.94 Appointed Leader of the Clare Youth Orchestra by Maoin Cheoil an Chláir.
Summer 1995 Maoin Cheoil an Chláir, appointed Leader of orchestra (to accompany Liam O'Flynn).
**TRAINING AND/OR QUALIFICATIONS:**
From 1994 to 1996, Grade 8 (Hons) from the Royal Irish Academy of Music (teacher Andrea Creach).
From 9.96 to 6.97, Maoin Cheoil an Chláir (teacher Kenneth Rice).
**REGULARLY PERFORMS WITH:**
Marie Quigley (piano).
**AVAILABILITY:**
General.
*See also page 212.*

## Cian O'Duill *Violin*

**Contact:** Mr Cian O'Duill
30, Summerstown Grove
Wilton, Co Cork
**Tel:** +353 21 546779
*See viola page 56.*

# Geraldine O'Grady *Violin*

**Contact:** Dr Geraldine O'Grady
12, Highfield Park
Dundrum
Dublin 14
**Tel:** +353 1 2986001

*"... An artist of the first rank"*

New York Times (Peter G Davis).

**KEY IRISH PERFORMANCES** (since January 1994):
1994 National Concert Hall, Dublin, promoted by RTÉ, appearing with Oonagh Keogh and the RTÉ Concert Orchestra.
1995 NCH, promoted by RTÉ, appearing with Oonagh Keogh and the RTÉCO.
1996 NCH, promoted by RTÉ, appearing with the National Symphony Orchestra of Ireland.
**KEY PERFORMANCES OUTSIDE IRELAND** (since January 1994):
1995 Sacramento, California, appearing with the Sacramento Symphony Orchestra.
1996 St Patrick's Cathedral, New York, appearing with the New York Chamber Ensemble.
1996 Tulane University, New Orleans, appearing with Oonagh Keogh.
1996 Mercyhurst College, Erie, Pennsylvania.
**SELECTED BROADCASTS AND/OR RECORDED WORK:**
'Heartship in Harmony' for Lunar Records, Dublin. 'The Lark in the Clear Air' for Cala Records London/New York. Ferguson and Moeran Sonatas with Charles Lynch (piano)) for EMI.
**PRIZES/AWARDS/APPOINTMENTS:**
Awarded Premier Prix, Premiére Nommée, Prix Sarasate, Prix Milanollo and Prix Christine Nillsson by the Conservatoire National Superieur de Paris. Artist-in-Residence, Buckneel College, Lewisburg, Pennsylvania.
**REGULARLY PERFORMS WITH:**
Oonagh Keogh (violin) (mother and daughter violin duo), Veronica McSwiney (piano).
**AVAILABILITY:**
General.
**ADDITIONAL INFORMATION:**
Studied with Jean Fournier in Paris. On return to Ireland was appointed leader of the National Symphony Orchestra of Ireland. Now follows a solo career. Has since toured extensively in Europe, the USA, South America and the West Indies. Has been soloist with many major orchestras, including the London Symphony Orchestra, the Kansas City Philharmonic and the Baltimore Symphony Orchestra. Was presented with an Honourary Degree of Doctor of Music, by the National University of Ireland in recognition of services to Irish music.

# Adrian Petcu *Violin*

**Contact:** Mr Adrian Petcu
7, Grosvenor Place
Wellington Road
Cork
**Tel/Fax:** +353 21 505153

**PRIZES/AWARDS/APPOINTMENTS:**
1978 Gold Medal at the International Competition, Poland. Head of Strings at the Cork School of Music.
**TRAINING AND/OR QUALIFICATIONS:**
Graduate of the Bucharest Conservatorium.
**REGULARLY PERFORMS WITH:**
Crawford Piano Trio, Jupiter Ensemble, D'Amici Flute Quartet.
**AVAILABILITY:** General.
**ADDITIONAL INFORMATION:**
Performances in native Romania have included solo and concerto appearances and also membership of various orchestras with whom he has toured Europe, Australia and New Zealand. Held teaching position at Music Lyceum, Bucharest. Musical activities in Ireland equally wide - solo violin and viola appearances with orchestras, duo recitals, chamber music performances and recordings. Also orchestral coach, conductor and adjudicator.

# Ioana Petcu-Colan *Violin*

**Contact:** Ms Ioana Petcu-Colan
7, Grosvenor Place
Wellington Road
Cork
**Tel/Fax:** +353 21 505153

*"Talented violinist in great recital."*

23.5.96 The Examiner.

**KEY IRISH PERFORMANCES** (since January 1994):
7.95 City Hall, Cork, appearing with Cork School of Music Symphony Orchestra.
11.95 John Field Room, National Concert Hall, Dublin.
2.96 University College Cork.
9.96 Bantry House, Co Cork, appearing with the West Cork Music Society.
**KEY PERFORMANCES OUTSIDE IRELAND** (since January 1994):
7.95 Valencia, Spain, promoted by the International Youth Orchestra Festival, appearing with the CSM Symphony Orchestra.
8.95 Schöntal, Germany, promoted by Klöster Schöntal, appearing with piano.
7.96 France, promoted by the Academy of Arts, Belgium.
**SELECTED REVIEWS** (since January 1994):
5.95 The Examiner (Tomás Ó Canainn).
5.96 The Examiner (John Gibson).
**PRIZES/AWARDS/APPOINTMENTS:**
1.96 String Finalist, RTÉ Young Musician of the Future.
11.96 Alfred J. Waley Prize (winner of Prokofiev concerto competition) from the Royal Academy of Music, London.
**TRAINING AND/OR QUALIFICATIONS:**
From 1993 to 1994, Medaille d'Or`a l'Unanimité, from Conservatoire de Region, Nantes (teacher Constantin Serban).
Since 1996 studying in Royal Academy of Music, London (Lydia Mordkovitch).
**REGULARLY PERFORMS WITH:**
Trio with Jan Càp, Patrick Zuk.
**AVAILABILITY:**
General.
**ADDITIONAL INFORMATION:**
Finalist in the 1997 string section of the Ulster Bank Music Foundation award. Won first prize from the Royal Academy of Music, London for the highest mark in performance. Has recently been awarded the loan of a Vuillaume violin from the collection of instruments at the RAM, London.

# Sebastien Petiet *Violin*

**Contact:** c/o Marie Petiet
23, Park Crescent House
Blackhorse Avenue
Dublin 7
**Tel:** +353 1 8681210
**Other instruments:** Guitar.

**PRIZES/AWARDS/APPOINTMENTS:**
From 1984 to 1988, Ist Prize awarded from the Conservatoire of Lyon, France.
1988 Leader with the St Etienne Chamber Orchestra.
From 1993 to 1994, Conductor with the Conservatoire of Andreizieux, France.
From 1994 to 1995, Member of the National Symphony Orchestra of Ireland.

**TRAINING AND/OR QUALIFICATIONS:**
From 1979 to 1983, Studied at the Cork School of Music.
From 1985 to 1986, Course certificate from the Hochschule Mozarteum, Salzburg.
**AVAILABILITY:** General.
*See violin page 299.*

# Alan Smale *Violin*

**Contact:** Mr Alan Smale
18, Phoenix View
James Street
Dublin 8
**Tel:** +353 1 6708289

**KEY IRISH PERFORMANCES** (since January 1994):
2.95 National Concert Hall, Dublin, promoted by RTÉ, playing the Hindemith Concerto with the National Symphony Orchestra of Ireland.
7.96 Lismore Castle, promoted by Judith Woodworth, as part of the AIB Festival of Music in Great Irish Houses, appearing with John Gibson.
9.96 Cork School of Music, promoted by the Cork Orchestral Society, appearing with John Gibson.
4.97 National Concert Hall, Dublin, promoted by RTÉ, playing the Raymond Deane Concerto with the NSOI.
**KEY PERFORMANCES OUTSIDE IRELAND** (since January 1994):
3.96 Venice, promoted by Jane O'Leary, appearing with Concorde.
5.96 Bacau, Romania, promoted by Jane O'Leary, appearing with Concorde.
4.97 Barbican, London, promoted by Jane O'Leary, appearing with Concorde.
5.97 Bucharest, Romanian, promoted by Jane O'Leary, appearing with Concorde.
**SELECTED BROADCASTS AND/OR RECORDED WORK:**
1995 James Wilson Concerto for Naxos/Marco Polo.
1996 'Celtic Connections', with Concorde for Capstone.
1997 'Krespel's Concerto' by Raymond Deane for Naxos/Marco Polo.
**PRIZES/AWARDS/APPOINTMENTS:**
From 1984 to 1993, Appointed Leader of the RTÉ Concert Orchestra.
Since 1993, Appointed Leader of the National Symphony Orchestra of Ireland.
**TRAINING AND/OR QUALIFICATIONS:**
From 1970 to 1972, Attended the Leeds College of Music.
From 1972 to 1976, LRAM from the Royal Academy of Music, London.
**REGULARLY PERFORMS WITH:**
Violin and piano duo with John Gibson or Anthony Byrne, Concorde, Prism.
**AVAILABILITY:**
By arrangement. Heavily committed to the schedule set by the NSOI.
**ADDITIONAL INFORMATION:**
A specialist in contemporary music but feels most at home in the classical and romantic repertoire. Has led orchestras and played solos professionally, for over 20 years. Guest Leader with the Ulster Orchestra.

# Nicola Sweeney *Violin*

**Contact:** Ms Nicola Sweeney
6, Lyttleton Road
Hornsey
London N8 0QB
England
**Tel:** +44 181 881 2612

*"She played with natural shape and a confidence inspiring insouciance in the face of technical challenges"* 5.4.95 Irish Times.

**KEY IRISH PERFORMANCES** (since January 1994):
8.94 National Concert Hall, Dublin, appearing with Junior Youth Orchestras.
4.95 NCH, appearing with Dublin Youth Orchestras.
6.95 St Ann's, Church, Dawson Street appearing with the Orchestra of St Cecilia.
8.95 NCH, appearing with RTÉ Concert Orchestra.
**KEY PERFORMANCES OUTSIDE IRELAND** (since January 1994):
4.95 Tour of Italy and Germany with Dublin Youth Orchestras performing Mendelssohn's Violin Concerto.
5.96 London with the Guildhall Orchestra, performing Prokofiev Violin Concerto No. 2.
5.97 Jersey with the Guildhall Chamber Orchestra playing Mozart's 'Sinfonia Concertante'.
**SELECTED BROADCASTS AND/OR RECORDED WORK:**
1991 Recital from St Michael's Church, Co Dublin, for RTÉ FM3.
8.95 'Tzigane' by Ravel and 'Berceuse' by Fauré for RTÉ.
4.97 'Late Late Show' for RTÉ.
**SELECTED REVIEWS** (since January 1994):
31.8.93 Irish Times (Pat O'Kelly).
30.8.94 Irish Times (Martin Adams).
5.4.95 Irish Times (Martin Adams).
**PRIZES/AWARDS/APPOINTMENTS:**
2.97 String Experience Scheme with the London Symphony Orchestra.
3.97 Awarded Birdie Warshaw and Maurice Warshaw prizes by the Guildhall School of Music and Drama, London
**TRAINING AND/OR QUALIFICATIONS:**
8.93 Masterclasses at the Vienna Hochschule with Ernst Kovacic.
From 1993 to 1997, B Mus Performance Degree from the GSMD.
5.96 Masterclass with Sylvia Rosenberg (USA).
5.97 Masterclass at the Eastman School of Music with Charles Castleman.
**AVAILABILITY:**
General, notice required during term time.
**ADDITIONAL INFORMATION:**
Additional prizes from the GSMD, London include: 1995 winner of Louis Pecskai Prize, 1996 winner of Alfred Gibson Memorial Prize. 1997 Finalist in Heineken Violin Competition and Ulster Bank Music Foundation Bursary. Frequently works with London Symphony Orchestra, National Symphony Orchestra of Ireland and the Irish Chamber Orchestra.

# Thérèse Timoney *Violin*

**Contact:** Dr Thérèse Timoney
7, Marley Rise
Rathfarnham
Dublin 16
**Tel:** +353 1 4936492
**Email:** johnkinsella@tinet.ie
**Other instruments:** Baroque violin.

**KEY PERFORMANCES OUTSIDE IRELAND** (since January 1994):
Performances with Hannover Band, the Academy of Ancient Music and Drottingholm Orchestra.
**AVAILABILITY:**
General.
**TRAINING AND/OR QUALIFICATIONS:**
D Mus, LRAM, Diploma in Psychology.

# Peadar Townsend *Violin*

**Contact:** Mr Peadar Townsend
Flat 2
8, Mayfield Road
Whalley Range
Manchester M16 8FT, England
**Tel/Mobile:** +44 161 2329315 / +44 421 366376
*See percussion/timpani page 31.*

## Hilary Travers *Violin*

**Contact:** Ms Hilary Travers
39, Brook Court
Monkstown
Co Dublin
**Tel:** +353 1 2809699
**Other instruments:** Piano, recorder, guitar.

**KEY IRISH PERFORMANCES** (since January 1994):
From 1992 to 1997, has performed at various venues in Dublin, promoted by University College, Dublin Music Department, appearing with Newman String Quartet.
From 1993 to 1997, National Concert Hall, Dublin, promoted by Royal Irish Academy of Music, appearing with Royal Irish Academy of Music Baroque Group.
8.95 Various venues, Dublin, appearing with Classical Grafitti.
3.96 UCD, promoted by UCD Music Society, appearing with UCD Baroque Orchestra.
**KEY PERFORMANCES OUTSIDE IRELAND** (since January 1994):
8.94 Hungary, promoted by and appearing with National Youth Orchestra.
**SELECTED BROADCASTS AND/OR RECORDED WORK:**
From 1992 to 1996, National Youth Orchestra concerts for RTÉ.
3.96 UCD Baroque Orchestra for a UCD recording.
**TRAINING AND/OR QUALIFICATIONS:**
From 1992 to 1996, BA (Music) from UCD.
Since 1996 Diploma in Performance from Royal Irish Academy of Music (teacher Deirdre Ward).
3.95 and 3.97, Masterclasses in the RIAM with Gregory Ellis and Elizabeth Charleson.
**REGULARLY PERFORMS WITH:**
Newman String Quartet, UCD Piano and Violin Duo, UCD Violin Duo.
**AVAILABILITY:**
General.
**ADDITIONAL INFORMATION:**
Will consider all performance opportunities. Flexible repertoire.

## Patricia Treacy *Violin*

**Contact:** Patricia Treacy
Shortstone
Hackballscross
Dundalk, Co Louth
**Tel:** +353 42 77110

**KEY PERFORMANCES OUTSIDE IRELAND** (since January 1994):
1996 Kensington, promoted by the Bank of Ireland.
1996 London, promoted by the BOI.
1997 Birmingham, promoted by the BOI.
**TRAINING AND/OR QUALIFICATIONS:**
1994 Course in Performance with Professor Mauricio Fucks, Montreal, Canada.
From 1994 to 1998, B Mus in Performance from the Guildhall School of Music and Drama, London.
1996 Masterclass in Ftan, Switzerland.
1997 Studied with Zukerman in Israel.
**AVAILABILITY:**
General.

## Deirdre Ward *Violin*

**Contact:** Deirdre Ward
Apartment 5
113, Strand Road
Sandymount, Dublin 4
**Tel:** +353 1 2600774
**Other instruments:** Viola, baroque violin.

**PRIZES/AWARDS/APPOINTMENTS:**
Since 1991, Professor of violin at the Royal Irish Academy of Music.
**ADDITIONAL INFORMATION:**
Has performed as soloist and chamber musician throughout Europe and America with community and youth orchestras. Was a regular guest artist at Cascale Head Festival, Oregon, USA. Also appeared with Houston's Da Camera Society, which included performances on baroque violin.

## Gillian Williams *Violin*

**Contact:** Gillian Williams
41, Kingshall
Chapelizod
Dublin 20
**Tel:** +353 1 6234906

*"... Real beauties of tone ... full command of wide ranging technical challenges"* Irish Times.

**KEY IRISH PERFORMANCES** (since January 1994):
7.96 National Concert Hall, Dublin, promoted by RTÉ, appearing with the National Symphony Orchestra of Ireland.
11.96 St Iberius Church, Wexford, promoted by Music Network and Music for Wexford.
3.97 Hugh Lane Municipal Gallery of Modern Art, Dublin.
4.97 O'Reilly Hall, University College, Dublin, appearing with Dublin Symphony Orchestra.
**KEY PERFORMANCES OUTSIDE IRELAND** (since January 1994):
7.94 Tchaikowsky Hall, Moscow.
**SELECTED BROADCASTS AND/OR RECORDED WORK:**
7.96 Tea-time Concert with the NSOI for RTÉ.
11.96 'Live at 3' for RTÉ.
**SELECTED REVIEWS** (since January 1994):
7.96 Irish Times.
7.96 Sunday Tribune.
3.97 Irish Times.
**PRIZES/AWARDS/APPOINTMENTS:**
1986 Winner of String Section of the Lombard and Ulster Music Foundation Competition.
1988 Winner of the Louis Pescki Memorial Prize at the Guildhall School of Music and Drama.
**TRAINING AND/OR QUALIFICATIONS:**
From 1986 to 1990, AGSM from the GSMD.
From 1990 to 1991 Advanced Solo Studies (teacher David Takeno, Head of Strings) at the GSMD.
**REGULARLY PERFORMS WITH:**
Rao-Williams Duo.
**AVAILABILITY:**
General.
**ADDITIONAL INFORMATION:**
Member of the Irish Chamber Orchestra.

# VIOLONCELLO

Also see orchestra members lists on page 140.

## William Butt *Cello*

**Contact:** Mr William Butt
20, Mulgrave Terrace
Dún Laoghaire
Co Dublin
**Mobile/Tel/Fax:** +353 87 2306311 / +353 1 2809771 / +353 1 2809771

**KEY IRISH PERFORMANCES** (since January 1994):
National Concert Hall, Dublin and Wexford Festival, 3 concertos with the National Symphony Orchestra of Ireland.
**SELECTED RECORDED WORK:**
6 Bach Cello Suites and Britten Cello Suites for BBC Northern Ireland. Other live radio broadcasts.
**PRIZES/AWARDS/APPOINTMENTS:**
1992 Winner of the Muriel Taylor Competition, the Martin Trust and other RSA Awards.
**TRAINING AND/OR QUALIFICATIONS:**
GRNCM and PPRNCM from the Royal Northern College of Music, Manchester (teacher Moray Welsh). Also studied at McGill University, Montreal.
**REGULARLY PERFORMS WITH:**
Prism.
**AVAILABILITY:**
General.
**ADDITIONAL INFORMATION:**
Has given many solo recitals throughout the UK. Currently presenting a series of BBC recitals featuring the solo suites of Bach and Britten. Left National Symphony Orchestra of Ireland (Sub-Principal) in 1997 to develop solo and chamber music career. Teacher in the Royal Irish Academy of Music, and the DIT Conservatory of Music and Drama, Dublin.

## Iosef Calef *Cello*

**Contact:** Iosef Calef
c/o The Cork School of Music
Union Quay
Cork
**Tel/Fax:** +353 21 270076 / +353 21 276595

**REGULARLY PERFORMS WITH:**
Crawford Piano Trio.
**ADDITIONAL INFORMATION:**
Came to Ireland from Romania in the 1980's. Graduate of the Bucharest Conservatory. Former member of the Bucharest Philharmonic and principal cellist with a number of chamber orchestras with whom he toured extensively throughout Eastern Europe, Greece, Italy and Germany. Teacher of cello and chamber music at the DIT Conservatory of Music and Drama, Dublin, Limerick School of Music and Cork School of Music.
*See conductors page 170.*

## Annette Cleary *Cello*

**Contact:** Ms Annette Cleary
2, Idrone Terrace
Blackrock, Co Dublin
**Tel/Fax:** +353 1 2841752

*"She has sweet tone and lyrical feeling ... the rapid transition of speed and mood were skillfully handled ... "* 2.97 Irish Times.

**KEY IRISH PERFORMANCES** (since January 1994):
1994 Royal Dublin Society, with the Irish Piano Trio, performing the complete cello and piano works of Beethoven.
1996 O'Reilly Hall, University College, Dublin promoted by RTÉ, appearing with the Irish Chamber Orchestra.
1996 Derry, promoted by the Two Cathedrals Festival.
1997 Hugh Lane Municipal Gallery of Modern Art, Dublin, promoted by Gavin O'Sullivan and Goethe Institute appearing with Peter Dains.
**KEY PERFORMANCES OUTSIDE IRELAND** (since January 1994):
1996 Osaka Music Festival, Japan, appearing with the Irish Piano Trio.
1997 Tour of Japan with the Irish Piano Trio.
**SELECTED BROADCASTS AND/OR RECORDED WORK:**
1991 Solo recital in Venice for RAI Television.
2.96 Tchaikovsky's 'Rococo Variations' for RTÉ.
6.96 Irish Piano Trio performance for French Radio.
**PRIZES/AWARDS/APPOINTMENTS:**
1991 Recipient of DAAD (German Academic Exchange Grant).
1992 Prize winner at the Siegfried Barchet International Cello Competition, Germany.
**TRAINING AND/OR QUALIFICATIONS:**
1987 BA from California State University.
1989 M Mus from the University of Southern California.
1993 KA from Hochschule für Musik, Stuttgart.
**REGULARLY PERFORMS WITH:**
Irish Piano Trio.
**AVAILABILITY:**
General.
**ADDITIONAL INFORMATION:**
After extensive study in the USA, is now performing regularly in European and American cities as a soloist. First Irish musician accepted to the Schleswig Holstein International Orchestra under Leonard Bernstein, which toured Europe and the Soviet Union. At present, Sub-principal Cellist with the RTÉ Concert Orchestra and teacher of cello at the Royal Irish Academy of Music. Has attended masterclasses with Antonio Janigro (Mozarteum Salzburg), Andre Navarra (Siena) and Paul Tortelier (Siena).

## Aisling Drury-Byrne *Cello*

**Contact:** Ms Aisling Drury-Byrne
18, Riversdale Avenue
Palmerstown
Dublin 20
**Tel:** +353 1 6260724

*" Her performance was utterly convincing and absorbing, a rare musical treat which showed what a fine musician she is"* 1.7.85 Irish Times.

**KEY IRISH PERFORMANCES** (since January 1994):
8.12.94 Hugh Lane Municipal Gallery of Modern Art, Dublin, appearing with Dublin Piano Trio.
14.2.97 John Field Room, National Concert Hall, Dublin, promoted by RTÉ, appearing with 'Music 97'.
4.6.97/5.6.97 Carton House, Maynooth, promoted by AIB Festival of Music in Great Irish Houses, appearing with Dublin Piano Trio and Bruno Giuranna.
8.6.97 Irish Museum of Modern Art, Dublin, appearing with Orla Boylan and the Dublin Piano Trio.
4.7.97 Killaloe, Co Clare.
**SELECTED BROADCASTS AND/OR RECORDED WORK:**
1994 'Nua Nós contemporary' - featuring works by Gerald Barry, recorded for NMC.
1996 CD featuring the works of Joan Trimble, recorded for Naxos.

**PRIZES/AWARDS/APPOINTMENTS:**
From 1958 to 1962, Winner of several Feis Ceoil competitions, Dublin.
**TRAINING AND/OR QUALIFICATIONS:**
From 1963 to 1968, Studied at the Conservatoire Nationale Supérieure, Paris.
**REGULARLY PERFORMS WITH:**
Dublin Piano Trio (piano, violin, cello).
**AVAILABILITY:**
Subject to NSOI schedule.
**ADDITIONAL INFORMATION:**
Principal Cellist with the National Symphony Orchestra of Ireland.

## Scott Heron *Cello*

**Contact:** Scott Heron
25, Indiana Avenue
Belfast BT15 5BZ
Northern Ireland
**Tel:** +44 1232 371255

**TRAINING AND/OR QUALIFICATIONS:**
Royal Academy of Music, London (teacher David Strange).
**REGULARLY PERFORMS WITH:**
Dennison String Quartet.
**AVAILABILITY:**
General.
**ADDITIONAL INFORMATION:**
Currently plays with the National Symphony Orchestra of Ireland, the RTÉ Concert Orchestra and the Ulster Orchestra on a freelance basis. Very interested in chamber music.

## Richard Jenkinson *Cello*

**Contact:** Mr Richard Jenkinson,
6, Grove Terrace
Highgate Road
London NW5 1PH
England
**Tel/Mobile/Fax:** +44 171 2678304 / +44 402 183493 / +44 1332 552860

*"Jenkinson made this work his own. Rapid string crossings, triple stopping brought this music to life with amazing vibrancy"*
6.95 Strad. (Kodaly Solo sonata)

**KEY IRISH PERFORMANCES** (since January 1994):
19.4.95 University of Limerick, Boccherini, promoted by the Irish Chamber Orchestra.
27.4.95 Kerry, promoted by the ICO.
28.4.95 Maynooth, promoted by the ICO.
16.11.95 O'Reilly Hall, University College Dublin, Mendelssohn Octet, promoted by the ICO.
**KEY PERFORMANCES OUTSIDE IRELAND** (since January 1994):
9.2.95 Caracas, Venezuela, promoted by British Council, appearing with Venezuelan Symphony Orchestra.
24.4.95 Purcell Room, South Bank, London, appearing with Robert Kulek, promoted by Kirkman Concert Society.
25.3.95 New York, USA, appearing with Rober Kulek.
14.11.95 Gateway, Shrewsbury, promoted by Live Music Now!
**SELECTED BROADCASTS AND/OR RECORDED WORK:**
5.95 'Tricky' album, for Island records.
8.95 Martinů Cello Works.
**SELECTED REVIEWS** (since January 1994):
4.95 Irish Times.
6.95 Music Weekly.

**PRIZES/AWARDS/APPOINTMENTS:**
7.94 Gold medal, awarded by The Guildhall School of Music and Drama, London.
10.94 Ist Prize, awarded by Vittorio Gui International Competition, Florence, Italy.
12.94 Appointed Principal Cello with the Irish Chamber Orchestra.
4.95 Cello Professor at the GSMD.
**TRAINING AND/OR QUALIFICATIONS:**
From 9.90 to 7.94, AGSM at the GSMD.
**REGULARLY PERFORMS WITH:**
Irish Chamber Orchestra, Hibernia String Trio, Tempo Nuovo Jenkinson, Kulek Duo.
**AVAILABILITY:**
General.

## Gerard Kelly *Cello*

**Contact:** Mr Gerard Kelly
11, Summerhill South
Cork
**Tel:** +353 21 316088
**Email:** grantkelly@tinet.ie

**KEY IRISH PERFORMANCES** (since January 1994):
10.96 Triskel Arts Centre, Cork.
1.97 Crawford Art Gallery, Cork, appearing with the Jupiter Ensemble.
4.97 Triskel Arts Centre, Cork, appearing with Evelyn Grant.
**KEY PERFORMANCES OUTSIDE IRELAND** (since January 1994):
10.96 St Martin-in-the-Fields, London, promoted by Justin Pearson, appearing with Locrian Chamber Orchestra.
2-3.97 London, promoted by Justin Pearson, appearing with Locrian Chamber Orchestra.
**SELECTED BROADCASTS AND/OR RECORDED WORK:**
Various.
**PRIZES/AWARDS/APPOINTMENTS:**
Senior Lecturer at the Cork School of Music.
**TRAINING AND/OR QUALIFICATIONS:**
From 1972 to 1978, KA Essen University, Germany (teachers Tortelier and Dorner).
**REGULARLY PERFORMS WITH:**
Jupiter Ensemble, d'Amici Quartet, Cork Pops Orchestra.
**AVAILABILITY:**
General.
**ADDITIONAL INFORMATION:**
Has toured nationwide as a soloist, chamber musician and orchestral player. Has also performed in Germany, France, USA and Canada.

## Jean Kelly *Cello*

**Contact:** Ms Jean Kelly
11, Summerhill South
Cork
**Tel:** +353 21 316088
**Email:** grantkelly@tinet.ie
*See concert harp page 7.*

## Vyvienne Long *Cello*

**Contact:** Ms Vyvienne Long
'Haddington'
32, Lower Mountown Road
Dún Laoghaire, Co Dublin
**Tel:** +353 1 2800505
**Other instruments:** Piano.

**KEY IRISH PERFORMANCES** (since January 1994):
3.96 Trinity College Dublin, promoted by Trinity Music Society, appearing with Deborah Kelleher.
6.96 National Concert Hall, Dublin, promoted by DIT Conservatory of Music and Drama Music Society, appearing with Deborah Kelleher.
5.97 NCH, Dublin, appearing with the National Symphony Orchestra of Ireland.
**PRIZES/AWARDS/APPOINTMENTS:**
3.96 Clive Twelvetrees Cup (special award) at Feis Ceoil, Dublin.
**TRAINING AND/OR QUALIFICATIONS:**
From 9.92 to 5.96, B Mus Performance from DIT CMD.
12.96 Awarded LTCL.
**REGULARLY PERFORMS WITH:**
Deborah Kelleher (piano), Festive Ensemble.
**AVAILABILITY:**
General.
**ADDITIONAL INFORMATION:**
Young freelance cellist willing to work on all creative projects including solo/chamber recitals and recordings.

# Christopher Marwood *Cello*

**Contact:** Mr Christopher Marwood
c/o October House
Ballyorban
Monkstown
Co Cork
**Tel/Fax:** +353 21 893027

**REGULARLY PERFORMS WITH:**
RTÉ Vanbrugh Quartet.

# Niall O'Loughlin *Cello*

**Contact:** Mr Niall O'Loughlin
9, Earlscourt
Old Cabra Road
Dublin 7

**KEY IRISH PERFORMANCES** (since January 1994):
12.94 National Concert Hall, Dublin, appearing with Padraig Ó Cuinneagáin.
4.95 NCH appearing with Réamonn Keary.
**KEY PERFORMANCES OUTSIDE IRELAND** (since January 1994):
7.94 Lyon, France, promoted by International String Workshops.
7.95 Dartington, England.
**SELECTED BROADCASTS AND/OR RECORDED WORK:**
23.1.90 'Music Room', for RTÉ.
4.94 Graduate recital, University of Texas.
**SELECTED REVIEWS** (since January 1994):
2.94 Irish Times.
5.95 Irish Times.
**PRIZES/AWARDS/APPOINTMENTS:**
1983 Certificate di Merito from the Accademia Chigiana, Siena.
1993 Scholarship for further study with Phyllis Young and to work in University of Texas as part of a string teaching project, awarded by University of Texas.
**TRAINING AND/OR QUALIFICATIONS:**
From 1963 to 1974, Scholarships and prizes, from Royal Irish Academy, Dublin.
From 1974 to 1978, RSAMD and ARCM Performance Diploma from the Royal Scottish Academy of Music.
From 1978 to 1979, Awarded a quartet scholarship, Western Michigan University.
**REGULARLY PERFORMS WITH:**
NSOI Haenjo Trio.
**AVAILABILITY:**
General.
**ADDITIONAL INFORMATION:**
Member of the National Symphony Orchestra of Ireland. Studied in Britain with Joan Dickson and at University of Texas with Phyllis Young. Appears frequently as a soloist and has broadcast on radio and television.

# Gerald Peregrine *Cello*

**Contact:** Gerald Peregrine
106, Stillorgan Wood
Stillorgan
Co Dublin
**Tel:** +353 1 2884207

*"Handled with firmness of musical resolve and solidly projected tone ... his performance at the moment certainly has the virtues of clarity and confidence"*
7.95 Irish Times (Michael Dervan) Elgar's Cello Concerto.

**KEY IRISH PERFORMANCES** (since January 1994):
6.95 Soloist with Junior Youth Orchestra, National Concert Hall, Dublin.
1.96 Soloist with National Symphony Orchestra of Ireland, NCH, Dublin, promoted by RTÉ.
5.96 Soloist with National Youth Orchestra, at the Bank of Ireland RTÉ proms.
1.97 Galway Music Festival appearing with Dearbhla Brosnan.
**SELECTED BROADCASTS AND/OR RECORDED WORK:**
9.93 Brahms and Bach for RTÉ, FM3.
6.96 Haydn's 'Concerto in C major' for RTÉ.
7.97 Beethoven String Trio for RTÉ.
**SELECTED REVIEWS** (since January 1994):
1.96 Irish Times.
7.97 Irish Times.
**PRIZES/AWARDS/APPOINTMENTS:**
5.93 Winner of the All Ireland Instrumental Bursary awarded by Irish National Teachers' Organisation.
1996 Winner in the String Final, and the selected Irish Representative in the RTÉ Young (European) Musician of the Future.
**TRAINING AND/OR QUALIFICATIONS:**
From 1993 to 1997, Studies with William Pleeth, OBE.
Since 1996 Scholar, at the Royal College of Music, London.
From 6.97 to 7.97, Attended masterclasses at the West Cork Chamber Music Festival, Bantry with Steve Doane.
From 7.97 to 8.97, Attended the Bourdoin Summer School, USA.
**AVAILABILITY:**
General.

# Arun Rao *Cello*

**Contact:** Mr Arun Rao
41, Kingshall
Chapelizod
Dublin 20
**Tel:** +353 1 6234906

*"Rao's ... un-histrionic and purely musical style was wholesome and rewarding"* 2.6.97 Irish Times.

**KEY IRISH PERFORMANCES** (since January 1994):
10.12.94 Peppercannister Church, Dublin, appearing with the Dublin Symphony Orchestra.
3.3.96 Wexford and Dublin, promoted by Music for Wexford, appearing with Gillian Williams.
4.96 St Patrick's Cathedral, Dublin, promoted by St Patrick's Cathedral and Alliance Française.
17.6.97 National Concert Hall, Dublin, promoted by RTÉ, appearing with the National Symphony Orchestra of Ireland.

**SELECTED BROADCASTS AND/OR RECORDED WORK:**
2.4.96 'Live at 3' for RTÉ.
5.96 'Solstice' CD for Penguin Editions, UK.
18.6.97 Lunchtime Concert from the NCH for RTÉ.
**PRIZES/AWARDS/APPOINTMENTS:**
7.86 Winner of the Fauré Medal at the Conservatoire Superieur de Bordeaux, France.
**TRAINING AND/OR QUALIFICATIONS:**
From 1984 to 1986, Awarded Silver Medal while studying under Robert Bec at the Conservatoire de Musique d'Agen.
From 1987 to 1991, AGSM from the Guildhall School of Music and Drama, London (teachers Raphael Wallfisch and Leonard Stehn).
**REGULARLY PERFORMS WITH:**
Rao-Williams Duo (with Gillian Williams on violin).
**AVAILABILITY:**
General.
**ADDITIONAL INFORMATION:**
Since moving to Dublin, has led a freelance career with the national orchestras and as a soloist. Teacher at the DIT Conservatory of Music and Drama and the Newpark Music Centre. Established the new cello department at the Leeson Park School of Music, Dublin in 1996.

# Miriam Roycroft *Cello*

**Contact:** Ms Miriam Roycroft
23, Ingledew Crescent
Roundhay
Leeds LS8 1BP
England
**Tel/Fax:** +44 113 2663966

*"Miriam Roycroft was well in command of the solo cello part of Tchaikovsky's 'Rococo Variations' "* 6.89 Irish Times.

**KEY IRISH PERFORMANCES** (since January 1994):
1989 National Concert Hall, Dublin, performing the 'Rococo Variations' conducted by Albert Rosen.
1993 NCH Dublin, performing Haydn's 'D Major Concerto', appearing with the National Symphony Orchestra of Ireland.
**KEY PERFORMANCES OUTSIDE IRELAND** (since January 1994):
7.96 Stockeld PK Harrogate, cello recital appearing with Darius Battiwalla.
11.96 York Arts Centre, promoted by York 20th Century Music Festival appearing with Pierrot Lunaire Beltane.
2.97 Knaresborough, Leeds, appearing with Leeds Symphony Orchestra performing the 'Lalo Concerto'.
**SELECTED BROADCASTS AND/OR RECORDED WORK:**
1986 Rococo duo for RTÉ.
**SELECTED REVIEWS** (since January 1994):
5.93 Yorkshire Post.
5.93 Musical Times.
**PRIZES/AWARDS/APPOINTMENTS:**
1st Prize in the Muriel Taylor cello competition in London.
1987 1st Prize at Worthing Music Competition, UK.
**TRAINING AND/OR QUALIFICATIONS:**
From 1973 to 1980, Royal Irish Academy of Music, Dublin, (teacher Aisling Drury-Byrne).
From 1981 to 1985, Royal Northern College of Music, Manchester, G Mus (Hons).
1992 Attended Summer School, Banff Centre for the Arts, Canada.
**AVAILABILITY:**
General.
**ADDITIONAL INFORMATION:**
Active career as a soloist, chamber musician and teacher. Performs frequently in Ireland, Switzerland, France, Canada and throughout Britain.

# Brendan Townsend *Cello*

**Contact:** Mr Brendan Townsend
Tollisstraat 12
6443 EH Brunssum
Netherlands
**Tel/Fax:** +31 45 525 1901
**Email:** townsend@cobweb.nl

**KEY PERFORMANCES OUTSIDE IRELAND** (since January 1994):
28.6.94 Maastricht, Netherlands, appearing with Igo Lange (piano).
16.11.95 Venlo, Netherlands, appearing with Igo Lange.
23.5.97 Eindhoven, Netherlands, promoted by Brenger Music, appearing with Ars Antiqua et Nova.
*See conductors page 175.*

# Mark Wilkes *Cello*

**Contact:** Mr Mark Wilkes
17, Windsor Road
Rathmines
Dublin 6
**Tel:** +353 1 4964575
*See viola da gamba page 120.*

# Steven Wise *Cello*

**Contact:** Mr Steven Wise
95, Woodland Park
Lambeg
Lisburn
Co Antrim
Northern Ireland BT27 4P6
**Tel:** +44 1846 676722

**REGULARLY PERFORMS WITH:**
Ireland String Quartet.

# Section two

## Small Ensembles

This section covers small ensembles (i.e. under nine members). For larger groups (i.e. choirs, orchestras, brass bands etc., please see the Large Performing Groups section (pages 139). Ensembles are also featured in the Contemporary Music section (page 135) and in the Period Musicians and Ensembles section (page 127).

The traditional, jazz and other music sections of the book also have group categories (pages 255, 288 and 301 respectively).

# SMALL ENSEMBLES

## Bebb-Mason Duo

**Contact:** Ms Ruth Bebb
13, Old Seahill Road
Craigavad
Co Down, BT18 0EG
Northern Ireland
**Tel:** +44 1232 424675

*"The viola ... that dark, sugary tone was the highlight of the evening."* Coleraine Chronicle

**FORMED:** 1983.
**MEMBERS IN GROUP:**
Ruth Bebb (violin, viola), Ashley Mason (viola).
**KEY IRISH PERFORMANCES** (since January 1994):
5.94 Heritage Centre, Bangor, appearing with the Orion Quartet.
2.95 Gallagher Community Recital Series, promoted by Castlereagh Arts.
4.95 Lough Moss Centre, Belfast, promoted by Castlereagh Arts
**AVAILABILITY:**
Subject to Ulster Orchestra schedule.
**ADDITIONAL INFORMATION:**
Repertoire includes all of violin/viola and 2 viola duets and ranges from Telemann to Mozart to 20th Century music including Scott Joplin and Bernstein. Music introduced by the players. Welcome new compositions.

## Belfast Wind Quintet

**Contact:** Colin Stark
41 Somerton Park
Belfast BT15 4DP
Northern Ireland
**Tel:** +44 1232 772325

**FORMED:** 1985.
**MEMBERS IN GROUP:**
Elizabeth Bennett (flute), Stephen Pickett (bassoon), Paul Schumann (clarinet), Colin Stark (oboe), Martin Wall (french horn).
**ADDITIONAL INFORMATION:**
Have performed at the Belfast Festival at Queen's and the Belfast Sonorities Festival of 20th Century music. All members are musicians with the Ulster Orchestra. Offer an extensive variety of programmes.
*See Elizabeth Bennett page 11 and Colin Stark page 25.*

## Bernardel Ensemble

**Contact:** Mr David MacKenzie
75, Oaklawn West
Leixslip
Co Kildare
**Tel:** +353 1 6245157
**Email:** dmack@indigo.ie

**FORMED:** 1995
**GROUP MEMBERS:**
Margaret Gleeson MacKenzie (piano), David MacKenzie (violin).
**KEY IRISH PERFORMANCES** (since January 1994):
4.96 St Matthias Church, Dublin.
6.96 Kylemore Abbey, Co Galway.
5.97 Dunshane House, Co Kildare.
**AVAILABILITY:**
General (travelling distance negotiable).
**ADDITIONAL INFORMATION:**
Variety of programmes available.

## Big Bad Bass

**Contact:** Mr Ricky Matson
27, Orange Lane
Magheralin
Craigavon
Co Armagh, BT67 0RG
Northern Ireland

*"Children were fascinated with the programme. A new and beneficial experience for them all at such a young age."*
5.95 Young Arts - Arts Council of Northern Ireland.

**FORMED:** 1987.
**GROUP MEMBERS:**
Gareth Hopkins (double bass), Ricky Matson (double bass), Michele Strong (double bass).
**KEY IRISH PERFORMANCES** (since January 1994):
3.94 Flowerfield Arts Centre, Portstewart.
6.95 Shankill Leisure Centre, Belfast, promoted by the Shankill Festival.
2.96 Newtownabbey Festival.
16.11.96 Library, Belfast, promoted by Belfast Festival at Queen's.
**SELECTED BROADCASTS AND/OR RECORDED WORK:**
6.5.94 'Kelly' for UTV.
**AVAILABILITY:**
General.
**ADDITIONAL INFORMATION:**
All members are players with the Ulster Orchestra. Varied repertoire.
*See Michele Strong page 10.*

## Cadenza

**Contact:** c/o Ms Barbara Devlin
3, Abbotsford Crescent
Strathaven
Scotland, ML10 6EQ
**Tel:** +44 1357 21234

**GROUP MEMBERS:**
Barbara Connolly (guitar), Andrea Kuypers (flute).
*See pages 19 and 16 respectively.*

## Carulli Trio

**Tel:** +353 1 4944119

**ADDITIONAL INFORMATION:**
A flute, violin and classical guitar ensemble. Repertoire ranges from light classical, popular, Irish classical guitar and baroque, to renaissance recorder music. Also perform as soloists and duos. Will consider all proposals.

# Castleward Wind Quintet

**Contact:** Mr Colin Irvine
38, Plantation Avenue,
Carrickfergus
Co Antrim BT38 9BJ
Northern Ireland
**Tel/Fax:** +44 1960 361695

**FORMED:** 1995.
**GROUP MEMBERS:**
Amanda Irvine (clarinet), Colin Irvine (flute), Colin Loughead (bassoon), Paul McCrisken (oboe), Dominic McHugh (horn).
**AVAILABILITY:**
Weekends, evenings.
*See Colin Irvine page 15.*

# Cecilian Duo

**Contact:** Ms Moya O'Grady
Inishowen
Kilmolin, Enniskerry
Co Wicklow
**Tel:** +353 1 2860044

**FORMED:** 1982.
**GROUP MEMBERS:**
Denise Kelly (harp), Moya O'Grady (cello).
**KEY IRISH PERFORMANCES** (since 1994):
1995 Ulster Television, Belfast, promoted by UTV.
From 1995 to 1997, Music Association of Ireland concert tours.
1996 National Concert Hall, Dublin promoted by Absolute Music.
1997 NCH Dublin, promoted by Absolute Music.
**SELECTED BROADCASTS AND/OR RECORDED WORK:**
1995 'Dreams' for Lunar Records.
'Oft in the Stilly Night' for Absolute Music.
**AVAILABILITY:**
General.
**ADDITIONAL INFORMATION:**
Have developed a versatile repertoire for their combined instruments, including music composed and arranged by Denise Kelly.
*See Denise Kelly page 7.*

# Classical Fusion

**Contact:** Bernard and Denise Traynor
26-27, Drury Street
Dublin 2
**Tel/Mobile:** +353 1 4518527 / +353 87 2345736

*" The finest performance of those songs I've ever heard"* 1997 Radio Ireland (Eamon Dunphy).

**FORMED:** 1994.
**GROUP MEMBERS:**
Denise Long Traynor (voice and piano), Bernard Traynor (guitar, electric guitar).
**KEY IRISH PERFORMANCES** (since January 1994):
2.96 Oak Room, Mansion House, Dublin promoted by the Instituto Cervantes during Dublin Guitar Week.
2.96 Bank of Ireland Arts Centre, Dublin promoted by the Instituto Cervantes during DGW.
**SELECTED BROADCASTS AND/OR RECORDED WORK:**
1997 Own cassette available.
**AVAILABILITY:**
General.
*See Bernard Traynor page 23 and Denise Long page 91.*

# Marie Comiskey and Leslie Cassidy

**Contact:** Ms Marie Comiskey
26, Sandyford Downs
Sandyford, Dublin 18
**Tel:** +353 1 2958742
**Email:** breilly@tinet.ie

**FORMED:** 1997.
**GROUP MEMBERS:**
Marie Comiskey (flute )Leslie Cassidy (guitar).
**AVAILABILITY:**
General.
*See Marie Comiskey page 11, Leslie Cassidy page 19.*

# Marie Comiskey and Thérèse Fahy

**Contact:** Ms Marie Comiskey
26, Sandyford Downs
Sandyford, Dublin 18
**Tel:** +353 1 2958742
**Email:** breilly@tinet.ie

**FORMED:** 1995.
**GROUP MEMBERS:**
Marie Comiskey (flute), Thérèse Fahy (piano).
**KEY IRISH PERFORMANCES** (since January 1994):
5.95 John Field Room, National Concert Hall, Dublin.
2.96 Royal Dublin Society, RDS, Ballsbridge, Dublin.
**AVAILABILITY:**
General.
*See Marie Comiskey page 11 and Thérèse Fahy page 37.*

# Crawford Piano Trio

**Contact:** Adrian Petcu
7, Grosvenor Place
Wellington Road
Cork
**Tel/Fax:** +353 21 505153

*"The Crawford Trio are quite outstandingly good; more recordings from them would be welcome"* 12.95 Gramophone.

**FORMED:** 1989.
**GROUP MEMBERS:**
Iosef Calef (cello), Jan Càp (piano), Adrian Petcu (violin).
**KEY IRISH PERFORMANCES** (since January 1994):
3.94 Waterford, Cork, Tralee, Carlingford and Clifden, promoted by Music Network.
6.94 Carton House, promoted by the AIB Festival of Music in Great Irish Houses.
8.94 St John's, Kilkenny, promoted by Kilkenny Arts week.
11.94 Cork, appearing at the Crawford Art Gallery, Cork.
**SELECTED BROADCASTS AND/OR RECORDED WORK:**
5.93 For RTÉ.
9.95 Philip Martin CD, for Altarus.
3.95 For RTÉ.
**SELECTED REVIEWS:**
20.6.92 The Examiner.

14.6.93 The Examiner.
12.3.94 Irish Times.
**AVAILABILITY:**
General, preferably weekends.
**ADDITIONAL INFORMATION:**
Formed by three East European musicians. In 1997 as part of Brahms/Schubert Celebration Year, organised and performed in a series of six concerts featuring all piano trios and piano quartets by Brahms and also completed their first three week tour of Japan. Trio in Residence of the Crawford Art Gallery, Cork. Are involved in a range of musical activities: solo appearances with orchestras, recitals, recordings, adjudicating and tutoring.
*See Adrian Petcu page 65, Iosef Calef page 68, Jan Càp page 33.*

# D'Amici Flute Quartet

**Contact:** Gerard Kelly
11, Summerhill South
Cork
**Tel:** +353 21 316088
**Email:** grantkelly@tinet.ie

**FORMED:** 1992.
**GROUP MEMBERS:**
Evelyn Grant (flute), Gerard Kelly (cello), Adrian Petcu (viola), Ruxandra Petcu-Colan (violin).
**KEY IRISH PERFORMANCES** (since January 1994):
Various performances at Triskel Arts Centre, Cork, Bantry House, Co. Cork, Village Arts Centre, Kilworth and University College, Galway.
**AVAILABILITY:**
General.
**ADDITIONAL INFORMATION:**
All Cork based friends (as the name suggests).
*See Evelyn Grant page 14, Gerard Kelly page 69, Ruxandra Petcu-Colan page 58, Adrian Petcu page 65.*

# Degani Ensemble

**Contact:** Ms Ruby Ashley
49, Weirview Drive
Stillorgan
Co Dublin
**Tel:** +353 1 2882467

*"Moeran's Fantasy Quartet and Bax's Oboe Quintet were vividly coloured and had some fire in the belly"* 11.94 Irish Times.

**FORMED:** 1983
**GROUP MEMBERS:**
Ruby Ashley (oboe d'amore, oboe, cor anglais), Lesley Bishop (horn), Deirdre Brady (flute), John Finucane (clarinet), David James (cello), John Leonard (bassoon), Neil Martin (viola), Alan Smale (violin).
**KEY IRISH PERFORMANCES** (since January 1994):
1.94 National Concert Hall, Dublin, RTÉ Young Musician of the Future Competition.
6.94 Aravon School, Bray, promoted by SAFE.
11.94 NCH, Dublin.
6.95 National University of Ireland, Maynooth.
**SELECTED BROADCASTS AND/OR RECORDED WORK:**
1992 Oboe quartets by Stamitz and Mozart, for RTÉ.
1992 Oboe quartets by Gatti and Stamitz, for RTÉ.
1993 Oboe quintets by Bliss and Bax, for RTÉ.
**AVAILABILITY:**
Subject to schedules.
**ADDITIONAL INFORMATION:**
Also expands to to use another violin, double bass and piano. Interested in performing large chamber works including music by Spohr etc. Involved in the composition section of RTÉ's Young Musician of the Future competition. Commissioned works include Gerald Barry's Oboe Quartet and Bernard Geary's Oboe Quartet. Also gives lecture recitals on contemporary works.
*See Ruby Ashley page 24, Deirdre brady page 11, John Finucane page 3, Alan Smale page 66.*

# Dennison String Quartet

**Contact:** Mrs Lesley Heron
25, Indiana Avenue
Belfast BT15 5BZ
Northern Ireland
**Tel:** +44 1232 371255

**FORMED:** 1985.
**GROUP MEMBERS:**
Lesley Heron (violin), Scott Heron (cello), Nicola Johnston (violin), David McCreadie (viola).
**KEY PERFORMANCES OUTSIDE IRELAND** (since January 1994):
29.1.95 Middlesex Hospital, London, promoted by Live Music Now!
30.1.95 Broadmoor Prison, England, promoted by Live Music Now!
**AVAILABILITY:**
General.
**ADDITIONAL INFORMATION:**
Specialises in easy listening music, ranging from traditional to jazz but includes many well known classical pieces, songs from the shows, etc. Part of the 'Live Music Now!' scheme.
*See Lesley Heron page 61, Scott Heron page 69 and David McCreadie page 56.*

# William Dowdall and John Feeley

**Contact:** Mr William Dowdall
13, Effra Road
Rathmines, Dublin 6
**Tel/Fax:** +353 1 4973381 / +353 1 8725292
or
John Feeley
14, Wesley Road
Rathgar, Dublin 6
**Tel/Fax:** +353 1 4905495

**GROUP MEMBERS:**
William Dowdall (flute), John Feeley (guitar).
*See William Dowdall page 13, John Feeley page 20.*

# Dublin Piano Trio

**Contact:** Ms Aisling Drury-Byrne
18, Riversdale Avenue
Palmerstown, Dublin 20
**Tel:** +353 1 6260724

*"Made clear once again its temperamental affinity for this music in performances full of warmth and excitement"* 8.12.94 Irish Times.

**KEY IRISH PERFORMANCES** (since January 1994):
8.12.94 Hugh Lane Municipal Gallery of Modern Art, Dublin.
4.6.97/5.6.97 Carton House, Maynooth, promoted by the AIB Festival of Music in Great Irish Houses, appearing with Bruno Giuranna.
8.6.97 Irish Museum of Modern Art, Dublin, appearing with Orla Boylan.
*See Aisling Drury-Byrne page 68.*

# Kenneth Edge and Benjamin Dwyer

**Contact:** Benjamin Dwyer
90, The Steeples
Chapelizod
Dublin 20
**Tel/Fax/Mobile:** +353 1 6234397 / +353 87 616391
**Email:** bdwyer@indigo.ie

**GROUP MEMBERS:**
Benjamin Dwyer (guitar), Kenneth Edge (saxophone)
*See Benjamin Dwyer page 20, Kenneth Edge page 52.*

# Fidelio Trio

**Contact:** Mary Dullea
Upper Flat
52, Finland Road
Brockley
London SE4 2JH, England
**Tel/Mobile:** +44 171 3589361 / +44 956 916510

*"In the 'Archduke Trio' in B flat, they deployed impressive discernment"*

11.95 Hampstead and Highgate Express.

**FORMED:** 1994.
**GROUP MEMBERS:**
Michael Atkinson (cello), Mary Dullea (piano), Darragh Morgan (violin).
**KEY IRISH PERFORMANCES** (since January 1994):
9.8.97 Primates Chapel, Palace Domain, Armagh, promoted by Kate Bond.
10.8.97 Ballywillan Presbyterian Church.
**KEY PERFORMANCES OUTSIDE IRELAND** (since January 1994):
11.96 Purcell Room, London, promoted by Tunbridge Wells International Young Concert Artists Competition Prizewinner's Concert.
5.97 Shatin Town Hall, Hong Kong promoted by Hong Kong Urban Council.
7.97 Petworth, England, promoted by Petworth Festival.
8.97 Stockton, England, promoted by Stockton International Riverside Festival.
**SELECTED BROADCASTS AND/OR RECORDED WORK:**
5.97 Lunchtime recital for Hong Kong Radio Four.
**PRIZES/AWARDS/APPOINTMENTS:**
8.95 Dartington International Summer School, bursary to study with Israel Piano Trio.
7.95 TWIYCAC Ensemble Class Winner (Tunbridge Wells).
**TRAINING AND/OR QUALIFICATIONS:**
8.96 Dartington International Summer School, workshop with the Israel Piano Trio and Simon Pearsley.
8.97 Music at Cubertou, masterclasses with Paul Roberts and David Dolan. Various masterclasses and workshops with Simon Rowland-Jones, Andrea Hess, Deref Hahn, David Alberman, and members of the Martinu Quartet.
**AVAILABILITY:**
General, but half term weeks and school holidays are preferable.
**ADDITIONAL INFORMATION:**
Debut in 1996 at the Purcell Room in the South Bank Centre performing Korngold's 'Trio Op. 1' and the UK premiere of Toru Takemitsu's 'Between Tides'. Has also commissioned new works from Deirdre Gribbin (funded by SE Arts) and Richard Causton.
*See Mary Dullea page 37, Darragh Morgan page 64.*

# Five Bells Wind Quintet

**Contact:** Mary Curran
Derryribbeen
Clogher
Westport
Co Mayo
**Tel:** +353 98 41983
*See French Horn page 23.*

# Five in the Bar

**Contact:** Mr Paul Lyttle
21, Kipkarren Park
Newtownards, Co Down BT23 7AQ
Northern Ireland
**Tel/Fax:** +44 1247 810820 / +44 1247 810820
**Email:** Lyttle @unite.co.uk

**FORMED:** 1992.
**GROUP MEMBERS:**
Rachel Adams (alto), Katy Griffiths (soprano), Paul Lyttle (bass), Richard McCullough, (tenor), Sharon West (soprano).
**KEY IRISH PERFORMANCES** (since January 1994):
21.9.94 Whiteabbey Presbyterian Church, promoted by the Whiteabbey Music Club.
21.5.96 Town Hall, Newtownards, Co Down promoted by Ards Arts Centre.
22.9.96 Christchurch Cathedral, Dublin.
29.11.97 Hillsborough Castle promoted by ABSA, Northern Ireland.
**SELECTED BROADCASTS AND/OR RECORDED WORK:**
11.95 Demonstration Tape available.
**PRIZES/AWARDS/APPOINTMENTS:**
10.95 1st prize winner at the Sligo International Choral Festival (Motet section).
**TRAINING AND/OR QUALIFICATIONS:**
10.9.95 Workshop with Jeremy Jackson.
**ADDITIONAL INFORMATION:**
Provide music for evening functions etc. Have an interest in sacred music from the renaissance era and are anxious to incorporate liturgical or concert performances of such works within their projects.

# Goudarzi-Tobin/ Keary Piano Duet

**Contact:** Ms Shirin Goudarzi -Tobin
27a, Baldoyle Road
Sutton
Dublin 13
**Tel:** +353 1 8390347

**FORMED:** 1992.
**GROUP MEMBERS:**
Shirin Goudarzi-Tobin (piano), Réamonn Keary (piano).
**KEY IRISH PERFORMANCES** (since January 1994):
2.94 Aula Maxima, Cork promoted by the Cork Orchestral Society.
4.96 Sutton Music Festival, Dublin, promoted by Sutton Park School.
4.97 and 5.97 Hugh Lane Municipal Gallery of Modern Art, Dublin, promoted by Dublin Corporation.
**AVAILABILITY:**
General.
**ADDITIONAL INFORMATION:**
Have both made several recordings for RTÉ and have appeared as soloists with the national orchestras. Their 1993 concert for two pianos in the Project Arts Centre, Dublin was praised by the Irish Times as one of the musical highlights of that year.
*See Réamonn Keary page 40.*

# Aedín Halpin and Luke Tobin

**Contact:** Aedín Halpin/Luke Tobin
27a, Baldoyle Road
Sutton
Dublin 13
**Tel:** +353 1 8390347

*"Partnership of rhythmic alertness and precise ensemble"* 25.8.94 Irish Times.

**FORMED:** 1992.
**GROUP MEMBERS:**
Aedín Halpin (recorders), Luke Tobin (guitar).
**KEY IRISH PERFORMANCES** (since January 1994):
1.4.95 University of Limerick.
8.2.96 Queen's University, Belfast.
6.10.96 Hugh Lane Municipal Gallery of Modern Art, Dublin.
1.11.96 John Field Room, National Concert Hall, Dublin.
**SELECTED REVIEWS** (since January 1994):
15.3.95 Irish Times.
9.10.96 Irish Times.
**AVAILABILITY:**
General.
**ADDITIONAL INFORMATION:**
Repertoire includes baroque to modern, plus arrangements of Irish traditional music for recorder and guitar.
*See Aedín Halpin page 122.*

# Hibernia String Trio

**Contact:** Ms Bróna Cahill
Clonheen House
Churchtown
Ardee
Co Louth
**Tel/Fax:** +353 41 55127 / +353 41 55294

**FORMED:** 1995.
**GROUP MEMBERS:**
Bróna Cahill (violin), Richard Jenkinson (cello) and Joachim Roewer (viola).
**KEY IRISH PERFORMANCES** (since January 1994):
2.97 Royal Dublin Society, Dublin promoted by the RDS appearing with Benjamin Frith.
5.97 Hugh Lane Municipal Gallery of Modern Art, Dublin promoted by Gavin O' Sullivan.
6.97 National Gallery of Ireland, Dublin promoted by the AIB Festival of Music in Great Irish Houses appearing with Hugh Tinney.
Killaloe, Co Clare promoted by the Irish Chamber Orchestra.
**KEY PERFORMANCES OUTSIDE IRELAND** (since January 1994):
7.96 Les Arc (France) promoted by Festival des Arc appearing with Francois Lulu.
**SELECTED BROADCASTS AND/OR RECORDED WORK:**
1.97 Recorded own CD music for clarinet and string trio.
**TRAINING AND/OR QUALIFICATIONS:**
2.96 Masterclass with David Talieno.
**AVAILABILITY:**
General.
**ADDITIONAL INFORMATION:**
Aim to explore and develop the string trio repertoire, placing great emphasis on producing a sound particular and true to their own expression. Have played in festivals throughout Ireland and on the continent. All members are performers with the Irish Chamber Orchestra.
*See Bróna Cahill page 57, Richard Jenkinson page 69.*

# Ireland String Quartet

**Contact:** Mr Nigel Ireland
100, Bramblewood
Ballytromery Road
Crumlin
Co Antrim, BT29 4FQ
Northern Ireland
**Tel:** +44 1849 423629

*"Easy listening repertoire - music to suit all tastes"* 2.6.95 Lisburn Star.

**FORMED:** 1995.
**GROUP MEMBERS:**
John Fitzpatrick (violin), Nigel Ireland (violin), Ralph Tartaglia (viola), Steven Wise (cello).
**KEY IRISH PERFORMANCES** (since January 1994):
6.95 Lord Mayor's inaugural banquet, Belfast City Hall, promoted by Dawn McKnight.
30.8.95 GLIAL International conference, Queen's University Belfast, promoted by Dawn McKnight.
7.10.95 Bank of Ireland Charity Ball, Europa Hotel, Belfast, promoted by Dawn McKnight.
**SELECTED BROADCASTS AND/OR RECORDED WORK:**
Regular appearances on 'Kelly' for UTV.
**SELECTED REVIEWS:**
17.5.95 Banbridge Times.
**AVAILABILITY:**
General.
**ADDITIONAL INFORMATION:**
Members originate from the USA, Scotland and Northern Ireland. Have previously recorded and toured with the Ulster Orchestra, the National Symphony Orchestra of Ireland, Rod Stewart, Elaine Page and Phil Coulter. Diverse repertoire spans well known classics and more modern/popular tunes and ballads.
*See Steven Wise page 71.*

# Irish Piano Trio

**Contact:** Michael d'Arcy
16, Viking Harbour
Usher's Island, Dublin 2
**Tel/Fax:** +353 1 6776051

*"... Their first outing was a remarkable success, showing a sophisticated blend of instruments and a clear ability to adopt a harmonious style"* 3.95 Sunday Tribune.

**FORMED:** 1994.
**MEMBERS IN GROUP:**
Michael d'Arcy (violin), Annette Cleary (cello), Dearbhla Collins (piano).
**KEY IRISH PERFORMANCES** (since January 1994):
3.95 Royal Dublin Society.
2.96 Town Hall, Waterford, promoted by Waterford Music Club.
5.96 Hugh Lane Municipal Gallery of Modern Art, Dublin, promoted by Gavin O'Sullivan.
10.96 Omagh, promoted by Music Network.
**KEY PERFORMANCES OUTSIDE IRELAND** (since January 1994):
11.97 Japanese tour, playing in Shingu, Wakayama, Tanabe, promoted by Kanemi Yaguchi, Tokyo.
**SELECTED BROADCASTS AND/OR RECORDED WORK:**
5.96 Live broadcast from Hugh Lane Municipal Gallery of Modern Art, Dublin for RTÉ.
7.96 l'Imaginaire Irlandais, for France Musique and a recital from the National Concert Hall live for Radio France.

**SELECTED REVIEWS** (since January 1994):
3.95 Evening Press.
5.96 Irish Times.
**AVAILABILITY:**
Unlimited.
**ADDITIONAL INFORMATION:**
Since 1994 have given recitals and broadcasts throughout Ireland.
1996 Participated in the International Chamber Music Competition in Osaka, Japan.
*See Michael d'Arcy page 61, Annette Cleary page 68, Dearbhla Collins page 34.*

# Lir Ensemble

**Contact:** Eilís Cranitch
Lungo Po, Antonelli 17
10153 Turin, Italy
**Tel/Fax:** +39 11 8122430 / +39 11 503361

*" These four swans play extremely well: in fact they have a special charm"* 23.2.94 La Repubblica.

**FORMED:** 1990.
**GROUP MEMBERS:**
Cristina Cogno-Merlat (soprano), Eilís Cranitch (violin), Nora Gilleece (cello), Pauline MacSweeney (harpischord).
**KEY PERFORMANCES OUTSIDE IRELAND** (since January 1994):
21.1.94 Turin, Italy promoted by Music Promotion.
19.2.94 Biella, Italy promoted by Circolo Culturale L. Lessona.
26.2.94 Campobasso, Italy, promoted by the Amici della Musica Campobasso.
**SELECTED BROADCASTS AND/OR RECORDED WORK:**
26.4.94 Live recording of a Geneva concert for Swiss Radio.
**SELECTED REVIEWS** (since January 1994):
24.2.94 La Stampa.
23.2.94 La Nuova Provincia.
**AVAILABILITY:**
General.
**ADDITIONAL INFORMATION:**
Repertoire embraces little known composers like Vallotti as well as well known composers from the baroque period. Also interested in specially commissioned works based on texts by Irish poets. Composers commissioned in the past include E Farrell, E Corroggia, G Mc Sweeney and F de Rossire.
*See Eilís Cranitch page 59.*

# Lowry String Quartet

**Contact:** Noel Lamont
60, Jordanstown Road
Newtownabbey
Co Antrim, BT37 0QG
Northern Ireland (h)
or
Hugh and Noeleen Carslaw
'The Music Company'
13, Sycamore Park
Jordanstown
Newtownabbey
Co Antrim, BT37 ONR
Northern Ireland (a)
**Tel:** +44 1232 862371 (h) or +44 1232 867980 (a)

**FORMED:** 1995.
**GROUP MEMBERS:**
Noeleen Carslaw (violin), Noel Lamont (viola), Clifford Lowry (violin), Kathryn Lowry (cello).
**AVAILABILITY:**
General.
**ADDITIONAL INFORMATION:**
Performances are mainly of a light-classical nature. Have played extensively throughout Northern Ireland. Members of group have recorded for BBC and UTV.
*See Noel Lamont page 56, Noeleen Carslaw page 57.*

# Brian and Sabine Ducrot-MacNamara

**Contact:** Brian MacNamara
9, The Heights
Broadale
Douglas
Cork
**Tel:** +353 21 895017

*"Their playing showed many qualities of natural musical partnership including excellent ensemble and expressive unanimity "* 7.95 Irish Times.

**FORMED:** 1984.
**GROUP MEMBERS:**
Brian MacNamara (piano), Sabine Ducrot MacNamara (flute).
**KEY IRISH PERFORMANCES** (since January 1994):
1995 Kilkenny Arts Week.
1995 Two Cathedrals Festival, Derry.
1995 John Field Room, National Concert Hall, Dublin.
1995 Crawford Art Gallery, Cork.
**SELECTED BROADCASTS AND/OR RECORDED WORK:**
1995 and 1997 for RTÉ.
**AVAILABILITY:**
General (prepared to travel any distance).
*See Brian McNamara page 44, Sabine Ducrot McNamara page 13.*

# Mosaic Music

**Contact:** Tony Ovenell
Nationwide House
Bank Place
Ennis, Co Clare
**Tel:** +353 65 42480
**Email:** cmmacto@iol.ie

**FORMED:** 1995.
**GROUP MEMBERS:**
Andrea Creech (violin, viola), Moira Gray (piano), Sharon Nye (cello), Tony Ovenell (flute).
**KEY IRISH PERFORMANCES** (since January 1994):
23.4.95 Old Ground Hotel, Ennis, promoted by Clare Music Makers.
18.10.95 St Mary's Church, Ballina, promoted by Ballina Music Group.
14.12.95 Belltable Arts Centre, Limerick.
12.04.96 St Columba's Church, Ennis, promoted by Clare Music Makers.
**AVAILABILITY:**
General.

# New Woodwinds

**Contact:** Ms Dorene Groocock
224, Lower Kilmacud Road
Goatstown, Dublin 14
**Tel:** +353 1 2983050

**FORMED:** 1994.
**GROUP MEMBERS:**
Tom Burke (oboe), Dorene Groocock (flute), Hilary Macken (bassoon) Conor Sheil (clarinet).
**KEY IRISH PERFORMANCES** (since January 1994):
23.9.95 Woodstown, Co Waterford, promoted by Woodstown Festival.
**ADDITIONAL INFORMATION:**
A restructuring of old 'Woodwinds' which performed quite widely in the past. Offer a varied program of classical pieces, Irish melodies, and popular hits - according to request. Also function as different trios within the quartet.
*See Conor Sheil page 5.*

# Geraldine O'Grady and Oonagh Keogh

**Contact:** Dr Geraldine O'Grady
La Pietra
12, Highfield Park
Dundrum, Dublin 14
**Tel:** +353 1 2986001

*"Geraldine and Oonaghs' sensitive playing had vibrant, even sense, sensual touch ... here was rich co-ordination, spirited style ..."*
11.89 Evening Herald.

**FORMED:** 1989.
**GROUP MEMBERS:**
Geraldine O'Grady (violin), Oonagh Keogh (violin), (Margaret O'Sullivan).
**KEY IRISH PERFORMANCES** (since January 1994):
5.95 Royal College of Surgeons, Dublin.
6.95 National Concert Hall, Dublin, appearing with Margaret O'Sullivan (piano).
**KEY PERFORMANCES OUTSIDE IRELAND** (since January 1994):
3.95 Crest Theatre, Sacramento City, California, USA, appearing with Sacramento Symphony Orchestra.
3.95 St Patrick's Cathedral, New York, appearing with New York Chamber Orchestra.
**SELECTED BROADCASTS AND/OR RECORDED WORK:**
12.93 'Heartstrings in Harmony', for Lunar Records.
6.95 'The Lark in the Clear Air', for Cala Artists (London and New York).
**SELECTED REVIEWS** (since January 1994):
Irish Times.
**REGULARLY PERFORMS WITH:**
Deborah Kelleher (piano).
**AVAILABILITY:**
General.
**ADDITIONAL INFORMATION:**
Performs regularly as a duo giving many recitals at home and abroad. Co-soloists with the RTÉ Concert Orchestra, the Sacramento Symphony Orchestra and the New York Chamber Ensemble.
*See Geraldine O'Grady page 65, Oonagh Keogh page 62.*

# Orion String Quartet

**Contact:** Ms Ruth Bebb
13, Old Seahill Road
Craigavad, Co Down BT18 OEG
Northern Ireland
**Tel:** +44 1232 424675

*"The Orion Quartet gave a committed and persuasive performance"*
11.96 Belfast Newsletter (Review of Pickett).

**FORMED:** 1984.
**GROUP MEMBERS:**
Ruth Bebb (violin), Stephen Begley (viola), Philip Davies (violin), Richard Glynn (cello).
**KEY IRISH PERFORMANCES** (since January 1994):
11.96 Flowerfield Arts Centre, Coleraine, promoted by Coleraine Borough Council Arts Committee.
11.96 Queen's University, Belfast, promoted by the Belfast Festival at Queen's.
4.2.97 Grammar School, Larne, promoted by Larne Borough Council Arts Committee.
11.5.97 Greyabbey House, Greyabbey, promoted by Belfast Music Society.
**SELECTED BROADCASTS AND/OR RECORDED WORK:**
2.93 Lunchtime concert including Janacek Quartet No 1 for BBC Radio Ulster.
6.95 Steve Pickett String Quartet for BBC Radio Ulster's 'Music Now'.
11.95 Live broadcast from the Belfast Festival at Queen's for BBC Radio Scotland.
**SELECTED REVIEWS** (since January 1994):
23.11.96 Belfast Newsletter.
**PRIZES/AWARDS/APPOINTMENTS:**
From 1989 to 1991, Ensemble-in-Residence at Queen's University, Belfast.
**TRAINING AND/OR QUALIFICATIONS:**
Easter 1994, Tuition with Levon Chilingirian and Philip Degroote of Chilingirian Quartet.
7.91 Orlando Festival, Holland, tuition with the Orlando and Talich Quartets.
**AVAILABILITY:**
General (except July) and subject to the Ulster Orchestra schedule.
**ADDITIONAL INFORMATION:**
Is principally interested in giving recitals and have performed a series of soirées at Balloo House, Killinchy, Northern Ireland. Have worked with Ulster Youth Dance and other educational groups.

# Pim Street String Quartet/ Pim Street Strauss Ensemble

**Contact:** Mr Gavin O'Sullivan
10, Pim Street
Dublin 8
**Tel:** +353 1 4531303
**Mobile:** +353 87 456971
**Email:** gavinosu@indigo.ie

**NUMBER IN GROUP:**
6-32 players.
**SELECTED BROADCASTS AND/OR RECORDED WORK:**
Gate Theatre, Dublin, recorded music for a production of Lady Windemere's Fan.
**AVAILABILITY:**
General.
**ADDITIONAL INFORMATION:**
Both ensembles are made up of professional musicians drawn from a pool of freelance players who regularly perform as solo artists, as members of the National Symphony Orchestra of Ireland, RTÉ Concert Orchestra, Irish Chamber Orchestra, Dublin Philharmonic Orchestra and other freelance orchestras for concerts and recording sessions. The Ensembles have flexible repertoires and will consider performing for all event types. Have performed at functions held in University College, Dublin, the Shelbourne Hotel and the Royal Hospital Kilmainham.

# Prelude Brass

**Contact:** Killyan Bannister
65, Larkfield Gardens
Harold's Cross
Dublin 6
**Tel:** +353 1 4922893

**AVAILABILITY:**
Subject to National Symphony Orchestra of Ireland schedule.
*See Killyan Bannister page 53.*

# Prism

**Contact:** c/o Thérèse Fahy
12, Malachi Road
Dublin 7
**Tel:** +353 1 6771508

**FORMED:** 1995.
**GROUP MEMBERS:**
William Butt (cello), Dominic Dudley (double bass), Thérèse Fahy (piano), Adèle Govier (viola), Alan Smale (violin).
**KEY IRISH PERFORMANCES** (since January 1994):
12.95 Hugh Lane Municipal Gallery of Modern Art, Dublin promoted by Gavin O'Sullivan.
9.96 Church of Ireland, Clifden, promoted by Clifden Community Arts Week.
4.97 Courthouse, New Ross, promoted by Music for New Ross.
**SELECTED BROADCASTS AND/OR RECORDED WORK:**
9.97 RTÉ FM3.
**AVAILABILITY:**
General.
**ADDITIONAL INFORMATION:**
Ensemble of professional musicians made up of principals of the National Symphony Orchestra of Ireland, including its Leader, Alan Smale. Aims to bring standard classical repertoire to audiences in Ireland and abroad.
*See William Butt page 68, Dominic Dudley page 9, Thérèse Fahy page 37, Adèle Govier page 55, Alan Smale page 66.*

# Quintessence

**Contact:** Ms Ottoline Maas
54, Railwayview Street
Bangor
Co Down, BT20 3BZ
Northern Ireland
**Tel:** +44 1247 455312

*"Such was the success of their performance last year . . . we had no hesitation in asking Quintessence to come back this year"*
1995 Belfast Festival at Queen's (programme).

**FORMED:** 1993.
**GROUP MEMBERS:**
Jennifer Hallet (violin), Francis King (piano), Ottoline Maas (violin), David McCreadie (viola), Michele Strong (double bass), Rachel van der Tang (cello). (Any combination of these players available).
**KEY IRISH PERFORMANCES** (since January 1994):
5.94 and 11.94 Queen's University, Belfast.
5.95 Elmwood Hall, Belfast, promoted by Friends of the Ulster Orchestra.
6.95 Dundonald High School, Belfast, promoted by Castlereagh Arts.
**SELECTED REVIEWS** (since January 1994):
15.11.94 Newsletter.

**AVAILABILITY:**
Subject to Ulster Orchestra schedule.
*See Michele Strong page 10, David McCreadie page 56 and Frances King page 41.*

# Quodlibet

**Contact:** Philip Richardson
16 Aberdelghy Park
Lisburn
Co Antrim BT27 4QF
Northern Ireland
**Tel:** +44 1846 664953

*"They have forged a fresh and viable musical coupling"* 11.96 Belfast Newsletter.

**FORMED:** 1994.
**GROUP MEMBERS:**
Rachel McGinley (cello), Philip Richardson (guitar).
**KEY IRISH PERFORMANCES** (since January 1994):
7.96 Foyle Arts Centre, Derry, promoted by Foyle Summer School of Music and Drama.
11.96 Belfast Festival at Queen's.
2.97 Queen's University, Belfast, promoted by Northern Irish Guitar Society.
4.97 Triskel Arts Centre, Cork.
**SELECTED REVIEWS** (since January 1994):
2.95 Irish News.
15.11.95 Lisburn Echo.
**AVAILABILITY:**
General.
**ADDITIONAL INFORMATION:**
Formed to create a new and exciting sound world. The term 'Quodlibet' means literally 'as it pleases'.
*See Philip Richardson page 22.*

# Rao-Williams Duo

**Contact:** Mr Arun Rao
41, Kingshall
Chapelizod
Dublin 20
**Tel:** +353 1 6234906

**GROUP MEMBERS:**
Arun Rao (cello), Gillian Williams (violin).
**ADDITIONAL INFORMATION:**
Musical partners for many years. Have performed duo recitals in England, Scotland and France. Repertoire includes Ravel's Sonata for vn. and vc. and 'Passacaille' by Handel. Performed Brahms Double Concerto in Dublin and London and have made television appearances on RTÉ.
*See Arun Rao page 70 and Gillian Williams page 67.*

# RTÉ Vanbrugh Quartet

**Contact:** Mr Simon Aspell
October House
Ballyorban
Monkstown, Co Cork
**Tel/Fax:** +353 21 373363
**Email:** vanbrugh@iol.ie

*"These performances of the Op. 18 set are so full of musical subtleties and buoyant, carefully considered ensemble playing, that further instalments will certainly be worth seeking out"* 21.3.97 The Guardian, London.

(Ref: recordings of the complete String Quartets by Beethoven)

**FORMED:** 1985.
**GROUP MEMBERS:**
Simon Aspell (viola), Elizabeth Charleson (violin), Gregory Ellis (violin), Christopher Marwood (cello).
**KEY IRISH PERFORMANCES** (since January 1994):
1995 and 1996 season, National Concert Hall, promoted by RTÉ performing the complete Beethoven String Quartet Cycle.
6.96 Bantry House, Co Cork, promoted by West Cork Chamber Music Festival.
1.97 Assembly Hall, Belfast in a live broadcast for BBC Radio 3.
**KEY PERFORMANCES OUTSIDE IRELAND** (since January 1994):
11.95 Suntory Hall, Tokyo, tour promoted by Japan Air Lines.
7.96 Luberon Festival for String Quartets, France.
4.97 Tour of Ontario, Canada.
**SELECTED BROADCASTS AND/OR RECORDED WORK:**
10.96 Beethoven 'String Quartet Op 18 No. 4' for GETV Sweden.
3.96 to 11.96, Complete Beethoven String Quartets for Intim Musik, Sweden.
1994 'Ceathrar' (contemporary Irish string quartets) for Chandos.
**SELECTED REVIEWS** (since January 1994):
27.2.97 Irish Times.
24.2.97 The Examiner.
6.4.97 Sunday Tribune.
**PRIZES/AWARDS/APPOINTMENTS:**
4.88 Ist Prize Portsmouth (now London) International String Quartet Competition.
12.95 REHAB/Telecom Éireann National Entertainment Classical Music Award.
**AVAILABILITY:**
General.
**ADDITIONAL INFORMATION:**
Now entering its second decade firmly established as one of Europe's most successful quartets. Reputation has grown since winning the Portsmouth (now London) International String Quartet Competition in 1988. Now present approximately one hundred concerts each year in more than twenty countries. Have been associated with RTÉ since 1986, and in that time have given close to three hundred recitals throughout Ireland. In June 1996 launched the first West Cork Chamber Music Festival at Bantry House, (were joined by Barry Douglas, Robert Cohen and Philippe Cassard). Artists in Residence at University College, Cork.

# Una Russell and John Feeley

**Contact:** Ms Una Russell
6, Kincora Terrace
Dundalk
Co Louth
**Tel/Fax:** +353 1 6603979 / +353 1 4023584 (w)

**FORMED:** 1996.
**GROUP MEMBERS:**
John Feeley (guitar), Una Russell (organ).
**KEY IRISH PERFORMANCES** (since January 1994):
20.6.96 Christchurch Cathedral, Dublin, promoted by Dublin International Organ and Choral Festival.
**AVAILABILITY:**
General.
*See John Feeley page 20, Una Russell page 29.*

# Song Circle

**Contact:** Colette McGahon
53, Hammond Street
Dublin 8
**Tel/Fax:** +353 1 4541042

*"The performers rose brilliantly to the occasion"*
Irish Times.

**FORMED:** 1994.
**NUMBER IN GROUP:**
Colette McGahon (mezzo soprano), Phillip O'Reilly (baritone), Andrew Synnott (piano), Kathleen Tynan (soprano).
**ADDITIONAL INFORMATION:**
A group of singers and pianists who all share a genuine interest in song. Aim is to present, at the highest level, interesting, varied and entertaining programmes of German Lieder, French melodie, American and English song. Repertoire includes Franz Schubert, and less familiar works such as those by Fauré and the Spanisches Liederbuch of Hugo Wolf. Commemorated the 100th anniversary of the death of Brahms in 1996 presenting some rarely heard Brahms Lieder along with the Liebeslieder Waltzes.
*See Colette McGahon page 103, Philip O'Reilly page 115, Kathleen Tynan page 98, Andrew Synnott page 50.*

# Sovereign Brass

**Contact:** Mr Colm Byrne
Pinewood
Boyerstown
Navan
Co Meath
**Tel:** +353 46 22130 / +353 46 21863

**FORMED:** 1995.
**GROUP MEMBERS:**
Colm Byrne (trumpet), Brian Daly (french horn), Pat Kenny (tuba), Niall O'Connor (trumpet), Gavin Roche (trombone).
**KEY IRISH PERFORMANCES** (since January 1994):
16.4.95 Glendelough Church, promoted by Tom Wallace performing with Andrew Synnott (organ).
10.5.95 University College, Dublin, promoted by Prof Seoirse Bodley/ UCD Graduation Committee.
21.6.95 Dublin Castle, promoted by the Small Firms Association.
1995 Bank of Ireland, RTÉ Proms.
**AVAILABILITY:**
Weekdays, weekends and on a project by project basis.
**ADDITIONAL INFORMATION:**
Aim primarily to entertain with a vast selection of music from the renaissance to modern day. Especially keen to perform brass quintet music written by contemporary Irish composers. As all members are music graduates, performers and teachers in their own right, they have an interest also in the educational aspect of brass instruments.

# String Fever *Palm-Court Trio*

**Contact:** Ms Noeleen Carslaw
13, Sycamore Park
Jordanstown, BT39 ONR
Northern Ireland
**Tel:** +44 1232 867980

**FORMED:** 1989.
**GROUP MEMBERS:**
Noeleen Carslaw (violin), Hilary Crawford (piano), Lorraine Stanley (cello).
**AVAILABILITY:**
General.

**ADDITIONAL INFORMATION:**
Performs regularly throughout Northern Ireland, at the Belfast Festival at Queen's, and at functions in the City Hall, Belfast. Have recorded for BBC Radio Ulster. Repertoire consists of light classical and jazz music.
*See Noeleen Carslaw page 157.*

# Trio Cervantes

**Contact:** Benjamin Dwyer
90 The Steeples
Chapelizod
Dublin 20
**Tel/Fax/Mobile:** +353 1 6234397 / +353 87 616391
**Email:** bdwyer@indigo.ie

*"... the finesse of the Trio Cervantes ..."* 9.95 Irish Times.

**FORMED:** 1995.
**NUMBER IN GROUP:**
Aran Corcoran (guitar), Benjamin Dwyer (guitar), Alan Grundy (guitar).
**KEY IRISH PERFORMANCES** (since January 1994):
1.9.95 The Abbey, Ballyshannon.
8.9.95 John Field Room, National Concert Hall, promoted by Instituto Cervantes.
11.11.95 Bank of Ireland Arts Centre, Dublin, promoted by Mostly Modern series.
2.96 BOI AC, promoted by Instituto Cervantes 'Dublin Guitar Week'.
**SELECTED BROADCASTS AND/OR RECORDED WORK:**
'Trio Cervantes' (own recording).
**SELECTED REVIEWS** (since January 1994):
9.95 Irish Times.
**AVAILABILITY:**
General.
*See Benjamin Dwyer page 20, Alan Grundy page 20.*

# Tuba Tapestry

**Contact:** Mr Ewan Easton
39, Ballyholme Road
Bangor
Co Down, BT20 5JR
Northern Ireland
**Tel/Fax:** +44 1247 275355

*"Music is always fun and enjoyable with Tuba Tapestry"* Diane Creighton, Curriculum Advisor, South Eastern Education and Library Board.

**FORMED:** 1990.
**GROUP MEMBERS:**
Stephen Barnett (tuba), Ewan Easton (keyboard).
**KEY IRISH PERFORMANCES** (since January 1994):
Various including: Ulster Orchestra "Friends" Recital, White Abbey, Belfast, Music Festival, Drogheda Band Club, Co Louth.
**TRAINING AND/OR QUALIFICATIONS:**
Members are professional musicians with the Ulster Orchestra.
**AVAILABILITY:**
Subject to Ulster Orchestra schedule.
**ADDITIONAL INFORMATION:**
Involved working with young people in Northern Ireland for some years. Duo's unwritten motto is 'music is fun'. Always looking for new and exciting ways to introduce children to music. Group encompasses most musical genres.
*See Ewan Easton page 54.*

# Ulster Brass

**Contact:** Ewan Easton
39, Ballyholme Road
Bangor
Co Down BT20 5JR
Northern Ireland
**Tel/Fax:** +44 1247 275355

*"... great educational value. The music was well chosen, and the musicians were enthusiastic, patient and inspiring"* Una Lawless, Music Co-ordinator, St Patrick's Primary School, Hilltown, Co Down.

**FORMED:** 1980.
**GROUP MEMBERS:**
Stephen Barnett (trombone), Hugh Carslaw (trumpet), Ewan Easton (tuba), Derek Parkins (french horn), Paul Young (trumpet).
**KEY IRISH PERFORMANCES** (since January 1994):
Various including: Belfast Festival at Queen's, St Anne's Cathedral, Belfast, Two Cathedrals Festival, Derry.
**AVAILABILITY:**
By arrangement and subject to Ulster Orchestra schedule.
**ADDITIONAL INFORMATION:**
Ensemble made up of principal members of the Ulster Orchestra. Aim to bring own enjoyment of performing music to as wide an audience as possible. Has performed extensively for both BBC radio and television. Members also teach at institutions such as Queen's University, University of Ulster, Campbell College, Bangor Grammar School, Belfast School of Music and the Ulster Youth Orchestra. Also involved in developing new music in the brass field.
*See Ewan Easton page 54.*

# John Vallery and Mary Beattie

**Contact:** Mr John Vallery
Green Cottage
Glenbrook
Co Cork
**Tel:** +353 21 841191

*"Their Bach Sonata No 2 in D was delightfully controlled and one remembers long-held viola notes while the piano sparkled"* 21.2.94 The Examiner.

**FORMED:** 1984.
**GROUP MEMBERS:**
Mary Beattie (piano), John Vallery (viola).
**KEY IRISH PERFORMANCES** (since January 1994):
17.5.95 Triskel Arts Centre, Cork.
26.5.95 National Concert Hall, Dublin.
6.8.95 Community School, Castletownbere.
23.8.95 St. John's, Kilkenny, promoted by Kilkenny Arts Week.
**KEY PERFORMANCES OUTSIDE IRELAND** (since January 1994):
1.94 Antwerp, Belgium, promoted by John Niland.
8.94 Port Erin, Isle of Man, International Viola Congress.
**SELECTED BROADCASTS AND/OR RECORDED WORK:**
5.94 RTÉ, FM 3.
**AVAILABILITY:**
General.
**ADDITIONAL INFORMATION:**
Are part of the teaching staff at Cork School of Music since 1975. Have commissioned works from Irish composers, such as Philip Martin and Séamas de Barra and always include at least one work by an Irish composer in each recital.

# Westport Ensemble

**Contact:** Mary Curran
Derryribbeen
Clogher, Westport
Co. Mayo
**Tel:** +353 98 41983
*See French Horn page 23.*

# Xenia Ensemble

**Contact:** Eilís Cranitch
Lungo Po Antonelli 17
10153 Turin
Italy
**Tel/Fax:** +39 11 8122430 / +39 11 503361
*See contemporary music groups page 138, Eilís Cranitch page 59.*

# Section three

## Singers

The singers in this section are sub-divided according to voice category

# SOPRANO

## Giselle Allen *Soprano*

**Contact:** Ms Giselle Allen
136B, Springbank Road
London SE13 6SU
or
58, Marmount Gardens
Belfast BT14 6NW
Northern Ireland
**Tel/Fax:** +44 181 695 1505 or +44 1232 713113 /
+44 181 695 1505

*"[Giselle Allen brought] passion and strong tone ... to 'Cressida' in 'Ischia' last summer"*

1995 Sunday Telegraph.

**KEY IRISH PERFORMANCES** (since January 1994):
24.6.96 Galway Music Festival, promoted by the Golden Voice of Athlone, appearing with Elizabeth Bicker.
8.8.96 National Concert Hall, Dublin, promoted by Golden Voice of Athlone, appearing with Elizabeth Bicker.
5.6.97 Castleward Opera, promoted by Castleward Opera Recital Series, appearing with Fiona McSherry.
**KEY PERFORMANCES OUTSIDE IRELAND** (since January 1994):
From 1994 to 1996, Britten Theatre, London, promoted by Royal Academy of Music Opera School.
16.10.95 Britten Theatre, London, promoted by Clonter Opera as 'Musetta'.
10.11.95 Birmingham Concert Hall, appearing with the City of Birmingham Symphony Orchestra under Sir Simon Rattle.
17.11.95 Royal Albert Hall, London, appearing with Sir David Wilcocks.
**SELECTED BROADCASTS AND/OR RECORDED WORK:**
17.11.95 Handel's Messiah from the Royal Albert Hall for Scorer Associates and BBC London Video.
**SELECTED REVIEWS** (since January 1994):
1995 Observer.
1997 Evening Sentinel.
1997 Sunday Telegraph.
**PRIZES/AWARDS/APPOINTMENTS:**
1.12.95 Various prizes, including recitals at the Golden Voice of Athlone.
3.3.96 Bruce Millar Opera Award, Scotland.
**TRAINING AND/OR QUALIFICATIONS:**
From 1989 to 1992, BA (Hons) in Music from Cardiff University.
From 1992 to 1994, Diploma in Vocal Studies from the Guildhall School of Music and Drama.
From 1994 to 1996, Dip RAM from the Royal Academy of Music, London.
**AVAILABILITY:**
General.
**ADDITIONAL INFORMATION:**
Has worked with some of Britain's distinguished conductors and sung in many of the major concert halls in Britain and Ireland. Repertoire in opera, ranges from Mozart to Puccini to Walton and also has a diverse Lieder and song repertoire. Winner of a number of opera awards.

## Eileen Bardin *Soprano*

**Contact:** Mrs Eileen Bardin
The Old School House
Rathdrum
Co Wicklow
**Tel:** +353 404 46920

**KEY IRISH PERFORMANCES** (since January 1994):
3.6.94 National Concert Hall, Dublin, promoted by DIT Conservatory of Music and Drama, Dublin appearing with other students.
4.5.95 St Ann's Church, Dawson Street, Dublin, promoted by the DIT CMD, appearing with Blanaid Murphy (piano).
22.2.95 No 29 Merrion Square, Dublin, promoted by Deirdre Kelleher, appearing with Liz Nolan, Patrick Connolly, Victoria Massey and John McKeown.
24.11.95 St Ann's Church, Dawson Street, Dublin, promoted by Mrs Deirdre Grier Delany, appearing with Sinéad Blanchfield.
**PRIZES/AWARDS/APPOINTMENTS:**
3.95 2nd Prize for duets, awarded by Feis Ceoil, Dublin.
3.95 Highly Commended for Early and 20th Century music, awarded by Feis Ceoil, Dublin.
**TRAINING AND/OR QUALIFICATIONS:**
From 1985 to 1989, BA Music, awarded by Waterford Institute of Technology.
From 1989 to 1990, H Dip in Education awarded by Trinity College, Dublin.
1992 ALCM piano.
**REGULARLY PERFORMS WITH:**
Madrigal group with Ronan Conroy (bass), Ciaran Nagle (tenor) Elspeth Hayes (alto), Cantique.
**AVAILABILITY:** General.
**ADDITIONAL INFORMATION:**
Has an interest in early music for some years. Formed a 4 person madrigal group which sings pieces by Lassus, Verdelot and Bennett. Teaches advanced piano, music theory and voice.

## Dorothy Bergin *Soprano*

**Contact:** Ms Dorothy Bergin
35, Mount Eagle Drive
Leopardstown Heights
Sandyford
Dublin 18
**Tel:** +353 1 2957096
**Other instruments:** Piano.

**KEY IRISH PERFORMANCES** (since January 1994):
1994 John Field Room, National Concert Hall, Dublin, narrator in 'The Rape of Lucretia', by Britten, appearing with DIT Opera.
Since 1994 John McCann Hall, The Pepper Cannister Church and St Ann's Church, Dublin appearing with Mairéad Hurley.
1995 NCH, 2nd Lady in 'The Magic Flute', appearing with DIT Opera.
1996 Clonliffe College, Dublin, soloist in Charpentier Mass.
**SELECTED BROADCASTS AND/OR RECORDED WORK:**
1996 'Focus on Youth', for Annalivia FM.
**PRIZES/AWARDS/APPOINTMENTS:**
3.95 German Government Cup, awarded at the Feis Ceoil, Dublin.
12.95 Lieder prize, awarded from the DIT Conservatory of Music and Drama, Dublin.
**TRAINING AND/OR QUALIFICATIONS:**
From 1991 to 1995, B Mus Performance (Hons) from DIT Conservatory of Music and Drama and Trinity College, Dublin.
1995 Masterclasses with Mikael Eliasen at the Royal Irish Academy of Music.
From 1995 to 1997, Diploma in Music Teaching from the DIT CMD (Hons).
**AVAILABILITY:**
General.

## Sinéad Blanchfield *Soprano*

**Contact:** Ms Sinéad Blanchfield
25, Larchfield
Kilkenny
Co Kilkenny
**Tel:** +353 56 63217

*"Some of the strongest moments were to be*

*found in the 'Zaïde' of Sinéad Blanchfield ... smooth and clearly-focussed singing brought to mind the style of the leading German lyric soprano's of the 1950's"* 2.96 Irish Times.

**KEY IRISH PERFORMANCES** (since January 1994):
11.95 Tour of Ireland with the Opera Theatre Company's production of Monteverdi's Orfeo as 'Euridice'.
2.96 Tour of Ireland and Belgium with the Opera Theatre Company and Transparant Muziektheater (Belgium) production of Mozart's 'Zaïde' as 'Zaïde', appearing with the RTÉ Concert Orchestra.
8.96 Recital at St Canice's Cathedral, Kilkenny, promoted by Kilkenny Arts Festival, accompanied by Trudi Carberry.
11.96 Duiske Abbey, Graiguenamanagh, promoted by Duiske Abbey Arts Festival, appearing with Mark Padmore (tenor) and Mairéad Hurley.
**KEY PERFORMANCES OUTSIDE IRELAND** (since January 1994):
2.96 Antwerp, Belgium, appearing with the Transparent Musiektheater production of Mozart's 'Zaïde' as 'Zaïde'.
6.97 Twickenham Arts Festival, appearing with Reckless Productions in the production of Mozart's 'Der Schauspieldirektor' as 'Madame Herz'.
6.97 Nottingham, appearing with Nottingham Bach Society in Stanford's Requiem.
5.97 Savoy Hotel, London, appearing with the Orchestra of Vienna.
**SELECTED BROADCASTS AND/OR RECORDED WORK:**
20.2.96 Opera Theatre Company production of 'Zaïde' as 'Zaïde' for RTÉ.
24.12.96 'Carols from Kilkenny', presented by Mary Kennedy for RTÉ.
12.2.97 'Gerry Ryan Tonight' for RTÉ.
**SELECTED REVIEWS** (since January 1994):
11.95 Irish Times (Michael Dervan).
11.95 Sunday Tribune (Ian Fox).
11.95 Huddersfield Examiner (Malcolm Cruise).
**TRAINING AND/OR QUALIFICATIONS:**
1991 Bachelor of Arts in Music (NCEA) from the Waterford Institute of Technology.
From 1991 to 1992, Higher Diploma in Education from Trinity College, Dublin.
From 1992 to 1995, Vocal studies (scholarships obtained) at the DIT Conservatory of Music and Drama, Dublin.
Since 1995, PPRNCM from the Royal Northern College of Music, Manchester.
**AVAILABILITY:**
General.

## Orla Boylan *Soprano*

**Contact:** Orla Boylan
13, Harbour Road
Skerries
Co Dublin
or
Harrison Parrott Limited
12, Penzance Place
London W11 4 PA
England (agent)
**Mobile/Tel:** +353 87 2324425 / +44 171 229 9166 (agent).

*"Boylan handled everything she sang with a natural, apparently effortless, performer's presence"* 5.95 Irish Times (Michael Dervan).

**KEY IRISH PERFORMANCES** (since January 1994):
1995/96 Cork City Hall and National Concert Hall, Dublin, promoted by Barra O'Tuama, appearing with Brenda Hurley and Tito Beltran.
1996 University of Limerick, Concert Hall, in Handel's 'Messiah' appearing with the Irish Chamber Orchestra, conductor Roger Vignoles.
9.96 NCH prize winners concert appearing with the RTÉ Concert Orchestra conductor Wojeck Drabowicz.
1997 NCH, in Haydn's 'Creation' as 'Gabriel' and 'Eva' appearing with Culwick Choral Society.
**KEY PERFORMANCES OUTSIDE IRELAND** (since January 1994):
1995 Salle Cortot, Paris, France appearing with Joon Kanno.
1995 St George's Hall, Liverpool in a performance of Verdi's Requiem, conducted by Nicholas Cleobury.
1996 Opera Theatre, Lombardy in a production of 'Cosi Fan Tutte' as 'Fiordiligi' appearing with Pomerigi Musicali Orchestra Milan.
1997 Teatro Communale, Bologna, in 'Turn of the Screw' as the 'Governess'.
**SELECTED BROADCASTS AND/OR RECORDED WORK:**
95 Lunchtime Recital with National Symphony Orchestra of Ireland for RTÉ FM3.
1996 Song recital, for RTÉ FM3.
1997 Song recital, with Hans Koppenburg for Frankfurt Radio.
**PRIZES/AWARDS/APPOINTMENTS:**
1995 Winner of the Veronica Dunne Bursary.
1996 Winner of the As.Li.Co, Milan (Association of Lyric Opera Companies).
**TRAINING AND/OR QUALIFICATIONS:**
From 9.94 to 4.96, Studied at the DIT Conservatory of Music and Drama, Dublin.
From 3.96 to 11.97, Milan, masterclasses with Leyla Gencer, Bob Kettleson, Renata Scotto.
**AVAILABILITY:**
Subject to schedule.

## Anne Buckley *Soprano*

**Contact:** Ms Anne Buckley
'Avalon'
Glenamuck Road
Carrickmines
Dublin 18
**Tel:** +353 1 2955881

## Theresa Cahill *Soprano*

**Contact:** Ms Theresa Cahill
NB Management
Ashley
Oakwood Drive
East Horsley
Surrey, KT24 6QF
England
**Tel:** +44 1483 282666

## Mary Callan Clarke *Soprano*

**Contact:** Ms Mary Callan Clarke
77a, Upper Brockley Road
London SE4 1TF
England
or
Helen Sykes Artists' Management
4th Floor
Parkway House, Sheen Lane
East Sheen
London SW14 8LS
England
**Tel/Fax:** +44 181 691 3783 (h) / +44 181 876 8276 (a) / +44 181 876 8277

*"A heart-rending Mimi, achieving the almost impossible task of appearing terminally consumptive while filling the auditorium with her gloriously soaring soprano."* 4.96 Surrey Advertiser.

**KEY IRISH PERFORMANCES** (since January 1994):
1995 Tour of Dublin, Galway, Wexford, promoted by Opera Theatre Company.
4.95 National Concert Hall, Dublin, appearing with Mark Armstrong and St Michael's Choral Society, Dún Laoghaire in Brahm's Requiem.
12.96/1.97 NCH 'New Years Eve Gala', promoted by RTÉ, appearing with Dennis O'Neill.
1.97 NCH appearing with the Guinness Choir in Mendelssohn's 'Paulus'.
**KEY PERFORMANCES OUTSIDE IRELAND** (since January 1994):
7/8.95 Granada/Athens/Peralada, promoted by the English Bach Festival, in Purcell's 'Fairy Queen'.
1-6.96 Tour of England, appearing in Crystal Clear Opera's production of Puccini's 'La Boheme' as 'Mimi'.
10/11.96 Tour of Scotland, in Scottish Opera Go Round's production of Mozart's 'Cosi Fan Tutte' as 'Fiordiligi'.
4/5.97 Tour of Scotland, promoted by Scottish Opera, in Essential Scottish Opera.
**SELECTED BROADCASTS AND/OR RECORDED WORK:**
2.95 Operatic arias with the RTÉ Concert Orchestra for RTÉ.
8.95 'Nervous Energy' (television play) for BBC Scotland.
2.97 'Theatre Nights' for RTÉ.
**SELECTED REVIEWS** (since January 1994):
3.96 Leicester Mercury.
8.96 Irish Times.
**PRIZES/AWARDS/APPOINTMENTS:**
1986 Winner of the Golden Voice of Ireland.
1988 Finalist, Shell/Scottish Opera International Competition.
**TRAINING AND/OR QUALIFICATIONS:**
From 1982 to 1987, DIT Conservatory of Music and Drama, Dublin (teacher Veronica Dunne).
From 1987 to 1988, Royal College of Music, London.
1988 Attended masterclasses with Ileana Cotrubas at the Britten-Pears School, Aldeburgh.
**AVAILABILITY:**
General.
**ADDITIONAL INFORMATION:**
In addition to work in opera, has performed extensively in concert and oratorio. Repertoire includes Haydn's 'Creation', Mozart's 'Exultate Jubilate' and 'Coronation' Mass, and Beethoven's Mass in C. (All have been recorded by RTÉ).

## Majella Cullagh *Soprano*

**Contact:** Ms Majella Cullagh
4a, Southborough Road
Hackney
London E97 EF
England
**Tel:** +44 171 9859225

## Colette Delahunt *Soprano*

**Contact:** Ms Colette Delahunt
35, Daletree Avenue
Ballycullen Grove
Knocklyon
Dublin 24
**Tel:** +353 1 4951069

*"Colette Delahunt gave an excellent performance of 'the fifteen-year-old'"* 1996 Evening Standard (review of proms).

**KEY IRISH PERFORMANCES** (since January 1994):
1994 National Concert Hall, Dublin promoted by RTÉ 'Music for Middlebrows'.
12.95 Glasnevin, Dublin, appearing with Our Lady's Choral Society and the National Symphonia in Charpentiers 'Te Deum'.
1995 Mater Dei, Dublin, promoted by RTÉ, appearing with Our Lady's Choral Society.
1997 Dublin International Handel Festival, appearing with RTÉ Chamber Orchestra in Handel's 'Messiah'.
**KEY PERFORMANCES OUTSIDE IRELAND** (since January 1994):
1996 St Martin-in-the-Field's, London, appearing with the London Concert Sinfonia in Handel's 'Messiah'.
1996 Glyndebourne, Sussex, appearing with the London Philharmonic in Berg's 'Lulu' as the '15-year-old'.
1996 Fairfield Hall, Croydon, appearing with the Croydon Philharmonic in Vivaldi's 'Gloria' and Bach's 'Jauchet Gott'.
1997 Fairfield Hall, Croydon, appearing with the Croydon Philharmonic
**SELECTED BROADCASTS AND/OR RECORDED WORK:**
1994 'Music for Middlebrows' for RTÉ.
1995 BBC Young Artist's Forum Recital for BBC.
1996 International Christmas Mass for RTÉ.
**PRIZES/AWARDS/APPOINTMENTS:**
1994 Overall overseas winner of the Royal Overseas League Music Competition.
1995 Winner of BBC Radio 3 recital from the Young Artists' Forum.
**TRAINING AND/OR QUALIFICATIONS:**
From 1988 to 1992, Performance Diploma from the College of Music, Dublin (teacher Nancy Calthorpe).
From 1992 to 1994, Post Graduate Certificate from Trinity College of Music, London.
From 1995 to 1997, Study with Iris del Aqua.
**AVAILABILITY:**
General.
**ADDITIONAL INFORMATION:**
Sings regularly for Glyndebourne Opera Festival and touring company. Has understudied the following roles: 'Susanna' in the 'Marriage of Figaro' (twice), 'Servilia' in 'La Clementza di Tito', 'Euridice' in 'The Second Mrs Kong' (twice). Also sings regularly at London venues, performing Lieder and French song programmes.

## Róisín Dempsey *Soprano*

**Contact:** Róisín Dempsey
Apt 2
130, Sandford Road
Ranelagh
Dublin 6
or
'Greenville'
Enniscorthy
Co Wexford
**Tel:** +353 1 4973873 / +353 54 33241

*"Sliabh Geal gCua has a solo melody line sung by Róisín Dempsey, soaring high above delicately textured harmonies"* 6.12.96 Irish Times (Nuala O'Connor) review of 'Deep Dead Blue' with Anúna.

**KEY IRISH PERFORMANCES** (since January 1994):
6.96 Eurovision Mass, Ballintubber, Co Mayo, promoted by RTÉ, appearing with Fr Liam Lawton and Ensemble.
11.96 St Patrick's Cathedral, Dublin, appearing with Anúna.
4.97 St Iberius, Wexford, in Wexford Festival Singers' production of Vivaldi's Gloria.
5.97 National Concert Hall, Dublin, appearing with Fr Liam Lawton and Ensemble.
**KEY PERFORMANCES OUTSIDE IRELAND** (since January 1994):
7.96 The Hammersmith Apollo, London, promoted by Tyrone Productions, appearing in 'Riverdance' The Show.
11.96 Theatre Monumental, Madrid, appearing with Anúna.

3.97 Gothenburg Cathedral, Sweden, appearing with Anúna.
2.97 St Patrick's, Chicago, appearing with Fr Liam Lawton and Ensemble.
**SELECTED BROADCASTS AND/OR RECORDED WORK:**
9.96 'Beautiful Tomorrow' soundtrack for modern dance ballet at the Project Arts Centre.
10.96 'Deep Dead Blue' with Anúna for Danú.
5.97 'The Sacred Story' for Gael Linn.
**SELECTED REVIEWS** (since January 1994):
5.96 Irish Music (review of 'Light the Fire' with L Lawton).
21.12.96 RTÉ Guide (review of 'Deep Dead Blue').
**TRAINING AND/OR QUALIFICATIONS:**
From 1990 to 1993, Degree in Music and Theology (Performance major) from the National University of Ireland, Maynooth.
1994 H Dip in Education from National University of Ireland, Maynooth.
**REGULARLY PERFORMS WITH:**
Anúna.
**AVAILABILITY:**
Some weekends, evenings, from June to September.
**ADDITIONAL INFORMATION:**
Specialises in liturgical music, both modern and ancient.

## Angela Feeney *Soprano*

**Contact:** Ms Angela Feeney
Josephspital Str 6
80331 München
Germany
or
32, Corinna Avenue
Upper Dunmurry Lane
Belfast BT17 0HR
**Tel/Fax:** +49 89 2604834 / +49 89 2603607 / +44 1232 626265 (Northern Ireland)

**REGULARLY PERFORMS WITH:**
Bel Canto Horn Piano Trio, West Belfast Bursary Ensemble.
**AVAILABILITY:**
General.

## Fionnuala Gill *Soprano*

**Contact:** Ms Fionnuala Gill
151, Árd na Mara
Malahide
Co Dublin
**Tel:** +353 1 8450698
**Other instruments:** Irish harp.

*"What one remembers most is the fresh-faced, mock-naivety of the newcomer Fionnuala Gill, playing 'Lisetta' as a coquette with a killer pounce"* 4.2.93 Irish Times (Michael Dervan) La Vera Costanza.

**KEY IRISH PERFORMANCES** (since January 1994):
5.97 Tour of Ireland with the Opera Theatre Company's production of 'The Magic Flute' as 'Pamina'.
**KEY PERFORMANCES OUTSIDE IRELAND** (since January 1994):
2.96 Findhorn, Scotland (recital of medieval Spanish music).
**SELECTED BROADCASTS AND/OR RECORDED WORK:**
5.97 Pamina's Aria from the "The Magic Flute' for RTÉ.
**PRIZES/AWARDS/APPOINTMENTS:**
1992 Semi-finalist in the National Mozart Competition, Southport.
1996 Awarded scholarship to the Royal Scottish Academy of Music and Drama.
**TRAINING AND/OR QUALIFICATIONS:**
1992 BA in Psychology from Trinity College, Dublin.
1993 LTCL (Perf) from Trinity College, London.
**AVAILABILITY:**
General.
**ADDITIONAL INFORMATION:**
Has also performed in the Opera Theatre Company productions of Haydn's 'La Vera Costanza' as 'Lisetta', Janacek's 'Jenufa' as 'Barena'/'Karolka' and Britten's 'Turn of the Screw' as 'Flora'. Although currently based in Scotland, is particularly interested in working in Ireland, in every aspect of singing (classical, traditional, jazz and sacred song).

## Deirdre Gilsenan *Soprano*

**Contact:** Ms Deirdre Gilsenan
Loughan
Kells
Co Meath
**Mobile:** +353 88 2756326
**Other instruments:** Piano.

*"Anúna have a celestial radiance that'a a testament to the sublime skilfulness of the singers"*
1995 Singapore Strait Times.

**KEY IRISH PERFORMANCES** (since January 1994):
12.96 'Live at 3' and 'Mary Kennedy Show' for RTÉ, appearing with Anúna.
2.97 St Canices Cathedral, Kilkenny, appearing with Anúna.
4.97 Guild Hall, Derry, Leading Soprano with Anúna.
6.97 National Concert Hall, Dublin, promoted by the Dublin Conservatory of Music, appearing with student and graduate singers in Offenbach's 'Christopher Columbas' as 'Fleurette'.
**KEY PERFORMANCES OUTSIDE IRELAND** (since January 1994):
1.97 Glasgow Concert Hall, Scotland, appearing as soprano soloist with Anúna.
2.97 Concert halls and churches in Gothenburg, Hamstad and Kungsbacka, Sweden, appearing as soprano soloist with Anúna.
4.97 St Peter's Church, Picadilly, London, appearing as soprano soloist with Anúna.
5.97 Christiansand Cathedral, Norway, appearing as soprano soloist with Anúna.
**SELECTED BROADCASTS AND/OR RECORDED WORK:**
12.96 'Jools Holland Christmas Special' (two pieces of music) live for Channel 4.
5.97 'Eurovision' (backing interval act) for RTÉ.
6.97 'Songs of Praise' for BBC.
**SELECTED REVIEWS** (since January 1994):
Spring 1995 Billboard.
10.96 Sunday Tribune.
2.97 Hallends Posten, Sweden and Svenska Dagbladet, Sweden.
**PRIZES/AWARDS/APPOINTMENTS:**
From 1993 to 1997, Awarded Distinction in Grade 6 Theory and Piano and Grade 5 Singing exams by the Associated Board of the Royal Schools of Music, London and the Dublin Conservatory of Music.
1997 Awarded Distinction and Certificate in 8 performances by the Ballymena Festival (affiliated to the British Federation of Festivals).
**TRAINING AND/OR QUALIFICATIONS:**
From 1987 to 1993, Studied up to Grade 6 Theory and Piano (Associated Board).
From 9.92 to 6.96, Bachelor of Design and Honours Degree in Textile Design at the National College of Art and Design, Dublin.
From 9.93 to 1997 Studied up to Grade 5 Singing at the Dublin Conservatory of Music.
From 9.96 to 2.97 Certificate in Business Start program from the Meath County Enterprise Board.
**REGULARLY PERFORMS WITH:**
Anúna, Teoranta, (Medieval), Céide (Irish Group), Matthew Gilsenan (tenor).

**AVAILABILITY:**
General.
**ADDITIONAL INFORMATION:**
Performances include oratorio, opera, French Art Songs and Lieder.

## Regina Hanley *Soprano*

**Contact:** Regina Hanley
c/o Neil Dalrymple
Music International
13, Ardilaun Road
London N5 2QR
England
**Tel/Fax:** +44 171 359 5183 / +44 171 226 9792

*"Regina Hanley's 'Jenufa' tore relentlessly at the heart strings. Her soprano is consistently beautiful, her diction clear"* Sunday Times (Rodney Milnes).

**KEY IRISH PERFORMANCES** (since January 1994):
Autumn 1994, Tour of Ireland with the Opera Theatre Company production of 'I Pagliacci' as 'Nedda'.
Autumn 1996, Tour of Ireland with the Opera Theatre Company production of 'Katya Kabanová' as title role.
Spring 1997, Dublin in the Opera Ireland production of 'Macbeth' as 'Dama'.
**KEY PERFORMANCES OUTSIDE IRELAND** (since January 1994):
Spring 1995, Collesium, London in the English National Opera production of 'The Rise and Fall of the City of Mahagonny' as 'Jenny's Girl'.
Spring 1996, Glyndebourne, Sussex, 'Eugene Onegin' covering 'Tatyana'.
**SELECTED REVIEWS** (since January 1994):
29.12.96 Sunday Independent.
**PRIZES/AWARDS/APPOINTMENTS:**
8.94 Mary Garden Singing Competition at the Aberdeen International Music Festival.
**TRAINING AND/OR QUALIFICATIONS:**
From 1986 to 1990, PPRNCM from the Royal Northern College of Music, Manchester.
**AVAILABILITY:**
General.

## Helen Hassett *Soprano*

**Contact:** Helen Hassett
5, College View
Blarney Road
Cork
**Tel:** +353 21 395495 (h) / +353 21 270076 (w)

*"The soprano soloist, Helen Hassett, ... communicated tonal beauty with clarity and chasteness ..."* 3.97 Irish Times (Michael Dervan).

**SELECTED BROADCASTS AND/OR RECORDED WORK:**
10.94 CD recording of 'Stabat Mater' composed by Colm Ó Foghlú.
11.96 CD recording 'Echoing' composed by Colm Ó Foghlú for Cló Iar-Chonnachta, Galway.
**SELECTED REVIEWS** (since January 1994):
2.94 The Examiner (Thomas Ó Canainn).
3.97 Irish Times (Martin Adams).
**TRAINING AND/OR QUALIFICATIONS:**
From 1989 to 1993, B Mus (Hons) from University College, Cork.
From 1990 to 1995, Cork School of Music (teacher Robert Beare).
From 1995 to 1996, Certificate of Advanced Studies from the Guildhall School of Music and Drama, London.
From 1996 to 1997, awarded CSM Diploma (teaching) (1st Hons), by the Cork School of Music.
**AVAILABILITY:**
Evenings.

## Shayron Hobbs *Soprano*

**Contact:** Ms Shayron Hobbs
110, Earlwood Estate
The Lough
Cork
**Tel:** +353 21 962370
**Other instruments:** Piano, guitar, tin whistle.

**KEY IRISH PERFORMANCES** (since January 1994):
5.97 National Concert Hall, Dublin, played role of Christine (Phantom of the Opera), appearing RTÉ Concert Orchestra.
7.97 Rosemary St Church, Belfast, appearing with Derek Collins and Patrick Davey.
**KEY PERFORMANCES OUTSIDE IRELAND** (since January 1994):
8.96 St Leonard's Auditorium, St Andrews, Scotland, as 'Giudilta' appearing with Paul Hamburger.
**SELECTED REVIEWS** (since January 1994): 5.97 Examiner.
**PRIZES/AWARDS/APPOINTMENTS:**
3.97 Winner, 'Dramatic Cup' for opera from Feis Ceoil, RDS, Dublin.
3.97 Winner, Rathmines and Rathgar Cup for Dramatic opera from Feis Ceoil, RDS, Dublin.
**TRAINING AND/OR QUALIFICATIONS:**
From 1988 to 1992, ALCM Diploma in Speech and Drama, Gold Medal (acting) from Cork School of Music and Drama.
From 1990 to 1993, BA (Hons) from UCC.
8.96 Masterclass in opera and operetta with Paul Hamburger.
Since 2.96, Studying with Irene Sandford at Royal Irish Academy of Music, Dublin.
**AVAILABILITY:**
General.
**ADDITIONAL INFORMATION:**
Currently on a singing scholarship at the Royal Irish Academy of Music, Dublin. Also a professional actress - full membership of Irish Actor's Equity and has experience in theatre, television and film. Speaks French, Spanish, German and Irish.

## Louise Irvine *Soprano*

**Contact:** Ms Louise Irvine
10, Devenish Crescent
Silverhill
Enniskillen
Co Fermanagh, BT74 5JP
Northern Ireland
**Tel:** +44 1365 323873

*"The first-rate local soloists were Louise Irvine ..."* 23.11.95 Belfast Telegraph.

**KEY IRISH PERFORMANCES** (since January 1994):
1994 Whitla Hall, Belfast, appearing in the Queen's University Choir and Orchestra production of Handel's 'Israel in Egypt'.
1994 First Presbyterian Church, Rosemary Street, Belfast, accompanied by Derek Collins and Séan Rafferty.
1995 Ulster Hall, Belfast, appearing in the Queen's University Choir and Orchestra performance of Mahler's 2nd Symphony.
1996 Ardhowen Theatre, Enniskillen, appearing with the Royal Ulster Constabulary Brass Band.
**KEY PERFORMANCES OUTSIDE IRELAND** (since January 1994):
1994 Italy and Germany, appearing solo with the Italian Institute Choir.

**SELECTED BROADCASTS AND/OR RECORDED WORK:**
1990 Lunchtime recital for BBC Radio Ulster.
**PRIZES/AWARDS/APPOINTMENTS:**
6.94 Winner of the May Turtle Award from the Queen's University, Belfast.
6.96 Awarded Bursary by the Arts Council Northern Ireland.
**TRAINING AND/OR QUALIFICATIONS:**
From 1982 to 1991, Grade 8 (Distinction) and Performer's Certificate with Andrew Batchelor, Omagh.
From 1991 to 1994 B Mus Degree (Hons) from Queen's University, Belfast.
From 1991 to 1997, followed advanced vocal training course with Veronica Dunne, at the Leinster Opera Studio, Dublin.
From 1994 to 1997, MA (Performance Studies) at Queen's University, Belfast.
**AVAILABILITY:**
December to January, March to April, June to September.
**ADDITIONAL INFORMATION:**
Has also been the soprano soloist in Mozart's Requiem with Hamilton Harty Choir and Orchestra in Belfast and in Vaughan William's 'Serenade to Music' with Queen's University Choir and Orchestra.
1997 winner of the Ian Gow Memorial Award.

# Anne-Marie Keaney *Soprano*

**Contact:** Ms Anne-Marie Keaney
'Willow Cottage'
41, Harfield Road
Sunbury-on-Thames
Middlesex TW16 5PT
England
**Tel:** +44 1932 783141

*"This singer is the loveliest sounding young Irish soprano I've heard ... on the evidence of this concert alone, her future development will be watched with especial interest"* 5.10.90 Irish Times.

**KEY IRISH PERFORMANCES** (since January 1994):
1995 National Concert Hall, Dublin appearing in Mozart's Requiem in D Minor, with Culwick Choral Society and the Orchestra of St Cecilia.
11.96 Bank of Ireland Arts Centre, Dublin appearing with Deborah Kelleher.
4.97 Dublin, appearing in Mozart's Requiem in D Minor and the Missa Brevis in D, with Tallaght Choral Society.
**KEY PERFORMANCES OUTSIDE IRELAND** (since January 1994):
12.96 Cambridge University, appearing with Cambridge Choral Society.
5.97 Recital, London.
6.97 Surrey, appearing with Elmbridge Choral Society in a performance of Rossini's 'Messe Solonnelle'.
7.97 Oxford, appearing with Bampton Summer Opera, in a production of 'Don Giovanni' by Gazzaniga as 'Maturina'.
**SELECTED BROADCASTS AND/OR RECORDED WORK:**
1982 Scór na nÓg winner recorded for RTÉ.
1983 Recording for RTÉ.
From 1987 to 1989, soloist with RTÉ Chamber Choir (now National Chamber Choir).
12.95 Carols at Christmas for RTÉ.
**SELECTED REVIEWS** (since January 1994):
4.95 Evening Press.
11.96 Irish Times.
7.97 Oxford Times.
**PRIZES/AWARDS/APPOINTMENTS:**
1986 Winner of Percy Whithead Cup, awarded by Feis Ceoil, Dublin.
1986 Winner of oratorio prize, awarded by Feis Ceoil, Sligo.
1987 Winner of Lieder competition, awarded by the DIT Conservatory of Music and Drama, Dublin.
1988 Winner of Michael O'Higgins Memorial Cup, awarded by Feis Maitiu, Dublin.
**TRAINING AND/OR QUALIFICATIONS:**
From 9.87 to 6.89, voice and theory and piano studies at the DIT CMD.
1991, Attended masterclasses with Geoffrey Parsons at the Royal Irish Academy of Music.
**REGULARLY PERFORMS WITH:**
Deborah Kelleher (piano), James Nelson (tenor).
**AVAILABILITY:** General.
**ADDITIONAL INFORMATION:**
Experienced as an oratorio soloist, having performed over thirty oratorios in a number of venues including the Church of St-Martin-in-the-Field's, St Alban's Abbey, Cambridge University, St Patrick's Cathedral and National Concert Hall, Dublin. Operatic roles have included 'Madame Goldentrill', 'Blonde', 'Susanna', 'Celidora', 'Gretel', 'Mrs Wrighten', 'Bacchis', 'Gianetta', 'Maturina', 'First Boy', 'Dew Fairy', 'Barbarina' .

# Virginia Kerr *Soprano*

**Contact:** Ms Virginia Kerr
c/o Mr Peter Hall
6, Windmill Street
London, W1 PLHF, England
**Tel/Fax:** +44 171 4368911 / +44 171 6314631
**Email:** musichall@compuserve.com

*"Radiant presence, sturdy tone and natural musicianship, made her ideal for the title role"*
7.96 The Times (Rodney Milnes) 'The Enchantress', New Sussex Opera.

**KEY IRISH PERFORMANCES** (since January 1994):
12.94 National Concert Hall, Dublin, Irish premiere of Sir Michael Tippett's 'Byzantium' in the presence of the composer to mark his 90th birthday, appearing with the National Symphony Orchestra of Ireland.
**KEY PERFORMANCES OUTSIDE IRELAND** (since January 1994):
Royal Opera House, Covent Garden 'Die Walkure' appearing with Placido Domingo in his London debut singing Wagner.
**SELECTED RECORDED AND/OR BROADCAST WORK:**
12.93 'Ultima Rerum' by Gerard Victory, for Naxos.
9.95 'Bower of Roses' (The Veiled Prophet) by Charles Villiers Standford for Naxos.
Numerous recordings for RTÉ and BBC Radio 3.
Her performance as the lead soprano in Weir's 'The Vanishing Bridegroom' was recorded by BBC.
**SELECTED REVIEWS** (since January 1994):
6.96 Sunday Tribune (Ian Fox).
7.96 Opera Magazine (John Allison).
7.96 Opera Now (George Hall).
**PRIZES/AWARDS/APPOINTMENTS:**
Winner of the Players Wills Vocal Bursary, Feis Ceoil, Dublin.
1981 Winner of the Golden Voice of Ireland.
5.96 Awarded the Margaret Burke Sheridan Medal for Excellence, Dublin.
**TRAINING AND/OR QUALIFICATIONS:**
Teaching and Performance Diplomas from the Royal Irish Academy of Music and the Guildhall School of Music and Drama, London.
**AVAILABILITY:**
Subject to schedule.
**ADDITIONAL INFORMATION:**
Operatic roles include 'Lelia' in the Pearl Fisher, 'Liu' in Turandot, 'Musetta' in La Boheme, 'Michaela' in Carmen, 'Elvira' in L'Italiana in Algeir', all performed with Opera Ireland. 'Governess' in the Turn of the Screw and 'Elettra' in Idomeneo for Opera Northern Ireland. 'Glasha' in Katya Kabanova for Glyndebourne Festival Opera, 'Anita' in Jonny Spielt and Donna Elvira for Scottish Opera. Has also sung the title role in Janacek's opera, Jenufa and 'Salome' in the Strauss' opera, Salome. Interpretations of contemporary music include 'Grete' in Schreker's Der Ferne Klang for Opera North and 'Judith' in Ian McQueen's Line of Terror at the Almeida Theatre, London. Sang the title role in the British premiere of Tchaikowsky's The Enchantress (see review above). Concert repertoire ranges from Bach to Webern and has sung under the baton of Paul Daniel, Richard Armstrong, John Mauceri, Sir Andrew Davis and Bernard Haitink, KBE.

## Lynda Lee *Soprano*

**Contact:** Ms Lynda Lee
1, Clyde Road
Dublin 4
**Tel:** +353 1 6603641

*"... She sang her part with an ideal combination of coloratura, flexibility and lyric warmth..."*
Opern Welt ('Xerxes' with the Hallé Handel Orchestra).

**KEY IRISH PERFORMANCES** (since January 1994):
1.94 Ulster Hall, Belfast, promoted by BBC, appearing with the Ulster Orchestra.
6.95 Ulster Hall, Belfast, promoted by BBC, appearing with the Ulster Orchestra in Beethoven's 9th Symphony.
2.96 National Concert Hall, Dublin, promoted by Our Lady's Choral Society, appearing with the National Symphony Orchestra of Ireland in Elgar's 'Kingdom Apostles'.
6.96 NCH promoted by RTÉ Opera Excerpts, appearing with the NSOI.
**KEY PERFORMANCES OUTSIDE IRELAND** (since January 1994):
12.96 Royal Festival Hall, appearing in Deruflé's Requiem and Poulenc 'Stabat Mater' with the London Philharmonic.
12.96 Queen Elizabeth Hall, London, soprano in Beethoven Mass in C.
1-3.97 Staatstheater, Karlsruhe, Germany, appearing with Deutsches Solisten as 'Agrippina'.
4-6.97 Staatstheater, Hallé, promoted by the Hallé Handelfestspiele, appearing in the title role of the Hallé Handel Orchestra production of 'Xerxes'.
**SELECTED BROADCASTS AND/OR RECORDED WORK:**
4.95 St Matthew Passion for United Recording and BBC.
9.95 'The Children of Lir' for Claddagh Records.
9.96 'Maritana' for Naxos.
**SELECTED REVIEWS** (since January 1994):
1.97 Opern Welt, Opera Now, Opera.
4.97 Irish Times.
6.97 Opern Welt, Opera, Opera Now and all main German newspapers.
**PRIZES/AWARDS/APPOINTMENTS:**
4.91 Vocal winner of the Lombard and Ulster Music Foundation Competition.
6.95 Finalist and winner of Radio Prize in the Belvedere International Competition, Austria.
**TRAINING AND/OR QUALIFICATIONS:**
From 1991 to 1995, DIT Conservatory of Music and Drama, Dublin (teacher Veronica Dunne). Has attended masterclasses with Brigette Fassbender and Carlo Bergonzi.
**AVAILABILITY:**
General.

## Denise Long *Soprano*

**Contact:** Denise Long
26/27, Drury Street
Dublin 2
**Mobile:** +353 87 2345736
**Other instruments:** Piano.

**KEY IRISH PERFORMANCES** (since January 1994):
Various appearances at the National Concert Hall, Dublin, John Field Room, NCH Mansion House, Dublin and the Bank of Ireland Arts Centre, Dublin appearing with Finbar Wright, Mairéad Hurley and Jonathan Webb.
**SELECTED BROADCASTS AND/OR RECORDED WORK:**
1992 'Gay Byrne Show' for RTÉ.
1997 With Eamon Dunphy for Radio Ireland.
1997 For Anna Livia FM.
**PRIZES/AWARDS/APPOINTMENTS:**
Vocal Arts Scholarship. Winner of the Mrs PJ Geoghegan Cup at the Feis Ceoil, Dublin.
**TRAINING AND/OR QUALIFICATIONS:**
B Mus from London University. Has attended masterclasses with Dr Bernadette Greevy and Professor Janice Chapman.
**REGULARLY PERFORMS WITH:**
Classical Fusion
**AVAILABILITY:**
General.

## Frances Lucey *Soprano*

**Contact:** Ms Frances Lucey
c/o Mr Matthew Sprizzo
477, Durant Avenue
Staten Island
New York 10308
USA
**Tel/Fax:** +1 718 948 5402 / +1 718 984 8996

*"... Unbelievable stage presence. The public was enthralled; whatever she sang [it] sent shivers down your spine"* 2.8.95 Süddentsche Zeitung.

**KEY IRISH PERFORMANCES** (since January 1994):
2.95 Gate Theatre, Dublin and tour of Ireland, promoted by Opera Theatre Company.
**KEY PERFORMANCES OUTSIDE IRELAND** (since January 1994):
16.8.95 Frick Collection, New York, promoted by Shaw Concerts and Matthew Sprizzo appearing with Donald Wages.
3.12.95 Carnegie Hall, New York, promoted by Matthew Sprizzo, appearing with American Composers Orchestra.
12.95 Bavarian State Opera, Munich as 'Gretel'.
**SELECTED BROADCASTS AND/OR RECORDED WORK:**
1993 'Carmina Burana' for RTÉ.
1994 Stanford Requiem for Naxos.
1995 Solo recording for Bavarian Radio and Amati.
**SELECTED REVIEWS** (since January 1994):
18.8.95 New York Times.
22.8.95 USA Today.
1995 New York Post.
**PRIZES/AWARDS/APPOINTMENTS:**
6.84 Soprano solo winner at the Feis Ceoil, Dublin.
Since 1989 permanant contract with Bavarian State Opera, Munich.
1992 Festival Prize, awarded by Friends of the Bavarian State Opera.
**TRAINING AND/OR QUALIFICATIONS:**
From 1980 to 1983, BA Music and French, awarded by University College, Dublin.
From 1980 to 1986, LRAM in Singing and Piano, awarded by DIT Conservatory of Music and Drama, Dublin.
From 1987 to 1989, Attended the opera studio of the Bavarian State Opera.

## Fiona McAndrew *Soprano*

**Contact:** Ms Fiona McAndrew
35 Crouch Hall Road
London N8 8HH
England
**Tel/Fax:** +44 181 3480954

*"Irish soprano, Fiona McAndrew was a splendid Donna Elvira ... in a delightful performance that held one's attention from start to finish."* 1996 Opera Magazine/ Sunday Tribune (Ian Fox).

**KEY IRISH PERFORMANCES** (since January 1994):
1996 National Concert Hall, Dublin, promoted by Tallaght Choral Society, appearing as soloist.
1996 Tour of Ireland and the UK*, appearing in the Pimlico Opera production of Don Giovanni as 'Donna Elvira'.
1997 Belfast, appearing in the Castleward Opera production of Carmen as 'Frasquita'.
1997 Tour of Ireland and the UK* appearing in Opera Theatre Company's production of 'My Love, My Umbrella' as 'My Love'.
**KEY PERFORMANCES OUTSIDE IRELAND** (since January 1994):
From 1994 to 1996, Guildhall School of Music and Drama, various roles.
8.97 Northamptonshire, promoted by Central Festival Opera, appearing in the 'The Magic Flute' as 'Pamina'. See also above*.
**SELECTED BROADCASTS AND/OR RECORDED WORK:**
1997 Recitals for RTÉ.
**SELECTED REVIEWS** (since January 1994):
6.95 Opera Magazine.
1995 The Times.
8.96 The Stage.
**PRIZES/AWARDS/APPOINTMENTS:**
1997 Finalist, Royal Overseas League Music Competition.
1997 Semi-finalist, Belvedere Hans Gabor International Singing Competition.
**TRAINING AND/OR QUALIFICATIONS:**
From 1985 to 1990 BA (Hons) from University of Western Australia.
From 1990 to 1992, Vocal course at the DIT Conservatory of Music and Drama, Dublin.
From 1991 to 1993, Studied at the Leinster Opera Studio, Dublin.
From 9.93 to 7.95 Opera Course at the GSMD, London.
**AVAILABILITY:** General.

# Carla Maney *Soprano*

**Contact:** Ms Carla Maney
57, Arran Street
Roath
Cardiff CF2 3HT
Wales
**Mobile/Tel:** +44 467 623329 / +44 1222 493301 / +44 1693 69292 (Northern Ireland)

*"... was a great pleasure to listen to in the role of Dhia from Mascagni's 'Iris'..."* 1.96 Opera Now.

**KEY IRISH PERFORMANCES** (since January 1994):
9.95 Opera House, Belfast, appearing with Opera Northern Ireland.
10/11.95 Theatre Royal, Wexford, promoted by Wexford Festival Opera.
11.95 Opera House, Belfast, appearing with Opera Northern Ireland.
11.95 Enniskillen, Co Fermanagh promoted by David Assater, appearing with Enniskillen Choral Society.
**KEY PERFORMANCES OUTSIDE IRELAND** (since January 1994):
3.96 Saint David's Hall, Cardiff, Wales, in a performance of 'Four Last Songs' (Strauss) promoted by the Welsh College of Music and Drama appearing with Christopher Adey.
1.97 Bradford, 'A Viennese Evening' promoted by Elizabeth Altman, appearing with English Camerata Orchestra.
5 - 10.97 Tour of Britain, promoted by International Artists, appearing with Mike Doyle in a tribute to Mario Lanza.
**SELECTED BROADCASTS AND/OR RECORDED WORK:**
1.95 '29 Bedford Street' with Séan Rafferty, recorded by BBC Northern Ireland.
3.95 'The Gerry Kelly Show' for UTV.
3.95 'The Séan Rafferty Show' for BBC.
**PRIZES/AWARDS/APPOINTMENTS:**
1994/1995 Sir Geraint Evans Scholarship, awarded by the Welsh College of Music and Drama.
1995 Silver medal, awarded by Worshipful Company of Musicians.
**TRAINING AND/OR QUALIFICATIONS:**
Royal Northern College of Music, Manchester and Welsh College of Music and Drama, Cardiff, Wales, (qualifications awarded LTCL and FTCL).
**AVAILABILITY:**
General (contract permitting).
**ADDITIONAL INFORMATION:**
A lyric soprano. Has performed the roles of the 'Cock', the 'Jay' the 'Innkeeper's Wife' and covered the role of the 'Vixen' in Janacek's 'The Cunning Little Vixen' (1995). Other performances include 'Dhia' in 'Iris' (Mascagni). Oratorio performances includes works by Handel and Purcell.

# Dorothy Maxwell *Soprano*

**Contact:** Ms Dorothy Maxwell
26, Deerpark Road
Mount Merrion
Co Dublin
**Tel:** +353 1 8370101 ext. 2612 (day) or +353 1 2982615 (evening)

*"Remarkably polished talent ... a real feel for style and a fine vocal legato ... a singer to be watched with real interest"* 2.94 Sunday Tribune.

**KEY IRISH PERFORMANCES** (since January 1994):
1994 Royal Dublin Society, promoted by RDS, Spotlight on Youth, appearing with Roy Holmes.
**SELECTED BROADCASTS AND/OR RECORDED WORK:**
1984 Radio Broadcast of the RTÉ Young Musician of the Future for RTÉ.
1984 'Let's Sing a Song' masterclasses for RTÉ.
1994 'BiBi' appearing with Roy Holmes for RTÉ.
**SELECTED REVIEWS** (since January 1994):
2.94 Evening Press.
2.94 Irish Times.
**PRIZES/AWARDS/APPOINTMENTS:**
1980 Carnegie Hall, New York as part of a talent evaluation competition.
From 1982 to 1984, Gold medal and cup winner at the Feis Ceoil and the Feis Maithiu.
1984 Vocal finalist as part of the RTÉ Young Musician of the Future.
1995 Semi finalist with the Belvedere International Singing Competition, Austria.
**TRAINING AND/OR QUALIFICATIONS:**
From 1979 to 1980, Studies at the Julliard School of Music, New York (teacher Elizabeth Bishop).
From 1981 to 1985, London studied with Constance Shacklock OBE.
From 1990 from 1995, Royal College of Music, London studied with Marion Stud Holme. Since 1990 vocal coaching with Peter Gelhorne, London.
**REGULARLY PERFORMS WITH:**
Roy Holmes (piano) Louisa Maxwell (soprano).
**AVAILABILITY:** General.
**ADDITIONAL INFORMATION:**
From 1987 to 1989, Professional cantor in University Church, Dublin. Stage appearances include the following leading roles in Gilbert and Sullivan productions:'Casilda' in 'The Gondoliers', 'Mabel' in the 'Pirates of Penzance' and 'Phylis' in 'Iolanthe'.

# Judith Mok *Soprano*

**Contact:** Judith Mok
Rocky Hill
The Green Road
Dalkey
Co Dublin
**Tel/Fax:** +353 1 2852013

*'We were all grateful for the wonderful moments offered by Judith Mok"* 3.10.95 Le Monde.

**KEY PERFORMANCES OUTSIDE IRELAND** (since January 1994):
9.94 Congresshall, Strasbourg appearing with Vienna Symphony Schoenberg Choir (Il Canto Sospeso).
10.95 Queen Elizabeth Hall, London appearing with London Sinfonietta.
3.97 Buenos Aires appearing with Fernando Pérez (piano).
6.97 Amsterdam, recital performance.
**SELECTED BROADCASTS AND/OR RECORDED WORK:**
1995 'Another Voice' for DO records.
1997 'For my Baby' for EMI.
**SELECTED REVIEWS** (since January 1994):
1996 Opera International.
1997 CD review.
**PRIZES/AWARDS/APPOINTMENTS:**
1980 3rd Prize winner, Concours de Paris.
1981 Awarded Lieder Prize in the Den Bosch International Vocal Competition.
**TRAINING AND/OR QUALIFICATIONS:**
From 1972 to 1978, Soloist and teacher at the Kon. Conservatory, The Hague.
From 1979 to 1981, Various masterclasses with E. Schivarhkopf, E and C Ludwig and others.
**REGULARLY PERFORMS WITH:**
As duo with Susanna Moncayo (mezzo soprano)
**AVAILABILITY:**
General.
**ADDTIONAL INFORMATION:**
Has a wide repertoire from baroque to contemporary. Works have also been composed for her. Has performed oratorio, Lieder and opera in many of the European festivals and halls with conductors such as Harnoncourt and Edo de Waart. Has made several TV and radio appearances.

## Geraldine Montague *Soprano*

**Contact:** Ms Geraldine Montague
40, Innismore
Crumlin Village
Dublin 12
**Tel:** +353 1 4560551
**Other instruments:** Piano, violin.

**KEY PERFORMANCES OUTSIDE IRELAND** (since January 1994):
11.96 Sir G Evans Hall, Welsh College of Music and Drama, Cardiff, German song recital.
3.96 Cardiff Scandinavian song recital.
5.97 Sir G Evans Hall, Welsh College of Music and Drama, Cardiff, lunchtime solo recital (Brahms).
5.97 Sir G Evans Hall, Welsh College of Music and Drama, Cardiff.
**PRIZES/AWARDS/APPOINTMENTS:**
3.97 Winner of Lieder Prize at the Feis Ceoil, Dublin.
1996, Scholarship awarded to the Guildhall School of Music and Drama, London.
**TRAINING AND/OR QUALIFICATIONS:**
From 1996 to 1997, Performance Diploma from the Welsh College of Music and Drama.
Since 9.97 B Mus at the Guildhall School of Music and Drama, London.

## Suzanne Murphy *Soprano*

**Contact:** Suzanne Murphy
c/o Ingpen and Williams Limited
International Artists Management
26, Wadham Road
London SW15 2LR
England
**Tel/Fax:** +44 181 8743222 / +44 181 8773113

*"Clarity of delivery ... poignantly understated emotional tension .... [ability to] ... alternate between coquette and distraught lover, are all testimony to formidable talent as both actress and singer"* Vancouver Opera production of Tosca.

**KEY IRISH PERFORMANCES** (since January 1994):
1994 Castletown House, promoted by Festival of Great Irish Houses, accompanied by Ingrid Surgenor (piano).
1995 Landsdowne Road, Dublin in the Voices of World concert, promoted by Oliver Barry, appearing with the RTÉ Concert Orchestra.
1996 Opera House, Belfast appearing with Opera Northern Ireland in a production of 'Fidelio'.
1997 Tour of Limerick, Dublin and Galway appearing with the Irish Chamber Orchestra.
**KEY PERFORMANCES OUTSIDE IRELAND** (since January 1994):
1994 Berlin Staatsoper appearing in 'Tosca'.
1994 Basel Opera Company, title role in 'La Vestale'.
1995 Minneapolis, USA in a production of 'Turandot' appearing with The Minnesota Opera.
1996 Berlin Staatsoper in 'Alceste'.
**SELECTED BROADCASTS AND/OR RECORDED WORK:**
1992 'Heroines of Verdi and Puccini' for Collins Classics.
1993 'There is an Isle' for Columbia.
1995 'Somewhere' for Columbia.
**PRIZES/AWARDS/APPOINTMENTS:**
1987 Winner of the National Entertainment Award from the Allied Irish Bank.
1989 Arts Award - Sunday Tribune.
1989 Made honourary fellow of the University of Mid Glamorgan.
1990 Irish Life Building Society Award for outstanding contribution to music.
**TRAINING AND/OR QUALIFICATIONS:**
DIT CMD (teacher Veronica Dunne).
**AVAILABILITY:**
Subject to schedule.

## Niamh Murray *Soprano*

**Contact:** Ms Niamh Murray
1, Coundon Court
Killiney Avenue
Killiney
Co Dublin
**Tel:** +353 1 2854123

*"Has immaculate diction ... glorious voice ... a recording star who sings opera, popular and traditional songs with equal facility."*
27.10.94 The Examiner.

**KEY IRISH PERFORMANCES** (since January 1994):
10.94 Theatre Royal, Wexford, promoted by Wexford Festival Opera, appearing in 'La Bohème' as 'Eufemia' with the National Symphony Orchestra of Ireland.
5.96 National Concert Hall, Dublin, promoted by the Culwick Choral Society, appearing with the Orchestra of St Cecilia.
4.97 National Concert Hall, Dublin, in St James' 'Verdi and Puccini Heroines', appearing with the Orchestra of St James.
5.97 University of Limerick Concert Hall, promoted by University of Limerick Proms, appearing with University of Limerick Orchestra.
**KEY PERFORMANCES OUTSIDE IRELAND** (since January 1994):
10.95 Malaga, Spain, appearing in celebrity gala concerts.
7.96 Gaiety Theatre, Douglas, promoted by the Isle of Man Opera Company, appearing with the Opera Island Orchestra.
3.97 Basilica di Maria Maggiore, Rome appearing with the choir and orchestra of Westminister Cathedral.
5.97 Rosary Basilica, Lourdes, appearing as soloist with St James' Choir and organist Jean Paul Lécot.

**SELECTED BROADCASTS AND/OR RECORDED WORK:**
10.94 'A Fairer Paradise' for Sony Records.
12.96 'Let the Bells Ring' for Ambush Records FMN.
3.97 'Songs of Praise' (Rome) for BBC.
**SELECTED REVIEWS** (since January 1994):
4/5.94 Irish Times.
10.94 Belfast Newsletter.
1.97 Irish Times.
**PRIZES/AWARDS/APPOINTMENTS:**
1987-91 (inclusive) Bursaries and scholarships from the Arts Council and Friends of the Vocal Arts in Ireland.
1990 Scholarship to study in Siena, Italy from Italian Government.
**TRAINING AND/OR QUALIFICATIONS:**
From 1980 to 1983, B Ed (with music) from Carysfort College of Education.
From 1987 to 1988, ALCM from the Royal Irish Academy of Music and London College of Music.
1990, Diploma masterclass at Chigiana di Musica, Siena (teacher Carlo Begonzi).
From 1991 to 1992, LLSM from Leinster School of Music.
**REGULARLY PERFORMS WITH:**
Culwick Choral Society, Dublin County Choir, Dublin Grand Opera Society, Irish Chamber Orchestra, Orchestra of St Cecilia, St James' Choir and Orchestra.
**AVAILABILITY:**
General.

# Regina Nathan *Soprano*

| | |
|---|---|
| **Contact:** | Ms Regina Nathan<br>19, Milling Road<br>Burnt Oak<br>Edgware, HA8 0PZ<br>England |
| **Tel/Fax:** | +44 181 9310811 |

**KEY IRISH PERFORMANCES** (since January 1994):
6.96 National Concert Hall, Dublin, promoted by MS Society.
11.96 St Patrick's Cathedral, Dublin in a performance of Faure's Requiem.
12.11.96 Aula Maxima, Maynooth.
13.1.97 The Point Depot, Dublin promoted by Enigma Productions, appearing with Frank Patterson.
**KEY PERFORMANCES OUTSIDE IRELAND** (since January 1994):
10.96 Glasgow, promoted by Scottish Opera as 'Adeina'.
11.96 Concertgebouw, Amsterdam, promoted by VARA Radio in Zdenka as 'Arabella'.
12.96 Nantes Opera House, in the production of 'La Traviata' as 'Violetta'.
2.97 Nantes Opera House, in Floyd's 'Susanna'.
**SELECTED BROADCASTS AND/OR RECORDED WORK:**
7.96 'The Bells' and 'Vocalise' for Carlton Classics.
11.96 'Faith of Our Fathers' CD for Enigma Productions.
2.97 'Faith of Our Fathers' video for Enigma Productions.
**PRIZES/AWARDS/APPOINTMENTS:**
1991 3rd Prize at the International Belvedere Competition, Austria.
1992 3rd Prize at the Geneva Concours International d'Executives Musicale.
**TRAINING AND/OR QUALIFICATIONS:**
From 1978 to 1982, BA from the National University of Ireland, Maynooth.
From 1982 to 1983, H Dip in Ed from the National University of Ireland, Maynooth.
From 1987 to 1988, Post Graduate Certificate from Trinity College of Music, London.
From 1988 to 1989, Studied at the National Opera Studio.
**AVAILABILITY:**
General.

# Méav Ní Mhaolchatha *Soprano*

| | |
|---|---|
| **Contact:** | Méav Ní Mhaolchatha<br>Flat 2<br>130, Sandford Road<br>Ranelagh, Dublin 6 |
| **Tel:** | +353 1 4973873 |
| **Other instruments:** | Irish harp. |

*"Haunting performances of Balfe and Moore"*
10.8.97 Sunday Tribune (Ian Fox).

**KEY IRISH PERFORMANCES** (since January 1994):
20.1.96 Ulster Hall, Belfast, promoted by The Ulster Orchestra, appearing as a soprano soloist with Anúna, Ulster Orchestra and Gerald McCrystal.
1.7.96 Temple Bar, Dublin (Meeting House Square), the televised opening of the European Presidency, appearing as a soprano soloist with Anúna.
10.96 National tour, appearing with The National Chamber Choir.
3.6.97 Newgrange Interpretive Centre, appearing as a soloist in a new work composed by Michael Holohan.
**KEY PERFORMANCES OUTSIDE IRELAND** (since January 1994):
11.96 Teatro Monumental, Madrid, promoted by Fernando Casas, appearing with Anúna.
11.96 Bridgewater Hall, Manchester, promoted by Manchester Hall, appearing with Anúna.
2.97 Gothenburg, Sweden, principal soloist with Anúna in Swedish concert series.
3.97, 3 week concert tour, USA, promoted by RTÉ, appearing with the RTÉ Concert Orchestra.
**SELECTED BROADCASTS AND/OR RECORDED WORK:**
1996 'Omnis' (New Edition), for Danú.
25.4.96 'Aujourd'hui L'Irlande', for Auvidis.
9.1.97 'The Spirit of Ireland', with the RTÉCO for Richmond Productions Ltd.
**TRAINING AND/OR QUALIFICATIONS:**
From 1987 to 1993, DIT Conservatory of Music and Drama, Dublin Grade 8 (voice).
1991 ALCM, (piano performance diploma).
1992 ARIAM (teachers diploma for Irish harp).
11.95, Attended a John Elwes, 'Mostly Modern' masterclass.
**REGULARLY PERFORMS WITH:**
Anúna, National Chamber Choir.
**AVAILABILITY:**
General.
**ADDITIONAL INFORMATION:**
A high lyric soprano specialising in contemporary Irish compositions. As principal soloist with Anúna, has toured extensively in Ireland and Europe. Has broadcast frequently on television and radio.

# Máire O'Brien *Soprano*

| | |
|---|---|
| **Contact:** | Ms Máire O'Brien<br>4, Brookwood Crescent<br>Artane<br>Dublin 5 |
| **Tel:** | +353 1 8310432 |
| **Email:** | mriggleman@msn,com. |

**KEY IRISH PERFORMANCES** (since January 1994):
1.94 National Concert Hall, Dublin, promoted by RTÉ, appearing with National Symphony Orchestra of Ireland.
12.95 NCH, Dublin, promoted by RTÉ.
6.96 Droichead Arts Centre, Drogheda, appearing with Michael Casey.
**KEY PERFORMANCES ABROAD** (since January 1994):
9.97 Weill Hall, Carnegie Hall, New York.
1997 Aspen Music Festival.

**SELECTED BROADCASTS AND/OR RECORDED WORK:**
6.94 'Neilson Symphony No 3', for Naxos Records.
**PRIZES/AWARDS/APPOINTMENTS:**
1994 Awarded scholarship to study at the Juilliard Opera Centre New York.
4.97 Winner of the Olga Kaussevitsky competition.
**TRAINING AND/OR QUALIFICATIONS:**
Studied in Dublin with Veronica Dunne.
From 1989 to 1994, LTCL from the DIT Conservatory of Music and Drama, Dublin.
From 1986 to 1990, BA Music from Trinity College, Dublin.
From 1994 to 1996, M Mus from the Juilliard School of Music, New York.
**REGULARLY PERFORMS WITH:**
RTÉ Concert Orchestra, Anthony Byrne (piano), Culwick Choral Group.
**AVAILABILITY:**
Subject to schedule.

# Anne O'Byrne *Soprano*

**Contact:** Ms Anne O'Byrne
Flat 1
68, Sydenham Park
London SE26 4DP
England
**Tel/Mobile:** +353 1 8213046 or +44 181 2913744 / +44 402 305187

*"Anne O'Byrne puts the emphasis on feeling and naturalness, without distortion to a well-made musical line"* 13.3.97 New York Times.

**KEY IRISH PERFORMANCES** (since January 1994):
Autumn 1995 National Concert Hall, Dublin, appearing in the Tallaght Choral Society production of Mendelssohn's 'Elijah', singing soprano solo.
3.96 Nationwide tour, appearing in the Opera Theatre Company production of Handel's 'Amadigi' as 'Oriana'.
**KEY PERFORMANCES OUTSIDE IRELAND** (since January 1994):
Autumn 1996 UK tour, appearing in the English Touring Opera production of Verdi's 'Rigoletto' as 'Gilda'.
Spring 1997 BAM Centre, New York and Portugal, appearing in the Opera Theatre Company production of Handel's 'Amadigi' as 'Oriana'.
Spring/summer 1997 UK tour, appearing in the Travelling Opera production of Mozart's 'Don Giovanni' as 'Elvira'.
6.97 Holland Park, London, appearing in the European Chamber Opera production of Mozart's 'Die Zauberflöte' as 'Pamina'.
**SELECTED BROADCASTS AND/OR RECORDED WORK:**
1991 Mozart's 'Exultate Jubilate' with the RTÉ Concert Orchestra for RTÉ.
12.91 Programme of operatic arias with the RTÉ Concert Orchestra for RTÉ.
Summer 1996 Travelling Opera production of 'Carmen' as 'Frasquita' for Carlton Classics.
**SELECTED REVIEWS** (since January 1994):
12.95 Opera Magazine.
24.5.96 Evening Herald.
Autumn 1996: Manchester Evening News.
**PRIZES/AWARDS/APPOINTMENTS:**
1990 Winner of vocal section in the Lombard and Ulster Music Foundation Award.
1995 Semi-finalist in the Belvedere International Singing Competition, Austria.
**TRAINING AND/OR QUALIFICATIONS:**
1988 Lieder masterclass with Paul Hamburger at the DIT Conservatory of Music and Drama, Dublin.
1989 Masterclass with Hugo Benelli at the Wexford Festival Opera.
From 1989 to 1991, Professional Performance Diploma from the Royal Northern College of Music, Manchester.
1991 Masterclasses in baroque music and movement with Jennifer Smith and Marshall Pinkoski at the Opera Theatre Company, Dublin.
**AVAILABILITY:**
General.

**ADDITIONAL INFORMATION:**
Interested in early music right through to contemporary: Monteverdi's '1610' Vespers, Mozart's 'C minor Mass', Britten's 'Les Illuminations, Maxwell Davies' 'Missa Super l'Homme Armé'.

# Maria O'Connell *Soprano*

**Contact:** Ms Maria O'Connell
13, Melesian Avenue
Feltrim Road
Swords
Co Dublin
**Tel:** +353 1 8405743

**KEY IRISH PERFORMANCES** (since January 1994):
11.96 Christchurch Cathedral, Dublin, soloist in Vivaldi's 'Gloria' with the Conservatory of Music Choir.
12.96 Pro-Cathedral, Dublin, soloist in Mozart's 'Missa Brevis in D' with the Palestrina Choir.
3.97 UCD Dublin, soloist in Mozart's Coronation Mass with the UCD Music Society.
6.97 Kildare, soloist with Our Lady's Choral Society.
**SELECTED BROADCASTS AND/OR RECORDED WORK:**
10.96 Soundtrack for the play 'Pitchfork Disney' and 5.97 soundtrack for the play 'Three Tall Women' both composed and recorded by sound engineer Fergal Andrews.
**PRIZES/AWARDS/APPOINTMENTS:**
11.95 Semi finalist in the John McCormack Golden Voice of Athlone Competition.
4.97 Vocal semi finalist for the Ulster Bank Music Foundation Award.
**TRAINING AND/OR QUALIFICATIONS:**
From 9.94 to 5.97, Diploma in Music from DIT Conservatory of Music and Drama, Dublin (teacher Deirdre Grier Delaney).
7.96 Masterclass with Eva Andor of the Liszt Academy, Budapest.
1.97 Masterclass with Bernadette Greevy.
**AVAILABILITY:**
General.
**ADDITIONAL INFORMATION:**
Has given numerous recitals around Dublin in venues such as the John Field Room, National Concert Hall, Dublin, St Ann's Church, St Stephen's Church (the 'Peppercannister') and the Alliance Française. Repertoire covers every period from Renaissance to 20th Century including oratorio, operatic and Lieder with a particular speciality in French song and Mozart repertoire. Also interested in Spanish Renaissance guitar songs.

# Anne-Marie O'Farrell *Soprano*

**Contact:** Ms Anne-Marie O'Farrell
28, Grange Manor Drive
Rathfarnham
Dublin 16
**Tel:** +353 1 4931873
*See Concert Harp page 8.*

# Mary O'Sullivan *Soprano*

**Contact:** Ms Mary O'Sullivan
5, Annamoe Road
North Circular Road
Dubin 7
**Tel:** +353 1 8385780

# Sinéad Pratschke *Soprano*

**Contact:** Ms Sinéad Pratschke
Top Floor Flat
6, Acre Lane
Brixton
London SW2 5SG
England
**Tel/Mobile:** +44 171 7376265 / +44 410 146465

*"Most impressive voice belonged to the 'Eurydice' of Sinéad Pratschke ... bright and affecting"* 4.96 Opera.

**KEY IRISH PERFORMANCES** (since January 1994):
1997 Dublin Castle, participant at the Veronica Dunne Singing Bursary Competition, accompanied by Veronica McSweeney.
**KEY PERFORMANCES OUTSIDE IRELAND** (since January 1994):
1995 Snape Maltings, Aldeburgh, as part of the Aldeburgh Early Music Festival, appearing with the 'Britten-Pears' Baroque Orchestra.
1996 Snape Maltings Proms, Aldeburgh, appearing with the 'Britten-Pears' Baroque Orchestra in the production of 'La Nozze di Figaro' as 'Barbarina'.
1997 St Wilfrid's Hall, London, Schubertiade with Graham Johnson.
1997 Palau de la Musica, Barcelona, appearing with the 'Opera Restor'd' production of 'The Dragon of Wantley' by Lampe as 'Margery'.
**SELECTED BROADCASTS AND/OR RECORDED WORK:**
1997 Excerpts from the Veronica Dunne Competition for RTÉ.
1998 'The Dragon of Wantley' CD for Hyperion.
**SELECTED REVIEWS** (since January 1994):
15.2.96 The Stage.
4.96 Opera.
11.96 Plymouth Herald.
**PRIZES/AWARDS/APPOINTMENTS:**
1996 Awarded the Ian Fleming Award by the Musician's Benevolent Fund.
1996 Highly Commended for the Maggie Teyte Prize.
**TRAINING AND/OR QUALIFICATIONS:**
From 1989 to 1993, B Mus (Perf) from the University of Western Ontario, Canada.
From 9.93 to 10.94, M Mus (Perf) from the Royal College of Music, London.
From 9.94 to 7.95 ARCM (PG) from the Royal College of Music, London (teacher Graziella Sciutti). Has also attended masterclasses at Tanglewood, Britten-Pears School and Banff Centre, Canada.
**REGULARLY PERFORMS WITH:**
Audrey Hyland (piano), Dario Bonell (guitar).
**AVAILABILITY:**
General.

# Eimear Quinn *Soprano*

**Contact:** Ms Eimear Quinn
c/o Pat Egan
24, Merchants Court
Merchants Quay
Dublin 8
**Tel/Fax:** +353 1 6797701 or +353 1 6798572 / +353 1 6797495
Email: equinn@clubi.ie

*"A beautiful young woman with a cherub's voice that floats in an ethereal cloud all of it's own making"* 1.12.96 Sunday Independent.

**KEY IRISH PERFORMANCES** (since January 1994):
3.96 Point Depot, Dublin at the National Song Contest.
3.97 Temple Bar Music Centre, Dublin, St Patrick's Day Concert appearing with the Donal Lunny Band.
11.96 St Patrick's Cathedral, Dublin in a concert in aid of the Red Cross.
**KEY PERFORMANCES OUTSIDE IRELAND** (since January 1994):
5.96 Spectrum, Oslo, Norway at the Eurovision Song Contest.
9.96 Philharmonic Hall, Liverpool appearing with the RTÉ Concert Orchestra and a traditional ensemble.
5.97 tour of Australia appearing with the Donal Lunny Band.
**SELECTED BROADCASTS AND/OR RECORDED WORK:**
With Anúna for Danú (007) and (008). 'Súlt' with Hummingbird Productions for RTÉ.
**SELECTED REVIEWS** (since January 1994):
14.12.96 RTÉ Guide.
17.5.97 Sunday Herald Sun, Melbourne, Australia.
**PRIZES/AWARDS/APPOINTMENTS:**
3.96 Winner of the National Song Contest.
5.96 Winner of the Eurovision Song Contest.
**TRAINING AND/OR QUALIFICATIONS:**
1993 Studied musicianship, Grade 8 at DIT Conservatory of Music and Drama, Dublin.
Since 1994, studying for BA Music.
1995 studied singing to Grade 8 at the DIT CMD.
**AVAILABILITY:**
General.
**ADDTIONAL INFORMATION:**
Founder member of Early Music Chamber Choir (5 voices), Zefiro', which specialises in choral works from Renaissance and Early Baroque periods. Currently recording 1st Solo Album in Nashville.

# Claire Roche *Soprano*

**Contact:** Ms Claire Roche
34, Hampton Crescent
St Helen's Wood
Booterstown
Co Dublin
**Tel:** +353 1 2835135
*See concert harp, page 8.*

# Alison Roddy *Soprano*

**Contact:** Ms Alison Roddy
31, Elm Mount Road
Beaumont
Dublin 9
**Tel/Fax:** +353 1 8315982

*"Alison Roddy's stage presence and vocal security are striking..."* 12.6.97 Irish Times.

**KEY IRISH PERFORMANCES** (since January 1994):
11.94 Cork Opera House, appearing with the IORC production of 'Orpheus in the Underworld' as 'Cupid'.
11.94 National Concert Hall, Dublin, promoted by RTÉ, appearing in a production of 'Carmen' as 'Frasquita'.
6.10.96 NCH, Dublin, appearing with the RTÉ Concert Orchestra in a production of 'Carmina Burana'.
11-15.6.97 NCH, Dublin, promoted by RTÉ, in the Opera Ireland production of 'Gipsy Baron' as 'Arsena'.
**KEY PERFORMANCES OUTSIDE IRELAND** (since January 1994):
4.96 National Arts Centre, Ottawa, Canada, in 'Carmen' as 'Frasquita'.
11.96 St James, Piccadilly, London, appearing with the University College, London Orchestra in 'Carmina Burana'.
5.97 Dome, Brighton, playing 'Lucile' in 'Danton's Death' in the Brighton Festival.
7.97 Tour of New Zealand with the New Zealand Symphony Orchestra, in the production of 'Das Rheingold' as 'Wellgunde'.

**SELECTED BROADCASTS AND/OR RECORDED WORK:**
10.95 'Carmina Burana' for RTÉ.
11.96 Rutter Magnificat for RTÉ.
6.97 'Gypsy Baron' as 'Arsena' for RTÉ.
**SELECTED REVIEWS** (since January 1994):
12.6.97 The Stage.
12.6.97 Irish Times.
12.8.97 Opera Now.
**PRIZES/AWARDS/APPOINTMENTS:**
1994 John McCormack Golden Voice Award by Athlone Chamber of Commerce.
1997 Awarded Reginald Cant Bursary.
**TRAINING AND/OR QUALIFICATIONS:**
Since 1996, PG Cert in Opera Performance from the Royal College of Music, London.
**AVAILABILITY:**
General.

# Nicola Sharkey *Soprano*

**Contact:** Ms Nicola Sharkey
30, Hale Road
Farnham
Surrey GU9 9QH
England
**Tel:** +44 1252 735886

**KEY IRISH PERFORMANCES** (since January 1994):
Spring 1994, Gaiety Theatre, Dublin, appearing with the Dublin Grand Opera Society and the National Symphony Orchestra in the production of 'Rigoletto' as 'Gilda'.
Summer 1994, RTÉ Proms, appearing with the RTÉ Concert Orchestra in the Viennese Evening.
Summer 1995 Castleward, Northern Ireland appearing with Castleward Opera in 'I Capuletti e i Montecchi' as 'Juliet'.
**KEY PERFORMANCES OUTSIDE IRELAND** (since January 1994):
Autumn 1994, Tour Wales and England with the Mid-Wales Opera production of 'Rigoletto' as 'Gilda'.
Spring 1995, Parma, Italy, playing 'Queen of the Night' in 'Die Zauberflöte' with John Eliot Gardiner.
Autumn 1995, London Coliseum in the English National Opera production of 'The Magic Flute' as 'Queen of the Night'.
Spring 1996 Grand Theatre, Leeds, in the Opera North production of 'Medea' as 'Glauce'.
**SELECTED BROADCASTS AND/OR RECORDED WORK:**
Spring 1994 'Rigoletto' live for RTÉ.
Summer 1995 'I Capuletti e i Montecchi' for Classic FM.
Spring 1996 'Medea' for BBC.
**TRAINING AND/OR QUALIFICATIONS:**
From 9.79 to 9.82, Studied with Veronica Dunne at the DIT Conservatory of Music and Drama, Dublin.
From 9.82 to 7.83, Studied with Maestro Campogalliani in Mantova.
**AVAILABILITY:**
General.

# Olive Simpson *Soprano*

**Contact:** Miss Olive Simpson
7, Emperor's Gate
London SW7 4HH
England
**Tel:** +44 171 3734453

**KEY PERFORMANCES OUTSIDE IRELAND** (since January 1994):
7.96 Great Elm Festival, Somerset, England, promoted by Maureen Lehane, appearing with Mark Deller and Stour Baroque in 'Acis and Galatea' as 'Galatea'.
2.97 Dartington, appearing with Scott Stroman and Western Sinfonia.
3.97 Royal Festival Hall, appearing with the City of Birmingham Symphony Orchestra (conductor Simon Rattle), singing 1st soprano in 'Sinfonia' by Berio.
6.97 Bonn, appearing with Ensemble Modern (director Steve Reich), singing 1st soprano in 'Hindenburg'.
**SELECTED BROADCASTS AND/OR RECORDED WORK:**
From 1973 to 1981, 12 albums with Swingle Singers for CBS, RCA and EMI.
1990 'Chameleon' for FLY CD 100.
From 1993 to 1997, 'Cardinall's Musick' (7 albums) for ASV.
**PRIZES/AWARDS/APPOINTMENTS:**
1991 Awarded Mor Vocal Award for 'Chameleon' by the Music Retailers Association.
**TRAINING AND/OR QUALIFICATIONS:**
From 1962 to 1970, studied with Carys Denton.
From 1965 to 1970 Royal Irish Academy of Music, Dublin.
1970, LRAM (teaching) from the Royal Academy of Music, London.
From 1971 to 1975, studied with Audrey Langford.
**REGULARLY PERFORMS WITH:**
Deller Consort, The Sixteen, Electric Phoenix.
**AVAILABILITY:**
General.
**ADDITIONAL INFORMATION:**
Interested in oratorio solo work. Most recent engagements in Dublin included a performance in 1993 of St John's Passion with the Guinness Choir. Specialises in Bach, Mozart, Handel, Haydn, Fauré. Experienced Early Music singer and recitalist. Also does consort singing, close microphone singing in studio setting or in contemporary music performance, and light music.

# Róisín Toal *Soprano*

**Contact:** Róisín Toal
Apt 3
Dillon House
Ardilaun Court
Patrick Street
Dublin 8
**Tel/Fax:** +353 1 4732887

*"Enjoy the artless, uninhibited performance... effortless, musical singing wedded to an engaging stage presence"* 3.4.97 Opera Now (L'Elisir D'Amore).

**KEY IRISH PERFORMANCES** (since January 1994):
4.96 Gaiety Theatre, Dublin, appearing in Opera Ireland's production of 'The Magic Flute' as 'Second Boy'.
12.96 Gaiety Theatre, Dublin, promoted by Opera Ireland, in the production of 'L'Elisir d'Amore' as 'Gianetta'.
7.94 Cork Opera House, appearing with Phil Coulter.
**SELECTED BROADCASTS AND/OR RECORDED WORK:**
9.96 Vivaldi Mass for RTÉ.
**SELECTED REVIEWS** (since January 1994):
4.97 Opera.
7.94 The Examiner.
**TRAINING AND/OR QUALIFICATIONS:**
From 9.88 to 5.93 DIT Conservatory of Music and Drama, Dublin (teacher Veronica Dunne).
From 9.93 to 6.96 Leinster School of Music, Dublin (teacher Veronica Dunne).
**REGULARLY PERFORMS WITH:**
National Chamber Choir, Leinster Opera Studio.
**AVAILABILITY:**
Weekends, evenings, during the summer.
**ADDITIONAL INFORMATION:**
A member of the National Chamber Choir and a former member of the RTÉ Chamber Choir and Chorus. Has concert, radio and commercial recording experience. Has sung professional chorus for Opera Ireland over the past three years.

# Úna Tucker *Soprano*

**Contact:** Ms Úna Tucker
49, Tressillian Road
Brockley
London SE4 1YG
England
**Tel:** +44 181 469 3087

**KEY IRISH PERFORMANCES** (since January 1994):
24.11.96 Monkstown Church, Dublin, promoted by the Dún Laoghaire Choral Festival singing soprano solo in Handel's 'Messiah'.
1.12.96 Delgany Church, Co Wicklow.
**KEY PERFORMANCES OUTSIDE IRELAND** (since January 1994):
From 16.3.94 London, appearing with Beaufort Opera in the production of 'The Magic Flute' as 'First Lady'.
26.11.95 Sussex Centre, appearing with Sussex Choral as soloist in Handel's 'Saul' as 'Michal'.
7/8.96 Holland Park, London, appearing with European Chamber Opera in the production of 'Don Giovanni' as 'Donna Elvira'.
18.1.97 Irish Club, London.
**SELECTED BROADCASTS AND/OR RECORDED WORK:**
1986 Choral Song Album with the Christchurch Cathedral Choir.
1987 'Nighthawks' for RTÉ. Weekly recordings with the RTÉ Chamber Choir.
**TRAINING AND/OR QUALIFICATIONS:**
From 1985 to 1990, Associate Diploma in Singing and Drama from the DIT Conservatory of Music and Drama, Dublin (teacher Evelyn Dowling).
From 1992 to 1996, private tuition with Robert Dean in London.
**AVAILABILITY:**
General.

# Kathleen Tynan *Soprano*

**Contact:** Ms Kathleen Tynan
c/o Helen Sykes Artists' Management
4th Floor
Parkway House
London SW14 8LS
England (a)
or
63 Dominick Street
Shandon
Cork (h)
**Tel/Fax:** +44 181 8768276 (a) or +353 21 501265 (h) /
+44 181 8768277 (a) or +353 21 904272 (h)

*"Even more compelling ... was Kathleen Tynan's 'Varvara', chillingly practical and enormously attractive vocally."* 10.96 The Independent (Jan Smaczny).

**KEY IRISH PERFORMANCES** (since January 1994):
4/5.95 Tour of Ireland promoted by Music Network, appearing with Dearbhla Collins and Colette McGahon ('What can we poor females do?').
11.95 John Field Room, National Concert Hall, Dublin, promoted by Song Circle and the NCH, appearing with Eleanor Malone.
9/10.96 Tour of Ireland, appearing in the Opera Theatre Company production of 'Katya Kabanova' as 'Varvara'.
5.97 New Ross and Tralee, promoted by Music Network, Music for New Ross and Siamsa Tire appearing with Dearbhla Collins, Colette McGahon.
**KEY PERFORMANCES OUTSIDE IRELAND** (since January 1994):
2.95 City Hall, Hamilton, Bermuda, promoted by the Bermuda Festival, appearing in the Midsummer Opera production of 'Le Nozze di Figaro' as 'Susanna'.
3.95 Tour of France, appearing in the Travelling Opera production of 'Le Nozze di Figaro' as 'Susanna'.
8.95 Barbican Hall, London, promoted by the Barbican Centre, appearing in the Travelling Opera production of 'Le Nozze di Figaro' as 'Susanna'.
8/9.97 Christ's Hospital, Kent and Tyne Opera House, Newcastle, promoted by the Broomhill Festival, in the EOS Chamber Orchestra/Northern Sinfonia production of 'Fidelio' as 'Marzelline'.
**SELECTED BROADCASTS AND/OR RECORDED WORK:**
5.88 'Rider to the Sea' by Vaughan Williams for National Video Corporation/RTÉ.
10.88 'The Devil and Kate' by Dvorak for National Video Corporation/ RTÉ.
9.97 'After a Childhood Spent Away from Ireland' by Fergus Johnston for RTÉ (1st performance).
**SELECTED REVIEWS** (since January 1994):
8.94 Opera (Rodney Hilnes).
2.95 Irish Times (Douglas Sealy).
**PRIZES/AWARDS/APPOINTMENTS:**
1985 Bursaries for study at Guildhall School of Music and Drama, London from the Arts Council/FVAI/Dublin VEC.
1987 Represented Ireland at the Cardiff Singer of the World Competition.
**TRAINING AND/OR QUALIFICATIONS:**
From 1977 to 1980, B Ed from St Patrick's College, Dublin.
From 1978 to 1985, LTCL Performance from Royal Irish Academy of Music (teacher Paul Deegan).
From 1985 to 1986, PDVT from the Guildhall School of Music and Drama (teacher Laura Sarti).
**REGULARLY PERFORMS WITH:**
Dearbhla Collins (piano), Colette McGahon (mezzo soprano), Jimmy Vaughan (piano), Song Circle.
**AVAILABILITY:**
General.
**ADDITIONAL INFORMATION:**
Opera: 'Zerlina' in 'Don Giovanni', 'Niece' in Peter Grimes (Dublin Grand Opera Society/Opera Ireland); 'Lucia' in 'Rape of Lucretia' (Opera Theatre Company); 'Belinda' in 'Dido and Aeneas' (English Bach Festival). Queen Elizabeth Hall, London; 'Mabel' in 'Pirates' and 'Eurydice' in 'Orpheus in the Underworld' (D'Oyly Carte).
Concerts: Irish Premiers including 'Deirdre' (Sweeney) with National Symphony Orchestra of Ireland; 'Exsultate Jubilate' and Kleine Orgel Messe' with London Festival Orchestra; Paukenmesse with NSOI at the National Concert Hall, Dublin.

# Louise Walsh *Soprano*

**Contact:** Ms Louise Walsh
89, Ridgmount Gardens
London, WC1E 7AY
England
**Tel:** +44 171 6379655

*"... With clear diction and instinct shows off her warm timbre and clear beautiful voice"*
1.95 Frankfurter Allgemeine.

**KEY IRISH PERFORMANCES** (since January 1994):
10.94 National Concert Hall, Dublin, in Haydn's St Cecilia Mass, appearing with the RTÉ Concert Orchestra.
11.94 Rowe Street Church, Wexford as part of Wexford Festival Opera appearing in Brahm's Requiem with the National Symphony Orchestra of Ireland conductor Yves Abel.
4.95 Mansion House, Dublin promoted by Opera Theatre Company, accompanied by Cornelus Witthoeft (piano).
9.95 Opera House, Belfast, in a Opera Northern Ireland production of 'The Cunning Little Vixen' appearing with the Ulster Orchestra.
**KEY PERFORMANCES OUTSIDE IRELAND** (since January 1994):
2.94 Sheldonian Theatre, Oxford, promoted by Stephanie Williams, in a performance of Carl Orff's 'Carmina Burana' appearing with the City of Birmingham Symphony Orchestra (conductor Christopher Robinson).

1.95 Town Hall Frankfurt, promoted by Deutsche Hessischer Rundfunk, accompanied by Jimmy Vaughan (piano).
5.95 St Clement Dane's Church, London in the Opera Theatre Company production of Handel's 'Tamberlane' as 'Asteria' appearing with the London Baroque Sinfonia conducted by Séamus Crimmins.
From 2.95 to 7.97 State Opera House, Stuttgart roles sung include 'Servilia' ('La Clemenza di Tito'), 'Xenia' ('Boris Godonov'), 'Marzelline' ('Fidelio') all appearing with the Stuttgart State Orchestra.
**SELECTED BROADCASTS AND/OR RECORDED WORK:**
11.96 'Die Welt auf Dem Mond' by Haydn for Süd-Deutsche Rundfunk, Stuttgart.
4.97 'A Song for Cardiff' with Jimmy Vaughan (piano) for RTÉ.
5.97 A 'Song for Cardiff' with the RTÉ Concert Orchestra for RTÉ.
**SELECTED REVIEWS** (since January 1994):
20.8.94 The Independent.
5.6.95 Opera Magazine.
**PRIZES/AWARDS/APPOINTMENTS:**
1994 Ist Prize (International Media Award), 2nd Overall Prize (The Warsaw Philharmonic Prize) and the Frankfurt-German, Iwate Prize at the Belvedere International Singing Competition.
**TRAINING AND/OR QUALIFICATIONS:**
From 9.83 to 6.89, Studied at the DIT Conservatory of Music and Drama, Dublin (teacher Mary Brennan).
From 9.89 to 6.93, PPRNCM, at the The Royal Northern College of Music, Manchester (teacher Caroline Ganshaw).
From 9.93 to 6.94, Attended the National Opera Studio, London.
**AVAILABILITY:**
General.
**ADDITIONAL INFORMATION:**
Freelance and works all over Europe. Repertoire also includes Irish songs and songs from musicals.

# Toni Walsh *Soprano*

**Contact:** Toni Walsh
34, Cúl na Gréine
Old Bawn
Tallaght
Dublin 24
**Tel:** +353 1 4527257

*"More than any other singer, Toni Walsh understood that, in Purcell, the music should ride on the back of the words and not the other way round"* 20.6.95 Irish Times (Martin Adams).

**KEY IRISH PERFORMANCES** (since January 1994):
11.95 National Concert Hall, Dublin in the Tallaght Choral Society production of 'Dido and Aeneas' as 'Sorceress'.
2.96 NCH, Dublin, promoted by Lyric Opera Productions, appearing with the Orchestra of St Cecilia in the production of 'La Traviata' as 'Anina'.
3.96 Bank of Ireland Arts Centre, Dublin, promoted by the Bank of Ireland, appearing with Alison Young (piano).
2.97 NCH, promoted by Lyric Opera Productions, in 'Il Travatore' as 'Inez' appearing with the Orchestra of St Cecilia.
**KEY PERFORMANCES OUTSIDE IRELAND** (since January 1994):
3.96 Êglise des Billettes, Paris in the University of Dublin Choral Society production of Handel's 'Messiah' singing soprano solo, conducted by Grainne Gormley.
**SELECTED BROADCASTS AND/OR RECORDED WORK:**
25.2.97 'Live at 3' for RTÉ.
**SELECTED REVIEWS** (since January 1994):
5.95 Irish Times.
2.96 Irish Times.
**TRAINING AND/OR QUALIFICATIONS:**
From 1985 to 1997, all grades and professional competitions.
1995 Gold Medal from the DIT Conservatory of Music and Drama, Dublin (teacher Mary Brennan).
From 1995 to 1997, Diploma in Vocal Teaching from the DIT CMD.
**AVAILABILITY:**
General.
**ADDITIONAL INFORMATION:**
Welcomes the opportunity to perform and is equally at home in opera, oratorio, the concert platform or organ loft.

# Franzita Whelan *Soprano*

**Contact:** Ms Franzita Whelan
29A, Chaucer Road
Acton Town
London W3 6DR
England
**Tel/Fax:** +44 181 993 4913

*"Inner passion rang through her powerful soprano"* 7.96 LRS vocal faculty.

**KEY IRISH PERFORMANCES** (since January 1994):
11.96 RDS, Dublin, promoted by Feis Ceoil, appearing with Andrew West (piano).
14.4.97 St Patrick's Cathedral, Dublin, promoted by Dublin Handel Festival, appearing with Prionnsias O' Duinn (conductor) in Handel's 'Messiah'.
22.5.97 National Concert Hall, Dublin, appearing with Alison Young.
14.5.97 Royal Hospital, Kilmainham, Dublin, Schubert recital appearing with Roger Vignoles.
**KEY PERFORMANCES OUTSIDE IRELAND** (since January 1994):
11.96 Liverpool Mozart Concert Orchestra singing Mozart concert arias.
12.96 France, appearing with the Besonçon Orchestra in Rossini's Sabat Mater.
4.2.97 Wigmore Hall, London, appearing with Andrew West.
6.5.97 Basingstoke, promoted by National Opera Studio, London, appearing with Bournemouth Orchestra, as 'Katya' and 'Mrs Ford'.
**SELECTED BROADCASTS AND/OR RECORDED WORK:**
1994 'Gay Byrne Show' for RTÉ.
1994 'Bibi' for RTÉ.
2.97 'FM3 Classical hour' for RTÉ.
**SELECTED REVIEWS** (since January 1994):
5.5.96 Daily Telegraph.
11.96 Irish Times.
1997 Opera.
**TRAINING AND/OR QUALIFICATIONS:**
From 1989 to 1992, Royal Irish Academy of Music (teachers M Smolenski and P Deegan).
From 1992 to 1996, Royal College of Music, London (teacher Margaret Kingsley).
From 1996 to 1997, National Opera Studio, London.
**AVAILABILITY:**
General.

# Marjorie Wright *Soprano*

**Contact:** Ms Marjorie Wright
7, Ardkeen Court
Warrenpoint
Co Down
Northern Ireland
**Tel/Fax:** +44 16937 72141 / +44 16937 52144

*"Festival chiefs sat basking in their coup in engaging Marjorie Wright after her return to settle in Warrenpoint"* 20.11.95 Belfast Newsletter.

**KEY IRISH PERFORMANCES** (since January 1994):
11.95 Belfast Festival at Queen's, Lyric Theatre (one woman show).

**SELECTED BROADCASTS AND/OR RECORDED WORK:**
8.95 'Anderson on the Road' for BBC Northern Ireland.
11.95 'PK Tonight Show' for BBC Northern Ireland.
2.97 Musical profile for Radio Ulster.
**SELECTED REVIEWS** (since January 1994):
20.11.95 Belfast Newsletter.
**PRIZES/AWARDS/APPOINTMENTS:**
1956 Associated Board Scholarship from the Royal College of Music.
1957 Clara Butt Leaving Award from the Royal College of Music, London.
**TRAINING AND/OR QUALIFICATIONS:**
1.95 ARCM and GRSM from Royal College of Music, London.
**AVAILABILITY:**
General.
**ADDITIONAL INFORMATION:**
Has one woman show 'Music for Everyone' which alternates popular songs and arias (self-accompanied) with anecdotes based on career. Also a writer with publications including a DIY singing lesson and cassette 'How to be a Bad Singer', and 'The Wright Way to Breathe'. Lectures and gives workshops based on writings. Lived and worked in Italy for 16 years.

## MEZZO-SOPRANO / CONTRALTO

### Nuala Anthony *Mezzo-Soprano*

**Contact:** Ms Nuala Anthony
55, Diamond Gardens
Finaghy
Belfast BT10 0HE
Northern Ireland
**Tel:** +44 1232 617356

*"Nuala Anthony's rich mezzo voice was heard to good effect in Henri Duparc's 'Trois Mélodies' "* 22.5.95 Irish News.

**KEY IRISH PERFORMANCES** (since January 1994):
26/27.2.94 Campbell College, Belfast appearing with the Castleward Opera Orchestra in the production of Mozart's, 'Marriage of Figaro' as 'Cherubino'.
29.3.94 Whitla Hall, Belfast, appearing with St George's Singers in Bach's St Mathew Passion.
30.3.96 St George's Church, Belfast, appearing with St George's Singers in Bach's B Minor Mass.
13.3.97 Ulster Hall, Belfast, appearing with the Methodist College Orchestra and Chorus.
**SELECTED BROADCASTS AND/OR RECORDED WORK:**
21.2.95 Songs by Brahms for BBC Radio Ulster.
6.2.96 'Music Now' singing Spanish and Italian Love songs for BBC Radio Ulster.
13.5.97 'Music Now' for BBC Radio Ulster.
**SELECTED REVIEWS** (since January 1994):
16.5.94 Belfast Telegraph.
1.4.96 Belfast Telegraph.
**TRAINING AND/OR QUALIFICATIONS:**
6.80 LTCL (singing), from Trinity College, London.
6.90 LRSM (piano).
**AVAILABILITY:**
Weekends.
**ADDITIONAL INFORMATION:**
Tutor of singing at the City of Belfast School of Music. Has sung with Studio Opera, Opera Northern Ireland and Castleward Opera. Repertoire includes: Handel's Messiah, Rossini's Stabat Mater, Bach's B Minor Mass and St Matthew Passion, Mozart's Requiem and Duruflé's Requiem.

### Patricia Bardon *Mezzo-Soprano*

**Contact:** Patricia Bardon
c/o Jonathan Groves
Ingpen and Williams Limited
International Artists' Management
26 Wadham Road
London SW15 2LR
England
**Tel/Fax:** +44 181 8743222 / +44 181 8773113

*"Gifted with a rich dark contralto which she combines with an effortless mastery of coloratura"*

12.92 Opera Magazine ('Arsace' from 'Semiramide').

**SELECTED BROADCASTS AND/OR RECORDED WORK:**
'Elijah' for Decca. 'Orlando' for Erato. 'Olga' (Eugene Onegin) for EMI and 'Giovanna' for Teldec (Rigoletto).
**SELECTED REVIEWS** (since January 1994):
10.96 Gramaphone.
6.97 Opera Now.
10.94 The Stage.
**PRIZES/AWARDS/APPOINTMENTS:**
1983 2nd Prize winner of Cardiff Singer of the World.
**REGULARLY PERFORMS WITH:**
Royal Opera House, Covent Garden, Welsh National Opera, Opera North as well as Opera Houses and orchestras throughout UK, Europe and the USA.
**AVAILABILITY:**
Subject to schedule.
**ADDITIONAL INFORMATION:**
Came to prominence as a prizewinner in the Cardiff Singer of the World Competition. Operatic roles include 'Arsace' in Semiramide at la Fenice, Venice. 'Orlando' at the Théatre des Champs Elysees, Paris and New York with Les Arts Florissants. 'Smeaton' in Anna Bolena at San Francisco Opera. 'Amastres' in Xerxes at the Statsok Munich. For the R.O.H. 'Hedwige' in 'William Tell' and 'Maddelana' in 'Rigoletto'. For W.N.O. roles include 'Carmen', 'Olga' and 'Flosshilde' in 'The Ring'. As a regular concert performer she has appeared at La Scala, Milan, Amsterdam Concertgebauw, Edinburgh Festival, Aix Festival, BBC Proms and extensively throughout UK, Europe and the USA.

### Johanna Byrne *Mezzo-Soprano*

**Contact:** Ms Johanna Byrne
36, Shannon Drive
Corbally
Limerick
**Tel:** +353 61 342829
**Other instruments:** Guitar, piano.

*"Miss Byrne can rarely have sung the delicate but taxing Schubert Litanei more effectively."*

9.95 Sunday Independent.

**KEY IRISH PERFORMANCES** (since January 1994):
1994 University of Limerick, appearing with Cara O'Sullivan and Patrick Zuk. 1996 Triskel Arts Centre, appearing with Clare Clements and Neil Sharp. 1996 John Field Room, National Concert Hall, Dublin, appearing with Clare Clements and Neil Sharp.
**KEY PERFORMANCES OUTSIDE IRELAND** (since January 1994):
6.96 Peterborough Cathedral, promoted by the Peterborough Music Festival, appearing with Clare Clements.
7.96 Holland Park Opera, London, promoted by Opera Europa, appearing with Holland Park Orchestra.
11.96 St Martin-in-the-Field's, London, appearing with Clare Clements.

5.97 Queen Elizabeth Hall, London, promoted by the National Opera Studio Showcase, appearing with Bournemouth Sinfonietta.
**SELECTED BROADCASTS AND/OR RECORDED WORK:**
1.95 Veronica Dunne Singing Bursury for RTÉ.
**SELECTED REVIEWS** (since January 1994):
16.5.97 The Times.
18.5.97 Sunday Telegraph.
**PRIZES/AWARDS/APPOINTMENTS:**
1.95 Sony Award (2nd prize) at the Veronica Dunne Singing Bursary.
6.96 Winner of the Elizabeth Harwood Award from the Royal Northern College of Music.
**TRAINING AND/OR QUALIFICATIONS:**
ARCM Diploma (merit) from the Royal College of Music, London.
From 9.93 to 6.96, PG Diploma (Distinction) from the Royal Northern College of Music, Manchester.
From 9.96 to 6.97, Studied at the National Opera Studio, London.
**AVAILABILITY:**
General.
**ADDITIONAL INFORMATION:**
Available for work as a recital artist, concert artist in oratorio or with orchestra and also in opera. Operatic repertoire includes 'Rosina' from'The Barber of Seville', 'Dorabella' from 'Cosi Fan Tutte', 'Cherubino' from 'Le Nozze di Figaro'. Oratorio repertoire includes Handel's 'Messiah', Haydn's 'Nelson' Mass and Bach's St Matthew Passion.

# Maeve Carey *Mezzo-Soprano/Contralto*

**Contact:** Ms Maeve Carey
7, Davis Avenue
Clonmel
Co Tipperary
**Tel:** +353 52 22542

**KEY IRISH PERFORMANCES** (since January 1994):
1997 Cobh Cathedral, Cork, appearing in University College Cork Choir production of Mozart's 'Coronation Mass', (singing contralto solo).
1997 White Theatre, Clonmel, Tipperary, appearing in a variety concert with Beithín Ní Mheara.
1997 Triskel Arts Centre, Cork, appearing in a Lieder recital with F Kelleher.
1997 St Luke's Church, Cork, appearing in the Cork East Choral Society performance of Vivaldi's 'Gloria', singing contralto solo.
**SELECTED BROADCASTS AND/OR RECORDED WORK:**
1994 'Late Late Show' for RTÉ.
1996 'Easter Ceremonies' for RTÉ.
1997 'Theatre Nights' for RTÉ.
**SELECTED REVIEWS** (since January 1994):
1996 Nationalist.
1997 The Examiner.
**PRIZES/AWARDS/APPOINTMENTS:**
1993 Winner at Moore's Melody competition in Avoca, Co Wicklow.
1995/7 Horne Scholarship (2 year) from the Cork School of Music
**TRAINING AND/OR QUALIFICATIONS:**
From 1993 to 1997, Studied with Maeve Coughlan at the Cork School of Music.
Since 1997, Attended the Royal Northern College of Music, Manchester.
Has taken masterclasses with R Bowman, P Hamburger, M Shanahan.
**REGULARLY PERFORMS WITH:**
'Harmony' Trio (voice, violin, piano), Carousel of Music.
**AVAILABILITY:**
General.
**ADDITIONAL INFORMATION:**
Available for oratorio, concert and recital work.

# Imelda Drumm *Mezzo-Soprano*

**Contact:** Ms Imelda Drumm
105, New Ireland Road
Rialto
Dublin 8
**Tel:** +353 1 4531701

*"Imelda Drumm acts and sings engagingly"*

6.2.94 Sunday Independent.

**KEY IRISH PERFORMANCES** (since January 1994):
From 1.94 to 2.94, Tour of Ireland appearing in the Opera Theatre Company production of Handel's 'Flavio' as 'Theodata'.
12.95 Gaiety Theatre, Dublin, in the Opera Ireland production of Rossini's 'La Cenerentola' as 'Tisbe'.
1997 Royal Dublin Society, Dublin, Bank of Ireland Proms, appearing with the RTÉ Concert Orchestra.
**KEY PERFORMANCES OUTSIDE IRELAND** (since January 1994):
1.95 New Sussex Opera tour, in a production of Rossini's 'Le Comte Ory' as 'Isolier' appearing with New Sussex Orchestra.
7.96 Glyndebourne Festival, promoted by Glyndebourne Festival Opera, as 'Dorabella' appearing with the London Philharmonic.
10.96 Glyndebourne Touring Opera Orchestra as 'Cherubino' appearing with GTOO.
10.97 Glyndebourne Tour as 'Isolier' appearing with GTOO.
**SELECTED BROADCASTS AND/OR RECORDED WORK:**
1997 Bank of Ireland Proms, recorded by FM3 Radio.
**SELECTED REVIEWS** (since January 1994):
17.5.94. Irish Times.
4.95/5.95 Opera Magazine.
**PRIZES/AWARDS/APPOINTMENTS:**
7.96 Richard Lewes / Jean Shanks Award, from Glyndebourne Festival Opera.
12.96 ESSO Award, from Glyndebourne Touring Opera.
**TRAINING AND/OR QUALIFICATIONS:**
From 1983 to 1993, Studied at the DIT Conservatory of Music and Drama, Dublin (teacher Anne-Marie O'Sullivan).
From 10.83 to 6.92, B BS (Hons) from Dublin City University.
Since 9.93, Studied at the Leinster School of Music (teacher Dr. Veronica Dunne).
From 9.96 to 6.97, Attended the National Opera Studio, London.
Since 5.97, Studies with Robert Dean, London.
**AVAILABILITY:**
Subject to schedule.
**ADDITIONAL INFORMATION:**
Apart from opera repertoire, also enjoys oratorio performances.

# Anne Marie Gibbons *Contralto*

**Contact:** Ms Anne Marie Gibbons
2, Holyrood Apartments
Holyrood Park
Ballsbridge
Dublin 4
**Tel:** +353 1 2839849

**KEY IRISH PERFORMANCES** (since January 1994):
12.96 Dublin alto soloist in Handel's 'Messiah'.
2.97 Dublin, appearing with TCD Choral Society and Orchestra.
5.97 St Ann's Church, Dawson St., Dublin.
**KEY PERFORMANCES OUTSIDE IRELAND** (since January 1994):
3.96 Paris and Burgundy, France, appearing as soloist is Handel's 'Messiah' with TCD Choral Society.
**SELECTED BROADCASTS AND/OR RECORDED WORK:**
4.93 and 10.96 'Late Late Show' for RTÉ.
**PRIZES/AWARDS/APPOINTMENTS:**
3.97 Contralto Solo Competition from the Feis Ceoil.
3.97 Margaret Burke Sheridan Cup from the Feis Ceoil.

**TRAINING AND/OR QUALIFICATIONS:**
From 1989 to 1995, studied at the DIT Conservatory of Music and Drama, Dublin.
**AVAILABILITY:**
General.

## Bernadette Greevy *Mezzo-Soprano*

**Contact:** Dr Bernadette Greevy
Artist in Residence
c/o Dublin Institute of Technology and Faculty of Applied Arts
c/o Rathmines Road
Dublin 6
**Tel/Fax:** +353 1 8313131

*"One of the most noble and beloved artists of our time"* Washington Post.

**PRIZES/AWARDS/APPOINTMENTS:**
The Harriet Cohen International Award for outstanding Artistry and the Order of Merit from Malta. Titled with Dame Commander of the Holy Sepulchre and has been bestowed the Pro Ecclesia et Pontifice, conferred by the Holy See. Life patron of the New Zealand Symphony Orchestra. Hon. life membership RDS (Royal Dublin Society).
**TRAINING AND/OR QUALIFICATIONS:**
Honorary Doctorates of Music from both the National University of Ireland and Trinity College, Dublin. AMB L'Argraiment de la Barcelona from University of Barcelona.
1996, Appointed the first Artist in Residence at the DIT Faculty of Applied Arts.
**AVAILABILITY:**
Subject to schedule.
**ADDITIONAL INFORMATION:**
Renowed as a Mahler singer and from 1992 sang the complete vocal output of Mahler with the Orquestra Filarmonica under Franz-Paul Decker at Teatro Colon, Buenos Aires. Operatic roles include 'Fricka' in Wagner's, 'Das Rheingold' and 'Die Walkure'. Eboli in Verdi's 'Don Carlo', 'Charlotte' in Massenet's 'Werther' and the title roles in 'Samson and Delilah', 'Orfeo', 'Herodiade' and 'Carmen'. Also performs Irish Folk Song arrangements and Anglo Irish Art Songs. Holds annual masterclasses and annual concert in the Irish Museum of Modern Art, Dublin. Has made recordings by the following composers: Brahms, Bach, Berlioz, Elgar, Duparc, Handel, Haydn and Irish/British Art folk songs.

## Amanda Irvine *Mezzo-Soprano* 

**Contact:** Mrs Amanda Irvine
38, Plantation Avenue
Carrickfergus, BT38 9BJ
Northern Ireland
**Tel:** +44 1960 361695
See clarinet page 4.

## Sonya Keogh *Mezzo-Soprano*

**Contact:** Ms Sonya Keogh
2, Friar Street
Cork
**Tel:** +353 21 315994

**KEY IRISH PERFORMANCES** (since January 1994):
18.2.97 Jury's Hotel, Cork, appearing in 'Bloody Mary' with Frank Buckley and Opera South.
22.3.97 St Peter's, Bandon, Cork, solo with Glaslinn Choir.
24.6.97 Crawford Art Gallery, Cork, appearing with John Gibson (contemporary music recital).
**KEY PERFORMANCES OUTSIDE IRELAND** (since January 1994):
5.96 and 5.97 Breisach, Germany, accompanied by Paul Hamburger.
**PRIZES/AWARDS/APPOINTMENTS:**
2.97 Winner of Margaret Dillon Award at the Feis Maitiú, Cork.
Summer 1997 awarded scholarship to study with Victoria de Los Angeles by the Italian Government.
**TRAINING AND/OR QUALIFICATIONS:**
From 1995 to 1997, regular masterclasses with Paul Hamburger.
Since 1996, studying for B Mus (Perf) at Cork School of Music.
**AVAILABILITY:**
General.

## Aylish Kerrigan *Mezzo-Soprano*

**Contact:** Ms Aylish Kerrigan
c/o Ms Joan Barry
1 Earlsfort Court
Lower Hatch Street
Dublin 2
**Tel/Fax:** +353 1 6614598

*"Artistic versatility and enormous vocal and dramatic talent"* Generalanzeiger, Bonn, Germany.

**KEY IRISH PERFORMANCES** (since January 1994):
2.94 Duffcarraig, Gorey, Co Wexford, appearing with Tracy Fleming (harp).
5.95 United Arts Club, Dublin, Markewitch Medal for young composers concert, appearing with Seoirse Bodley.
**KEY PERFORMANCES OUTSIDE IRELAND** (since January 1994):
5.95 University Witten, Herdecke, appearing with Seoirse Bodley (piano).
6.95 Boelblingen Schopeheim, appearing with Tracey Fleming.
7.95 Minsk, Russia, appearing with Minsk Philharmonic Orchestra.
**SELECTED BROADCASTS AND/OR RECORDED WORK:**
'I am wind on Sea' for RTÉ/Echo. 'Aylish Kerrigan on Broadway' for RTÉ/Echo.
**SELECTED REVIEWS:**
8.8.94 Leipziger Volkzeitung.
26.6.95 Ruhr Nachrichten.
13.8.95 Sindelfinger Zeitung.
**PRIZES/AWARDS/APPOINTMENTS:**
1980, Joint 2nd place awarded by Nevada Opera.
1980 2nd place awarded by East Bay Opera.
1981 Metropolitan Opera finalist.
**TRAINING AND/OR QUALIFICATIONS:**
1983 Masters Degree in Vocal Performance, from University of Oregon.
1986 Diploma from Stuttgart Musikhochschule.
**REGULARLY PERFORMS WITH:**
Christian Brembeck (piano/conductor), Andreas Kersten (piano) and Gabriele Schinnerling (piano).
**AVAILABILITY:**
General.
**ADDITIONAL INFORMATION:**
Special interest in contemporary Irish music. Honorary Professor of Music at the Conservatory of Music,Wuhan, China.

## Kate McCarney *Mezzo-Soprano*

**Contact:** Ms Kate McCarney
c/o Musicmakers
Little Easthall
St Paul's, Walden near Hitchen
Hertfordshire SG4 8DH
England (agent)
**Tel/Fax:** +44 1438 871708 / +44 1438 871777
**Email:** 100620.2341@compuserve.com

*"Kate McCarney had a sumptuous and eloquent approach in a dramatic and moving performance of the angel"*

7.95 West Sussex County Times (Dream of Gerontius).

**KEY IRISH PERFORMANCES** (since January 1994):
1994 Grand Opera House, Belfast, promoted by Opera Northern Ireland production of the 'Barber of Seville' as 'Rosina'.
1994 GOH, Belfast, promoted by ONI in the production of 'Eugene Onegin' as 'Olga'.
1995 GOH, Belfast, promoted by ONI in the production of 'Cunning Little Vixen' as 'Fox'.
1997 GOH, Belfast, promoted by ONI in the production of 'Madame Butterfly' as 'Suzuki'.
**KEY PERFORMANCES OUTSIDE IRELAND** (since January 1994):
1995 London Coliseum, promoted by English National Opera, in the production 'Belle Vivette' as 'Loulou'.
1996 State Auditorium, Mexico, as 'Carmen', appearing with the Mexico State Orchestra.
1996 Eindhoven, Netherlands, appearing with the Brabants Orchestra.
1996 Town Hall, Leeds, appearing with the BBC Philharmonic Orchestra as the alto solo in the Deruflé Requiem.
**SELECTED BROADCASTS AND/OR RECORDED WORK:**
1996 'Country House Opera at Trafalgar Park' for Tosca Records Ltd.
1996 Duruflé Requiem for BBC Radio Three.
1997 Broadcast of official opening of the Waterfront Hall, Belfast, for BBC 2.
**SELECTED REVIEWS** (since January 1994):
1997 Irish News.
1997 Belfast Telegraph.
**PRIZES/AWARDS/APPOINTMENTS:**
1983 Elsie Sykes Fellowship from the Royal Northern College of Music.
1983 John Noble Bursary from Scottish Opera.
**TRAINING AND/OR QUALIFICATIONS:**
From 1969 to 1976, Studied at the Belfast School of Music.
From 1976 to 1980, GRNCM and PPRNCM from the Royal Northern College of Music, Manchester.
From 1983 to 1984, National Opera Studio, London.
**AVAILABILITY:**
General.
**ADDITIONAL INFORMATION:**
Other roles performed include: 'Siebel' ('Faust') for Opera Northern Ireland, 'Rosina' and 'Carmen' for Welsh National Opera and 'Meg Page' ('Falstaff') and 'Carmen' for Opera Theatre Company, Dublin. Was one of four soloists at televised gala concert to mark official opening of Belfast's Waterfront Hall in May 6th 1997. (Other soloists present were Dame Kiri Te Kanawa, Dennis O' Neill and Gregory Yurisich).

# Colette McGahon *Mezzo-Soprano*

**Contact:** Colette McGahon
c/o Mr Gerry Keenan
Real Good Management
17, Dame Court, Dublin 2
**Tel/Mobile/Fax:** +353 1 6688108 / +353 87 542366
+353 1 6674530
**Email:** realgood@clubi.ie

*"... Has a glorious voice, a sheerly beautiful voice"* Irish Times (Charles Acton).

**KEY IRISH PERFORMANCES** (since January 1994):
From 16-22.9.95 Grand Opera House, Belfast, promoted by Opera Northern Ireland.
6.10.95 National Concert Hall, Dublin, promoted by the RTÉ Concert Orchestra.
16/17.11.95 NCH, Dublin, appearing with the National Symphony Orchestra of Ireland.
13.12.95 Promoted by the Irish Chamber Orchestra.
**KEY PERFORMANCES OUTSIDE IRELAND** (since January 1994):
20.5.95 Eden Court Theatre, Inverness, promoted by Inverness Choral Society.
**SELECTED BROADCASTS AND/OR RECORDED WORK:**
2.95 Bach Cantatas.
10.95 'Seven Deadly Sins' (Kurt Weill) for RTÉ.
1996 Stanford Requiem for Naxos.
**SELECTED REVIEWS** (since January 1994):
22.5.95 Inverness Courier.
11.10.95 Irish Times.
**PRIZES/AWARDS/APPOINTMENTS:**
1979 Awarded Ely O'Carrol Gold Medal by the DIT Conservatory of Music and Drama, Dublin.
1979 Golden Voice of Ireland.
1982 Finalist with the Kathleen Ferrier Memorial Competition.
1985 Finalist with the Friends of Covent Garden Bursary with the National Opera Studio, London.
**TRAINING AND/OR QUALIFICATIONS:**
From 1980 to 1982, Opera course with the Guildhall School of Music and Drama.
From 1983 to 1984, Attended the National Opera Studio.
**REGULARLY PERFORMS WITH:**
Song Circle.
**AVAILABILITY:**
General.
**ADDITIONAL INFORMATION:**
Has also performed in musicals ie has appeared as 'Mother Abbess' in 'Sound of Music' at the Olympia Theatre and 'Nettle Fowler' in 'Carousel' at the Tivoli Theatre. Very interested in contemporary music.

# Sara McGuinness *Mezzo-Soprano*

**Contact:** Ms Sara McGuinness
26 Oakhill,
Surbiton
Surrey KT6 6DY
England
or
c/o English National Opera
London Coliseum
St Martin's Lane
London WC2N 4ES
England
**Tel/Fax:** +44 181 399 0620 (h) or +44 171 836 0111 (w) /
+44 181 3990620

*"She has a fine and very expressive mezzo voice and as a performer is both very musical and intelligent."* 6.96 A Ingram.

**KEY PERFORMANCES OUTSIDE IRELAND** (since January 1994):
1996 English National Opera, London, in the production of 'Salome' as a 'Slave', appearing with S Burgess and D Leveaux (producer).
1996 English National Opera, London, in the production of 'The Cunning Little Vixen' as 'Bridesmaid' appearing with J Watson and J Summers.
1996 English National Opera, London, appearing with L Garviet and D Poutney (Producer).
**SELECTED BROADCASTS AND/OR RECORDED WORK:**
1994 'Peter Grimes' (English National Opera) for Channel 4.
1996 'Don Quixote'(ENO) for BBC Radio 4.
1997 'Damnation of Faust' (ENO) for Channel 4.
**SELECTED REVIEWS:**
6.91 Opera.
4.95 Opera Now.
**PRIZES/AWARDS/APPOINTMENTS:**
1987 to 1989, winner of Cripplegate Scholarship, awarded by Guildhall School of Music and Drama, London.
1989 and 1990, Alec Redshaw Memorial Bursary, awarded by Gridt Grimsby International Singing Competition.

**TRAINING AND/OR QUALIFICATIONS:**
1987 LRSM Singing from the Royal School of Music, London.
From 1987 to 1989, post graduate vocal training, at the Guildhall School of Music and Drama, London.
1990 Singers course, at the British Kodály Institute.
1992 Studies in opera, Lieder, French song and oratorio, at the Britten-Pears School for Advanced Studies.
1994 to 1996 Victor Morris Masterclasses.
**REGULARLY PERFORMS WITH:**
Vocal Interludes, English National Opera.
**AVAILABILITY:**
General.
**ADDITIONAL INFORMATION:**
Building on the experience gained with the National Chamber Choir, 'Laudate' CD/tape and regular solo engagements in Ireland, has established a professional career in London. Is now working on an individual contract with English National Opera.

# Eimear Mangan *Mezzo-Soprano*

**Contact:** Ms Eimear Mangan
16, Glenageary Woods
Glenageary
Co Dublin
**Tel:** +353 1 2842086
**Other instruments:** Piano, flute.

*"Eimear Mangan ... seems to have considerable musical intelligence ... a singer worth watching"*
26.10.95 Irish Times (Martin Adams).

**KEY IRISH PERFORMANCES** (since January 1994):
1995 House of Lords, Dublin, promoted by Ellen Lynch, appearing with Patrick Zuk (piano).
1996 Irish Museum of Modern Art, promoted by Ellen Lynch, appearing with Patrick Zuk (piano).
1997 Bank of Ireland Arts Centre, promoted by Ellen Lynch, appearing with Patrick Zuk (piano).
1997 Gaiety Theatre, Dublin, promoted by Opera Ireland in the production of Verdi's 'Macbeth' as one of 'the witches'.
**SELECTED BROADCASTS AND/OR RECORDED WORK:**
1993 'Songs of Praise' for BBC.
1995 Veronica Dunne Bursary performance recording for RTÉ FM3.
1995 'Classical Choice' for Anna Livia Radio.
**PRIZES/AWARDS/APPOINTMENTS:**
1996 Winner of the Trustee Savings Bank Vocal Bursary, Dublin.
**TRAINING AND/OR QUALIFICATIONS:**
1996 Masterclasses with Dr Bernadette Greevy.
**REGULARLY PERFORMS WITH:**
Patrick Zuk (piano).
**AVAILABILITY:**
General.
**ADDITIONAL INFORMATION:**
Currently studying the music of Bach, Rossini and Mahler, with David Harper in London.

# Katy Miller *Mezzo-Soprano*

**Contact:** Ms Katy Miller
9, North Great George's Street
Dublin 1
**Tel/Fax:** +353 1 8727517 / +353 1 8787784

**KEY IRISH PERFORMANCES** (since January 1994):
1995 The Gaiety, Dublin, promoted by DGOS, appearing in 'La Cenerentola' and 'Faust'.
1995 The Olympia, Dublin, promoted by Encore Productions, in a production of 'Annie' as 'Mrs Greer'.
1995 The Gaiety, Dublin, promoted by Velour Cabaret, singing songs by Gershwin.
1995 Galway Arts Centre appearing with the Irish Modern Dance Theatre.
**PRIZES/AWARDS/APPOINTMENTS:**
1989/1990 highly commended for interpretation at the Feis Ceoil, Dublin.
1990 oratorio prize, awarded by the DIT Conservatory of Music and Drama, Dublin.
**TRAINING AND/OR QUALIFICATIONS:**
From 1984 to 1988, BA English and Philosophy.
From 1988 to 1989 Certificate of Music, from the DIT CMD.
From 1988 to 1989, Associated Board Grade 8 Theory and Singing.
From 1989 to 1991, B Mus (Performance) from the DIT CMD.
**AVAILABIITY:**
General.
**ADDITIONAL INFORMATION:**
Professional acting experience with Fishamble Theatre Company.

# Louise Muckell *Mezzo-Soprano*

**Contact:** Louise Muckell
17, Roches Road
Rathkeale
Co Limerick
**Tel:** +353 69 64033

**KEY IRISH PERFORMANCES** (since January 1994):
12.95 Gaiety Theatre, Dublin, appearing in the chorus of the Dublin Grand Opera Society production of 'Faust'.
**SELECTED BROADCASTS AND/OR RECORDED WORK:**
6.97 'Demo' tape, made at Den Studios, Limerick.
**TRAINING AND/OR QUALIFICATIONS:**
From 1986 to 1992, ALCM and LRSM from the Limerick School of Music (teacher Jean Holmes).
From 1992 to 1994, LTCL (teacher Veronica Dunne).
From 1994 to 1996, studied with Evelyn Dowling.
**AVAILABILITY:**
General.
**ADDITIONAL INFORMATION:**
Performer anxious to branch out as a soloist or part of a group.
Repertoire covers both classical and contemporary music.

# Ann Murray *Mezzo-Soprano*

**Contact:** Ann Murray
c/o Lies Askonas Ltd.
6, Henrietta Street
London WC2E 8LA
England (a)
**Tel/Fax:** +44 171 3797700 / +44 171 2421831

*"Let it also be recorded that in 'Aure,deh,per pieta', Murray sang a slowly ascending phrase that ranks as the most divinely beautiful sound I've heard all year"*
1997 Daily Telegraph (Rupert Christiansen) (Giulio Cesare).

**KEY PERFORMANCES OUTSIDE IRELAND** (Since January 1994):
Operatic performances have taken her to Paris, Brussels, Geneva, Dresden, Zurich, Frankfurt, Madrid, London, the Aldeburgh, Edinburgh and Munich and Salzburg Festivals, and both the Konzerthaus and Musikverein in Vienna.
**SELECTED BROADCASTS AND/OR RECORDED WORK:**
Extensive discography.
**PRIZES/AWARDS/APPOINTMENTS:**
1997 Hon. Doctorate of Music from National University of Ireland.
1997 Kammersängerin of the Bavarian State Opera, Munich.

**TRAINING AND/OR QUALIFICATIONS:**
Studied at the Royal Manchester College of Music (teacher Frederick Cox).
**AVAILABILITY:**
Subject to schedule.
**ADDITIONAL INFORMATION:**
Dublin born, now resident in Surrey. Has established close links with the English National Opera, for whom she has sung 'Charlotte', 'Rosina', 'Beatrice' and the title roles in Handel's 'Xerxes' and 'Ariodante', and at the Royal Opera House, Covent Garden, where her roles have included 'Cherubino', 'Dorabella', 'Donna Elvira', 'Rosina' and 'Oktavina'. Has performed with the Chicago Lyric Opera, and the Metropolitan Opera, New York, the Vienna State Opera and the Bavarian State Opera. Is a regular guest at La Scala, Milan where roles have included 'Donna Elvira', 'Sextus' and 'Cherubino' under Muti. As a concert singer, has performed with the Orchestre de Paris, the Philadelphia Orchestra and the Berlin Philharmonic.

## Edel O'Brien *Contralto*

**Contact:** Ms Edel O'Brien
Carnanes
Kilrush
Co Clare
**Tel:** +353 65 51320

**KEY IRISH PERFORMANCES** (since January 1994):
1994 Maynooth, Galway and Dublin, appearing with John O'Keeffe (organ), performing 'O Domino Nostra'.
**KEY PERFORMANCES OUTSIDE IRELAND** (since January 1994):
5.95 St John's Church, Hanover Square, London, promoted by Trinity College of Music, London appearing as soloist in Mozart's Requiem.
10.96 Church of St George the Martyr, Southwark, promoted by TCM.
11.96 Southport as semi finalist in the National Mozart Competition.
3.97 St John's, Smith Square, London, appearing as soloist in 'Les Noces'.
**PRIZES/AWARDS/APPOINTMENTS:**
1992 Ist Prize winner Contralto Solo and Margaret Burke Sheridan Cup from Feis Ceoil, Dublin.
1994 Scholarship from Trinity College of Music, London.
**TRAINING AND/OR QUALIFICATIONS:**
From 1990 to 1994 BA (Hons), and 1995 MA (Hons) in Performance and Related Studies in music, both from the National University of Ireland, Maynooth.
1997 Fellowship from Trinity College of Music, London.
**AVAILABILITY:**
April, July, August, September, October, December.
**ADDITIONAL INFORMATION:**
Has also played the part of 'Clarissa' in Prokofiev's 'Love for Three Oranges' for TCM. Offered an Italian Government Scholarship to continue vocal studies in Italy in the academic year 1997-1998.

## Sylvia O'Regan *Mezzo-Soprano*

**Contact:** Sylvia O'Regan
169, Glenageary Park
Dún Laoghaire
Co Dublin
**Tel:** +353 1 2854108

*"Sylvia O'Regan was outstanding as 'Mercedes' "*
The Citizen, Ottawa, Canada (Carmen).

**KEY IRISH PERFORMANCES** (since January 1994):
1994 Royal Dublin Society, Dublin promoted by RTÉ, in 'La Traviata' at RTÉ Proms with RTÉ Concert Orchestra as 'Annina'.
1996 Royal Hospital Kilmainham, appearing with Bernadette Greevy, accompanied by Patrick Zuk (piano) in 'The Exaltation of Larks'.
1997 University College, Dublin, promoted by UCD Music Society, appearing in 'Israel in Egypt', accompanied by UCD Music Society Choir and Orchestra.
**KEY PERFORMANCES OUTSIDE IRELAND** (since January 1994):
1996 National Arts Centre, Ottawa, Canada, promoted by Seagram, appearing in a production of 'Carmen' as 'Mercedes' accompanied by Arts Centre Orchestra.
**SELECTED BROADCASTS AND/OR RECORDED WORK:**
1994 'Annina' in Verdi's 'La Traviata' for RTÉ.
1996 'I Want to Sing in Opera' for RTÉ .
1996 Pergolesi's 'Stabat Mater' for RTÉ.
1996 'Exaltation of Larks' for RTÉ.
1997 'Late Late Show'.
**SELECTED REVIEWS** (since January 1994):
4.96 Ottowa Citizen.
10.96 Irish Times.
**PRIZES/AWARDS/APPOINTMENTS:**
1992/93 Scholarships to Britten-Pears School.
1994/95 Outstanding Musician Scholarship Awards from Dublin VEC.
**TRAINING AND/OR QUALIFICATIONS:**
From 1980 to 1984, BA (Music and English) at University College, Dublin.
From 1994 to 1995, Attended the Britten-Pears School.
From 1995 to 1996, Tuition with Suzanne Danco, Italy.
**AVAILABILITY:**
General.
**ADDITIONAL INFORMATION:**
Has sung solo in opera, oratorio and concerts as well as giving recitals. Also performs jazz and 'comedy' pieces.

## Ethna Robinson *Mezzo-Soprano*

**Contact:** Ms Ethna Robinson
c/o Owen White Management
39, Hillfield Avenue
London N8 7DS, England
**Tel/Fax:** +44 181 340 9571 / +44 181 340 4056

**KEY IRISH PERFORMANCES** (since January 1994):
5.95 National Concert Hall, Dublin, appearing with the National Symphony Orchestra of Ireland.
12.96 Limerick, appearing with the Irish Chamber Orchestra.
**KEY PERFORMANCES OUTSIDE IRELAND** (since January 1994):
1.96 to 3.96 Grand Theatre, Leeds, promoted by Opera North in the production of 'Luisa Miller' as 'Federica'.
9.96 to 10.96 Coliseum, London promoted by English National Opera in the production of 'A Midsummer Night's Dream' as 'Hermia'.
1.97 Coliseum, London promoted by English National Opera in the production of 'The Italian Girl in Algiers' as 'Zulma'.
4.97 to 5.97 Coliseum, London promoted by English National Opera in the production of 'Madame Butterfly' as 'Suzuki'.
**SELECTED BROADCASTS AND/OR RECORDED WORK:**
Numerous broadcasts for BBC.
**TRAINING AND/OR QUALIFICATIONS:**
From 1975 to 1979, DIT Conservatory of Music and Drama, Dublin (teacher Nancy Culthorpe).
From 1979 to 1981, Birmingham School of Music, (teacher Pamela Cooke).
From 1981 to 1984, Guildhall School of Music and Drama, London (teacher Noelle Barker).
**AVAILABILITY:**
General.

## Linda Snell *Contralto/Mezzo-Soprano*

**Contact:** Mrs Linda Snell
36, Clifton Road, Bangor
Co Down BT20 5EP
Northern Ireland
**Tel:** +44 1247 459122

**KEY IRISH PERFORMANCES** (since January 1994):
1994 Armagh Cathedral, appearing in the Belfast Baroque Consort production of 'Messiah'.
1995 Bangor Leisure Centre, appearing with the SEELB Youth Orchestra in 'Sea Pictures' by Elgar.
1995 St George's, Belfast, appearing with St George's Orchestra and David Byers in 'Petite Messe Solennelle' by Rossini.
1995 Grand Opera House, Belfast, in the Opera Northern Ireland production of 'The Cunning Little Vixen' as 'Lapak the Dog' appearing with the Ulster Orchestra and Kenneth Montgomery.
**KEY PERFORMANCES OUTSIDE IRELAND** (since January 1994):
1994 Fort Regent, Jersey, appearing with the Jersey Festival Chorus and Orchestra.
1995 Symphony Hall, Birmingham, appearing with the Hallé Choir and Symphony Orchestra.
**SELECTED BROADCASTS AND/OR RECORDED WORK:**
1992 Last Night of the Proms, Fairfield Halls, Croydon, for Classical Recording Services.
**PRIZES/AWARDS/APPOINTMENTS:**
1994 Appointed Vocal Coach for the Ulster College of Music.
**TRAINING AND/OR QUALIFICATIONS:**
From 1974 to 1992, Studied with G Frank Capper.
Since 1992 Studied with Enid Hartle (London).
**AVAILABILITY:**
General.
**ADDITIONAL INFORMATION:**
Wide repertoire - opera, oratorio, Lieder, French and English Art Songs. Operatic roles have included' Giovanna' in Verdi's 'Rigoletto', 'Azucena' in 'Il Trovatore', 'La Principessa' in Puccini's 'Suor Angelica' and 'Frugola' from 'il Tabarro'. Has performed on the concert platform with several symphony orchestras and given recitals with piano. Teaches privately and at the Ulster College of Music. Has adjudicated and taken masterclasses in Glasgow.

## Marie Walshe *Mezzo-Soprano*

**Contact:** Ms Marie Walshe
58, College Park
Corbally
Limerick
**Tel:** +353 61 344 282

**KEY IRISH PERFORMANCES** (since January 1994):
1996 Cork Opera House, appearing in the Opera South production of 'Carmen'.
1996 Gaiety Theatre, Dublin appearing in the Dublin Grand Opera Society production of 'The Magic Flute'.
1996 Everyman Theatre, Cork, appearing in the Kinsale Opera production of 'Yeoman of the Guard' as 'Phoebe'.
1997 Cork Opera House, appearing in the 'Sound of Music' as 'Mother Abbess'.
**KEY PERFORMANCES OUTSIDE IRELAND** (since January 1994):
1995 Bath Festival, Beethoven Symphony ix, appearing with Bournemouth Symphony Orchestra.
1995 Ivor Novello Gala Evening, St David's, Cardiff, appearing with the BBC Welsh Symphony.
1995-96 Tour of Britain, appearing in a City of Birmingham Touring Opera production of 'Falstaff' as 'Meg Page'.
**SELECTED BROADCASTS AND/OR RECORDED WORK:**
1993 Rossini's 'Sabat Mater' with Our lady's Choral Society for RTÉ.
1993 Mozart Arias with the National Symphony Orchestra of Ireland for RTÉ.
1996 Verdi's Requiem at the Cork International Choral Festival for RTÉ.
**PRIZES/AWARDS/APPOINTMENTS:**
1988 Awards, from the Friends of the Vocal Arts in Ireland.
1988 Scholarship to Siena, awarded by the Irish Philharmonic Society
**TRAINING AND/OR QUALIFICATIONS:**
From 1984 to 1988, Awarded 1st Prize in the final exams at the DIT Conservatory of Music and Drama, Dublin.
**AVAILABILITY:**
General.
**ADDITIONAL INFORMATION:**
Singing professionally in Ireland and abroad since 1986. Roles have included 'Dorabella', 'Phoebe', 'Valencienne', 'Mother Abbess', 'Cherubino', 'Ross Weisse', 'Suzuki', 'Fenena', 'Isolier', 'Varvara', 'Hermia', 'Nancy', 'Siebel', 'Orlovsky', 'Olga' and 'Carmen'. Large repertoire of arias, duets, trios and quartets from many years of gala operatic concerts. Oratorios include Rossini's Stabat Mater, Bach's B Minor Mass, Handel's Messiah, Mozart's Requiem, Verdi's Requiem, Elgar's 'The Dream of Gerontius', Mendelssohn's 'Elijah' and Vivaldi's Gloria.

## Yvonne Woods *Mezzo-Soprano*

**Contact:** Ms Yvonne Woods
Liberties
Greenore Road
Carlingford
Co Louth
**Tel:** +353 42 73466

**KEY IRISH PERFORMANCES** (since January 1994):
Town Hall, Dundalk, Co Louth, solo recital.
St Ann's Church, Dawson Street, Dublin.
**KEY PERFORMANCES OUTSIDE IRELAND** (since January 1994):
St Mary Abbots Church, London, solo recital.
Royal College of Music, London, solo recital.
**SELECTED BROADCASTS AND/OR RECORDED WORK:**
8.96 Soundtrack for the video 'Riverdance the Show'.
'Live at 3' for RTÉ.
Patrick Cassidy's 'The Children of Lir' for RTÉ.
**TRAINING AND/OR QUALIFICATIONS:**
Since 9.94 ARCM Post Graduate Diploma from Royal College of Music, London with Margaret Cable and James Lockhart.
8.94 Oxenford International Summer School.
Has attended masterclasses with Roger Vignoles, Paul Hamburger, Laura Sarti, Carlo Bergonzi, Veronica Dunne, Bernadette Greevy, Robert Tear, Graziella Sciutti and Philip Langridge.
**AVAILABILITY:**
General.
**ADDITIONAL INFORMATION:**
Spent 4 years on a working scholarship with the (RTÉ) Chamber Choir which involved weekly recordings and numerous live television broadcasts.

# COUNTER TENOR, TENOR

## Alan Boyd *Counter-Tenor*

Contact: Mr Alan Boyd
15, Willowholme Drive
Belfast BT6 8PA
Northern Ireland
Tel: +44 1232 455801

**KEY IRISH PERFORMANCES** (since January 1994):
12.2.94 St George's Church, Belfast, appearing with the St George's Singers and Orchestra, performing Purcell's 'Ode on St Cecilia's Day'.
8.10.94 Belfast Cathedral, promoted by Northern Ireland Hospice, appearing with Hospice promoted chorus in Handel's 'Messiah'.
12.12.95 Omagh, promoted by Omagh Music Society, appearing with Omagh Choral Society, performing Handel's 'Samson'.
15.2.96 Harty Room, Queen's University, Belfast, appearing with Stephen Sandford, performing Purcell Duets.
**KEY PERFORMANCES OUTSIDE IRELAND** (since January 1994):
20.12.96 Grimsby, promoted by Andrew Cantrill, appearing with church choral group and orchestra in Handel's 'Messiah'.
**SELECTED BROADCASTS AND/OR RECORDED WORK:**
2.3.86 'The Singer's Art', 'The Lord, Even the Most Mighty God Hath Spoken', by Roseingrave recorded by BBC Ulster.
22.11.86 'Ah how sweet it is to Love' by Purcell for BBC Ulster.
7.2.89 'Love's Philosophy', recital of lute songs, recorded by BBC Ulster.

**SELECTED REVIEWS** (since January 1994):
9.2.94 Belfast Telegraph.
15.3.94 Belfast Telegraph.
**REGULARLY PERFORMS WITH:**
Sineet Chamber Choir, Ulster College of Music, Madrigal Group.
**AVAILABILITY:**
General.
**ADDITIONAL INFORMATION:**
Began musical life as a boy chorister in St Anne's Cathedral, Belfast. Has sung as a soloist with many of the Province's choral groups. Studied singing with Donald Cairns and Paul Deegan.

## Louis Browne *Tenor*

**Contact:** Mr Louis Browne
28, Park Road
Glenageary
Co Dublin
**Tel:** +353 1 2853091

**KEY IRISH PERFORMANCES** (since January 1994):
1.94/95 National Concert Hall, Dublin, promoted by World of Gilbert and Sullivan.
5.94/95 Thomas Moore evenings (various venues).
1.96/97 NCH, promoted by World of Gilbert and Sullivan.
**KEY PERFORMANCES OUTSIDE IRELAND** (since January 1994):
9.94 Queen's Hall, London, promoted by the BBC.
3.95 Concert Hall, Glasgow, promoted by Ian Southerland.
3.96 Symphony Hall, Boston, promoted by the Irish Society.
4.8.97 Sabre Rooms, Chicago, promoted by Rego Records.
**SELECTED BROADCASTS AND/OR RECORDED WORK:**
1989 'Louis Browne Recalls' for Rex/NBC (Irish Magic Irish Music).
1992 'An Evening in Ireland' for Rego/WEA.
1996 'Irelands Favourite Tenor' for Chart.
**TRAINING AND/OR QUALIFICATIONS:**
From 1960 to 1963, Guildhall School of Music and Drama, London.
**AVAILABILITY:**
General.

## Ted Courtney *Tenor*

**Contact:** Mr Ted Courtney
Kingsford
Newtownsmith
Sandycove
Co Dublin
**Tel/Fax:** +353 1 2804519 / +353 1 2082072

*See clarinet page 3.*

## Morgan Crowley *Counter Tenor/Tenor*

**Contact:** Morgan Crowley
259, Howth Road
Dublin 5 (h)
or
c/o Hilary Gagan Associates
Caprice House
3, New Burlington Street
London W1X 1FE (a)
**Tel:** +353 1 8335805
**Email:** morganstar@compuserve.com

*See baritone (4 octave range) page 112.*

## Paul Deegan *Tenor*

**Contact:** Mr Paul Deegan
14, Mount Place
Phibsboro
Dublin 7
**Tel:** +353 1 8303266

## John Elwes *Tenor*

**Contact:** John Elwes
Kilballyquilty
Carrick-on-Suir
Co Waterford
**Tel/Fax:** +353 51 646286

*See period Tenor page 126.*

## Matthew Gilsenan *Tenor*

**Contact:** Mr Matthew Gilsenan
Loughan
Kells
Co Meath
**Tel/Mobile:** +353 46 44437 / +353 88 2760591

*"Effortless projection ... won comments from pseudo-Pavarottis and Pattersons"*
27.3.97 Evening Herald (Michael Dungan) Handel's Messiah.

**KEY IRISH PERFORMANCES** (since January 1994):
26.3.97 Temple Theatre, Temple Street, Dublin, promoted by Marion Doherty, appearing with the Dublin Baroque Players and Brian McKay as tenor solo in Handel's 'Messiah'.
10.5.97 Westmanstown Centre, Clonsilla, Dublin 15, promoted by Imelda O'Rourke as 'Camill' in the 'Merry Widow'.
28.5.97 John Field Room, National Concert Hall, Dublin, promoted by Feis Ceoil, accompanied by Mairéad Hurley.
**KEY PERFORMANCES OUTSIDE IRELAND** (since January 1994):
12.95 Key Theatre, Peterborough, appearing in the Peterborough Opera production of the 'Flying Dutchman' as a 'Sailor'.
**SELECTED BROADCASTS AND/OR RECORDED WORK:**
1992 Various radio work with the National Chamber Choir for RTÉ.
1997 Choral excerpts for documentary.
1997 'Eurovision' with Boyzone for RTÉ.
**PRIZES/AWARDS/APPOINTMENTS:**
1992 Winner of Dermot Troy Trophy for Oratorio at the Feis Ceoil, Dublin.
1997 Overall vocal winner for the Ballymena Borough Council Arts Award.
**TRAINING AND/OR QUALIFICATIONS:**
From 1988 to 1992, up to Grade 4 at the DIT Conservatory of Music and Drama, Dublin (teacher Mary Brennan).
From 1996 to 1997, Studied with Natasia Yufe in California.
Since 1997, Studying Grade 5 at the DIT CMD (teacher Mary Brennan).
20.6.97 to 11.7.97, Attended masterclasses with Evaandor and received Kodály Solfège training.
**AVAILABILITY:**
General.
**ADDITIONAL INFORMATION:**
Currently singing with the National Chamber Choir.

# Bryan Hoey *Tenor*

**Contact:** Mr Bryan Hoey
66, Hampton Court
Vernon Avenue
Clontarf
Dublin 3
**Tel:** +353 1 8337331

**KEY IRISH PERFORMANCES** (since January 1994):
1995 National Concert Hall, Dublin, appearing with Trinity College Dublin Orchestra in 'Carmina Burana'.
1996 National Concert Hall, Dublin, promoted by the ICB, appearing with the Garda Band.
1996 NCH, promoted by Culwick Choral Society, appearing with Dublin City Youth Orchestra.
**KEY PERFORMANCES OUTSIDE IRELAND** (since January 1994):
1994 Isle of Man, promoted by Island Opera as 'Nemorino'.
1996 Three performances on the Isle of Man, promoted by IOMT.
1997 Isle of Man, one man show promoted by Ramsey Musical Society.
**SELECTED BROADCASTS AND/OR RECORDED WORK:**
1984 Handel's 'Messiah'.
1990 Soundtrack to film 'Hear my Song'. Also various recordings for television including twelve 'Live at 3' peformances for RTÉ.
**TRAINING AND/OR QUALIFICATIONS:**
1964, Studied with Martin Dempsey. Has also attended the Brendan Smith Acting Academy.
**PRIZES/AWARDS/APPOINTMENTS:**
Joseph O'Mara Memorial cup winner from the Feis Ceoil, Dublin.
**AVAILABILITY:**
General.
**ADDITIONAL INFORMATION:**
Has made several public performances in the last 3 years. Has experience in opera, theatre, musicals, radio, television. Has performed Handel's 'Messiah' on numerous occasions and has given a number of recitals featuring songs of Moore and French.

# Declan Kelly *Tenor*

**Contact:** Mr Declan Kelly
c/o Helen Sykes
First Floor
Parway House
Sheen Lane, East Sheen
London SW14 8LS
England
**Tel/Fax:** +44 181 8768276 / +44 181 8768277

*"Declan Kelly's lyrical tenor voice was the highlight of this production, perfectly expressing the dilemma ... and forming an admirable vocal partnership with Marilyn Hill Smith."*
24.7.96 Evening Gazette (Terry Gilder).

**KEY IRISH PERFORMANCES** (since January 1994):
3.96 Tour of Ireland promoted by RTÉ and Opera Theatre Company, appearing with the RTÉ Concert Orchestra.
10.96 Tour of Ireland promoted by OTC, appearing with Dearbhla Collins, Regina Hanley, James Nelson, Iain Paton.
1.97 St Patrick's College, Dublin, promoted by St Patrick's College of Education, appearing with Kathleen Tynan, Eoin Power.
5.97 Tour of Ireland promoted by OTC, appearing with Ger O'Connor, Colette MacGahon, Fionnuala Gill, Margaret Preece, Tom Guthrie.
**KEY PERFORMANCES OUTSIDE IRELAND** (since January 1994):
6.95-5.96 Tour of UK, promoted by D'Oyly Carte Opera, appearing with John Owen Edwards, Sally-Ann Sheperdson, Gareth Jones as 'Nanki-Poo'.
3.97 Tour of Belgium and Holland, promoted by Musick Theater Transparant, appearing with Rosie Ashe, Joe Corbett, Annette Brinthop ('La Squadra').
6.97 Holland Park, London, promoted by the European Chamber Opera, appearing with Andrea Quinn, Anne O'Byrne and the Holland Park Opera - as 'Tamino'.
7.97 Batignano, Italy, promoted by Musica nel Chiostra, appearing with Susie Clarke in the Batignano Festival as 'Eurillo'.
**SELECTED BROADCASTS AND/OR RECORDED WORK:**
11.92 'Songs for Christmas' for Owen Brady and Warner Music.
10.94 'Cursaí' for RTÉ.
3.96 'Zaide' for RTÉ.
**SELECTED REVIEWS** (since January 1994):
1.10.94 Irish News.
1.5.96 The Scotsman.
**PRIZES/AWARDS/APPOINTMENTS:**
1991 John McCormack Cup and Tenor Gold Medal at the Feis Ceoil.
1994 National Opera Studio Bursary, awarded by the Friends of Covent Garden.
**TRAINING AND/OR QUALIFICATIONS:**
From 1983 to 1986, B Ed (Hons) from St Patrick's College of Education.
From 1988 to 1993, Grade 8 from the Royal Irish Academy of Music (teacher Paul Deegan).
From 1993 to 1994, Studied with the National Opera Studio, London.
**AVAILABILITY:**
General.
**ADDITIONAL INFORMATION:**
Has performed in numerous concerts and oratorios, and has worked with the National Symphony Orchestra of Ireland and RTÉ Concert Orchestra. Has given recitals in Ireland, Great Britain, Italy and the United States. Currently studying with Margaret Lobo.

# Stuart Kinsella *Tenor*

**Contact:** Stuart Kinsella
Carrickvale
Carrickbrennan Road
Monkstown
Co Dublin
**Tel:** +353 1 2801464 or +353 1 6778099
**Email:** cccdnb@indigo.ie

**KEY IRISH PERFORMANCES** (since January 1994):
10.96 Tour of Ireland with the National Chamber Choir.
1.97 All Hallows College, Dublin, appearing with Zefiro (vocal quintet) at the RTÉ Liturgical Music Competition.
3.97 John Field Room, National Concert Hall, Dublin appearing with Cantique at a Dr Brian Boydell appreciation concert.
6.97 Christ Church Cathedral, Dublin, appearing with Christ Church Cathedral Choir (Gala Concert).
**KEY PERFORMANCES OUTSIDE IRELAND** (since January 1994):
1995, Durham Cathedral, appearing with Christ Church Cathedral Choir.
1996 Westminster Abbey, appearing with Christ Church CC.
1997 Chartres Cathedral and Sainte Chappelle, France, appearing with the Christ Church CC.
**SELECTED BROADCASTS AND/OR RECORDED WORK:**
8.96 'Deep Dead Blue' with Anúna.
11.96 Vol III of Stanford Music for Priory Records.
6.97 Soundtrack recording for the 'Séan Ó'Riada' documentary for RTÉ with the Irish Film Orchestras
**PRIZES/AWARDS/APPOINTMENTS:**
1995 Appointed position of Lay Vicar Choral of Christ Church Cathedral Choir.
10.96 Appointed to National Chamber Choir.
**REGULARLY PERFORMS WITH:**
Christ Church Cathedral Choir, Zefiro, Tactus, Cantique, NCC.
**AVAILABILITY:**
General.

# Emmanuel Lawler *Tenor*

**Contact:** Emmanuel Lawler
Apt 3 Viscount House
6A Love Lane
Pinner
Middlesex HA5 3EF
England
or
c/o Gerry Keenan
Real Good Management
17, Dame Court
Dublin 2

**Tel/Mobile/Fax:** +353 1 6688108 / +353 87 542366 / +353 1 6674530

**Email:** realgood@clubi.ie

*"Tenors are scarce, but even if they were not, Emmanuel Lawler would be one to treasure very greatly"* Irish Times.

**KEY IRISH PERFORMANCES** (since January 1994):
Point Depot, Dublin 'Messiah for Somalia'.
RTÉ Proms in a production of Donizetti's 'Don Pasquale' as 'Ernesto'.
National Concert Hall, Dublin, premier of John Buckley's 'Te Deum'.
**SELECTED BROADCASTS AND/OR RECORDED WORK:**
'The Children of Lir' by Patrick Cassidy, appearing with the London Symphony Orchestra.
Various appearances on television in Europe and North America.
**PRIZES/AWARDS/APPOINTMENTS:**
Winner of the Gold Medal (whilst still attending school) at Feis Ceoil, Dublin.
**TRAINING AND/OR QUALIFICATIONS:**
DIT Conservatory of Music and Drama, Dublin (teachers Veronica Dunne and Jeannie Reddin).
BA (Music and Irish) from National University of Ireland, Maynooth.
LTCL (vocal training).
1990 and 1991, Studied with Carlo Bergonzi at the Accademia Musicale di Siena (Chigiana).
**AVAILABILITY:**
General.
**ADDITIONAL INFORMATION:**
Commenced singing as a boy in the Palestrina Choir, Pro Cathedral , Dublin and sang extensively as a treble soloist. Currently based in London where engagments have included two appearances in the Convent Garden Festival singing the world premier of Hoyland's "Vexilla Regis' in 1996, and Bach's solo cantata 'Meine Seele Ruhmt' in 1997. Repertoire includes concert, oratorio and opera spanning from the earliest compositions/rescontructions, to new music.

# Niall Morris *Tenor*

**Contact:** Mr Niall Morris
c/o Mr Colin Ure
Harlequin Agency
203, Fidlas Road
Cardiff CF4 5NA, Wales

**Tel/Fax:** +44 1222 750821 / +44 1222 755971

*"Best of all, that rising young Irish tenor, as 'Davie'... has charm of personality and charm of vocal manner"* 9.94 Opera Magazine.

**KEY IRISH PERFORMANCES** (since January 1994):
10.95 Tour of Ireland with the Opera Theatre Company production of 'Orfeo'.
12.95 Goffs, Co Kildare 'Three Tenors Concert' appearing with J Nelson and P Hennessy.
**KEY PERFORMANCES OUTSIDE IRELAND** (since January 1994):
From 1.94 to 6.94, Tour of England with 'H.M.S Pinafore' appearing with D'Oyly Carte as 'Ralph'.
7.94 Almeida Opera Festival, singing 'SirenSong' by Jonathan Dore.
7.95 Almeida Opera Festival, London singing 'Powder Her Face' by Tom Ades, appearing with Jill Gormez.
9.95 Tour of Wales, with Mid Wales Opera in a production of 'L'Elisir d'Amore' as 'Nemorino'.
**SELECTED BROADCASTS AND/OR RECORDED WORK:**
7.95 'The Spanish Lady' by Elgar, recorded by BBC Music Magazine.
12.95 'Powder Her Face' Tom Ades recorded by BBC and EMI.
**PRIZES/AWARDS/APPOINTMENTS:**
From 1991 to 1993, Awarded Foundation Scholarship, by the Wolfson Foundation.
From 1991 to 1993, Awarded Council Fellowship, by the British Council.
1992, Communications Bursary, from OTC.
**TRAINING AND/OR QUALIFICATIONS:**
From 1987 to 1989 BA Music awarded by Kings College, London.
From 1991 to 1993, opera scholarship, awarded by Guildhall School of Music and Drama, London.
From 1992 to 1993, attended the National Opera Studio, London.
**REGULARLY PERFORMS WITH:**
English Touring Opera, Castleward Opera.
**AVAILABILITY:**
General.

# Ciarán Nagle *Tenor*

**Contact:** Mr Ciarán Nagle
Elgan House
Woodbrook Downs
Bray, Co Wicklow

**Tel/Mobile/Fax:** +353 1 282 1068 / +353 88 533 456 / +353 1 282 0460 or +353 1 282 9209

**Email:** edgewood@indigo.ie

**KEY IRISH PERFORMANCES** (since January 1994):
5.95 National Concert Hall, Dublin appearing in 'Dido and Aeneas' as 'Aeneas'.
8.96 Boyle Arts Festival, Boyle, Co Roscommon, appearing with Deborah Kelleher and Doreen Curran.
1996 National Concert Hall, Dublin, appearing in Lyric Opera Company production of 'La Traviata' as 'Guiseppe'.
10.96 Taibhdearc Na Gaillimhe, Galway, appearing in 'Lucia Di Lammermoor' as 'Edguardo'.
**TRAINING AND/OR QUALIFICATIONS:**
8.96 Masterclasses with Mark Shanahan and Annette Thompson.
From 1990 to 1997, DIT Conservatory of Music and Drama, Dublin (studied with Edith Forrest, Alison Young).
Since 1996 studying with Brian MacKay.
**REGULARLY PERFORMS WITH:**
Emer Hartnet (soprano), Margaret Killian (mezzo-soprano), Nyle Wolf (baritone).
**AVAILABILITY:**
General.
**ADDITIONAL INFORMATION:**
Is available for oratorio, opera, recital, concerts, musicals, corporate and voice-over work.

# James Nelson *Tenor*

**Contact:** Mr James Nelson
41, Harfield Road
Sunbury on Thames
Middlesex TW16 5PT
England

**Tel/Fax:** +44 1932 783141 / +44 171 2269792 (fax for agent only)

*"Real find of this production ... played and sung with integrity ... enormously funny and poignant at the same time"* 11.94 The Stage.

**KEY IRISH PERFORMANCES** (since January 1994):
1995 Opera Theatre Company tour, in the production of 'Wiener Blut' as 'Joseph'.
From 1995 to 1996, numerous venues including the National Concert Hall, Dublin in the 'Irish Three Tenors' series.
1996 Opera Theatre Company tour, in the production of 'Katya Kabanova' as 'Tichon'.
1996 RTÉ Proms in the production of 'Madame Butterfly' as 'Goro'.
**KEY PERFORMANCES OUTSIDE IRELAND** (since January 1994):
1994 Scottish Opera tour, in the production of 'Grand Duchess of Gerolstein' as 'Prince Paul'.
1994 Tel Aviv, Israel, promoted by New Israel Opera in the production of 'Sweeney Todd' (playing four roles).
1994 Bern and Zürich Cathedrals, appearing with Evangelische Singemeinde, in Frank Martin's 'Golgotha'.
1995 Theatre Royal Scotland appearing with Scottish Opera.
**SELECTED BROADCASTS AND/OR RECORDED WORK:**
1996 and 1997 'Theatre Nights' for RTÉ.
1996 'Rose of Tralee', 'Late Late Show' and 'Live at 3' for RTÉ.
**SELECTED REVIEWS** (since January 1994):
1994 Opera Magazine.
1996 Independent, London.
**TRAINING AND/OR QUALIFICATIONS:**
From 1981 to 1984, BA in Music and French from University College, Dublin.
From 1981 to 1995, B Mus (Hons) from University College, Dublin.
From 1987 to 1988, Summer Music course at Bushey, England.
From 1989 to 1990, Mayer - Lismann Opera Course at the Royal Opera House, London.
**REGULARLY PERFORMS WITH:**
Scottish Opera, OTC, choral societies and orchestras.
**AVAILABILITY:**
General.
**ADDITIONAL INFORMATION:**
Native of Sligo. Winner of a number of awards including Lieder Prize and Plunket Greene Trophy, Feis Ceoil. With Music International Agency (London) and student of David Harper. Has performed almost 50 roles in opera/operetta and 60 oratorios, at home and abroad. Interested in baroque through to contemporary music.

## Frank Patterson *Tenor*

**Contact:** Dr Frank Patterson
c/o Frank Murphy
3, Bethel Terrace
Trafalgar Road
Greystones
Co Wicklow
**Tel:** +353 1 2082766 (w) / +353 1 2876370 (h)

**KEY IRISH PERFORMANCES** (since January 1994):
National Concert Hall, Dublin appearing with Eily O'Grady. The Point Depot, Dublin, appearing with 'Faith of our Fathers' choral group
**KEY PERFORMANCES OUTSIDE IRELAND** (since January 1994):
Several, in America and Canada including Carnegie Hall, New York, The White House, Washington DC, Boston State House and the Roy Thompson Hall, Toronto, all appearing with Eily O'Grady.
**SELECTED BROADCASTS AND/OR RECORDED WORK:**
Has recorded 36 albums with Philips and various other companies.
**PRIZES/AWARDS/APPOINTMENTS:**
1984 presented with the Papal Award, the Knighthood of St Gregory. Received a Doctorate of Music, from Salve Regina University, Rhode Island, New York. Received a Doctorate of Fine Arts, from Manhattan College, New York.
**TRAINING AND/OR QUALIFICATIONS:**
Studied in Dublin with Hans Walderar Rosen. Studied in Paris with Janine Micheau.

**ADDITIONAL INFORMATION:**
Has also performed as a soloist in film eg. 'The Dead' 'The Coen Brothers' 'Millers Crossing' and 'Michael Collins'.

## Andrew Synnott *Tenor*

**Contact:** Andrew Synnott
98, Wilfield Road
Sandymount, Dublin 4
**Tel:** +353 1 2696023
*See piano page 50.*

## Ronan Tynan *Tenor*

**Contact:** Mr Ronan Tynan
Brittas Cottage
Tullaroan, Co Kilkenny
**Tel:** +353 56 69397

**KEY IRISH PERFORMANCES** (since January 1994):
1994 Debut at the National Concert Hall, Dublin and winner of the RTÉ/BBC singing competition.
1994/1996 Performed excerpts from Tosca, La Boheme and Don Giovani as a member of the Leinster Opera Studio in Ireland.
1996 Voices of the World, with RTÉ.
**KEY PERFORMANCES OUTSIDE IRELAND** (since January 1994):
1995 'Don Ricardo' with the Opera Arnani at the Royal Northern College, Manchester.
1995 'Mylio Le Roio'ys' for the Royal Northern College, Manchester.
9.96 Theatre Francais De La Musique Compiegne (Paris) in a production of 'La Jollie Fille De Perth' by Bizet as Henri Smith.
**PRIZES/AWARDS/APPOINTMENTS:**
1992 Winner of the Tenor and John McCormack Trophy at the National Singing Festival, Dublin.
**TRAINING AND/OR QUALIFICATIONS:**
1993 Masterclass with Ugo Bennelli, Genoa, Italy.
1994 Post Graduate Training in the Royal Northern College, Manchester, England.
1994 Masterclass with James King, Munich, Germany.
1994 Masterclass with Soto Papulcas, Essen, Germany.
**ADDITIONAL INFORMATION:**
Has performed in concerts with the RTÉ Concert Orchestra, the Ulster Orchestra and Cork Pops Orchestra. Was a finalist and runner up in the Webster Boot Esso Award Competition for young opera singers in England. European finalist in the World International Pavarotti Competition, Italy

## Finbar Wright *Tenor*

**Contact:** Finbar Wright
c/o Fifty Seventh Street Limited
24, Upper Mount Street
Dublin 2 (Agent)
**Tel/Fax:** +353 1 6766751 / +353 1 6766786
**Email:** Street57@indigo.ie

**ADDITIONAL INFORMATION:**
Born in Kinsale, Co Cork. Began his professional career in music in 1990. Has recorded four solo albums all of which have achieved platinum status - 'Because', 'Whatever You Believe', 'A Tribute to John McCormack' and 'Lift the Wings'.
Co-hosted own television series on RTÉ and is a regular contributor to television and radio programmes in Ireland and Britain.
Highlights of career include performing with Spanish soprano Montserrat Caballe at the Point Depot, Dublin and entertaining the President of the United States, Bill Clinton, at the State Banquet given in his honour at St Patrick's Hall, Dublin Castle. Has toured extensively in Australia and the United States.

# BARITONE, BASS

## Paschal Allen *Bass-Baritone*

**Contact:** Mr Paschal Allen
13, Earlsfield Road
London, SW18 3DB
England
**Tel/Fax:** +44 181 874 2341 / +44 181 870 7389

*"The deep clarity and resonance of the voice was most impressive"* The Times.

**KEY IRISH PERFORMANCES** (since January 1994):
9.94 National Concert Hall, Dublin, accompanied by Blanaid Murphy.
**KEY PERFORMANCES OUTSIDE IRELAND** (since January 1994):
5.95 Palermo Opera House, Sicily, promoted by the British Council, appearing with the Royal Opera, Convent Garden.
6.95 Le Mans Cathedral, appearing with St Ann's Choir, Wandsworth
**SELECTED BROADCASTS AND/OR RECORDED WORK:**
1981 'Bohemian Girl' for RTÉ.
1985 'Manon Lescaut' for Deutsche Gramophon.
1995 'Salome' for BBC.
**PRIZES/AWARDS/APPOINTMENTS:**
1963 Awarded gold medal from the Guildhall School of Music and Drama, London.
1964 Awarded the Sir Thomas Beecham Opera Scholarship, by the Beecham Foundation.
**TRAINING AND/OR QUALIFICATIONS:**
From 1960 to 1964, AGSM, from Guildhall School of Music and Drama, London.
**REGULARLY PERFORMS WITH:**
Celtic Journey (piano, soprano and bass) and Catherine Allen (piano, singer and actress).
**AVAILABILITY:** General.

## Conor Biggs *Bass-Baritone*

**Contact:** Mr Conor Biggs
Arduinkaai 33
1000 Brussels, Belgium
**Tel/Fax:** +32 2 223 11 89 / +32 2 223 42 22
**Other instruments:** Piano, organ.

*"A most rewarding recital of French, German and Irish songs ... Biggs is completely at home in the German language"* 1990 Music Ireland.

**KEY IRISH PERFORMANCES** (since January 1994):
From 10.95 to 11.95, Trinity College, Dublin, Ballyshannon, Ennis, Cork, Belfast and Enniskillen in the Opera Theatre Company production of Monteverdi's 'Orfeo' as 'Caronte'.
**KEY PERFORMANCES OUTSIDE IRELAND** (since January 1994):
8.95 Banff Arts Centre, Canada, as 'Father' in Stravinsky's 'Les Noces'.
10.96 Konzerthaus, Berlin, as 'Deus' in Carissimi's 'Historia di Ezechia'.
6.97 Telaviv, Israel, appearing with Israel Camerata, as 'Pilatus' in 'St John's Passion'.
4.97 Jugendtheater, Vienna, as 'Wienertaschenoper' in Max Davies' 'Resurrection'.
**SELECTED BROADCASTS AND/OR RECORDED WORK:**
10.94 'Works for 40 Solo Voices' for Sony (Huelgas).
12.95 'William Byrd' for Arsonor (Laudantes).
6.97 'Vlaamsepassiemuziek' for Accent (Currende).
**PRIZES/AWARDS/APPOINTMENTS:**
1988 Awarded Brigitte Fassbaender Prize for Lieder Interpretation by the Royal Northern College of Music, Manchester.
**TRAINING AND/OR QUALIFICATIONS:**
From 1985 to 1992, Studied with Evelyn Dowling.
From 1987 to 1989, Studied with John Cameron at the Royal Northern College of Music, Manchester.
1995, Studied with Mary Morrison at the Banff Arts Centre, Canada.
**REGULARLY PERFORMS WITH:**
Currende, Ex Tempore.
**AVAILABILITY:**
General.
**ADDITIONAL INFORMATION:**
Specialises in baroque, renaissance and contemporary music. Experienced in stage and concert performances.

## Geoffrey Blower *Baritone*

**Contact:** Mr Geoffrey Blower
35a, Drumhirk Road
Comber
Co Down, BT23 5NN
**Tel:** +44 1238 528157

## Alan Boyd *Baritone*

**Contact:** Mr Alan Boyd
15, Willowholme Drive
Belfast BT6 8PA
Northern Ireland
**Tel:** +44 1232 455801
*See Counter Tenor page 106.*

## Shane Brennan *Baritone*

**Contact:** Mr Shane Brennan
Director
Schola Cantorum
St Finian's College
Mullingar
Co Westmeath
**Tel/Mobile:** +353 44 42906 or +353 44 44957 / +353 88 528029
*See organ page 26.*

## Bruno Caproni *Baritone*

**Contact:** Mr Bruno Caproni
c/o Portland Wallis Artists Management
50 Great Portland Street
London W1N 5AH
England
**Tel/Fax:** +44 171 636 6785 / +44 171 636 6786

**KEY PERFORMANCES OUTSIDE IRELAND** (since January 1994):
1996/1997 Opernhaus, Kiel, appearing in the production of 'Christoforo Colombo' playing title role.
1-4.97 Tour of Wales and England with the Welsh National Opera production of 'Carmen' as 'Escamillo'.
8.97 Royal Opera House, Covent Garden with The Royal Opera in the production of 'Macbeth' playing title role.
9.97 Opernhaus, Köln, appearing in the Cologne Opera production of 'Aida' as 'Amonasro'.
**PRIZES/AWARDS/APPOINTMENTS:**
1988 Winner of the Frederic Cox Award.
1989 Winner of the Ricordi Prize for Opera.

**TRAINING AND/OR QUALIFICATIONS:**
From 9.83 to 6.89, PPRNCM from the Royal Northern College of Music, Manchester (teacher Frederic Cox).
**REGULARLY PERFORMS WITH:**
Cologne Opera, The Royal Opera.
**AVAILABILITY:**
General.

# Aidan Coleman *Baritone/Bass Baritone*

**Contact:** Mr Aidan Coleman
28, Lisalea, Frascati Park
Blackrock
Co Dublin
**Tel:** +353 1 2835117
**Other instruments:** Piano, guitar.

**KEY IRISH PERFORMANCES** (since January 1994):
25.4.97 Hotel Conrad, Dublin for the KPMG Association 1997 annual dinner.
**KEY PERFORMANCES OUTSIDE IRELAND** (since January 1994):
4.94 Hotel Atlas - Asni, Marrakech for the Uruguay Round of the Gatt Conference.
**SELECTED BROADCASTS AND/OR RECORDED WORK:**
3.97 'Réalta '97 - Uaigneas' for Raidió Na Gaeltachta.
**PRIZES/AWARDS/APPOINTMENTS:**
4.91 Artist in Residence, Tyrone Guthrie Centre, Annaghmakerrig.
11.96 Finalist in Raidió Na Gaeltachta's 'Réalta '97' competition.
**AVAILABILITY:**
General.
**ADDITIONAL INFORMATION:**
Writer, composer, performer, director, sound engineer, multitrack recording engineer. Repertoire: 1,400 songs in all styles, sings in several languages, 3.5 octaves. Multi-instrumentalist, trained actor. Arts seminars speaker 'Financial know-how for the artist' (BA Com Degree graduate, University College, Dublin).

# Joseph Corbett *Baritone*

**Contact:** Mr Joseph Corbett
50, Goldhurst Terrace
London NW6 3HT
England
**Tel:** +44 171 624 6280
**Other instruments:** Piano, piano accordion.

*"A voice which eloquently reveals his strong operatic background"* 23.2.96 Eastern Daily Press.

**KEY IRISH PERFORMANCES** (since January 1994):
8-10.94 Tour of Ireland with the Opera Theatre Company, playing 'Silvio' in 'Pagliacci' and 'Gino' in 'Frankie's'.
4.95 Cork Opera House, appearing in the Opera South production of 'H.M.S. Pinafore' (Capt. Corcoran).
11.95 Cork City Hall, guest soloist at the Garda Band Gala Concert.
12.95 John Field Room, National Concert Hall, Dublin, accompanied by Patrick Zuk (French song recital).
**KEY PERFORMANCES OUTSIDE IRELAND** (since January 1994):
1-2.95 Royal Opera House, Covent Garden, appearing in the production of 'Der Rosenkavalier' as 'Leopold'.
1-3.96 Norwich Playhouse, appearing in the Norwich Playhouse production of 'Kiss Me Kate' as 'Petruchio'.
2-4.97 Tour of Belgium and the Netherlands, appearing in the Musiektheater Transparant production of 'Trouble in Tahiti' as 'Sam'.
6.97 Vilnius, Lithuania, as part of the Lithuanian International Theatre Festival, appearing with Shameless and Opera Circus.
**SELECTED BROADCASTS AND/OR RECORDED WORK:**
10.93 'Guys and Dolls' and ''D' Wing' for BBC.
8.95 'The Art of Romance' for Channel 4.
4.1.97 'The County Mayo' (Song Cycle) by Joan Trimble, for Naxos.
**SELECTED REVIEWS** (since January 1994):
21.10.95 Examiner.
9.12.96 Examiner.
**PRIZES/AWARDS/APPOINTMENTS:**
3.81/3.82 Male Voice Winner of Limerick Civic Week's 'Golden Voice of Ireland'.
From 1983 to 1986, Awarded 4 Cripplegate Scholarships by the Guildhall School of Music and Drama, London.
**TRAINING AND/OR QUALIFICATIONS:**
From 1979 to 1982, Studied with Paul Deegan at the Royal Irish Academy of Music, Dublin.
1982, Lieder course at Britten-Pears School, Aldeburgh.
From 1982 to 1986, followed postgraduate course and course in opera at the Guildhall School of Music and Drama, London.
1987 Opera course at Britten-Pears School, Aldeburgh.
**AVAILABILITY:**
General.
**ADDITIONAL INFORMATION:**
Has sung for Wexford Festival Opera, Opera Theatre Company, Opera Northern Ireland and Opera South, and in Britain for Pimlico Opera, Opera '80 and English Bach Festival. Oratorio repertoire includes most standard works. Has also sung in musicals, and regularly sings lighter repertoire in concert.

# Morgan Crowley *Baritone*

**Contact:** Morgan Crowley
259, Howth Road
Dublin 5 (h)
or
c/o Hilary Gagan Associates
Caprice House
3, New Burlington Street
London W1X 1FE (a)
**Tel:** +353 1 8335805
**Email:** morganstar@compuserve.com
**Other instruments:** Piano, bodhrán, recorder.

*"... A vocally rare being with a heaven-sent voice, hugely versatile acting ability, fluid natural dancer ... can truly make an audience swoon"* 1996 The Independent (David Benedict).

**KEY IRISH PERFORMANCES** (since January 1994):
1994 National Concert Hall, Dublin, appearing in the Leinster Opera Studio production of 'Die Zauberflöte' as 'Papageno'.
1995 NCH, appearing with Conor Linehan (piano).
1995 Point Theatre, Dublin, promoted by Maurice Cassidy and Abhann Productions, appearing in 'Riverdance, The Show'.
1996 Millstreet Arena, Cork, promoted by Maurice Cassidy and Abhann Productions, appearing in 'Riverdance, The Show'.
**KEY PERFORMANCES OUTSIDE IRELAND** (since January 1994):
1994 Queen Elizabeth Hall, London, promoted by EBF Opera, in Purcell's 'Dido and Aeneas' playing 'Spirit'.
1995 Theatre on the Bay, Capetown, South Africa, appearing as Solo Lead of the World Premiere of 'Music of the Night' by Andrew Lloyd Webber with Cantabile (singing solo lead).
1996 Royal Opera House, Covent Garden, London, appearing in World Premiere of Opera Trilogy with Cantabile and Covent Garden Festival Opera.
1996 Radio City Music Hall, New York, promoted by Maurice Cassidy and Abhann Productions in 'Riverdance, The Show' (as lead singer and dancer).
**SELECTED BROADCASTS AND/OR RECORDED WORK:**
1993 'Lovejoy' for BBC.

1995 'Friday Night is Music Night' for BBC.
1997 'Riverdance', Spotlight Interview, Perth, Australia.
**SELECTED REVIEWS** (since January 1994):
1994/5 Articles in German and South African Publications by Wilhelm Grutter.
1996 Observer (Andrew Porter).
**PRIZES/AWARDS/APPOINTMENTS:**
1990 Winner of the John McCormack Award for the 'Best Overall Singer' at the Feis Ceoil, Dublin.
1991 Awarded the Luciano Pavarotti Award for 'Best Performer' by RTÉ.
**TRAINING AND/OR QUALIFICATIONS:**
From 1988 to 1993, Singing and Piano Diplomas from the DIT Conservatory of Music and Drama, Dublin and Leinster Opera Studio.
From 1990 to 1992, Diploma in Theatre Studies from Trinity College, Dublin.
From 1990 to 1996, Various dance styles studied at the Dublin Dance Centre and Dance Attic, London.
From 1993 to 1996, Private coaching from David Mason and Michael Chance.
**AVAILABILITY:**
Dependent on current contractual obligation, usually 2 months notice maximum required.
**ADDITIONAL INFORMATION:**
Trained in Dublin, London, Paris and New York with tutors in all disciplines of the Performing Arts. Has performed in several musicals (e.g. 'West Side Story', 'Carousel', 'Grand Night for Singing' - European Premiere), and operas such as 'Tosca', 'Die Zauberflöte', 'Orfeo', 'Dido and Aeneas'. Lead with Europe's vocal quartet, Cantabile. Has performed with Placido Domingo, Cleo Laine, Harry Connick and Celine Dion. 4 octave vocal range.

## Austin Gaffney *Baritone*

**Contact:** Mr Austin Gaffney
20, Vintage Court
Dublin 8
**Tel/Fax:** +353 1 4547130 / +353 1 6621509

**AVAILABILITY:**
General.
**ADDITIONAL INFORMATION:**
Specialises in theatre and musicals.

## Owen Gilhooly *Baritone*

**Contact:** Owen Gilhooly
c/o Royal College of Music
Prince Consort Road, London SW7 2BS
**Mobile:** +44 973 673760
**Other instruments:** Piano.

**KEY IRISH PERFORMANCES** (since January 1994):
9.95 University of Limerick Concert Hall appearing with David Wray.
12.96 O'Reilly Hall, University College, Dublin appearing with the Garda Band.
3.97 Carlow appearing as soloist in 'St John's Passion' with the Orchestra of St Cecilia.
**KEY PERFORMANCES OUTSIDE IRELAND:**
11.95 Hastings, appearing as soloist with Hastings Choral Society.
5.96 London, appearing as soloist with the Royal College of Music Sinfonietta.
11.96 London, appearing as soloist with the University College London Orchestra.
11.96 Drury Lane, London, promoted by Irish Heritage Opera Evening, and appearing with Úna Murphy (piano).
**SELECTED BROADCASTS AND/OR RECORDED WORK:**
1.97 Veronica Dunne Singing Competition for RTÉ.
**PRIZES/AWARDS/APPOINTMENTS:**
5.96 Peter Pears Exhibition Scholarship from the Royal College of Music, London.
**TRAINING AND/OR QUALIFICATIONS:**
From 1989 to 1994, Limerick School of Music with J Holmes.
Since 1995 Royal College of Music, London with Graziella Sciutti.
**AVAILABILITY:**
General.

## Patrick Healy *Baritone*

**Contact:** Mr Patrick Healy
1, Cavendish Mansions
Hazelbourne Road
London SW12 4NX
England
**Tel/Fax:** +44 181 6752086 / +44 1332 740 423
*See piano page 38.*

## Martin Higgins *Baritone*

**Contact:** Mr Martin Higgins
14 Kinross Avenue
Cardonald
Glasgow, G52 3JB
Scotland
**Tel/Fax:** +44 141 8101997 / +44 141 8101997

**KEY IRISH PERFORMANCES** (since January 1994):
12.94 Gaiety Theatre, Dublin, promoted by DGOS, appearing in Puccini's 'La Bohème' as 'Shavnard' with the RTÉ Concert Orchestra.
1.95 John Field Room, National Concert Hall, Dublin, promoted by Opera Theatre Company, appearing with Mairéad Hurley.
3.95 Gaiety Theatre, Dublin, promoted by DGOS, appearing in Verdi's 'Rigoletto' as 'Marullo'.
5.96 University of Limerick Concert Hall, appearing as soloist in 'The Children of Lir'.
**KEY PERFORMANCES OUTSIDE IRELAND** (since January 1994):
7.95 Holland Park, London, promoted by Opera Europa, appearing in 'Pagliaci' as 'Silvio'.
4.96 Cottier Theatre, Glasgow, promoted by Mayfest, appearing in 'Lucia Di Lammermoor' as 'Enrico'.
9.96 Tour of Scotland, promoted by Scottish Opera, appearing in Mozart's 'Cosi Fan Tutte' as 'Giuglielmo'.
5.96 Tour of Scotland, promoted by SO.
**SELECTED BROADCASTS AND/OR RECORDED WORK:**
1991 'The Children of the Last Music' by Gerard Victory for RTÉ.
1994 Verdi's 'La Traviata' for RTÉ.
1995 'A Passionate Man' for RTÉ.
**PRIZES/AWARDS/APPOINTMENTS:**
8.91 Awarded a six week opera training workshop in Siena by the Italian Government.
9.91 Awarded funding grant 'British Young Singers Award' for further study at the National Opera Studio, London.
**TRAINING AND/OR QUALIFICATIONS:**
From 1987 to 1991, Studied with Dr Veronica Dunne.
From 8.91 to 9.91, Accademia Chigana, Siena studied with Carlo Bergonzi.
From 9.91 to 7.92, Opera Training Course at the National Opera Studio, London.
**AVAILABILITY:**
General.
**ADDITIONAL INFORMATION:**
Operatic performances include 'Ravenal' (Showboat), 'Publio' ('La Clemenza Di Tito'), 'Guglielmo' and 'Don Alfonso' ('Cosi Fan Tutte'), 'Silvio' ('i Pagliacci'), 'Shavnard', 'Marcello' ('La Boheme'), 'Sid' (Albert Herring), 'Berandino' ('Benvenutto Cellini'), 'Enrico' ('Lucia di Lammermoor'), 'Figaro' ('The Barber of Seville') and 'Harley' ('A Passionate Man').

# James Ludden *Bass*

**Contact:** Mr James Ludden
96, Millview Lawns
Malahide
Co Dublin
**Tel/Mobile/Fax:** +353 1 8452182 / +353 88 585918 / +353 1 8450107

**KEY IRISH PERFORMANCES** (since January 1994):
2.94 Grand Hotel, Malahide, Dublin, promoted by the Malahide Musical Society.
12.94 National Concert Hall, Dublin, promoted by the Goethe Institute, appearing with the Hibernian Chamber Choir conducted by John Finucane.
23.2.95 Royal Dublin Hotel, O'Connell Street, promoted by the National Council for Higher Education, appearing with Pádhraic Ó Cuinneagáin.
**SELECTED BROADCASTS AND/OR RECORDED WORK:**
1993 for Frank Patterson CD.
1994 'Aida' chorus for Naxos.
**PRIZES/AWARDS/APPOINTMENTS:**
1993 and 1994, 2nd Prize, solo bass, awarded at the Feis Ceoil, Dublin.
1992 and 1995, 2nd Prize, solo bass, awarded at the Feis Maitiu.
**TRAINING AND/OR QUALIFICATIONS:**
Since 1986, Private vocal training.
From 1990 to 1993, attended vocal workshops at the DIT Conservatory of Music and Drama, Dublin.
**ADDITIONAL INFORMATION:**
From 1990 to 1994, Singer with the DIT CMD Choral Society. Member of the Goethe Institute Choir. Cantor in St Sylvester's Choir, Malahide. Interested in opera, oratoria and Lieder.

# Séamas Ludden *Baritone*

**Contact:** Mr Séamas Ludden
96, Millview Lawns
Malahide
Co Dublin
**Tel:** +353 1 8452182 / +353 1 8450107

**KEY IRISH PERFORMANCES** (since January 1994):
5.95 Christ Church Cathedral, Dublin, appearing with the Dún Laoghaire Chamber Choir, as a baritone solo in the Duruflé Requiem.
5.95 St Patrick's College, Drumcondra, Dublin, appearing with the College Choral Society production of Handel's 'Messiah'.
**SELECTED BROADCASTS AND/OR RECORDED WORK:**
1994 'Aida' chorus for Naxos.
1995 'Schubert Mass' for RTÉ, ITV, BBC.
**PRIZES/AWARDS/APPOINTMENTS:**
4.92 1st Prize winner in the Feis Ceoil, Dublin.
12.92 Scholarship and prize for singing, awarded by DIT Conservatory of Music and Drama, Dublin.
4.93 1st Prize bass solo, awarded by Feis Maitiú.
4.93 1st Prize winner in the Feis Ceoil, Dublin.
**TRAINING AND/OR QUALIFICATIONS:**
From 10.90 to 6.91, One year certificate in music received from the DIT CMD.
From 1991 to 1992, Studied music theatre and operatic studies at the DIT CMD.
From 1991 to 1992, Royal Irish Academy of Music, (teacher B McNamara).
1992 Studied piano at the DIT CMD (teacher B Parker).
**AVAILABILITY:**
General.
**ADDITIONAL INFORMATION:**
Member of the Palestrina choir and DGOS Professional Chorus. Has worked with the National Chamber Choir. Light operas include 'Showboat and 'The Arcadians'. Member of chorus in Rigoletto (May 1992) for RTÉ. Has experience in conducting and accompanying choirs.

# Mario di Marco *Baritone*

**Tel/Fax:** +49 621 411455 / +49 621 412173

*"A man who possesses a velvet baritone with a metal centre and enormous power"* 10.96 Opern Welt.

**KEY PERFORMANCES OUTSIDE IRELAND** (since January 1994):
Sings in all major Opera Houses.
**SELECTED BROADCASTS AND/OR RECORDED WORK:**
1983 'Il Trovatore', as 'Di Luna', for RTÉ.
1987 'La Forza del Destino', as 'Don Carlos' for SDR, Germany.
1997 'Don Carlo', as 'Posa' for Lithuania Far East Block Television.
**SELECTED REVIEWS** (since January 1994):
3.96 Hamburger Abendblatt, ('Otello'), with R Kallo and S Sweet.
4.96 Der Neue Werker (Vienna), 'Simon Boccanegra'.
9.96 Opern Welt, ('Guglielmo Tell').
**PRIZES/AWARDS/APPOINTMENTS:**
1989/90 Appointed Kammersinger at the Vienna State Opera.
1991 Appointed Kammersinger at the Hamburg State Opera.
**TRAINING AND/OR QUALIFICATIONS:**
From 1970 to 1976, Studied at the Royal Irish Academy of Music, Dublin. Also studied with Charles Germant Hearn in Dublin, Tio Gabbi and Enzo Ferrari in Italy.
**REGULARLY PERFORMS WITH:**
Carreras, Domingo, Ava Marton, Margaret Price.
**AVAILABILITY:**
Subject to schedule.
**ADDITIONAL INFORMATION:**
Has performed Verismo Opera world wide for almost 20 years. Repertoire of 60 operas.

# Frank O'Brien *Baritone*

**Contact:** Mr Frank O'Brien
4, Brookwood Crescent
Artane
Dublin 5
**Tel:** +353 1 8310432

**KEY IRISH PERFORMANCES** (since January 1994):
2.6.94 Bank of Ireland Proms, Dublin, appearing with RTÉ Concert Orchestra.
1995 National Concert Hall, Dublin, performing Elgar's 'The Apostles', appearing with the National Symphony Orchestra of Ireland.
8.96 NCH, Dublin, in a production of the 'Gypsy Baron' as 'Homondy' appearing with the RTÉ Concert Orchestra.
6.97 NCH, Dublin, in a production of 'Bohemian Girl', appearing with RTÉCO and Choir.
**KEY PERFORMANCES OUTSIDE IRELAND** (since January 1994):
1993 San Diego and New York, USA.
**PRIZES/AWARDS/APPOINTMENTS:**
1994 Presented with the Vocal Heritage Award (John McCormack Medal) for services to singing in Ireland.
Gold medalist winner at various Feiseanna.
**TRAINING AND/OR QUALIFICATIONS:**
1960's DIT Conservatory of Music and Drama, Dublin (teacher Veronica Dunne).
1996 ARCM, London (teacher M Annovazzi).
**REGULARLY PERFORMS WITH:**
Opera Ireland, RTÉ Concert Orchestra, Opera Theatre Company.
**AVAILABILITY:**
General.
**ADDITIONAL INFORMATION:**
Singing for twenty years. Repertoire includes opera, oratorio and Lieder. Has given solo recitals in Kilkenny, Wexford, and Galway. Works also as a soloist with choral groups.

## Gerard O'Connor *Bass-Baritone*

**Contact:** Mr Gerard O'Connor
c/o Music International
18 Ardilaun Road
London N5 2QR
England
**Tel/Fax:** +44 171 3595183 / +44 171 2269792

**KEY IRISH PERFORMANCES** (since January 1994):
1995, Opera House, Belfast in the Opera Northern Ireland production of 'Cunning Little Vixen' as 'Parson' and 'Badger'.
1996 The Gaiety, Dublin, in the Opera Ireland production of 'La Boheme' as 'Colline'.
1997 The Gaiety, Dublin, in the Opera Ireland production of 'The Barber of Seville' as 'Antonio'.
1997 Opera House, Belfast in the Castleward Opera production of 'La Boheme' as 'Colline'.
**KEY PERFORMANCES OUTSIDE IRELAND** (since January 1994):
1995 Holland Park, London, in the Opera Europe production of 'Rigoletto'.
1996 Belgium and Holland in the Opera Theatre Company production of Mozart's 'Zaide' as 'Osmin'.
1997 Holland Park, London, in the Holland Park Opera production of Mascagni's 'Iris' as 'il Cieco'.
**SELECTED BROADCASTS AND/OR RECORDED WORK:**
'La Boheme' and 'Rigoletto' for RTÉ Proms series.
**PRIZES/AWARDS/APPOINTMENTS:**
1995 Awarded the Guinness Bursary by National Opera Studio, London.
**TRAINING AND/OR QUALIFICATIONS:**
From 1990 to 1993, (teacher Rev Sr Peter Cronin).
From 1993 to 1994, (teacher Veronica Dunne).
From 1994 to 1995, attended the National Opera Studio.
From 1994 to 1997, (teacher Robert Dean).

## Jack O'Kelly *Baritone*

**Contact:** Mr Jack O'Kelly
2a, Kelvin Road
Roath
Cardiff, CF2 5ET
Wales
**Tel:** +44 1222 450967

*"Made a splendid debut ... a singer of real distinction"*

1988 Sunday Tribune (Tu Rex Gloriae' in the 'Te Deum' by Dvorak).

**AVAILABILITY:**
Subject to contract.
**ADDITIONAL INFORMATION:**
Currently on contract to Welsh National Opera but is available by arrangement. Roles have included 'Nourabad' in 'Les Pecheurs du Perles', 'Marullo' in 'Rigoletto', 'Alessio' in 'La Sonambula' and 'Jose Castro' in 'Fancivilla del West'.

## Philip O'Reilly *Bass-Baritone*

**Contact:** Mr Philip O'Reilly
16, St John's Road
Sandymount
Dublin 4
**Tel/Fax:** +353 1 2692207 / +353 1 2838129

*"... A real find, with a rich resonant bass baritone"* 9.94 Sunday Tribune (Ian Fox).

**KEY IRISH PERFORMANCES** (since January 1994):
26.5.95 Royal Dublin Society, Dublin, appearing with the RTÉ Concert Orchestra in a production of 'Don Pasquale'.
21.6.95 Samuel Beckett Centre, Trinity College, Dublin promoted by Swift Productions, conducted by Colman Pearce.
26.10.95 National Concert Hall, Dublin, promoted by Dublin County Choir.
17.11.95 St Mary's, Clonmel, promoted by Our Lady's Choral Society, appearing with the RTÉ Concert Orchestra.
**KEY PERFORMANCES OUTSIDE IRELAND** (since January 1994):
10.95 Bournemouth, England in an production of Haydn's 'Creation' appearing with Bournemouth Symphony Orchestra and Chorus.
11.95 Sheffield City Hall, appearing in a production of Mendelssohn's 'Elijah' with the Sheffield Philharmonic Orchestra.
12.95 Tokyo, promoted by Tokyo Handel Society, appearing with Tokyo Symphony Orchestra.
**SELECTED BROADCASTS AND/OR RECORDED WORK:**
1995 Bach Cantatas with the Orchestra of St Cecilia.
1995 'Don Pasquale' for RTÉ.
**AVAILABILITY:**
General.

## Peter Wells *Bass*

**Contact:** Mr Peter Wells
10c, Woodland House
Rushpark
Co Antrim BT37 9SG
Northern Ireland
**Tel:** +44 1232 867768

*See recorder page 123.*

## Nyle Wolfe *Baritone*

**Contact:** Mr Nyle Wolfe
'Shangri-La'
Halfmoon Lane
South Douglas Road
Cork
**Tel/Mobile:** +353 21 891249 / +44 956 473004

*"Wolfe has a sensitive appreciation of texts ... [and]...consistently pleasing quality [of voice]"*

15.6.96 Irish Times (Martin Adams).

**KEY IRISH PERFORMANCES** (since January 1994):
6.96 National Concert Hall, Dublin, appearing with David Wray (piano) singing Schumann's Liederkreis.
11.96 Cork Opera House, promoted by Opera South, in a production of Bizet's 'Carmen' as 'Dancario'.
3.97 Cork City Hall, promoted by Kinsale Opera, in a production of 'The Merry Widow' as 'Danilo'.
4.97 Queen's University, Belfast, in Haydn's 'Creation'.

**SELECTED BROADCASTS AND/OR RECORDED WORK:**
3.94 'The Pirates of Penzance' as 'Pirate King' for RTÉ.
4.94 'Late Late Show' for RTÉ.
12.96 Schumann's 'Leiderkreis' for RTÉ.
**SELECTED REVIEWS** (since January 1994):
17.3.97 Examiner.
**PRIZES/AWARDS/APPOINTMENTS:**
1.95 Winner of RTÉ FM3 Prize at the Veronica Dunne Singing Competition.
6.95 Winner of the Mary Garden International Singing Competition, at the Aberdeen Youth Festival.
**TRAINING AND/OR QUALIFICATIONS:**
From 8.91 to 3.93, Studied at the Cork School of Music (teacher John Carolan).
From 3.93 to 6.96, Studied at the Leinster School of Music (teacher Veronica Dunne).
From 8.96 to 6.97, Studied at the Royal Academy of Music, London (teacher Mark Wildman)
**AVAILABILITY:**
General.
**ADDITIONAL INFORMATION:**
Singer and actor. Has appeared with main companies and societies. Performs many diverse styles of music: musicals, recitals, opera, oratorio, to banquets at Bunratty Castle, etc.

# Section four

## Period Instrumentalists, Singers and Ensembles



Performers who have made a special study of early instrumental technique and performance practice are listed below under four broad categories, strings (bowed and plucked), wind, keyboard, voice.

The ensembles listed are those which specialise in period performance.



*(listed by name)

# PERIOD INSTRUMENTALISTS
## Strings (bowed and plucked)

## Siobhán Armstrong *Early Harps*

**Contact:** Ms Siobhán Armstrong
Kilballyquilty
Carrick-on-Suir
Co Waterford
**Tel/Fax:** +353 51 646286
or
25, Queensdown Road
London E5 8NN
England
**Tel/Fax:** +44 181 9864173

*". . . Superb harp playing . . ."* 1992 Karjalainen, Finland.

**KEY IRISH PERFORMANCES** (since January 1994):
5.96 Sligo Early Music Festival, promoted by the Early Music Organisation of Ireland, appearing with John Elwes.
5.97 An Taibhdhearc, as part of the Galway Early Music Festival.
1997 Rothe House, Kilkenny, appearing with John Elwes, Maya Homburger, Malcolm Proud.
**KEY PERFORMANCES OUTSIDE IRELAND** (since January 1994):
2.95 Madrid, appearing with the Freiburger Barock Orchester, conducted by Thomas Hengelbrock.
3.96 Amsterdam, appearing with Les Talens Lyriques, conducted by Christophe Rousset, in Monteverdi's 'Poppea'.
5.97 Boston Early Music Festival, 'Italian Extravaganza', appearing with Tragicomedia.
8.97 Drottningholm Royal Theatre, Sweden, appearing with the Royal Theatre Orchestra, in Rossi's 'Orfeo'.
**SELECTED BROADCASTS AND/OR RECORDED WORK:**
1995 Purcell's 'Songs of Welcome and Farewell' with Tragicomedia for Teldec Classics.
1996 Monteverdi's 'L'Incoronazione di Poppea' conducted by John Eliot Gardiner for Deutsche Grammophon.
1996 Laudi's 'Il Sant' Alessio', conducted by William Christie for Erato.
**PRIZES/AWARDS/APPOINTMENTS:**
1986 1st Prize winner at the Concours International de Harpe Celtique, Brittany.
**TRAINING AND/OR QUALIFICATIONS:**
From 1983 to 1987, BA (Hons) Music from Trinity College, Dublin.
**REGULARLY PERFORMS WITH:**
John Elwes (tenor).
**AVAILABILITY:**
General.
**ADDITIONAL INFORMATION:**
One of only a number of individuals worldwide who research and play harps from earlier centuries. Has an extensive collection of instruments and performs and records internationally with various ensembles for historically aware performance. Lectures and gives both solo and chamber music concerts. Also available, when in Ireland, as a duo with the tenor John Elwes.

## Cormac de Barra *Baroque Harp*

**Contact:** Mr Cormac de Barra
21, Northbrook Avenue
Ranelagh
Dublin 6
**Tel/Mobile:** +353 1 4963324 / +353 87 445562
**Email:** cormac.d@usa.net
*See Irish harp page 227.*

## Maria Christina Cleary

### *Historical Harps*

**Contact:** Ms Maria Christina Cleary
Ryswykseweg 340-9
2516 HM Den Haag
The Netherlands
**Tel/Fax:** +31 70 3952605
*See concert harp page 6.*

## Paul Conway *Viola da Gamba*

**Contact:** Mr Paul Conway
37, Monastery Drive
Dublin 22
**Tel:** +353 1 4593847
**Other instruments:** Piano/keyboards, treble viol, bass viol, SATB recorders.

**TRAINING AND/OR QUALIFICATIONS:**
Diploma in Music Teaching from University College, Dublin.
**REGULARLY PERFORMS WITH:**
Marion Doherty, Honor OBrolchain, Anna Pories.
**AVAILABILITY:**
General.
**ADDITIONAL INFORMATION:**
Studied with John Beckett at Royal Irish Academy of Music and has been tutored by leading instructors in various chamber music summer schools specialising in viols, recorders and voice in Ireland, UK and Italy.

## John Feeley *Lute*

**Contact:** John Feeley
14, Wesley Road
Rathgar
Dublin 6
**Tel/Fax:** +353 1 4905495
*See classical guitar page 20.*

## Douglas Gunn *Viola da Gamba*

**Contact:** Mr Douglas Gunn
Ballaghmore Castle
Borris-in-Ossory
Co Laois
**Tel:** +353 505 23093
**Email:** dgunn@iol.ie
**WWW:** http://www.iol.ie/~dgunn/
*See recorders page 121.*

## Camilla Gunzl *Baroque Violin, Viola*

**Contact:** Ms Camilla Gunzl
7, Larchfield Park
Roebuck
Dublin 14
**Tel:** +353 1 2982731
*See violin page 61.*

## Gráinne Hambly *Baroque Harp*

**Contact:** Ms Gráinne Hambly
Knockrickard
Claremorris
Co Mayo
**Tel/Fax:** +353 94 60209 / +353 94 60273
**Email:** grainne@mayo-ireland.ie
*See Irish harp page 228.*

## Maya Homburger *Baroque Violin*

**Contact:** Ms Maya Homburger
Carrickmourne
Thomastown
Co Kilkenny
**Tel/Fax:** +353 56 58708 / +353 56 58709
**Email:** maya@tinet.ie

*"Maya Homburger's sense of line is absolutely unerring, and her controlled use of vibrato particularly impressive".*

(Early Music Review) of Bach sonatas (see below)

**KEY IRISH PERFORMANCES** (since January 1994):
16.3.97 and 23.3.97, Hugh Lane Municipal Gallery of Modern Art, appearing with Malcolm Proud (harpsichord).
**KEY PERFORMANCES OUTSIDE IRELAND** (since January 1994):
5.96 Schlosskonzerte Spiez, promoted by Schlosskonzerte Spiez, appearing with Malcolm Proud and friends.
8.96 Münsterkonzerte, Berne, appearing with continuo group.
12.96 Forum fúr Altemusik, Zurich appearing with Barry Guy (double bass).
**SELECTED BROADCASTS AND/OR RECORDED WORK:**
1993 Telemann 'Solo Fantasies' for Maya Records.
1995 Bach Sonatas for harpsichord and violin, for Maya Records.
**SELECTED REVIEWS** (since January 1994): 1
993 Strad.
3.97 Irish Times.
**TRAINING AND/OR QUALIFICATIONS:**
From 1977 to 1980, Diploma (soloist) from Conservatory of Music, Berne, Switzerland.
**REGULARLY PERFORMS WITH:**
Malcolm Proud (harpsichord), Barry Guy (double bass).
**AVAILABILITY:**
General.
**ADDITIONAL INFORMATION:**
Plays both classical and contemporary music as a duo with Barry Guy.

## Michael McCartney *Period Guitars*

**Contact:** Mr Michael McCartney
8, Alexandra Terrace
Novara Avenue
Bray
Co Wicklow
**Tel/Fax:** +353 1 2867168
**Email:** mgmccart@indigo.ie
*See classical guitar page 21.*

## Tom O'Farrell

### *Viola da Gamba, Guitars, Lute*

**Contact:** Mr Tom O'Farrell
12, Restelouet
22340 Plévin, France
**Tel:** +33 2 962 96792
*See guitar page 224.*

## Catríona O'Leary *Baroque Harp*

**Contact:** Catríona O'Leary
c/o 86, Ard na Mara
Malahide, Co Dublin (a)
or
Apt. 6D
West 11th Street
NY 10014, New York
USA (Home)
**Tel/Fax:** +353 1 8450444 (a) or +1 212 645 0989 (h) / +353 1 8456979
*See singers page 126.*

## Brian Payne

### *Lute, Archlute, Orpharion, Vihuela*

**Contact:** Mr Brian Payne
13, High Street
Killyleagh
Co Down, BT 30 9QF
Northern Ireland
**Tel:** +44 1396 828567
**Email:** 106363.3140@compuserve.com
**WWW:** http://ourworld.compuserve.com/homepages/brian-payne-2

*"... The lute playing of Brian Payne shows considerable musical ability and a fine technical mastery of his instrument"* 2.97 Down Recorder.

**KEY IRISH PERFORMANCES** (since January 1994):
5.96 Queen's University, Belfast, promoted by Queen's Early Music Festival, appearing with Stephen Sandford (counter tenor).
5.96 Dalriada House, University of Ulster, Jordanstown, appearing with Fiona Donaghy (soprano).
2.97 Down Arts Centre, promoted by Ards Arts, appearing with Susan Lines (soprano).
4.97 Stranmillis, promoted by Stranmillis College Music Society, appearing with Stephen Sandford (counter tenor).
**SELECTED REVIEWS** (since January 1994):
10.96 Belfast Telegraph.
2.97 Ards Chronicle.
**TRAINING AND/OR QUALIFICATIONS:**
Since 1988, Tuition with Tom Finucane and Jakob Lindberg.
**REGULARLY PERFORMS WITH:**
Stephen Sandford (counter tenor), Susan Lines (soprano).
**AVAILABILITY:**
General.
**ADDITIONAL INFORMATION:**
Particularly interested in the music found in the important collections of 16th and early 17th Century lute manuscripts from Irish and English sources, especially those with Irish associations. Has accompanied various song recitalists.

## Andrew Robinson *Viols*

**Contact:** Mr Andrew Robinson
35, Marlborough Road
Donnybrook
Dublin 4
**Tel:** +353 1 6685349
**Email:** akr@tinet.ie

**REGULARLY PERFORMS WITH:**
Dublin Viols, Consort of St Sepulchre.

## Deirdre Ward *Baroque Violin*

**Contact:** Deirdre Ward
Apartment 5
113, Strand Road
Sandymount
Dublin 4
**Tel:** +353 1 2600774
*See violin page 67.*

## Mark Wilkes

### *Viola da Gamba, Cello, Treble Viol*

**Contact:** Mr Mark Wilkes
17, Windsor Road
Rathmines, Dublin 6
**Tel:** +353 1 4964575

**KEY IRISH PERFORMANCES** (since January 1994):
11.6.94 Lismore Cathedral, promoted by West Waterford Early Music Festival, appearing with Dublin Consort of Viols.
8.11.95 No 29 Merrion Row, promoted by Feis Ceoil and ESB, appearing with Canzona.
24.5.97 Sligo, promoted by Sligo Early Music Festival, appearing with the Dublin Consort of Viols.
1.2.97 St Bartholomew's, Ballsbridge, Dublin, appearing with Tactus.
**SELECTED BROADCASTS AND/OR RECORDED WORK:**
1995 BBC Northern Ireland.
1995 'Words Upon the Window Pane' (film).
**TRAINING AND/OR QUALIFICATIONS:**
From 1978 to 1989, Studied at the Royal Irish Academy of Music (teacher Olwyn Lewis).
From 1991 to 1994, BA (Hons) in Music and Art History from University College, Dublin.
1993 LTCL (Teaching) from Trinity College, London.
From 1994 to 1995, B Mus (Hons) from UCD.
**REGULARLY PERFORMS WITH:**
Dublin Consort of Viols, Tactus, Canzona.
**AVAILABILITY:**
General.
**ADDITIONAL INFORMATION:**
Principally a viola da gamba player. Specialises in continuo playing, as well as gamba music from the late 18th Century.

# WIND

## David Agnew *Recorders*

**Contact:** Mr David Agnew
Beaufort House
Butterfield Avenue
Rathfarnham
Dublin 14
**Tel/Fax:** +353 1 4945939
**Email:** oboeking@iol.ie
*See oboe page 24.*

## Ruby Ashley *Oboe d'Amore*

**Contact:** Ms Ruby Ashley
49, Weirview Drive
Stillorgan
Co Dublin
**Tel:** +353 1 2882467
*See oboe page 24.*

## David Carmody

### *Hand Horn and Cornetto*

**Contact:** David Carmody
33, Westfield Road
Harold's Cross
Dublin 6w
**Tel:** +353 1 4923486
*See French Horn page 23.*

## Aisling Casey *Oboe d'Amore*

**Contact:** Ms Aisling Casey
12, Beverly
Ovens
Co Cork
**Tel:** +353 21 870676
*See oboe page 25.*

## Paul Conway *Recorders*

**Contact:** Mr Paul Conway
37 Monastery Drive
Dublin 22
**Tel:** +353 1 4593847
*See Viola da Gamba page 118.*

# Emma Coulthard

## *Historical Flutes and Recorders*

**Contact:** Ms Emma Coulthard
8, Alexandra Terrace
Novara Avenue
Bray
Co Wicklow
**Tel:** +353 1 2867168
**Email:** mgmccart@indigo.ie
**Other instruments:** Voice (soprano).

**KEY IRISH PERFORMANCES** (since January 1994):
10.94 St Finian's Church, Dublin, promoted by John O'Sullivan, appearing as soloist with Dublin Orchestral Players.
12.94 Droichead Arts Centre, Drogheda, appearing with Michael Holohan.
6.95 St Ann's Church, Dawson Street, Dublin, appearing with Michael McCartney (guitar).
**KEY PERFORMANCES OUTSIDE IRELAND** (since January 1994):
7.95 St Donal's Castle, Wales, promoted by Early Music Wales, appearing with Jelma van Amersfort (lute).
9.95 Snug Harbour Cultural Center, New York, promoted by Snug Harbour Cultural Center and the Department of Foreign Affairs, appearing with Michael McCartney (guitar).
**SELECTED BROADCASTS AND/OR RECORDED WORK:**
1991 'The Wounds of Art' for Paul Hayes.
1992 Mass for RTÉ (with the RTÉ Concert Orchestra).
1994 Trim Castle Heritage Centre Cassette.
**PRIZES/AWARDS/APPOINTMENTS:**
1991 Contemporary Music Cup at the Feis Ceoil.
1991 Boydell Cup for Chamber Music, awarded by Trinity College, Dublin.
**TRAINING AND/OR QUALIFICATIONS:**
From 1976 to 1991, ARIAM (flute) from Royal Irish Academy of Music.
From 1985 to 1991, BA (Hons) Music from Trinity College, Dublin.
1995 Baroque Flute Studies with Rachel Brown.
1996 Studied period flute with Lisa Besnosiuk.
**REGULARLY PERFORMS WITH:**
Michael McCartney (guitar).
**AVAILABILITY:**
General, particularly during school holidays.
**ADDITIONAL INFORMATION:**
Has been active as flautist and singer, performing a wide spectrum of music from medieval and renaissance to contemporary music and has performed premiers of Irish works. Has recently specialised in historical flutes (from the 18th and 19th Centuries).

# Morgan Crowley *Recorders*

**Contact:** Morgan Crowley
259, Howth Road
Dublin 5 (h)
c/o Hilary Gagan Associates
Caprice House
3, New Burlington Street
London W1X 1FE
England (a)
**Tel:** +353 1 8335805
**Email:** morganstar@compuserve.com
*See baritone page 112.*

# Eleanor Dawson

## *Baroque and Renaissance Flutes*

**Contact:** Ms Eleanor Dawson
7a, Martello Avenue
Sandycove
Co Dublin
**Tel:** +353 1 2803870

**KEY IRISH PERFORMANCES** (since January 1994);
3.96 Waterford Institute of Technology, appearing with Malcolm Proud.
5.96 Queen's University, Belfast, Sonorities Festival.
5.96 Model Arts Centre, Sligo, appearing with Malcolm Proud.
1.97 Hugh Lane Municipal Gallery of Modern Art, Dublin.
**KEY PERFORMANCES OUTSIDE IRELAND** (since January 1994):
5.94 Sutton House, London, appearing with Elizabeth Kenny (lute).
12.94 Oxford, London, appearing with Elizabeth Kenny and Reiko Idise.
2.95 City University, London, solo performance.
5.96 Windsor, London, appearing with Katherine May (harpsichord).
**SELECTED BROADCASTS AND/OR RECORDED WORK:**
9.92 Recital with Malcom Proud, for RTÉ.
8.94 'Airs and Brunettes', for Dervorguilla Records.
7.95 Recital with Laurence Cummings, for RTÉ.
**SELECTED REVIEWS** (since January 1994):
5.96 Irish Times.
5.96 Belfast Telegraph.
1.97 Irish Times.
**TRAINING AND/OR QUALIFCATIONS:**
From 1982 to 1985, Studied with Edward Beckett.
From 1984 to 1988, BA from University of Oxford.
From 1988 to 1989, Postgraduate at Royal College of Music, London (teacher Lisa Beznosink).
From 1989 to 1992, MA from Queen's University, Belfast.
**REGULARLY PERFORMS WITH:**
Malcolm Proud, Canzona, Tactus, Parsley and Opera Theatre Company.
**AVAILABILITY:**
General.
**ADDITIONAL INFORMATION:**
Interested in developing education and period-instrument performance in Ireland. Helped to organise the Sligo Early Music Festival in 1996 and 1997 and has performed at both the Huddersfield Contemporary Music Festival and the Darlington Festival. Gives lecture/recitals in England and in 3rd level institutions in Ireland.

# Douglas Gunn *Recorders*

**Contact:** Mr Douglas Gunn
Ballaghmore Castle
Borris-in-Ossory
Co Laois
**Tel:** +353 505 23093
**Email:** dgunn@iol.ie
**WWW:** http://www.iol.ie/~dgunn/
**Other instruments:** Viola da Gamba

**REGULARLY PERFORMS WITH:**
The Douglas Gunn Ensemble, The Vendon Duo.
**AVAILABILITY:**
General.

## Aedín Halpin *Recorders*

**Contact:** Ms Aedín Halpin
28, Simmonscourt Castle
Simmonscourt Road
Ballsbridge
Dublin 4 (h)
or
c/o Royal Irish Academy of Music
36-38 Westland Row
Dublin 2 (w)
**Tel:** +353 1 6608146(h) / +353 1 6764412 (w)
**Other instruments:** Flute.

*"... Deft assurance ...persuasive sense of line ... a brilliant display of musical feeling and technical dexterity"* 10.96 Irish Times.

**KEY IRISH PERFORMANCES** (since January 1994):
6.10.96 Hugh Lane Municipal Gallery of Modern Art, Dublin, appearing with Luke Tobin (guitar).
1.11.96 John Field Room, National Concert Hall, Dublin, appearing with Luke Tobin.
24.5.97 Royal Hospital Kilmainham, Dublin, appearing with the Dublin Baroque Players, (playing Vivaldi Concerti for Recorder in D and G).
9.7.97 St Ann's Church, Dawson Street, Dublin, appearing with the Orchestra of St Cecilia (playing Vivaldi Concerto in C for Sopranino).
**SELECTED BROADCASTS AND/OR RECORDED WORK:**
19.11.92 Appearing with John Feeley (lute) and Ann Robinson (viol) for RTÉ.
15.11.93 Appearing with Luke Tobin (guitar) for RTÉ.
16.8.94 Appearing with the RTÉ Concert Orchestra for RTÉ.
**SELECTED REVIEWS** (since January 1994):
8.94 Irish Times.
25.8.94 Irish Times.
**PRIZES/AWARDS/APPOINTMENTS:**
1981 Winner of woodwind section of RTÉ Young Musician of the Future Competition.
1995 Appointed full-time recorder and flute teacher at the Royal Irish Academy of Music, Dublin.
**TRAINING AND/OR QUALIFICATIONS:**
From 1979 to 1989, ARIAM (flute and piano) and LTCL (recorder) from the Royal Irish Academy of Music.
From 1985 to 1989, BA Mod in Music from Trinity College, Dublin.
From 1989 to 1992, Studied with Pedro Memelsdorf, Italy.
**REGULARLY PERFORMS WITH:**
Luke Tobin (guitar), Canzona (Renaissance/Baroque mixed ensemble).
**AVAILABILITY:**
General.
**ADDITIONAL INFORMATION:**
Exploits the versatility of the instrument with its repertoire ranging from 1600 up to the present day. Has performed as a soloist with orchestras and various ensembles (including guitar, piano, harpsichord, harp, lute, viol) for State and private functions.

## Philip Horan *Recorder*

**Contact:** Mr Philip Horan
17, Elm Mount Park
Beaumont
Dublin 9
**Tel:** +353 1 8316096
**Other instruments:** Piccolo and shakuhachi.
*See flute page 15.*

## Adrian Hughes *Recorders*

**Contact:** Mr Adrian Hughes
33, Cúl na Gréine
Old Bawn
Tallaght
Dublin 24
**Tel:** +353 1 4510101
*See bassoon page 2.*

## Emer McDonough *Recorder*

**Contact:** Ms Emer McDonough
3, Greenlawns
Sandyford Road
Dublin 16
**Tel:** +353 1 2956754
*See flute page 16.*

## Cecilia Madden *Recorder*

**Contact:** Ms Cecilia Madden
44, Downey Street
Killalee
Limerick
Co Limerick
**Tel:** +353 61 400820
*See oboe page 25.*

## Ríona Ó Duinnín *Recorder*

**Contact:** Ríona Ó Duinnín
Old Road
Carlingford
Co Louth
**Tel:** +353 42 73331
*See flute page 17.*

## Catríona O'Leary *Recorder*

**Contact:** Catríona O'Leary
86, Ard na Mara
Malahide, Co Dublin (a)
Apt. 6D, West 11th Street
NY 10014, New York
USA (h)
**Tel/Fax:** +353 1 8450444 (a) or +1 212 645 0989 (h) / +353 1 8456979
*See singers page 126.*

## Ruth O'Sullivan *Baroque Flute*

**Contact:** Ms Ruth O'Sullivan
6, Clarinda Park East
Dún Laoghaire, Co Dublin
**Tel/Fax:** +353 1 2804501 or + 353 1 2807268 / +353 1 2301406
*See flute page 18.*

## Kathleen Raymond *Recorder*

**Contact:** Ms Kathleen Raymond
72, Stack's Villas
Tralee
Co Kerry
**Tel:** +353 66 26973
*See flute page 18.*

## Jenny Robinson *Recorder*

**Contact:** Jenny Robinson
35, Marlborough Road
Dublin 4
**Tel:** +353 1 6685349

*"One of the outstanding concerts of the festival [Galway Early Music Festival] .... beautiful music, beautifully played ... "*

6/97 Early Music Organisation of Ireland Newsletter (Maura Ó Cróinín).

**ADDITIONAL INFORMATION:**
Principal recorder player in several period-instrument groups including the consort of St Sepulchre and Good Company. Has also been Solo/Principal Recorder of the National Symphony Orchestra of Ireland, the Irish Chamber Orchestra, the Cantata Players (under John Beckett), and the RTÉ Concert Orchestra.

## Emma Roche *Baroque Flute*

**Contact:** Ms Emma Roche
Cruachan
Sarsfields Court
Glanmire
Co Cork
**Tel:** +353 21 866198
*See flute page 18.*

## Rachel Talbot *Recorder*

**Contact:** Ms Rachel Talbot
117, Templeogue Road
Dublin 6w
**Tel:** +353 1 4907512
**Email:** rtalbot@clubi.ie
*See soprano page 127.*

## Hilary Travers *Recorder*

**Contact:** Ms Hilary Travers
39, Brook Court
Monkstown
Co Dublin
**Tel:** +353 1 2809699
*See violin page 67.*

## Peter Wells *Recorder*

**Contact:** Mr Peter Wells
10c, Woodland House
Rushpark
Co Antrim BT37 9SG
Northern Ireland
**Tel:** +44 1232 867768
**Other instruments:** Bass singer.

*"Wells' playing brimmed with energy and purpose ... he caught impeccably the flavour of the pieces ... "* 9.4.97 Irish Times.

**KEY IRISH PERFORMANCES** (since January 1994):
6.2.97 Harty Room Belfast, promoted by the Queen's University Belfast Music Society, appearing with Nigel McClintock (harpsichord).
3.4.97 Bank of Ireland Arts Centre, Dublin, promoted by the 'Mostly Modern' series.
28.6.97 St George's Church, Belfast, as part of the June recital series, appearing with Nigel McClintock (organ).
10.97 Harty Room, Belfast, promoted by the Belfast Early Music Festival, appearing with Jan Smaczney (harpsichord).
**KEY PERFORMANCES OUTSIDE IRELAND** (since January 1994):
26.4.95 Bachzaal, Amsterdam, promoted by Ensemble, appearing with Andrew Uren (bass clarinet) and Penelope Steel (piano).
16-23.7.95 Tour of New Zealand, promoted by St Cecilia Music, appearing with Douglas Mews (organ).
29.11.96 Exeter College, Oxford, promoted by Exeter College Music Society, appearing with Graeme McCullough (organ).
**SELECTED BROADCASTS AND/OR RECORDED WORK:**
5.7.95 For Radio New Zealand (national broadcast).
17.6.97 For RTÉ.
10.97 For BBC Radio Ulster.
**SELECTED REVIEWS** (since January 1994):
3.6.94 Irish News (Belfast).
17.6.97 Irish Times.
30.6.97 Belfast Telegraph.
**PRIZES/AWARDS/APPOINTMENTS:**
4.94 Postgraduate Fellowship (tenable for 1 year) awarded by the Netherlands Organisation for International Co-Operation in Higher Education.
**TRAINING AND/OR QUALIFICATIONS:**
9.85 LTCL (Perf) from Trinity College, London.
From 2.86 to 10.89, B Mus (Perf) from the University of Auckland, New Zealand.
From 9.93 to 6.95, Cert Post Grad St (Utrecht) from the Utrecht School of Arts (teacher Marion Verbruggen).
**AVAILABILITY:**
General.
**ADDITIONAL INFORMATION:**
Ireland's only full-time, Dutch-trained recorder virtuoso. A student of Marion Verbruggen. Specialises in historic performance practice as well as lively interpretation of lesser exposed early music. Also has an interest in contemporary recorder music.

# PERIOD KEYBOARDS

## David Adams

### *Harpsichord and other Early Keyboards*

**Contact:** Mr David Adams
3, Belgrave Place
Rathmines, Dublin 6
**Tel:** +353 1 4962079
**Other instruments:** Organ, piano.

*"Impressive enough to put an extra sprint in one's step on the way out of the Concert Hall"*
12.4.95 Irish Times.

**KEY IRISH PERFORMANCES** (since January 1994):
21.8.94 Project Arts Centre, Dublin.
21.11.94 Chapel, Trinity College, Dublin.
7.4.95 National Concert Hall, Dublin.
12.11.96 Ulster Hall, Belfast, promoted by BBC Northern Ireland.
**KEY PERFORMANCES OUTSIDE IRELAND** (since January 1994):
21.6.94 St Bavo, Haarlem, promoted by Town of Haarlem.
4.12.94 Stuttgart, promoted by Musik für Jahrhunderte.
4.96 Berlin, promoted by Hochschule der Künste.
2.2.97 Stuttgarte, promoted by New Music Festival, appearing with Ensemble Surplus.
**SELECTED BROADCASTS AND/OR RECORDED WORK:**
2.97 Maxwell Davies 'Solstice of Light' for NOS.
7.2.97 'Music Now' for BBC.
5.97 Recording for Naxos (with Brian Havergal).
**SELECTED REVIEWS** (since January 1994):
22.11.94 Irish Times.
**PRIZES/AWARDS/APPOINTMENTS:**
1985 Prizewinner at the International Early Music Competition, Bruges.
1986 1st Prize at the International Organ and Choral Festival, Dublin.
**TRAINING AND/OR QUALIFICATIONS:**
From 1978 to 1982, BA Music (Hons) from Trinity College, Dublin.
From 1983 to 1989, Recitalist's Diploma from the Freiburg Musikhochschule.
From 1985 to 1987, Recitalist's Diploma from the Sweelinck Conservatory, Amsterdam.
1982 FRCO from the Royal College of Organists. Is preparing a Doctoral dissertation for the Free University in Amsterdam.
**AVAILABILITY:**
General.
**ADDITIONAL INFORMATION:**
Repertoire encompasses the entire literature for organ and harpsichord. Is particularly involved with early music and contemporary music. Teacher and performer, has taught at the Musikhochschule in Freiburg the Royal Conservatory in The Hague, and the Hochschule der Künste in Berlin.

## Emer Buckley *Harpsichord*

**Contact:** Ms Emer Buckley
23, Rue de Rungis
75013, Paris, France
**Tel:** +33 1 45895858

*"... Wove a rich tapestry of sound and accomplished the little miracle of making the music of some 300 years ago comprehensible and appealing"* 29.11.96 Irish Times (Douglas Sealy).

**KEY IRISH PERFORMANCES** (since January 1994):
11/12.96 Tour of Ireland promoted by Music Network appearing with the Lachrimae Consort.
**KEY PERFORMANCES OUTSIDE IRELAND** (since January 1994):
1997 Festival St Loup, appearing with the Lachrimae Consort.
1997 Festival Pontoise.
29.8.95 Utrecht, The Netherlands, promoted by Utrecht Early Music Festival, appearing with Isabelle Poulenard.
8.95 Amsterdam, promoted by Amsterdam Early Music Festival, appearing with Isabelle Poulenard.
**SELECTED BROADCASTS AND/OR RECORDED WORK:**
1988 Works by Peter Philips, for Harmonia Mundi, France.
1990 Suites of J.S. Bach, for Harmonia Mundi, France.
1995 Works of Diego Ortiz with the Lachrimae Consort, for Mandala.
**PRIZES/AWARDS/APPOINTMENTS:**
1991 Appointed Professor of Harpsichord and Baroque Chamber Music at Lille National Conservatory, France.
**TRAINING AND/OR QUALIFICATIONS:**
M Mus from University College, Dublin.
**REGULARLY PERFORMS WITH:**
The Lachrimae Consort (viol, violin and baroque harpsichord), Les Voix Humaines (viol, baroque violin and harpsichord and Isabelle Poulenard, soprano).
**AVAILABILITY:**
General.
**ADDITIONAL INFORMATION:**
Has produced a series of recordings with the Lachrimae Consort devoted to Italian and Spanish 17th century music. Although resident in Paris, takes every opportunity to play in Ireland. Available for masterclasses and introductory courses to the harpsichord and its technique.

## Paul Conway *Period Pianofortes*

**Contact:** Mr Paul Conway
37, Monastery Drive
Dublin 22
**Tel:** +353 1 4593847
*See viola da gamba page 118.*

## Adrian Hughes *Period Pianofortes*

**Contact:** Mr Adrian Hughes
33, Cúl na Gréine
Old Bawn
Tallaght
Dublin 24
**Tel:** +353 1 4510101
*See bassoon page 2.*

## Desmond Hunter *Harpsichord*

**Contact:** Dr Desmond Hunter
16, The Hermitage
Drumbeg Road
Belfast BT17 9NH
Northern Ireland
**Tel/Fax:** +44 1232 622696 / +44 1232 366870
**Email:** d.hunter1@ulst.ac.uk

**KEY PERFORMANCES OUTSIDE IRELAND** (since January 1994):
27.4.95 Kent State University, Ohio, appearing solo (harpsichord).
**AVAILABILITY:**
General (prepared to travel any distance).
*See organ page 28.*

## David Lee *Harpsichord*

**Contact:** Mr David Lee
10, Corbawn Drive
Shankill
Dublin 18
**Tel:** +353 1 2821303
*See organ page 28.*

## Margo McGeeney *Harpsichord*

**Contact:** Ms Margo McGeeney
Geeha South
Kinvara
Co Galway
**Tel:** +353 91 637505
**Other instruments:** Tin whistle, guitar.

*"... Lively facility, expressive phrasing ... lyrical warmth ... excellent ornamentation and rhythmic feeling ..."* 6.10.87 Münchner Merkur, Germany.

**KEY IRISH PERFORMANCES** (since January 1994):
8.9.97 Geeha South, Kinvara, Co Galway.
**SELECTED BROADCASTS AND/OR RECORDED WORK:**
1974 and 1975 radio recording for RTÉ.
**SELECTED REVIEWS** (since January 1994):
Times, London.
Daily Telegraph, London.
**PRIZES/AWARDS/APPOINTMENTS:**
1969 Scholarship, awarded to study at Accademia Chigiana, Siena, Italy.
**TRAINING AND/OR QUALIFICATIONS:**
1968 Accademia Chigiana, Siena, Italy.
1969 Accademia Chigiana, Siena, Italy, awarded Performers Diploma.
From 1966 to 1969, private tuition with Jane Clark, London.
**AVAILIABILITY:**
Subject to schedule and activities based in own arts centre*.
**ADDITIONAL INFORMATION:**
*Operates own arts centre from home, with an emphasis on highlighting harpsichord music. Concerts feature a presentation of Elizabethan art and architecture. Regular performer in England, Germany and Ireland.

## Brian MacKay *Harpsichord*

**Contact:** Mr Brian MacKay
Front Flat
8, Kenilworth Road
Dublin 6
**Tel/Fax:** +353 1 4974812 / +353 1 4902822
*See piano page 43.*

## Malcolm Proud

### *Harpsichord and Period Pianofortes*

**Contact:** Mr Malcolm Proud
St Canice's Cottage
St Canice's Cathedral
Kilkenny
**Tel/Fax:** +353 56 61497
**Other instruments:** Organ, piano.

*"... A player with a brilliant technique and an acute musical sensibility"*
7.89 Gramophone (Nicholas Anderson).

**KEY IRISH PERFORMANCES** (since January 1994):
27.10.95 National Concert Hall, Dubin, promoted by Bach Organ Series.
9.6.96 Birr Castle, Co Offaly, promoted by AIB Festival of Music in Great Irish Houses, appearing with John Elwes and Sarah Cunningham.
16/23.3.97 Hugh Lane Municipal Gallery of Modern Art, Dublin, appearing with Maya Homburger.
12.4.97 Christ Church Cathedral, Dublin, International Handel Festival appearing with James Bowman and David Watkin.
**KEY PERFORMANCES OUTSIDE IRELAND** (since January 1994):
8.11.94 Ritz-Carlton Huntingdon Hotel, Pasadena, USA promoted by Da Camera Society, appearing with The Chandos Baroque Players.
6.8.95 Pembroke College, Cambridge, England, promoted by Cambridge Summer Music.
18.8.95 Magnano Festival, Italy, appearing with Maya Homburger.
4.12.96 Antwerp Opera House, promoted by De Vlaamse Opera.
**SELECTED BROADCASTS AND/OR RECORDED WORK:**
1985 'Malcolm Proud Harpsichord-plays' for Claddagh.
1994 'Henry Purcell - Eight Suites', for Meridian.
1995 'JS Bach - Six Sonatas for violin and harpshichord' for Maya recordings.
**SELECTED REVIEWS** (since January 1994):
10.11.94 Los Angeles Times.
30.10.95 Irish Times.
6.96 BBC Music Magazine.
**PRIZES/AWARDS/APPOINTMENTS:**
8.74 Royal Danish Government scholarship, awarded by Conservatory of Music, Copenhagen.
8.82 1st Prize winner of the International Harpsichord Competition, awarded by Edinburgh International Festival.
**TRAINING AND/OR QUALIFICATIONS:**
From 9.69 to 6.73, B Mus from Trinity College, Dublin.
From 9.74 to 6.75, Studied at Copenhagen Conservatory.
From 9.80 to 6.81, Final Diploma in harpsichord performance, from Sweelinck Conservatory, Amsterdam.
**REGULARLY PERFORMS WITH:**
Maya Homburger (baroque violin), John Elwes (tenor), Chandos Baroque Players.
**AVAILABILITY:**
General. Can travel with own harpsichord.
**ADDITIONAL INFORMATION:**
Has performed extensively throughout Britain, Continental Europe and North America.

## Andrew Synnott *Harpischord*

**Contact:** Andrew Synnott
98, Wilfield Road
Sandymount
Dublin 4
**Tel:** +353 1 2696023
*See piano page 50.*

# PERIOD SINGERS

## Eileen Bardin *Soprano*

**Contact:** Mrs Eileen Bardin
The Old School House
Rathdrum, Co Wicklow
**Tel:** +353 404 46920
*See soprano page 85.*

## Emma Coulthard *Soprano*

**Contact:** Ms Emma Coulthard
8, Alexandra Terrace
Novara Avenue
Bray
Co Wicklow
**Tel:** +353 1 2867168
**Email:** mgmccart@indigo.ie
*See historical flutes and recorders page 121.*

## John Elwes *Tenor*

**Contact:** John Elwes
Kilballyquilty
Carrick-on-Suir
Co Waterford
**Tel/Fax:** +353 51 646286

**SELECTED BROADCASTS AND/OR RECORDED WORK:**
Dowland's 'First Book of Ayres' [Vérany] for Gramophone.
Monteverdi's 1610 Vespers [BMG] with Frieder Bernius.
Purcell's 'The Tempest' [Archiv] with John Elliot Gardiner.
**REGULARLY PERFORMS WITH:**
Siobhán Armstrong (period harps), Hugh Tinney (piano), Benjamin Dwyer (guitar).
**AVAILABILITY:**
General.
**ADDITIONAL INFORMATION:**
Began musical career as Head Chorister in Westminister Cathedral, London. Under the name John Hahessy, had success as a boy soprano, with BBC Broadcasts and recordings with conductors such as Benjamin Britten, who dedicated his 'Corpus Christi Carol' to him. At the age of 14 sang 'Issac' in the world premiere recording of Britten's Canticle 'Abraham and Issac' appearing with Peter Pears. Has also worked with Gustav Leonhardt, Michael Corboz and Roger Norrington. Stage performances include the title roles in Monteverdi's three extant operas 'Orfeo', 'L'Incoronazione di Poppea' and 'Il Ritorno d'Ulisse'. His solo recitals encompass Elizabethan song with Renaissance lute music of the 17th Century with baroque harp, Lieder and chansons with piano, and contemporary music with guitar.

## Fionnuala Gill *Soprano*

**Contact:** Ms Fionnuala Gill
151, Ard na Mara
Malahide
Co Dublin
**Tel:** +353 1 8450698
*See soprano page 88.*

## Deirdre Gilsenan *Soprano*

**Contact:** Ms Deirdre Gilsenan
Loughan
Kells
Co Meath
**Mobile:** +353 88 2756326
*See soprano page 88.*

## Helen Hassett *Soprano*

**Contact:** Helen Hassett
5, College View
Blarney Road
Cork
**Tel:** +353 21 395495 (h) / +353 21 270076 (w)
*See soprano page 89.*

## Judith Mok *Soprano*

**Contact:** Judith Mok
Rocky Hill
The Green Road
Dalkey
Co Dublin
**Tel/Fax:** +353 1 2852013
*See soprano page 92.*

## Catríona O'Leary *Soprano*

**Contact:** Ms Catríona O'Leary
86, Ard na Mara
Malahide
Co Dublin (a)

or

Apt 6D
270, West 11th Street
NY 10014
New York
USA (h)
**Tel/Fax:** +353 1 8450444 (a) or +1 212 645 0989 (h) / +353 1 8456979
**Email:** nascaire@quicklink.com
**Other instruments:** Recorder, baroque harp.

**KEY PERFORMANCES OUTSIDE IRELAND** (since January 1994):
12.96 New York, performance accompanied by viola da gamba.
2.97 Bremen, Germany, promoted by BMG, appearing with The Harp Consort.
3.97 Tour of USA, promoted by BMG, appearing with The Harp Consort.
5.97 New York, performance accompanied by viola da gamba
**SELECTED BROADCASTS AND/OR RECORDED WORK:**
5.96 'Carolan's Harp', with The Harp Consort, for BMG.
9.96 'I am stretched on your Grave' for Black Box Music.
5.97 'The Play of Daniel' 13th Century French music-drama, with The Harp Consort, for BMG.
**PRIZES/AWARDS/APPOINTMENTS:**
1994 Awarded Faculty Circle Honor Scholarship to the Conservatory of Music, Brooklyn College.
1994 Winner of the Avery History Writing Prize by the Conservatory of Music, Brooklyn College.

**TRAINING AND/OR QUALIFICATIONS:**
From 1991 to 1994, B M (summa cum laude) from Brooklyn College.
**REGULARLY PERFORMS WITH:**
The Harp Consort (with Andrew Lawrence King), Sequentia.
**AVAILABILITY:**
By arrangement.
**ADDITIONAL INFORMATION:**
A specialist in early and Irish music. Has performed on such (BMG) recordings as: 'Shining Light' 12th Century Aquitanian polyphony with Sequentia; 'Symphony of Saints', music by Hildegard, with Sequentia. Recently recorded a solo CD of traditional Irish laments.

## Rachel Talbot *Soprano*

**Contact:** Ms Rachel Talbot
117, Templeogue Road
Dublin 6w
**Tel:** +353 1 4907512
**Email:** rtalbot@clubi.ie
**Other instruments:** Recorder, piano, clarinet, organ, violin.

*"Perhaps the most striking solo was [Purcell's sacred song 'In the dismal dungeon of despair'] sung with a flair both idiomatic and dramatic by Rachel Talbot"* 19.6.95 Irish Times.

**KEY IRISH PERFORMANCES** (since January 1994):
6.94 Lismore Early Music Festival, appearing with Dublin Viols.
1995 Lismore Early Music Festival, appearing with Christchurch Cathedral Choir.
1996 Sligo Early Music Festival, appearing with Canzona.
**SELECTED BROADCASTS AND/OR RECORDED WORK:**
1997 With the National Chamber Choir for CD.
1997 With Zefiro in the Liturgical Music Competition for RTÉ.
**TRAINING AND/OR QUALIFICATIONS:**
From 1989 to 1993, BA Mod from Trinity College, Dublin.
Since 1995, Studying with Evelyn Dowling.
1995, Attended masterclasses in Norway with Ian Partridge.
1996, Attended Early Music masterclasses in Portugal with Jill Feilman.
**REGULARLY PERFORMS WITH:**
National Chamber Choir, Polyphonia, Zefiro and Canzona.
**AVAILABILITY:**
Weekends, evenings, and in particular mid-July to mid-August.

## Peter Wells *Bass*

**Contact:** Mr Peter Wells
10c, Woodland House
Rushpark
Co Antrim BT37 9SG
Northern Ireland
**Tel:** +44 1232 867768
*See recorders page 123.*

# PERIOD ENSEMBLES

## Carulli Trio

**Tel:** +353 1 4944119
*See ensembles page 73.*

## Chandos Baroque Players

**Contact:** Malcolm Proud
St Canice's Cottage
St Canice's Cathedral
Kilkenny
**Tel/Fax:** +353 56 61497

*"The Chandos Baroque Players matched technical skill with interpretive fervor in an impressive US debut"* 10.11.94 Los Angeles Times.

**FORMED:**
1981.
**GROUP MEMBERS:**
Sarah Bealby-Wright (baroque violin), Rachel Beckett (recorder and baroque flute), Barry Guy (double bass), Maya Homburger (baroque violin), Rosemary Nalden (baroque viola), Malcolm Proud (harpsichord, chamber organ), Jeremy Ward (baroque bassoon), David Watkin (baroque cello).
**KEY IRISH PERFORMANCES** (since January 1994):
30.3.95 Assembly Hall, Derry, 1.4.95 Elmwood Hall, Belfast.
3.4.95 Bantry House, Co Cork.
10.4.95 Coach House, Dublin Castle, all promoted by Music Network and appearing with Robin Blaze (countertenor).
**KEY PERFORMANCES OUTSIDE IRELAND** (since January 1994):
11.94 Montreal, Canada.
11.94 Pasadena, USA, promoted by De Camera Society.
7.1.95 Southampton, UK, promoted by Turner Sims Concert Hall.
15.5.96 Spiez, Switzerland.
**SELECTED BROADCASTS AND/OR RECORDED WORK:**
1988 Vivaldi 'La Pastorella' for Hyperion.
1990 Zelenka 'Lamentations' for Hyperion.
1991 A. Scarlatti, 'Cantatas' for EMI.
**SELECTED REVIEWS** (since January 1994):
25.5.96 Spiez.
**AVAILABILITY:**
General.
**ADDITIONAL INFORMATION:**
Specialise in playing baroque music using period instruments. Is an extremely flexible group as regards size - any number of players from a duo with violinist Maya Homburger and harpsichordist Malcolm Proud to a group capable of performing Bach's 'Brandenburg Concertos'. Also perform with singers in a repertoire which includes Bach's 'Cantatas'.
*See Malcolm Proud page 125, Maya Homburger page 119, Barry Guy page 295.*

## Consort of St Sepulchre

**Contact:** Andrew Robinson
35, Marlborough Road
Dublin 4
**Tel:** +353 1 6685349
**Email:** akr@tinet.ie

*"One of the outstanding concerts of the festival .... beautiful music, beautifully played and sung..."* June 1997 Early Music Organisation of Ireland Newsletter
Maura Ó Cróinín, Galway Early Music Festival.

**FORMED:**
1969.
**GROUP MEMBERS:**
Lucienne Purcell (singer), Jenny Robinson, Vanessa Sweeney, Barra Boydell (recorders), Honor ÓBrolcháin, Lucy Robinson, Andrew Robinson (viols).

**KEY IRISH PERFORMANCES** (since January 1994):
5.96 Sligo Model Arts Centre, promoted by Sligo Early Music Festival.
26.10.96 Barryscourt Castle, Carrigtwohill, Cork.
24.2.97 National University of Ireland, Maynooth, Co Kildare, promoted by the Music Department.
25.5.97 St Patrick's School Hall, Galway, promoted by the Galway Early Music Festival.
**SELECTED BROADCASTS AND/OR RECORDED WORK:**
1974 'Medieval and Renaissance Music' for EMI Ireland IEMC6005 (LP).
1976 'Lette the Coppe Goo Rounde' for EMI Ireland IEMC 6008 (LP).
1993 Music for 'Caravaggio In Dublin' documentary for RTÉ.
**AVAILABILITY:**
General.
**ADDITIONAL INFORMATION:**
St Sepulchres perform the secular music of AD1450 - 1650 Europe. Viols and recorders make accompaniments by turns sweet, intricate and hearty to the unique alto voice of Lucienne Purcell.
*See Jenny Robinson page 123.*

# Delicious Musicke

**Contact:** Mr Brian Payne
13, High Street
Killyleagh, Co Down BT 30 9QF
Northern Ireland
**Tel:** +44 1396 828567
**Email:** 106363.3140@compuserve.com
**WWW:** http://ourworld.compuserve.com/homepages/BRIAN_PAYNE_2

*"Sandford has always impressed us with the unique and very musical quality . . . No praise could be too high for the quiet beauty of Payne's lute support."* 10.96 Belfast Telegraph "Rathcol".

**FORMED:**
1995.
**GROUP MEMBERS:**
Susan Lines (soprano), Brian Payne (lute), Stephen Sandford (counter-tenor).
**KEY IRISH PERFORMANCES** (since January 1994):
18.0.96 Harty Room, Belfast, promoted by Queen's University School of Music.
17.10.96 Early Music Festival at Queen's, promoted by the Arts Council of Northern Ireland and Queen's University Music Department.
13.2.97 Down Arts Centre, promoted by Down Arts.
14.2.97 Ards Arts Centre, promoted by Ards Arts.
**SELECTED REVIEWS** (since January 1994):
2.97 Down Recorder.
**PRIZES/AWARDS/APPOINTMENTS:**
1996 Overall Vocal Prize from the Judge Thompson Vocal Championship.
**AVAILABILITY:**
General.
**ADDITIONAL INFORMATION:**
Perform Elizabethan lute songs accompanied with lute and orpharion including works by Ford, Campion, Dowland, Danyel and their contemporaries. Offers a programme of music by John Dowland with relevance to Elizabethan Ireland.
*See Brian Payne page 119.*

# Douglas Gunn Ensemble

**Contact:** Douglas Gunn
Ballaghmore Castle
Borris-in-Ossory, Co Laois
**Tel:** +353 505 23093
**Email:** dgunn@iol.ie
**WWW:** http://www.iol.ie/~dgunn/dge.htm

*"An exceedingly beautiful concert ... an evening of music that could only be described as enchanting"* 26.8.95 The Midland Tribune.

**FORMED:**
1967.
**GROUP MEMBERS:**
Douglas Gunn (recorders and viola da gamba), Brian MacKay (harpischord), Deirdre Ní Shé (recorders), Carol O'Connor (baroque cello).
**KEY IRISH PERFORMANCES** (since January 1994):
18.6.96 Bank of Ireland Arts Centre, Dublin promoted by the Bank of Ireland.
6.9.96 King House, Boyle, Co Roscommon, promoted by Roscommon Arts Office.
8.12.96 St Michan's Church, Dublin.
10.5.97 Ballaghmore Castle, Co Laois, promoted by Grace Pym.
**SELECTED BROADCASTS AND/OR RECORDED WORK:**
11.91 'O' Carolan's Feast' (C,D) for Ossian (Oss CD65).
6.94 Programme for RTÉ FM3.
7.96 CD featuring the music by Daniel, Thomas and Ralph Roseingrave for Melrose Music (mm CD-101).
**AVAILABILITY:**
General.
**ADDITIONAL INFORMATION:**
Broadcast on radio and television and have released a number of commercial recordings. Repertoire ranges from 16th Century to late baroque and includes Irish baroque music. Have performed at several festivals in Ireland and the UK.
*See Brian Mackay page 43.*

# Dublin Viols

**Contact:** Mr Andrew Robinson
35, Marlborough Road
Donnybrook
Dublin 4
**Tel:** +353 1 6685349
**Email:** akr@tinet.ie

*"... A variety of instrumental combinations ... a lively sense of rhythm ... extraordinarily rich pieces"* 16.3.93 Irish Times.

**FORMED:**
1985.
**GROUP MEMBERS:**
Honor OBrolchain (treble viol), Lucy Robinson (tenor viol), Anne Robinson (tenor viol), Andrew Robinson (bass viol), Mark Wilkes (treble viol),
**KEY IRISH PERFORMANCES** (since January 1994):
6.94 Lismore Cathedral, Co Waterford, promoted by Lismore Early Music Festival and Jan Van Potter, appearing with Rachel Talbot (soprano).
12.3.95 Lutheran Church, Dublin, promoted by the Purcell Series and John O'Sullivan.
21.11.95 BBC Radio, Belfast, promoted by David Byers, BBC Northern Ireland.
**SELECTED BROADCASTS AND/OR RECORDED WORK:**
1974/1976 'Consort of St Sepulchre' for EMI Ireland.
1992 Backing for 'Dead Can Dance' album.
21.11.95 Purcell Commemoration, for BBC Northern Ireland.
**AVAILABILITY:**
General.
**ADDITIONAL INFORMATION:**
An offshoot of the 70's band The Consort of St Sepulchre. Andrew Robinson (director) has taught in the Royal Irish Academy of Music, the Wien Barock Summer School (Austria), and the Orpheon Summer School, Italy.

## Five in the Bar

**Contact:** Mr Paul Lyttle
21, Kipkarren Park
Newtownards
Co Down BT23 7AQ
Northern Ireland
**Tel/Fax:** +44 1247 810820 / +44 1247 810820
**Email:** lyttle @unite.co.uk
*See ensembles page 76.*

## Lir Ensemble

**Contact:** Eilís Cranitch
Lungo Po Antonelli 17
10153 Turin
Italy
**Tel/Fax:** +39 11 8122430 / +39 11 503361
*See ensembles page 78.*

## Sligo Early Music Ensemble

**Contact:** Rod Alston
Eden
Rossinver
Co Leitrim
**Tel:** +353 72 54122

**FORMED:**
1990.
**NUMBER IN GROUP:**
13.
**MUSICAL/ARTISTIC DIRECTOR:**
Rod Alston.
**KEY IRISH PERFORMANCES** (since January 1994):
28.6.95 Drumcliffe Church, in a performance of Pergolesi's Sabat Mater, appearing with Siobhan Terry.
18.4.96 'The Faerie Queen' promoted by Mackree Castle, Colooney appearing with the Amarillis Singers.
28.9.96 Parkes Castle, Dromohaire, appearing with David Lane (oboe).
24.11.96 Model Arts Centre, Sligo, in a concert featuring Lucie O'Hara (recorder) and Eleanor Dawson (flute).
**TRAINING AND/OR QUALIFICATIONS:**
Have undertaken workshops with Barra Boydell, Eleanor Dawson, Malcolm Proud and Thérèse Timoney.
**AVAILABILITY:**
General.
**ADDITIONAL INFORMATION:**
Have given a number of 'historical' concerts ie. In 1997, performed compositions which dated from circa 1750 in Strokestown House, Co. Roscommon.

## The Vendon Duo

**Contact:** Mr Douglas Gunn
Ballaghmore Castle
Borris-in-Ossory
Co Laois
**Tel:** +353 505 23093
**Email:** dgunn@iol.ie
**WWW:** http://www.iol.ie/~dgunn/vendon.htm

**FORMED:**
1996.
**GROUP MEMBERS:**
Hazel Etherington (piano, harpsichord, organ, Irish harp), Douglas Gunn (recorders).
**AVAILABILITY:**
General.
**ADDITIONAL INFORMATION:**
Perform a wide range of music from the 16th Century to the late 20th Century, including music by Irish composers. A variety of timbres is produced by the different recorders (renaissance, baroque and modern) and by piano, harpsichord, Irish harp and, where available, organ.

# Section five

## Contemporary Instrumentalists, Singers and Ensembles



The musicians in this section expressed a keen interest in contemporary music in their questionnaires (either by ticking the word 'Other' in the section of the questionnaire for music genre and writing the word 'contemporary' or, by mentioning it in their additional information). It is important to note that one should obviously consider the sections which deal with classical instrumentalists, singers, (composers), groups and large performing groups as many of these are also active performers of contemporary pieces and welcome the opportunity to perform them even though it was not explicitly stated on their questionnaires.



*(listed in name order)

# CONTEMPORARY INSTRUMENTALISTS

## Ruby Ashley *Oboe*

**Contact:** Ms Ruby Ashley
49, Weirview Drive
Stillorgan
Co Dublin
**Tel:** +353 1 2882467
*See oboe page 24.*

## Joy Beatty *Viola*

**Contact:** Ms Joy Beatty
6, Upper Celtic Park
Enniskillen
Co Fermanagh, BT74 6JA
Northern Ireland
**Tel:** +44 1365 322753
*See viola page 55.*

## Shane Brennan *Organ*

**Contact:** Mr Shane Brennan
Director
Schola Cantorum
St Finian's College
Mullingar
Co Westmeath
**Tel/Mobile:** +353 44 42906 or +353 44 44957 /
+353 88 528029
*See organ page 26.*

## Anthony Byrne *Piano*

**Contact:** Mr Anthony Byrne
190, Dunluce Road
Clontarf
Dublin 3
**Tel:** +353 1 8335085 / +353 87 618706
**Email:** Byrne@indigo.ie.
*See piano page 33.*

## Maria Christina Cleary
*Concert Harp*

**Contact:** Ms Maria Christina Cleary
Ryswykseweg 340-9
2516 HM, Den Haag
The Netherlands
**Tel/Fax:** +31 70 3952605
*See concert harp page 6.*

## Neil Cooney *Piano*

Contact: Mr Neil Cooney
15, Pinewood Avenue
Glasnevin
Dublin 11
Tel/Fax: +353 1 8422475 / +44 181 8835844
*See piano page 35.*

## Eilís Cranitch *Violin*

**Contact:** Eilís Cranitch
Lungo Po Antonelli 17
10153 Turin
Italy
**Tel/Fax:** +39 11 8122430 / +39 11 503361
*See violin page 59.*

## Raymond Deane *Piano*

**Contact:** Mr Raymond Deane
c/o Contemporary Music Centre
95, Lower Baggot Street
Dublin 2
**Tel/Fax:** +353 1 6612105 / +353 1 6762639
*See piano page 36.*

## William Dowdall *Flute*

**Contact:** Mr William Dowdall
13, Effra Road
Rathmines
Dublin 6
**Tel/Fax:** +353 1 4973381 / +353 1 8725292
*See flute page 13.*

## Susan Doyle *Flute*

**Contact:** Ms Susan Doyle
11, Springfield Drive
Templeogue
Dublin 6W
**Tel:** +353 1 4900316
*See flute page 13.*

## Aisling Drury-Byrne *Cello*

**Contact:** Ms Aisling Drury-Byrne
18, Riversdale Avenue
Palmerstown
Dublin 20
**Tel:** +353 1 6260724
*See cello page 68.*

## Benjamin Dwyer *Classical Guitar*

**Contact:** Mr Benjamin Dwyer
90, The Steeples
Chapelizod, Dublin 20
**Tel/Fax/Mobile:** +353 1 6234397 / +353 1 6234397 / +353 87 616391
**Email:** bdwyer@indigo.ie
*See classical guitar page 20.*

## John Feeley *Classical Guitar*

**Contact:** John Feeley
14, Wesley Road
Rathgar, Dublin 6
**Tel/Fax:** +353 1 4905495 / +353 1 4905495
*See classical guitar page 20.*

## John Gibson *Piano*

**Contact:** Mr John Gibson
41, Cloverhill Estate
Blackrock
Cork
**Tel:** +353 21 357676
*See piano page 38.*

## Gerard Gillen *Organ*

**Contact:** Professor Gerard Gillen
Department of Music
National University of Ireland
Maynooth
Co Kildare
**Tel/Fax:** +353 1 7083768 or +353 1 2880880
+353 1 6289432
*See organ page 27.*

## Alan Grundy *Classical Guitar*

**Contact:** Alan Grundy
c/o The Dublin School of Guitar
26/27, Drury Street
Dublin 2
**Tel/Fax:** +353 1 6714732 or +353 1 6249199/
+353 1 6796049
*See classical guitar page 20.*

## Barry Guy *Double Bass*

**Contact:** Mr Barry Guy
Carrickmourne
Thomastown
Co Kilkenny
**Tel/Fax:** +353 56 58708 / +353 56 58709
**Email:** maya@tinet.ie
*See page 295.*

## Beatrix Hermann *Organ*

**Contact:** Mrs Beatrix Hermann
139, Richmond Park
Bray
Co Wicklow
**Tel:** +353 1 2867488
*See organ page 28.*

## John Hogan *Saxophone*

**Contact:** Mr John Hogan
47, Hermitage Drive
Rathfarnham
Dublin 16
**Tel:** +353 1 4947412
*See saxophone page 296.*

## Maya Homburger *Baroque Violin*

**Contact:** Ms Maya Homburger
Carrickmourne
Thomastown
Co Kilkenny
**Tel/Fax:** +353 56 58708 / +353 56 58709
**Email:** maya@tinet.ie
*See baroque violin page 119.*

## Philip Horan *Flute*

**Contact:** Mr Philip Horan
17, Elm Mount Park
Beaumont
Dublin 9
**Tel:** +353 1 8316096
*See flute page 15.*

## Fionnuala Hunt *Violin*

**Contact:** c/o The Office of the Irish Chamber Orchestra
Foundation Building
University of Limerick
Limerick
**Tel/Fax:** +353 61 202620 or +353 61 202659 or
+353 61 202583 / +353 61 202617
**Email:** ico@ul.ie
*See violin page 62.*

## Denise Kelly *Concert Harp*

**Contact:** Denise Kelly
66, Dartmouth Square
Ranelagh
Dublin 6
**Tel:** +353 1 6689366
*See concert harp page 7.*

## Frances King *Piano*

**Contact:** Mr Frances King
2, Chippendale Vale
Bangor
Co Down, BT20 4QJ
Northern Ireland
**Tel:** +44 1247 459336
*See piano page 41.*

## Catriona McElhinney Grimes *Piano*

**Contact:** Ms Catriona McElhinney Grimes
264, Marina Village
Malahide
Co Dublin
*See piano page 42.*

## Anne-Marie O'Farrell *Concert Harp*

**Contact:** Ms Anne-Marie O'Farrell
28, Grange Manor Drive
Rathfarnham
Dublin 16
**Tel:** +353 1 4931873
*See concert Harp page 8.*

## Tom O'Farrell *Guitar*

**Contact:** Mr Tom O'Farrell
12 Restelouet
22340 Plévin
France
**Tel:** +33 2 962 96792
*See guitar page 224.*

## Nicholas O'Halloran *Piano*

**Contact:** Mr Nicholas O'Halloran
'Pinewood'
Shanakiel
Co Cork
**Tel:** +353 21 308307
*See piano page 47.*

## Honor O'Hea *Piano*

**Contact:** Honor O'Hea
Mount Grellan House
Kilbrogan
Bandon
Co Cork
**Tel/Fax:** +353 23 41569
*See piano page 47.*

## Patrick O'Keeffe *Clarinet*

**Contact:** Mr Patrick O'Keeffe
126, North Main Street
Youghal
Co Cork
**Tel:** +353 24 92820
*See clarinet page 5.*

## Eilís O'Sullivan *Flute*

**Contact:** Ms Eilís O'Sullivan
Ivy Bridge
Ballyhillogue
Mourne Abbey
Mallow, Co Cork
**Tel:** +353 22 29159
*See flute page 17.*

## Charles Stephen Lawrence Parker *Piano*

**Contact:** Mr Stephen Parker
19, Raglan House
Ballsbridge Court
Ballsbridge
Dublin 4
**Tel:** +353 1 6603557
*See piano page 49.*

## Niamh Quigley *Viola*

**Contact:** Ms Niamh Quigley
14, Meadowgrove
Blackrock, Cork
**Tel:** +353 21 357399
*See viola page 56.*

## Miriam Roycroft *Cello*

**Contact:** Ms Miriam Roycroft
23, Ingledew Crescent
Roundhay, Leeds LS8 1BP
England
**Tel/Fax:** + 44 113 2663966
*See cello page 71.*

## Una Russell *Organ*

**Contact:** Ms Una Russell
6, Kincora Terrace
Dundalk, Co Louth
**Tel/Fax:** +353 1 6603979 / +353 1 4023584
*See organ page 29.*

## Alan Smale *Violin*

**Contact:** Mr Alan Smale
18, Phoenix View
James Street
Dublin 8
**Tel:** +353 1 6708289
*See violin page 66.*

## Fintan Sutton *Clarinet*

**Contact:** Mr Fintan Sutton
20, Old Court Manor
Firhouse, Dublin 24
**Tel:** +353 1 4519089
*See clarinet page 6.*

## Peter Sweeney *Organ*

**Contact:** Mr Peter Sweeney
4, Orwell Park
Rathgar
Dublin 6
**Tel:** +353 1 4966740
*See organ page 30.*

## Louise Thomas *Piano*

**Contact:** c/o Ms Alison Thomas
17, Old Ballymun Road
Glasnevin
Dublin 9
**Tel:** +353 1 8374353
*See piano page 50.*

# CONTEMPORARY SINGERS

## Eileen Bardin *Soprano*

**Contact:** Mrs Eileen Bardin
The Old School House
Rathdrum
Co Wicklow
**Tel:** +353 404 46920
*See soprano page 85.*

## Conor Biggs *Bass-Baritone*

**Contact:** Mr Conor Biggs
Arduinkaai 33
1000 Brussels
Belgium
**Tel/Fax:** +32 2 223 11 89 / +32 2 223 42 22
*See bass, baritone page 111.*

## Ursula Connolly *Singer*

**Contact:** Ms Ursula Connolly
9, Temple Court
Palatine Square
Arbour Hill
Dublin 7
**Tel:** +353 1 6717589
*See page 244.*

## Róisín Dempsey *Soprano*

**Contact:** Róisín Dempsey
Apt 2
130, Sandford Road
Ranelagh
Dublin 6
or
'Greenville'
Enniscorthy
Co Wexford
**Tel:** +353 1 4973873 / +353 54 33241
*See soprano page 87.*

## John Elwes *Tenor*

**Contact:** John Elwes
Kilballyquilty
Carrick-on-Suir
Co Waterford
**Tel/Fax:** +353 51 646286
*See tenor period page 126.*

## Sonya Keogh *Mezzo-Soprano*

**Contact:** Ms Sonya Keogh
2, Friar Street
Cork
**Tel:** +353 21 315994
*See mezzo-soprano page 102.*

## Aylish Kerrigan *Mezzo-Soprano*

**Contact:** c/o Ms Joan Barry
1, Earlsfort Court
Lower Hatch Street
Dublin 2
**Tel/Fax:** +353 1 6614598
*See mezzo-soprano page 102.*

## Emmanuel Lawler *Tenor*

**Contact:** Emmanuel Lawler
Apt 3 Viscount House
6A Love Lane, Pinner
Middlesex HA5 3EF
England
or

c/o Gerry Keenan
Real Good Management
17 Dame Court
Dublin 2
**Tel/Mobile/Fax:** +353 1 6688108 / +353 87 542 366 / +353 1 6674530
*See tenor page 109.*

## Colette McGahon *Mezzo-Soprano*

**Contact:** Colette McGahon
c/o Mr Gerry Keenan
Real Good Management
**Tel/Mobile/Fax:** +353 1 6688108 / +353 87 543666 / +353 1 6674530
*See mezzo-soprano page 103.*

## Judith Mok *Soprano*

**Contact:** Judith Mok
Rocky Hill
The Green Road
Dalkey
Co Dublin
**Tel/Fax:** +353 1 2852013
*See soprano page 92.*

## Louise Muckell *Mezzo-Soprano*

**Contact:** Louise Muckell
17, Roches Road
Rathkeale
Co Limerick
**Tel:** +353 69 64033
*See mezzo-soprano page 104.*

## James Nelson *Tenor*

**Contact:** Mr James Nelson
41, Harfield Road
Sunbury on Thames
Middlesex TW16 5PT
England
**Tel/Fax:** +44 1932 783141 / +44 171 2269792 (fax for agent only)
*See tenor page 109.*

## Méav Ní Mhaolchatha *Soprano*

**Contact:** Méav Ní Mhaolchatcha
Flat 2
130 Sandford Road
Ranelagh
Dublin 6
**Tel:** +353 1 4973873
*See soprano page 94.*

## Anne O'Byrne *Soprano*

**Contact:** Ms Anne O'Byrne
Flat 1
68, Sydenham Park
London SE26 4DP
England
**Tel/Mobile:** +353 1 8213046 or +44 181 2913744 / +44 402 305187
*See soprano page 95.*

## Olive Simpson *Soprano*

**Contact:** Miss Olive Simpson
7, Emperor's Gate
London SW7 4HH
England
**Tel:** +44 171 3734453
*See soprano page 197.*

# CONTEMPORARY ENSEMBLES

## Athem Brass

**Contact:** Athem Brass
3, Butterfield Grove
Rathfarnham
Dublin 14
**Mobiles:** +353 87 2330228 or +353 88 2715534 / +353 88 2726421
*See page 301.*

## Bebb-Mason Duo

**Contact:** Ms Ruth Bebb
13, Old Seahill Road
Craigavad
Co Down, BT18 0EG
Northern Ireland
**Tel:** +44 1232 424675
*See classical ensembles page 73.*

## Cantique

**Contact:** Hilly Dunford
22, Corbawn Close
Shankill
Co Dublin
**Tel/Fax:** +353 1 2821682

*"... A well balanced, well blended choir capable of a fine, rich tone and effective dynamic flexibility"* 30.8.96 Evening Herald.

**FORMED:** 1989.
**NUMBER IN GROUP:** 20.

**MUSICAL/ARTISTIC DIRECTOR:**
Blánaid Murphy.
**KEY IRISH PERFORMANCES** (since January 1994):
9-11.95 Irish Museum of Modern Art, Dublin, promoted by RTÉ and IMMA appearing with Andrew Synnott and Cabrini String Quartet.
5.96/97 Cork International Choral Festival.
12.96 Trinity College, Dublin, appearing with Andrew Johnstone.
25.3.97 National Concert Hall, Dublin.
**SELECTED BROADCASTS AND/OR RECORDED WORK:**
9-11.95 'Purcell in the Twentieth Century' for RTÉ.
5.96 'A Night at the Festival' for Cork Festival Records.
3.97 Dr Brian Boydell Celebrations for RTÉ.
**SELECTED REVIEWS** (since January 1994):
24.10.95 Irish Times (Martin Adams).
26.3.97 Irish Times (Michael Dervan).
5.5.97 Irish Times (Martin Adams).
**TRAINING AND/OR QUALIFICATIONS:**
5.96/97 Cork International Choral Festival, attended seminar on contemporary music.
**AVAILABLE:**
General.
**ADDITIONAL INFORMATION:**
Group attracts singers and composers who are interested in exploring unusual vocal resources. Promotes the work of Irish composers, including the commissioning and premiere performance of new compositions. Specialises in the realisation of the most challenging contemporary choral works.

# Concorde

**Contact:** Dr Jane O'Leary
1, Avondale Road
Highfield Park
Galway
**Tel/Fax:** +353 91 522867 / +353 91 582153

*"Concorde is in many ways the keystone to contemporary music in Ireland"* 1994 Sunday Tribune.

**NUMBER IN GROUP:** 7.
**FORMED:** 1976.
**GROUP MEMBERS:**
David James (cello), Richard O'Donnell (percussion), Jane O'Leary (piano and ensemble director), Paul Roe (clarinet), Alan Smale (violin) Madeleine Staunton (flutes), Tina Verbeke (soprano).
**KEY IRISH PERFOMANCES** (since January 1994):
Annual series of concerts at both the National Concert Hall, promoted by the NCH and RTÉ and also at the Hugh Lane Municipal Gallery of Modern Art, Dublin.
7.97 Galway Arts Festival.
**KEY PERFORMANCES OUTSIDE IRELAND** (since January 1994):
10.96 New Music Festivals in Latvia, the Netherlands, Italy and Romania.
4.97 Barbican Centre, London, promoted by the 'From the Heart' Festival.
5.97 Bucharest, Romania, 7th International New Music Week.
**SELECTED BROADCASTS AND/OR RECORDED WORK:**
1995 'Contemporary Music from Ireland', Vol 1 CD for CMC.
1997 'Celtic Connections' for Capstone Records (USA).
1997 'Contemporary Music from Ireland' Vol 2 CD for CMC.
**SELECTED REVIEWS** (since January 1994):
1996/97 Irish Times.
**PRIZES/AWARDS/APPOINTMENTS:**
Member of the European Conference of Promoters of New Music. Supported by the Arts Council, IMRO and RTÉ.
**ADDITIONAL INFORMATION:**
Enjoy the challenge of the new and aim to pass on this excitement to the listener. Programmes feature spoken introductions, composers involvement and a variety of instrumental groupings and contemporary styles.
*See Jane O'Leary page 185, Alan Smale page 66.*

# Crash Ensemble

**Contact:** Donnacha Dennehy
c/o Music and Technology Department
5 Trinity College
Dublin 2
**Tel/Fax:** +353 1 6082503 / +353 1 6709509
**Email:** ddennehy@tcd.ie

*"Boundless energy and riotous abandon"*
24.10.97 Irish Times (Michael Dervan)

**GROUP MEMBERS:**
David Adams (piano), Stethie Buttrich (vocals), Donnacha Dennehy (electronics), John Godfrey (piano and guitar), Natasha Lohan (vocals/actress), Gerry O'Brien (video artist), Hugh Reynolds (video artist), Michael Seaver (clarinet), Andrew Synnott (conductor/keyboards).
**MUSICAL/ARTISTIC DIRECTOR(S):**
Donnacha Dennehy, Andrew Synnott.
**KEY IRISH PERFORMANCES** (since January 1994):
23.10.97 Samuel Beckett Centre, Trinity College, Dublin.
**AVAILABILITY:**
Subject to schedule.
**ADDITIONAL INFORMATION:**
Aims to widen the repertoire of music presented to Irish audiences by performing works of leading Irish composers from home and abroad. Performs music which involves a strong multi-media component. Intention is to present challenging music in a stimulating and entertaining way.
*See David Adams page 124, Donnacha Dennehy page 181, Michael Seaver page 5, Andrew Synnott page 50.*

# Degani Ensemble

**Contact:** Ms Ruby Ashley
49, Weirview Drive
Stillorgan
Co Dublin
**Tel:** +353 1 2882467
*See groups page 75.*

# Fidelio Trio

**Contact:** Mary Dullea
Upper Flat
52 Finland Road
Brockley
London SE4 2JH
England
**Tel/Mobile:** +44 171 3589361 / +44 956 916510
*See classical ensembles page 76.*

# Madrigal '75

**Contact:** Dr Geoffrey Spratt
Director
Cork School of Music
Union Quay
Cork
**Tel/Fax:** +353 21 270076 / +353 21 276595
*See large performing groups page 158.*

# National Chamber Choir

**Contact:** Ms Karina Lundstrom
Dublin City University
Glasnevin
Dublin 9
**Tel/Fax:** +353 1 7045665 / +353 1 7045603
*See large performing groups page 153.*

# Pago Libre

**Contact:** John Wolf Brennan
Hofmattstr. 5
CH-6353 Weggis
Switzerland
**Tel:** +41 41 3902777 / +41 41 3902761
**Email:** brennan@swissonline.ch

*"Their music is a risky business, often resulting in freely licensed frictions, and because it all comes along with unpretentious lightness, there's no lack of humourous moments either"*

Jürg Solothurnmann, Radio DRS, Berne.

**FORMED:** 1989.
**GROUP MEMBERS:**
Daniele Patumi (double bass), Arkady Shilkloper (french horn and alphorn), Tscho Theissing (violin), John Wolf Brennan (piano, organ).
**KEY IRISH PERFORMANCES:**
20.2.97 Bank of Ireland Arts Centre, Mostly Modern Festival, appearing with Groupe Lacroix.
**AVAILABILITY:**
General.
**ADDITIONAL INFORMATION:**
Improvisation is at the core of their music. Draw on the various musical and ethnic roots of its members (the traditions of jazz, folk and classical music in Umbria, Ireland, Russia, Vienna and Switzerland), giving the group a contemporary profile.
*See John Wolf Brennan page 32.*

# Quodlibet

**Contact:** Philip Richardson
16 Aberdelghy Park
Lisburn
Co Antrim BT27 4QF
**Tel:** +44 1846 664953
*See classical ensembles page 80.*

# RTÉ Vanbrugh Quartet

**Contact:** Mr Simon Aspell
October House
Ballyorban
Monkstown
Co Cork
**Tel/Fax:** +353 21 373363
**Email:** vanbrugh@iol.ie
*See classical ensembles page 80.*

# Slí Nua

**Contact:** Mr Fintan Sutton
20, Old Court Road
Firhouse
Dublin 24
**Tel:** +353 1 4519089

**FORMED:** 1995.
**GROUP MEMBERS:**
Cheramie Allum (viola), William Butt (cello), Dominic Dudley (double bass), Brona Fitzgerald (violin), Hillary Macken (bassoon), Matthew Manning (oboe), Richard O'Donnell (percussion), Fintan Sutton (clarinet).
**KEY IRISH PERFORMNCES** (since January 1994):
10.95 Hugh Lane Municipal Gallery of Modern Art, Dublin, promoted by the Goethe Institut.
11.96 Bank of Ireland Arts Centre, promoted by the 'Mostly Modern' Series.
5.97 Maynooth, Co Kildare, promoted by IMRO.
**SELECTED RECORDED WORK:**
10.95 With Frank Corcoran for RTÉ.
11.96 'Mostly Modern' for RTÉ.
**AVAILABILITY:**
General.
**ADDITIONAL INFORMATION:**
Specialises in contemporary Irish music.
*See William Butt page 68, Dominic Dudley page 9, Fintan Sutton page 6.*

# Sovereign Brass

**Contact:** Mr Colm Byrne
Pinewood
Boyerstown
Navan
Co. Meath
**Tel:** +353 46 22130 / +353 46 21863
*See classical ensembles page 81.*

# Trio Cervantes

**Contact:** Benjamin Dwyer
90, The Steeples
Chapelizod
Dublin 20
**Tel/Fax/Mobile:** +353 1 4978333 / +353 87 616391
**Email:** bdwyer@indigo.ie
*See classical ensembles page 82.*

# Ulster Brass

**Contact:** Ewan Easton
39, Ballyholme Road
Bangor
Co Down BT20 5JR
Northern Ireland
**Tel/Fax:** +44 1247 275355
*See classical ensembles page 82.*

# Ulster Youth Flute Orchestra

**Contact:** Mr Paul Lyttle
21, Kipkarren Park
Newtownards
Co Down BT23 7AQ
Northern Ireland
**Tel/Fax:** +44 1247 810820
*See large performing groups page 146.*

# Xenia Ensemble

**Contact:** Eilís Cranitch
Lungo Po Antonelli 17
10153 Turin
Italy
**Tel/Fax:** +39 11 8122430 / +39 11 503361

*"The excellent and exciting [Xenia Ensemble] performed G. Kancheli's "Night Prayers" for String Quartet"* La Repubblica, Italy.

**FORMED:** 1995.
**GROUP MEMBERS:**
Christine Anderson (violin), Eilís Cranitch (violin), Michelle Minne (viola), Maria-Carla Notarstefano (piano), Elizabeth Wilson (cello).
**KEY PERFORMANCES OUTSIDE IRELAND** (since January 1994):
5.9.95 Turin, Italy, promoted by Settembre Musica Festival Internazionale.
16.3.96 St Peterburg, Russia promoted by the Contemporary Music Festival.
15.11.96 Turin, Italy promoted by the Galleria D'Arte Moderna.
6.7.97 Ravenna, Italy promoted by the Ravenna Festival Internazionale.
**SELECTED BROADCASTS AND/OR RECORDED WORK:**
15.11.76 'Cosmic Tangents' Art Video for Euphron/Edison.
**SELECTED REVIEWS** (since January 1994):
7.9.95 La Repubblica, Italy.
11.7.96 La Repubblica.
12.7.96 Il Resto del Carlino, Italy.
**AVAILABILITY:**
General.
**ADDITIONAL INFORMATION:**
Specialises in 20th Century music and has presented programmes on such topics as: Russian Avant Garde, female composers, mysticism in contemporary music and poetry in music. The Ensemble also inaugurated on 8.7.97 the first of an ongoing series in Turin of 'Meet the Composer' with guest composer Giya Kancheli. Presents unfamiliar and interesting music, which has resulted in both commissioning new works by young composers, and undertaking research into variety of areas of neglected music, from the Italian Baroque to lesser known early 20th Century composers from Italy, Russia and England.
*See Eilís Cranitch page 59.*

# Section six

## Large Performing Groups and Choirs

# LARGE PROFESSIONAL PERFORMING GROUPS

## Irish Chamber Orchestra

**Contact:** John Kelly
The Foundation Building
University of Limerick
Limerick
Co Limerick
**Tel/Fax:** +353 61 202620 / +353 61 202617
**Email:** ico@ul.ie

*"... A team of excellent young musicians - their enthusiasm convinces the audience concert by concert. They have the capacity to conquer the world".* 12.4.97 Günter Pichler, Principal Violinist and founder of the Alban Berg Quartet.

**FORMED:** 1970.
**NUMBER IN GROUP:** 16-25.
**MUSICAL/ARTISTIC DIRECTOR:** Fionnuala Hunt.
**KEY IRISH PERFORMANCES** (since January 1994):
Since 1995, numerous regional tours nationwide.
95/97 Spring series, University Concert Hall, Limerick appearing with various artists.
96/97 Killaloe International Festival, Co Clare, appearing with various artists.
**KEY PERFORMANCES OUTSIDE IRELAND** (since January 1994):
6.96 France, as part of l'Imaginaire Irlandais.
11.96 Nine venue tour of the Netherlands, promoted by the Nederlands Impressariaat.
10.11.97 Seventeen venue tour in the USA, promoted by Columbia Artists, appearing with John O'Conor.
**SELECTED REVIEWS:**
6.95 Irish Times (Michael Dervan).
7.96 Sunday Tribune (Ian Fox).
4.97 Irish Times (Martin Adams).
**AVAILABILITY:**
General.
**ADDITIONAL INFORMATION:**
Chief Executive: John Kelly, Administrator: Imelda Dervin.
Office Manager: Margaret McConnell, Tour Manager: Terence O'Reilly.

**MEMBERS**
**Violins**
Fionnuala Hunt
Gillian Williams
Bróna Cahill
Kenneth Rice
Anita Vedres
Oonagh Keogh
Rebecca Jones
Louis Roden
Diane Daly

**Viola**
Rachael Walker
Joachim Roewer
Mark Coates Smith

**Cellos**
Richard Jenkinson
Richard Angell
Ben Chappell

**Double Bass**
Malachy Robinson

## Irish Film Orchestra(s)

**Contact:** Catríona Walsh
The Villa
Ellesmere Avenue
North Circular Road
Dublin 7
**Mobile/Fax:** +353 87 471195 / +353 1 8221492

**FORMED:** 1988.
**NUMBER IN GROUP:** Pool of 4-90 musicians.
**SELECTED BROADCASTS AND/OR RECORDED WORK:**
Has recorded with Placido Domingo, Julian Lennon, 'Riverdance the show' etc.
**ADDITIONAL INFORMATION:**
Orchestra(s) comprise of combinations of players from the National Symphony Orchestra of Ireland, RTÉ Concert Orchestra and the Irish Chamber Orchestra, plus other freelance musicians.

## National Symphony Orchestra of Ireland

**Contact:** Mr Simon Taylor
Music Department
RTÉ
Donnybrook
Dublin 4
**Tel/Fax:** +353 1 2082779 / +353 1 2082511

**FORMED:** 1947/48.
**NUMBER IN GROUP:** 88.
**KEY IRISH PERFORMANCES** (since January 1994):
Regular appearances at the National Concert Hall, Dublin.
10.96 Rowe Street Church during Wexford Festival Opera.
2.97 Belfast Waterfront Hall.
3.97 Ulster Hall, Belfast.
3.97 University College, Galway.
**KEY PERFORMANCES OUTSIDE IRELAND** (since January 1994):
16.2.97 Festival Theatre Edinburgh.
17.2.97 Royal Concert Hall, Glasgow.
18.2.97 Royal Festival Hall, Glasgow.
**SELECTED BROADCASTS AND/OR RECORDED WORK:**
Extensive Contract with Naxos/Marco Polo.
**AVAILABILITY:**
General.
**PRINCIPAL CONDUCTOR:**
Kasper de Roo.
**CONDUCTOR LAUREATE:**
Albert Rosen.

**First Violins**
Alan Smale
Elaine Clark
Clodagh Vedres
Timothy Kirwan
Catherine Briscoe
Anna Kane
Camilla Gunzl
Claire Crehan
Catherine McCarthy
Patrick Fitzgerald Mooney
Ting-Zhong Deng
Audrey McAllister
Ann-Marie Twomey
Anne Harte
David Clarke
Bronagh Fitzgerald

**Second Violins**
David McKenzie

Vanessa Caminiti
Keith Packer
Elias Maguire
Mary Wheatley
Cornelia Sexton
Briege McGoldrick
Fiona McAuslan
Rosalind Brown
Rosemary Doyle
Paul Fanning
Joanne Fleming
Dara O'Connell
Melanie Briggs
Evelyn McGrory

**Violas**
Adèle Govier
Cheremie Allum
Seamus O'Grady
Margaret Adams
John O'Mahony Adams
Neil Martin
Randal Devine
Helena Plews
Aine O'Neill
Margarete Lutz
Niamh Nelson
Cliona O'Driscoll

**Cellos**
Aisling Drury-Byrne
Niall O'Loughlin
Linda Kelly
Peter Hickey
Una Ní Chanainn
Claire Fitch
Siobhan Lynch
Delia Lynch
Moya O'Grady
Celine Barry
Stephen Sensbach

**Basses**
Dominic Dudley
Wolfgang Eulitz
Waldemar Kozak
Christopher Long
Aura Stone
Mark Jenkins
Daniel Whibley
Lucy Shaw

**Flutes**
William Dowdall
Catriona Ryan
Madeline Staunton

**Piccolo**
Catríona Ryan

**Oboes**
Matthew Manning
Deborah Clifford
Sile Daly

**Cor Anglais**
Deborah Clifford

**Clarinets**
John Finucane
Paul Roe
Fintan Sutton

**Bass Clarinet**
Fintan Sutton

**Bassoons**
Michael Jones
Robert Dulson
Hilary Macken

**Contra Bassoons**
Hilary Macken

**Horns**
Lesley Bishop
Fergus O'Carroll
Ian Dakin
Tom Briggs
David Atcheler

**Trumpets**
Graham Hastings
Killiyan Bannister
Thomas Rainer

**Trombones**
Seán Cahill
Gavin Roche

**Bass Trombone**
Sean Fleming

**Tuba**
Francis Magee

**Timpani**
Martin Metrustry

**Percussion**
Richard O'Donnell
Angela Boot (Dakin)

**Harp**
Andreja Mališ̌

# Orchestra of St Cecilia

**Contact:** Lindsay Armstrong
Manager
32, Shelbourne Road
Ballsbridge
Dublin 4
**Tel/Fax:** + 353 1 6675835

*"Crisp ensemble, neat shaping and lively rhythm set a standard which was maintained throughout the concert"* 29.11.95 Irish Times

**YEAR FORMED:**
1995
**NUMBER IN GROUP:**
20
**AVAILABILITY:**
General.

# RTÉ Concert Orchestra

**Contact:** Mr Simon Taylor
Music Department
RTÉ
Donnybrook
Dublin 4
**Tel/Fax:** +353 1 2082779 / +353 1 2082511

**FORMED:** 1926.
**NUMBER IN GROUP:** 45.
**KEY IRISH PERFORMANCES** (since January 1994):
Regular seasons in National Concert Hall, Dublin Gaiety Theatre Operas, O'Reilly Hall at University College, Dublin, Galway Cathedral, Athlone Regional Technical College and Waterford Institute of Technology.
**KEY PERFORMANCES OUTSIDE IRELAND** (since January 1994):
9.6.97 Philharmonic Hall, Liverpool.
3.97 United States.
**SELECTED BROADCASTS AND/OR RECORDED WORK:**
Extensive contract with Naxos/Marco Polo.
**AVAILABILITY:**
General.
**PRINCIPAL CONDUCTOR:**
Proinnsias Ó Duinn.

**First Violins**
Michael d'Arcy
Michael Healy
Mircea Petcu
Jennifer Murphy
Pamela Forde
Sunniva Fitzpatrick
Eileen Murphy
Ruth Murphy

**Second Violins**
Paul O'Hanlon
Arthur McIver
Donal Roche
Elizabeth MacNally

**Violas**
Padraig O'Connor
Ruth Mann
Thomas Kane
Michelle Lalor

**Cellos**
David James
Anette Cleary
Catherine Behan
Hilary Moffatt

**Basses**
Martin Walsh
Seamus Doyle O'Connell

**Flutes**
Elizabeth Petcu
Deirdre Brady

**Piccolo**
Deirdre Brady

**Oboes**
Peter Healy
David Agnew

**Clarinets**
Michael Seaver
Jean Lechmar

**Bassoons**
John Leonard
Carole Block

**Horns**
David Carmody
Declan McCarthy
Fearghal Ó Ceallacháin

**Trumpets**
Bernard McNeill
David Martin
Eoin Daly

**Trombones**
David Weakley
John Tate
Patrick Kennedy

**Timpani**
John Fennessy

**Percussion**
Paul McDonnell

**Harp**
Maria Cleary

# Ulster Camerata

**Contact:** Mr Philip Walton
10, Lancaster Avenue
Bangor
Co Down
Northern Ireland
**Tel/Fax:** +44 1247 462891
**Email:** philwal@iol.ie

*"Splendid sonorities and considerable intensity marked this fine performance"* 3.92 Belfast Telegraph.

**FORMED:** 1992.
**NUMBER IN GROUP:** Pool of between 13-30 members.
**MUSICAL/ARTISTIC DIRECTOR:** Philip Walton.
**KEY IRISH PERFORMANCES** (since January 1994):
11.94 Elmwood Hall, Belfast, promoted by Belfast Arts Festival.
21.10.95 Leisure Centre, Omagh, promoted by Omagh Arts Festival.
11.95 Elmwood Hall, Belfast, promoted by DPS Financial Services.
**SELECTED REVIEWS** (since January 1994):
11.94 Belfast Telegraph.
11.94 Ulster Newsletter.
**AVAILABILITY:**
General.

# Ulster Orchestra

**Contact:** Mr Michael Henson
Chief Executive
Elmwood Hall at Queen's University
89, University Road
Belfast BT7 1NF
Northern Ireland
**Tel/Fax:** +44 1232 664535 / +44 1232 662761

*"The Ulster Orchestra proved that they can be equal to any visiting orchestra in terms of style, technique and sonority"* 2.97 Belfast Newsletter.

**FOUNDED:** 1966.
**NUMBER IN GROUP:** 63.

**PRINCIPAL CONDUCTOR/ARTISTIC ADVISOR:**
Dmitry Sitkovetsky.
**LEADER:**
Lesley Hatfield.
**KEY PERFORMANCES OUTSIDE IRELAND** (since January 1994):
8.95 Royal Albert Hall, London promoted by the BBC.
10.96 Tour of Germany and Austria.
**PRIZES/AWARDS/APPOINTMENTS:**
1.97 AIB and First Trust Better Ireland Award.

**First Violins**
Lesley Hatfield
Lucy Griffith
Beveley Scott
Philip Clegg
Philip Davies
Jonathan Griffin
Chad Koelmeyer
Gill Leeming
Otti Maas
Alex Mackenzie
Claire Thatcher

**Second Violins**
Michael Alexander
Helen Wakelam
Bernie McBrierty
Patsy Fenton
Kevin Harrell
Jenny Lomas
John McKernan
Guera Maunder
Karen Sexton
Maggie Wilson

**Violas**
Ashley Mason
Ruth Bebb
Stephen Begley
Elizabeth Dean
Richard Guthrie
David McCreadie
Ralph Tartaglia
Philip Walton

**Cellos**
John Leeming
Morag Stewart
Sarah Shephard
Richard Glynn
Jeremy Lawrence
Kathyrn Lowry
Linda Miller

**Double Bass**
Barry Young
Gareth Hopkins
Michele Strong
Helen Glynn
Ricky Matson

**Flutes**
Colin Fleming
Meg Young
Elizabeth Bennett

**Piccolo**
Elizabeth Bennett

**Oboes**
Christopher M Blake
Colin Stark

**Cor Anglais**
Colin Stark

**Clarinets**
Christopher King
Paul Schumann

**Bass Clarinet**
Paul Schumann

**Bassoons**
Charles Miller
Stephen Pickett

**Contra Bassoon**
Stephen Pickett

**Horns**
Christopher J Blake
Martin Wall
Grenville Moore
Derek Parkins

**Trumpet**
Paul Young
Hugh Carslaw

**Trombones**
Martin Wilson
Stephen Barnett

**Bass Trombone**
Adrian Morris

**Tuba**
Ewan Easton

**Timpani**
David Openshaw

**Percussion**
Malcolm Neale

# LARGE SEMI PROFESSIONAL AND AMATEUR PERFORMING GROUPS

## Belfast Harp Orchestra

**Contact:** Janet Harbison
Brookfield Mill
333, Crumlin Road
Belfast BT14 7EA
Northern Ireland
**Tel/Fax:** +44 1232 352555 / +44 1232 740288
**Email:** jharbison@harps.dnet.co.uk

*"Ireland's most accomplished . . . radical traditional harpers"*
12.11.95 '29 Bedford St' on BBC (Seán Rafferty).

**FORMED:** 1992.
**NUMBER IN GROUP:** 20 - 25.
**MUSICAL/ARTISTIC DIRECTOR:** Janet Harbison.
**KEY IRISH PERFORMANCES** (since January 1994):
22.1.97 Belfast Waterfront Hall.

9.5.97 Rialto Theatre, Derry.
11.5.97 Mayo Abbey, Co Mayo.
**KEY PERFORMANCES OUTSIDE IRELAND** (since January 1994):
6.95 Bonn, Germany, promoted by Bonn Summer Festival.
3-4.96 Tour of UK, promoted by Roy Hastings.
2-5.7.97 Oban and Iona, Scotland, promoted by Iona Abbey Ltd, Argyll and Bute Council, AOC Scotland.
**SELECTED BROADCASTS AND/OR RECORDED WORK:**
10.95 'Carillon' (CD and cassette).
2.97 'Blue Peter', for BBC (for 17.3.97).
**SELECTED REVIEWS** (since January 1994):
1.97 Belfast Telegraph.
1.97 Irish News.
**ADDITIONAL INFORMATION:**
Presents a spectacle of harps accompanied by other instruments, singers and dancers.

# City of Belfast Sinfonia

**Contact:** 129, Belmont Road
Belfast BT4 2AD
Northern Ireland
**Tel:** +44 1232 673326

*"... Nicely balanced and thoroughly stylish ..."*
17.11.96 Irish Times.

**FORMED:** 1996.
**NUMBER IN GROUP:** 30.
**MUSICAL/ARTISTIC DIRECTOR:**
Julian G Maunder.
**KEY IRISH PERFORMANCES** (Since January 1994):
3.96 Town Hall, Portadown promoted by Craigavon Arts.
5.96 St Anne's Cathedral, Belfast promoted by Johnsons/Belfast Cathedral Summer Recital Series.
11.96 Elmwood Hall, Belfast promoted by Belfast Festival at Queen's appearing with George Zukerman (bassoon) and Ron Halder (actor).
**SELECTED REVIEWS** (since January 1994):
17.5.96 Belfast Telegraph.
17.11.96 News Letter.
17.11.96 Irish News.
**AVAILABILITY:**
General.
**ADDITIONAL INFORMATION:**
In conjunction with the performance of pieces from the chamber orchestra repertoire, aims to promote local soloists and composers. Very flexible repertoire.

# Cork Pops Orchestra

**Contact:** Gerard Kelly
11, Summerhill South
Cork
Co Cork
**Tel:** +353 21 316088
**Email:** grantkelly@tinet.ie

**FORMED:** 1990.
**NUMBER IN GROUP:** 25-35.
**MUSICAL/ARTISTIC DIRECTOR:**
Evelyn Grant.
**KEY IRISH PERFORMANCES** (since January 1994):
Between 11.96 and 3.97, ten performances at Everyman Palace Theatre, Cork, promoted by Gerard Kelly.
7.12.96 City Hall Cork, promoted by the Lord Mayor.
**AVAILABILITY:**
General.
**ADDITIONAL INFORMATION:**
Known in Munster as the 'Festival Orchestra'. Founded in 1990 to celebrate the arrival of the 'tall ships' visit to Cork. Performs annually for the Cork Lord Mayor's concert.

# Dublin Baroque Players

**Contact:** Mr Liam Fitzgerald
52, Highfield Road
Rathgar
Dublin 6
**Tel:** +353 1 4970350

**ADDITIONAL INFORMATION:**
Longest established chamber orchestra in Ireland. Wide-ranging repertoire of orchestral and choral works. Special interest in performing the symphonies and concertos of the 18th Century.

# Dublin Symphony Orchestra

**Contact:** Ms Simone Orr
19, Louvain
Ardilea
Dublin 14
**Tel:** +353 1 2887212

**FORMED:** 1967.
**NUMBER IN GROUP:** 50.
**MUSICAL DIRECTOR:**
John Hughes.
**KEY IRISH PERFORMANCES** (since January 1994):
25.6.95 National Concert Hall, Dublin, appearing with Stuart O'Sullivan.
3.97 Dublin, appearing with Gillian Williams (violin).
8.6.97 Drogheda, appearing with Annette Cleary (cello).
15.6.97 Dublin, appearing with Annette Cleary.
**ADDITIONAL INFORMATION:**
Amateur orchestra which was established to provide an opportunity to study, perform and stimulate the interest of young people in classical music. Provides members with a platform to gain experience of performing with a symphony orchestra. New members, especially string players, are always welcome.

# Galway Concert Orchestra

**Contact:** Mr Patrick Heaney
'Bella Vista'
Rusheen Bay
Barna Road
Galway
**Tel:** +353 91 591686

*"Since its foundation in 1992, the orchestra has become an integral part of the cultural life of Galway"* 3.95 Show Times.

**FORMED:** 1992.
**NUMBER IN GROUP:** 55.
**KEY IRISH PERFORMANCES** (since January 1994):
2.12.94 Dánlannan Chláir, Ennis, Co Clare.
3.12.94 Seapoint Ballroom, Galway.
11.5.95 Ardilaun Hotel, Galway, appearing with Rustern Hairutdinov (piano).
13.5.95 Sacred Heart School, Westport, Co Mayo appearing with Rustern Hairutdinov.
11.95 University of Limerick Concert Hall, AIMS 30th Anniversary concert (also recorded for three regional radio stations).

# Hibernian Chamber Orchestra

**Contact:** Ms Julie Hodgers
7, St Andrew's Green
The Fairways
Lucan
Co Dublin
**Tel/Fax:** +353 1 6211370
**Email:** nickh.tinet.ie

**FORMED:** 1981.
**NUMBER IN GROUP:** 35-60.
**MUSICAL/ARTISTIC DIRECTOR:**
John Finucane.
**KEY IRISH PERFORMANCES** (since January 1994):
22.2.97 Peppercanister Church, Dublin.
28.3.97 St Patrick's Cathedral, Dublin, promoted by the Carmichael Centre, appearing with the Goethe Institute Choir.
14.6.97 Taney Parish Centre, Dundrum, Dublin.
11.12.97 National Concert Hall, Dublin appearing with the Goethe Institute Choir.
**AVAILABILITY:**
General.
**ADDITIONAL INFORMATION:**
Performs extensively in Dublin and all over Ireland with many Irish professional musicians. Repertoire stretches across the musical spectrum, ranging from early works to newly commissioned pieces.

# Irish Youth Wind Ensemble

**Contact:** Mr Pat Mullen
12, Strand Road
Portmarnock
Co Dublin
**Tel/Fax:** +353 1 8460248 or +353 1 8557481 /
+353 1 8557508

**FORMED:** 1985.
**NUMBER IN GROUP:** 55.
**MUSICAL/ARTISTIC DIRECTOR:**
James Cavanagh.
**KEY IRISH PERFORMANCES** (since January 1994):
7.96 National Concert Hall, Dublin appearing with Tim Reynish and Finghin Collins.
7.96 Wexford, appearing with James Cavanagh.
**KEY PERFORMANCES OUTSIDE IRELAND** (since January 1994):
8.95 Music Hall, Aberdeen, promoted by Aberdeen International Youth Festival, appearing with James Cavanagh.
**SELECTED BROADCASTS AND/OR RECORDED WORK:**
8.95 'Irish Youth Wind Ensemble in Aberdeen' for BBC Radio Three.
8.95 'Irish Youth Wind Ensemble in the National Concert Hall' for RTÉ.
**SELECTED REVIEWS** (since January 1994):
8.95 Irish Times.
**TRAINING AND/OR QUALIFICATIONS:**
From 1985 to 1996, residential courses with the members of the national orchestras.
**AVAILABILITY:**
General.
**ADDITIONAL INFORMATION:**
Consists of young brass and percussion players from the island of Ireland. Group is re-auditioned every year and meet for a residential course before giving a series of countrywide concerts. Specialises in music specifically composed for the medium.

# Limerick Baroque Players

**Contact:** Dr Gareth Cox
Music Department
Mary Immaculate College
South Circular Road
Limerick
**Tel/Fax:** +353 61 314588 / +353 61 313632

**FORMED:** 1995.
**NUMBER IN GROUP:** 20.
**MUSICAL/ARTISTIC DIRECTOR:**
Dr Gareth Cox.
**KEY IRISH PERFOMANCES** (since January 1994):
St Michael's Church, Limerick, appearing with University of Limerick Choral Society.
Glenstal Abbey, Murroe, appearing with Cyprian Love.
St Joseph Church, Limerick appearing with Limerick Choral Union.
Waterford Institute of Technology, appearing with the University of Limerick Choral Society and Waterford IT Choir.

# National Youth Orchestra of Ireland

**Contact:** Mrs Joanna Crooks
37, Molesworth Street
Dublin 2
**Tel/Fax:** +353 1 6613642

*"... New in character, altogether better regulated and more even in achievement"* 5.1.97 Irish Times.

**FORMED:** 1970.
**NUMBER IN GROUP:** 225.
**MUSICAL/ARTISTIC DIRECTORS:**
Music Committee and Board of the National Youth Orchestra.
**GROUP MEMBERS:**
National Youth Orchestra: 102 musicians over and under 18 years (symphonic). Junior National Youth Orchestra: 102 musicians - under 18 years (symphonic). Both orchestras have 64 string players and 38 wind and brass players.
**KEY IRISH PERFORMANCES** (since 1984):
12.7.96 National Concert Hall, Dublin.
4.8.96 NCH, Dublin.
3.1.97 City Hall, Cork.
4.1.97 NCH, Dublin.
**KEY PERFORMANCES OUTSIDE IRELAND** (since January 1994):
2.8.97 Music Hall, Aberdeen, Scotland as part of the International Youth Festival.
9.8.97 Stevenson Hall, Glasgow, Scotland as part of the British Festival of Youth Orchestras.
**SELECTED RECORDED WORK:**
4.1.97 Recording for RTÉ FM3.
4-5/4.97 RTÉ Bank of Ireland Young Proms recording for RTÉ.
**ADDITIONAL INFORMATION:**
Member of the European Federation of National Youth Orchestras, the Irish Association of Youth Orchestras, and Jeunesses Musicales Ireland. Annual auditions take place in Dublin, Cork, Galway and Dundalk in October and November for the following season. Works under guest conductors. Tour abroad on alternate summers.

# Ulster Youth Flute Orchestra

**Contact:** Mr Paul Lyttle
21, Kipkarren Park
Newtownards
Co Down BT23 7AQ
Northern Ireland
**Tel/Fax:** +44 1247 810820
**Email:** lyttle@uniteco.uk

**FORMED:** 1995.
**MUSICAL/ARTISTIC DIRECTORS:**
Paul Lyttle and Katy Griffiths.
**KEY IRISH PERFORMANCES** (since January 1994):
23.8.96 St Georges Church, Belfast.
4.4.97 St Patrick's Church, Newtownards, Co Down.
**SELECTED BROADCASTS AND/OR RECORDED WORK:**
23.8.96 'The Magic of the Flute' (own recording).
**PRIZES/AWARDS/APPOINTMENTS:**
6.97 British Reserve Award from the National Association of Youth Orchestras.
**TRAINING AND/OR QUALIFICATIONS:**
8.95 Workshop with Trevor Wye.
**AVAILABILITY:**
General.
**ADDITIONAL INFORMATION:**
Group comprising of young and highly trained players from across Ulster. Committed to promoting original repertoire and to commissioning new works for this medium. Can provide a programme of up to one hour and is particularly suited to educational work and projects which encompass music for wind ensembles.

# Wexford Sinfonia

**Contact:** Ms Ruth Miller
Newtown
Killinick, Co Wexford
**Tel:** +353 53 58849

**FORMED:** 1993.
**NUMBER IN GROUP:** 50.
**MUSICAL/ARTISTIC DIRECTOR:**
Fergus Sheil.
**KEY IRISH PERFORMANCES** (since January 1994):
1.96 Wexford and Piltown, Co Waterford, appearing with Orla Boylan.
6.96 Wexford and Dublin, appearing with Nicola Cleary.
1.97 Waterford and Wexford, appearing with Conor Linehan.
6.97 National Concert Hall, Dublin and Wexford, appearing with Dublin Orchestral Players and Pauline McGlynn.
**ADDITIONAL INFORMATION:**
Draws its fifty or more instrumentalists from all over County Wexford, as well as Waterford, Kilkenny, Wicklow and Dublin. Performs two programmes a year in January and June, presenting one in Wexford with the second location varying each year.

# ACCORDION, BRASS, SILVER & CONCERT, FLUTE, PIPE AND OTHER BANDS

**Useful contact addresses in the area of band performance in Ireland include:**
**Irish Association of Brass and Concert Bands,** Ms Gillian Mohan, 28, Millmount Terrace, Drogheda, Co. Louth.
**Tel.:** +353 41 35799
**Irish Pipe Band Association,** Mr Brian McMahon, 39, Pondfields, New Ross, Co. Wexford.
**Tel./Fax:** +353 51 22531.
**Email:** ipba@iol.ie
**North of Ireland Bands Association,** Mr William J Clements, 28, Knockfergus Park, Green Island, Carrickfergus BT38 8SN, Northern Ireland.

## ACCORDION BANDS

*Please note that the numbers placed after each entry title, indicate the number in the group and the year of the band's formation.

# Ahoghill Junior Accordion Band

***20/1937***

**Contact:** C. Young
14, Laurel Park
Ahoghill BT42 1LN
Ballymena, Co Antrim
Northern Ireland
**Tel:** +44 1266 871834

## BRASS, SILVER & CONCERT BANDS

*Please note that the numbers placed after each entry title, indicate the number in the group and the year of the band's formation.

# Ardee Concert Band *100/1860*

**Contact:** Mr John Byrne
Ash Walk, Ardee, Co Louth
**Tel:** +353 41 56091

**MUSICAL/ARTISTIC DIRECTOR:** H Kelly.
**PRIZES/AWARDS/APPOINTMENTS:**
1995/1996 1st Prize, awarded by the National Band Championships, organised by the Irish Association of Brass and Concert Bands
**SELECTED BROADCASTS AND/OR RECORDED WORK:**
1988 'Bandstand', for RTÉ radio.

# Drogheda Brass Band *35/1886*

**Contact:** Mr Christy Smith
121, Brookville Park, Drogheda, Co Louth
**Tel/Fax:** +353 41 33591 / +353 41 34977

**MUSICAL/ARTISTIC DIRECTOR:**
Michael Maher.
**PRIZES/AWARDS/APPOINTMENTS:**
Current 2nd prize winner in the championship section of the National Band Championships and runners up in the North of Ireland Band Championships (2nd Grade Brass)
**AVAILABILITY:**
General.
**ADDITIONAL INFORMATION:**
Consistent amateur band with many contests and concert successes to its name. Has appeared on RTÉ.

# James Fitzgerald Memorial Band *18/1850*

**Contact:** Gerard Toomey
Church Street
Mitchelstown
Co Cork
**Tel:** +353 25 24411

**Musical/Artistic Director:**
Séan Chamberlain.
**AVAILABILITY:**
By appointment.
**ADDITIONAL INFORMATION:**
Brass band which also incorporates a dixiland jazz band called "The Galtee Stompers"

# Loc Garman Band *30/1932*

**Contact:** Mr David Clancy
22, Pinewood Estate
Wexford
Co Wexford
**Tel:** +353 53 45630

**MUSICAL/ARTISTIC DIRECTOR:**
John Clancy.
**GROUP INSTRUMENTS:**
Cornet, euphonium, tenor horn, flugel horn, trombone, tuba, percussion.
**KEY IRISH PERFORMANCES** (since January 1994):
94/95/96, performances in Wexford town, Enniscorthy, Waterford and Dublin.
**KEY PERFORMANCES OUTSIDE IRELAND** (since January 1994):
1994 Fishguard, Wales, promoted by Goodwick Brass Band.
1994 Zurich promoted by ABS Pumps Limited.
1997, London, promoted by the Bands Association.
**SELECTED BROADCASTS AND/OR RECORDED WORK:**
1983 'In the Spotlight' cassette for Dogen Recordings.
1988 Bandstand radio programme for RTÉ.
1991 'Songs of Praise' for BBC.
**PRIZES/AWARDS/APPOINTMENTS:**
1987 2nd prize awarded with the European Brass Band Association.
From 1989 to 1996, winners in the Irish National and Regional Championships.
**AVAILABILITY:**
General.

# Lourdes Brass Band *50/1959*

**Contact:** Ms Jennifer Black
c/o The Bandroom, Batchelors Lane
Drogheda, Co Louth
**Tel:** +353 41 33450

**MUSICAL/ARTISTIC DIRECTOR:**
Mr Harry Kelly.
**KEY IRISH PERFORMANCES** (Since January 1994)
11.95 Performance in honour of a visit by President Robinson to Drogheda, promoted by Drogheda Corporation.
7.96 St Patrick's Church, Dungannon, Co Tyrone promoted by Fr L Boyle.
7.96 Clonakility, Co Cork promoted by the Festival of West Cork.
8.96 Participants in Drogheda Band Festival.
**SELECTED BROADCASTS AND/OR RECORDED WORK:**
2.95 Recording of "Mass of Fire" by Michael Holohan for RTÉ.
**PRIZES/AWARDS/APPOINTMENTS:**
1997 1st Prize, senior section, all Ireland championships presented by the Irish Association of Brass and Concert Bands.
**AVAILABILITY:**
General.
**ADDITIONAL INFORMATION:**
Accompanied by the Lourdes Majorettes for marching displays.

# Murley Silver Band *35/1927*

**Contact:** David Trimble
12, Nelson Park
Fivemiletown
Co Tyrone, BT 75 0QQ
Northern Ireland
**Tel/Fax:** +44 13655 21392

**KEY IRISH PERFORMANCES** (since January 1994):
28.3.97 Windsor Park, Belfast for the North of Ireland V Portugal International Football Match.
24.5.97 Bray, Co Wicklow, performance coordinated by Mr Patrick Murphy of the Assocation of Irish Festivals and Events.
24.5.97 Performance at Dublin Zoo.
25.5.97 Powerscourt Gardens, Enniskerry, Co Wicklow.
**SELECTED BROADCASTS AND/OR RECORDED WORK:**
1996 'Strike up the Band' for BBC Radio Ulster.
**PRIZES/AWARDS/APPOINTMENTS:**
Senior Champion Award from BBC Northern Ireland competition.
**AVAILABILITY:**
General.
**ADDITIONAL INFORMATION:**
Formed in 1927, drawing members from the local rural community. During the 1960's commenced contesting and won through to the championships section of the North of Ireland Bands Association by 1980, where they have remained ever since. As well as contesting, perform at festivals and charity concerts (North and South). Have a wide repertoire.

# Rathfarnham Concert Band *250/1980*

**Contact:** St Mary's Boys National School
Grange Road
Rathfarnham, Dublin 14
**Tel:** +353 1 4525580 / +353 1 4931477 (school)

**MUSICAL/ARTISTIC DIRECTORS:**
Rory Doyle, Vincent Kennedy, Jack Manning, John Maher, Ronan O'Reilly.
**KEY IRISH PERFORMANCES** (Since January 1994):
12.94, 12.95 and 12.96 National Concert Hall, Dublin.
4.96 National Band Championships promoted by the Irish Association of Brass and Concert Bands.
**AVAILABILITY:**
General.
**ADDITIONAL INFORMATION:** Largest concert band group in Ireland. Has won numerous national and international music competitions and travels extensively in Europe. Twenty band participants are currently members of the National Youth Orchestra of Ireland.

# St Catherine's Concert Band

*35/1922*

**Contact:** Paul McAteer
31, Churchview
Bessbrook
Co Armagh BT35 7ET
Northern Ireland
**Tel:** +44 1693 838581

**MUSICAL/ARTISTIC DIRECTOR:**
Luke Burke.
**PRIZES/AWARDS/APPOINTMENTS:**
Winners in the All-Ireland Band Championships.
**AVAILABILITY:**
General.
**ADDITIONAL INFORMATION:**
75 years in existence. Originally began a marching brass and reed band and are now a concert band.

# St George's Brass Band *36/1936*

**Contact:** Neville Bryan (Hon Sec)
34, Clonrosse Drive
Malahide Road
Dublin 13
**Tel:** +353 1 8473111

**MUSICAL DIRECTOR:**
Mr P.J. Regan.
**KEY IRISH PERFORMANCES** (since January 1994):
3.96 Portmarnock Country Club, for the Band's celebration of 60 years in existence.
6.96 National Botanic Gardens, Dublin appearing with the Burtle Silver Band from England.
**PRIZES/AWARDS/APPOINTMENTS:**
2nd Prize National Band Championships of Ireland.
**ADDITIONAL INFORMATION:**
Traditional 'English style' brass band which perform a wide range of music at several venues throughout Dublin. Rehearsal night, Mondays 8pm - 10pm in St Thomas Church Hall, Cathal Brugha Street, Dublin 1. New members welcome. Visiting players to Ireland will be made very welcome.

# Silver Sounds *20/1980*

**Contact:** Mr Michael Fottrell
69, Michael Street
New Ross
Co Wexford
**Tel/Fax:** +353 51 425063 / +353 51 422326

*"They are an inspiration to the beginners ..."*
4.96 New Ross Standard

**KEY IRISH PERFORMANCES** (since January 1994):
1994 South East Championships, Waterford.
1995 Southern Championships, Clonakilty, promoted by the West Cork Festival Committee.
1996 National Championships.
1997 St Michael's Theatre, New Ross, promoted by the Kennedy Trust, solo recital.
**SELECTED BROADCASTS AND/OR RECORDED WORK:**
10.86 'Silver Sounds' own recording.
8.88 'Hands' for RTÉ.
8.90 'Good as Gold' own recording.
**SELECTED REVIEWS** (since January 1994):
1997 New Ross Standard.
**PRIZES/AWARDS/APPOINTMENTS:**
1991 1st Prize IAB and CB, Dublin.
1996 1st Prize IAB and CB, Dublin.
**AVAILABILITY:**
General.
**ADDITIONAL INFORMATION:**
An amateur band who proudly serve their local community.

# SIPTU Band *30/1913*

**Contact:** Mr Shay Hackett (Secretary)
Services Industrial Professional Technical Union
Liberty Hall
Dublin 1
**Tel/Fax:** +353 1 6749731

**MUSICAL/ARTISTIC DIRECTOR:**
Michael Rodgers.
**GROUP INSTRUMENTS:**
Flute, oboe, clarinet, bassoon, saxophones, horn, cornet, trumpet, euphonium, tuba, trombone, percussion.
**KEY IRISH PERFORMANCES** (since January 1994):
Annual May Day parade.
1996 St Patrick's Day Parade, Dublin.
Dun Laoghaire Festival.
**AVAILABILITY:**
Weekends.
**ADDITIONAL INFORMATION:**
Rehearse every Thursday at 8pm and Sunday at 11am, in Liberty Hall, Dublin 1 (excluding Sundays falling on bank holiday weekends). All players, Grade IV+ are welcome.

# Templemore Band *34/1948*

**Contact:** Mr Robin Black
10, Quayside
Ballyvester
Donaghadee
Co Down, Northern Ireland
**Tel:** +44 1247 883804

**MUSICAL/ARTISTIC DIRECTOR:**
Mrs Jean Savage.
**PRIZES/AWARDS/APPOINTMENTS:**
Spring 1996, 2nd section champions with the Brass Band League (NI).
**AVAILABILITY:**
General.

# The Army No 1 Band *45/1923*

**Contact:** The Director
Defence Forces School of Music
Cathal Brugha Barracks
Rathmines
Dublin 6
**Tel/Fax:** +353 1 8046420 / +353 1 4961346

**MUSICAL/ARTISTIC DIRECTOR:**
Comdt Joseph Ryan.
**KEY IRISH PERFORMANCES** (since January 1994):
21.10.95 National Concert Hall, Dublin, appearing with Finghin Collins.
19.10.96 National Concert Hall, Dublin, appearing with Ronan Tynan.
28.2.97 City Hall, Cork, appearing with Colette Kidney.
18.10.97 National Concert Hall, Dublin, appearing with Majella Cullagh and James Nelson.

**KEY PERFORMANCES OUTSIDE IRELAND** (since January 1994):
6.95 Saumur, France, appearing with other Military bands.
12.96 Münster, Germany, appearing with other Military bands
**SELECTED BROADCASTS AND/OR RECORDED WORK:**
'The Army No 1 Band' for EMI Records.
**ADDITIONAL INFORMATION:**
Defence Forces Bands perform music ranging from classical to jazz and pop arrangements to original music for wind band.

# The Band of The Curragh Command *35/1925*

**Contact:** c/o The Director
Defence Forces Schol of Music
Cathal Brugha Barracks
Rathmines
Dublin 6
**Tel/Fax:** +353 1 8046420 / +353 1 4961346

**MUSICAL/ARTISTIC DIRECTOR:**
Capt. Mark Armstrong.
*See The Army No 1 Band page 148.*

# The Band of The Southern Command *35/1924*

**Contact:** c/o The Director
Defence Forces School of Music
Cathal Brugha Barracks
Rathmines
Dublin 6
**Tel/Fax:** +353 1 8046420 / +353 1 4961346

**MUSICAL/ARTISTIC DIRECTOR:**
Capt Liam Daly.
*See The Army No 1 Band page 148.*

# The Band of The Western Command *35/1936*

**Contact:** c/o The Director
Defence Forces School of Music
Cathal Brugha Barracks
Rathmines
Dublin 6
**Tel/Fax:** +353 1 8046420 / +353 1 4961346

**MUSICAL/ARTISTIC DIRECTOR:**
Lt Declan Whitston.
*See The Army No 1 Band page 148.*

# The Garda Band *31/1923*

Contact: Superintendent J.F. King
Director of Music
Garda Band, Garda Headquarters
Phoenix Park, Dublin 8
Tel/Fax: +353 1 6771156 Ext. 2040 / +353 1 6795180

**MUSICAL/ARTISTIC DIRECTOR:**
Superintendent J.F. King.

# The Steadfast Band *35/1951*

**Contact:** Leslie Knight
c/o 43, Clonkeen Drive
Foxrock
Dublin 18
**Tel/Fax:** +353 1 2896026

**KEY IRISH PERFORMANCES** (since January 1994):
11.96 National Concert Hall, Dublin, promoted by the Alzheimer Society.
12.96 National Concert Hall, Dublin, appearing with Dublin County Choir and Niamh Murray.
5.97 Dublin, promoted by Clontarf Orthopedic Hospital, appearing with Dublin Welsh Male Choir.
**SELECTED BROADCASTS AND/OR RECORDED WORK:**
5.96 Michael Collins film.
12.96 CD and tape recording 'Let the Bells Ring'.
**PRIZES/AWARDS/APPOINTMENTS:**
2nd place in the Senior Section, awarded by the Irish Association Brass and Concert Bands.
**ADDITIONAL INFORMATION:**
Perform at charity concerts in aid of Church/Parish funds and make guest appearances. Varied repertoire.

# Warrenpoint Silver Band *26/1950*

**Contact:** B Thomas
38, Great Georges Street
Warrenpoint
Newry BT34 3HS
Northern Ireland
**Tel:** +44 16937 74033

## FLUTE BANDS

*Please note that the numbers placed after each entry title, indicate the number in the group and the year of the band's formation.

# Ballyclare Victoria Flute Band *40/1919*

**Contact:** Mr Donald Doods
10, Bay Park
Larne BT40 1BZ
Co Antrim
Northern Ireland
**Tel/Fax:** +44 1574 277685

**MUSICAL/ARTISTIC DIRECTOR:**
Colin Irvine.
**KEY IRISH PERFORMANCES** (since January 1994):
2.94 Avoniel Leisure Centre, Belfast promoted by Northern Ireland Flute Band League.
11.95 Ulster Hall, Belfast promoted by the North of Ireland Bands Association.
**KEY PERFORMANCES OUTSIDE IRELAND** (since January 1994):
5.96/97 Airdie Town Hall, Glasgow promoted by the Scottish Flute Band League.
**SELECTED BROADCASTS AND/OR RECORDED WORK:**
5.95/5.96/5.97 'Strike up the Band' a Blackthorn Production for BBC.
**AVAILABILITY:**
General.

## Ballykeel Conservative Flute Band *25/1900*

**Contact:** Mr Ronald Jeffrey
14, Wanstead Avenue
Dundonald
Belfast BT16 OEU
Northern Ireland
**Tel:** +44 1232 485834

**MUSICAL/ARTISTIC DIRECTOR:**
William McMurray.
**AVAILABILITY:**
General.

## Droma Mór Rann na Feirsde *36/1976 (Silver Flute Marching Band)*

**Contact:** Joe McGowan
Dún Caolog
Maullaghmore
Cliffoney, Co Sligo
**Tel/Fax:** +353 71 66207

**MUSICAL/ARTISTIC DIRECTOR:**
Fergus Cobaine.

## Seapatrick Flute Band *23/1873*

**Contact:** E Morton
16, Flough Road
Corbet, Banbridge
Co Down BT32 3SU
Northern Ireland
**Tel:** +44 1820 622597

# PIPE BANDS

*Please note that the numbers placed after each entry title, indicate the number in the group and the year of the band's formation.

## Antrim Pipe Band *22/1921*

**Contact:** M McCullough
20, Firfields
Antrim BT41 4DL
Northern Ireland
**Tel:** +44 1849 467397

## Ballanaleck Pipe Band *49/1948*

**Contact:** D.W. Nixon
Toneytigue
Ballanaleck
Enniskillen, Co Fermanagh
Northern Ireland
**Tel:** +44 1365 348502

## Clontibret O'Neill Pipe Band *40/1972*

**Contact:** Peadar Morgan
Listinny
Monaghan
Co Monaghan
**Tel:** +353 47 80632

**MUSICAL/ARTISTIC DIRECTOR:**
Pipe Major Michael Duffy.
**KEY PERFORMANCES OUTSIDE IRELAND** (since January 1994):
17.3.96 Birmingham, England, promoted by St Patrick's Day Committee, Birmingham.
14.6.97 Cookstown, Co Tyrone, promoted by Scottish Pipe Band Association.
**AVAILABILITY:**
Evenings.

## Convoy Pipe Band *30/1900*

**Contact:** Mrs Elizabeth Craig
Broadlea
Raphoe
Co Donegal
**Tel:** +353 74 45446

**MUSICAL/ARTISTIC DIRECTOR:**
Mervyn Elvier.
**GROUP INSTRUMENTS:**
Bagpipes, snare, tenor and bass drums.
**KEY IRISH PERFORMANCES** (since January 1994):
7.94 Kilkenny city, promoted by the Irish Pipe Band Association.
3.96 Raphoe, promoted by the IPBA.
5.96 Fivemiletown, promoted by the IPBA.
6.97 Enniskillen, promoted by the IPBA.
**AVAILABILITY:**
Prepared to travel any distance.
**ADDITIONAL INFORMATION:**
Attends competitions most Saturdays from April to September, in Ireland and Scotland. Had the honour of representing Ireland in Scotland at a civic reception in Glasgow, prior to competing in the World Championships.

## Cranmore and District Pipe Band *20-30/1979*

**Contact:** Ms Michelle McMorrow
44, Cranmore Drive
Sligo
**Tel:** +353 71 61120

**MUSICAL/ARTISTIC DIRECTORS:**
Tonya Curran and Jennifer Tiernan.
**AVAILABILITY:**
General.

# Crozier Memorial Pipe Band

*24/1947*

**Contact:** Mr Iuan Conly
57, Salters Grange Road
Armagh
Co Armagh BT61 8EX
Northern Ireland
**Tel:** +44 1861 527294

**MUSICAL/ARTISTIC DIRECTOR:**
D Hawthorne.
**AVAILABILITY:**
General.

# Fintan Lalor Pipe Band *17/1912*

**Contact:** Jim King
c/o 30, Cedar Park
Leixlip
Co Kildare
**Tel:** +353 1 6067900
**Email:** jim.king@ccm.ir.intel.com

**MUSICAL/ARTISTIC DIRECTOR:**
Finbarr Connolly (Pipe Band).
**KEY IRISH PERFORMANCES** (since January 1994):
1996 All Ireland Pipe Band Championships, Kilkenny.
1996 Pipe Band Competition, Howth.
**AVAILABILITY:**
General.
**ADDITIONAL INFORMATION:**
Non profit making, self financed. Are former world champions and have won several prizes.

# Killeshin/Durrow Pipe Band

*20/1935*

**Contact:** Mr Noel Whelan
Fortlee House
Killeshin Road
Carlow
**Tel:** +353 503 47769

**KEY IRISH PERFORMANCES** (since January 1994):
6.96 Kilkenny City, promoted by Smithwicks Championships.
6.97 National Concert Hall, Dublin.
**KEY PERFORMANCES OUTSIDE IRELAND** (since January 1994):
1992 France, Cultural Festivals, promoted by French Tourism.
1993 France, Cultural Festivals, promoted by French Tourism.
1995 Scotland.
**PRIZES/AWARDS/APPOINTMENTS:**
1986/1987 Champion of Champions (Grade 4), awarded by Irish Pipe band Association.
**ADDITIONAL INFORMATION:**
Many members possess All-Ireland medals in solo piping and drumming, including one member who is an the All-Ireland Champion Accordion Player of 1996. Have performed for President Mary Robinson.

# Manorcunningham Pipe Band

*20/1935*

**Contact:** 'Alta Vista'
Manorcunningham
Letterkenny
Co Donegal
**Tel/Fax:** +353 74 57274

**MUSICAL/ARTISTIC DIRECTOR:**
Robert Wallace.
**AVAILABILITY:**
General.

# Narraghmore Pipe Band *30/1916*

**Contact:** Susan Feery
Enterprise Centre
Melitta Road
Kildare
Co Kildare
**Tel/Fax:** +353 45 521190 / +353 45 521198
**Email:** mdassociates@tinet.ie

**PRIZES/AWARDS/APPOINTMENTS:**
1994 Champion of Champions, awarded by the Royal Scottish Pipe Band Association.
1994 2nd Prize, awarded the All-Ireland Pipe Band Championships.
6.95 1st Prize, awarded by the East of Ireland Championships, Howth, Co Dublin.
4.6.97 2nd Prize, awarded by the Mid Ulster Championships, High School, Cookstown, Co Tyrone.
**KEY PERFORMANCES OUTSIDE IRELAND** (since January 1994):
8.94 Lorient, France, promoted by Irish Breton Association.
10.94 Perrenporth, England, promoted by Lavender Peran Festival.
7.95 Valencia, Spain, promoted by International Europeade Committee.
10.96 tour of Brittany, France.
**ADDITIONAL INFORMATION:**
Have represented Ireland at international cultural events. Are familiar with the contest arena both in Ireland and abroad.

# St Cronan's Pipe Band (Balla)

*16/1971*

**Contact:** Mr Martin O'Dowd
Rathduff
Balla
Castlebar
Co Mayo
**Tel:** +353 94 65281

**KEY IRISH PERFORMANCES** (since January 1994):
17.3.97 Castlebar, Co Mayo.
17.3.97 Kiltimagh, Co Mayo.
25.7.97 Balla, Co Mayo.
**AVAILABILITY:**
General.
**ADDITIONAL INFORMATION:**
Pipe music is a tradition in Mayo, with ten pipe bands based in the County. This group performs regularly thoughout Sligo, Mayo, Roscommon and Galway. Past performers in the St Patrick's Day Parade in New York.

# St Fin Barr's Pipe Band *20/1930*

**Contact:** Mr Michael Mulcahy
3, Bridgeview Heights
Old Mallow Road
Cork
**Tel/Fax:** +353 21 306188 (h) or +353 21 966222 (w) / +353 21 318927

**MUSICAL/ARTISTIC DIRECTOR:**
Mr Michael Mulcahy.
**KEY IRISH PERFORMANCES** (since January 1994):
1997 Munster Championships, Blarney, Co Cork.
**KEY PERFORMANCES OUTSIDE IRELAND** (since January 1994):
1995 Lorient, Brittany, promoted by Festival Interceltique.
1996 La Coruna, Spain, promoted by the Celtic Festival.
**PRIZES/AWARDS/APPOINTMENTS:**
1980 All Ireland Champions (Grade 3), awarded by the Irish Pipe Band Association.
1994 3rd place (Grade 3), awarded by the Irish Pipe Band Association.
**AVAILABILITY:**
General.
**ADDITIONAL INFORMATION:**
Regularly competes at provincial and national level. Has represented Ireland at the International Folk Festival (Lorient) four times. Solo pipers, drummers etc. from the band are open to all performance opportunities.

# St Laurence O'Toole *27/1910*

**Contact:** Harry McGlone
1, Woodford Green
Clondalkin
Dublin 22
**Tel:** +353 1 4592181 / +353 1 4580676

**MUSICAL/ARTISTIC DIRECTOR:**
Terry Tully.
**KEY IRISH PERFORMANCES** (since January 1994):
Have taken part in several Irish and Scottish pipe band competitions.
**AVAILABILITY:**
General.
**ADDITIONAL INFORMATION:**
Competing band (Grade 1 Competition) but are willing to do some engagements. Some members take part in solo contests in Ireland and Scotland and are also willing to play for events.

# Tamlaght O'Crilly Pipe Band *40/1944*

**Contact:** T Derby
52, Lugarnagoose Road
Curren, Knockcloghrim
Magherafelt BT46 8QY
Northern Ireland
**Tel:** +44 1648 469309

# Thomas Davis Pipe Band *20/1924*

**Contact:** Mr Colm Dwane
15, Glenannaar
Mallow, Co Cork
**Tel:** +353 22 22426

**MUSICAL/ARTISTIC DIRECTOR:**
Colm Dwane.
**KEY IRISH PERFORMANCES** (since January 1994):
6.96 Ballyvourney, promoted by GAA Gaeltacht Football finals.
7.96 Ballybunion, Co Kerry promoted by the Ballybunion Bachelor Festival.
8.96 Puck Fair, Killorglin, Co Kerry.
5.97 Mallow Racecourse, Mallow, Co Cork promoted by Cork Racecourse (Mallow) Company.
**SELECTED BROADCASTS AND/OR RECORDED WORK:**
10.96 'Rakes of Mallow' vol 111 cassette.
6.97 rededication of St. Mary's Church, Mallow for County Sound Radio, Cork.
**AVAILABILITY:**
General.
**ADDITIONAL INFORMATION:**
Have travelled to Boston at the invitation of the America/Ireland fund to perform at their annual fundraising dinner and also to Tréguier, Brittany, France.

# Trillick Pipe Band *21/1946*

**Contact:** Mr James Henderson
"Fairwinds"
Drummurry Gardens
Ballinamallard
Co Fermanagh BT94 2 EG
Northern Ireland
**Tel:** +44 1365 388202

**MUSICAL/ARTISTIC DIRECTOR:**
Mr A Jamison.
**GROUP INSTRUMENTS:**
10 Bagpipes, 6 snare/side drums, 3 tenor drums, 1 bass drums, 1 drum major.
**KEY IRISH PERFORMANCES** (since January 1994):
12.5.97 Belleek, Co Fermanagh promoted by the Education and Library Board.
27. 6.97 Trillick, Co Fermanagh promoted by the local Community Association.
13.7.97 Enniskillen promoted by the Fermanagh District Council.
**TRAINING AND/OR QUALIFICATIONS:**
1994 to 1996, Piping and Drumming Certificates awarded from the Royal Scottish Pipe Band Association.
**AVAILABILITY:**
General.
**ADDITIONAL INFORMATION:**
Sport the muted MacNaughton tartan with dark green matching jackets. Full set of new bagpipes and drums were acquired in 1997. Regular musical performances include concerts, parades and charity appearances. Well disciplined as a marching combination.

# Waterford City Pipe Band *35-30/1980*

**Contact:** Mr John Stone
13, Hawthorne Drive
Hillview
Waterford
Co Waterford

**MUSICAL/ARTISTIC DIRECTOR:**
John Stone.
**GROUP INSTRUMENTS:**
Highland bagpipes, side, tenor and bass drums.
**KEY IRISH PERFORMANCES** (since January 1994):
Contests organised by the Irish Pipe Band Association.
**PRIZES/AWARDS/APPOINTMENTS:**
Grades 1 and 2, College Board Awards from the Irish Pipe Band Association.

**AVAILABILITY:**
Evenings.
**ADDITIONAL INFORMATION:**
Formed to promote the art of piping and drumming in Waterford.

## OTHER BANDS

*Please note that the numbers placed after each entry title, indicate the number in the group and the year of the bands formation.

### Fifty Fifth (55th) Old Boys Band *35/1920*

**Contact:** F.S. McCrea
32, Church Road
Ballynure
Ballyclare
Co Antrim
Northern Ireland
**Tel:** +44 1960 342107

**MUSICAL/ARTISTIC DIRECTOR:**
Ernest Ruddock.
**AVAILABILITY:**
General.

### Sídhe Gaoithe *16/1990*

**Contact:** Joe McGowan
Dún Caolog
Maullaghmore
Cliffoney
Co Sligo
**Tel/Fax:** +353 71 66207

### The Bells of Mayo *11/1995 (Carillon)*

**Contact:** Ms Niamh O'Kelly
The Old School House
Rossduane
Kilmeena
Westport
Co Mayo
**Tel/Fax:** +353 98 41030

**MUSICAL/ARTISTIC DIRECTOR:**
Niamh O'Kelly.
**KEY IRISH PERFORMANCES** (since January 1994):
9.2.97 Abbey Church, Dublin, promoted by Hibernian Insurance, appearing with Mayo County Choir.
14.3.97 Ballintubber Abbey, promoted by the National Council for the Blind, appearing with Mayo County Choir.
22.5.97 Castlebar, The Welcome Inn, appearing with the Mayo County choir.
7.6.97 Taibhhearc Theatre, Galway.
**SELECTED BROADCASTS AND/OR RECORDED WORK:**
6.96 The 'Gay Byrne Radio Show' for RTÉ.
9.6.96 and 20.12.96 'Nationwide' for RTÉ.
**AVAILABILITY:**
General.

## PROFESSIONAL CHOIRS AND CHORAL GROUPS

### Anúna

**Contact:** Michael McGlynn
PO Box 4468
Churchtown
Dublin 14
**Tel/Fax:** +353 1 2835533
**Email:** info@anuna.ie
**WWW:** http://www.anuna.ie

*"With voices and harmonies woven from the mouths of angels, Anúna may just be the most intriguing vocal group on the classical pop scene today"* CD review, USA.

**NUMBER IN GROUP:** 11-17 (pool of 30 singers).
**KEY IRISH PERFORMANCES** (since January 1994):
1.96 Ulster Hall, Belfast appearing with the Ulster Orchestra.
7.96 Performance as part of the opening of the EU presidency, Dublin
**KEY PERFORMANCES OUTSIDE IRELAND** (since January 1994):
2.96 Theatre de la Ville, Paris.
7.96 Brittany, France with the Festival de Cournaille.
11.96 Bridgewater Hall, Manchester.
**SELECTED BROADCASTS AND/OR RECORDED WORK:**
1993 'Anúna' (re - released in 1995 on the Celtic Heartbeat Universal MCA label).
1995 'Riverdance the album' features 4 tracks by Anúna.
1996 'Deep Dead Blue' for Danú 005.
**SELECTED REVIEWS** (since January 1994):
10.96 Sunday Tribune.
1996 Le Monde, France.
1997 Gothenburg Post, Sweden.
**PRIZES/AWARDS/APPOINTMENTS:**
1994, National Entertainment Award, classical award category.
**ADDITIONAL INFORMATION:**
Group name derives from 'An Uaithne', which collectively describes the three ancient types of Irish music - suantraí (lullaby), geantraí (happy song) and goltraí (lament). Founded by young Dublin composer Michael McGlynn.

### National Chamber Choir

**Contact:** Ms Karina Lundstrom
Dublin City University
Glasnevin
Dublin 9
**Tel/Fax:** +353 1 7045665 / +353 1 7045603

*"... Under the conductorship of Colin Mawby ... has consolidated its position as a musically satisfying, resourceful, well balanced and finely drilled ensemble of 17 singers"* 10.96 Belfast Telegraph.

**FORMED:** 1991.
**NUMBER IN GROUP:** 17.
**MUSICAL/ARTISTIC DIRECTOR:**
Colin Mawby.

**GROUP MEMBERS:**
5 sopranos, 4 altos, 4 tenors, 4 basses.
**KEY IRISH PERFORMANCES** (since January 1994):
10.96 St Georges, Belfast promoted by NCC.
11.12.96 Gaeity Theatre, Dublin, appearing with Opera Theatre Company and the RTÉ Concert Orchestra in a production of La Bohemé.
19.12.96 University of Limerick Concert Hall appearing with the Irish Chamber Orchestra.
22.12.96 National Concert Hall, Dublin, Christmas programme promoted by RTÉ and the European Broadcasting Union.
**SELECTED BROADCASTS AND/OR RECORDED WORK:**
8.96 'The Torc of Gold' on cassette.
3.97 International Women's Day recording for RTÉ.
5.97 'The National Chamber Choir at the National Gallery of Ireland' recorded on cassette.
**PRIZES/AWARDS/APPOINTMENTS:**
1.96 Winners of the AIB Better Ireland Award.
**AVAILABILITY:**
General.
**ADDITIONAL INFORMATION:**
Specialises in contemporary music and music from the baroque era. Devotes a considerable amount of its budget to music in the community and music education at all levels.

# AMATEUR AND SEMI-PROFESSIONAL CHOIRS AND CHORAL GROUPS

**Useful contact addresses in the area of choral performance in Ireland include:**
**Cumann Náisiúnta na gCór,** (Association of Irish Choirs), Ms Barbara Heas, Drinan Street, Cork.
**Tel/Fax:** +353 21 312296 / +353 21 962457
**AIMS, The Association of Irish Musical Societies,** Ms Mary Mullen, 24 Glenbourne Green, Leopardstown Valley, Dublin 18.
**Tel:** +353 1 2940775

*Please note that the numbers placed after each entry title indicate the number in the group and the year of the group's formation.

## Antrim Choral Society *40/1975*

**Contact:** R Horn
81, Magheralane Road
Randalstown
Co Antrim
**Tel:** +44 18494 72445

## Ards Choral Society *60+/1947*

**Contact:** Mr Ian Bell
20, Kinwood Drive
Perry Road, Bangor
Co Down BT19 6UQ
Northern Ireland
**Tel:** +44 1247 451 081

**MUSICAL/ARTISTIC DIRECTOR:**
Mr Ian G Bell.
**KEY IRISH PERFORMANCES** (since January 1994):
10.96 Queen's Hall, Newtownards, Co Down, appearing with Stephen Hamill (organ).
12.96 Queen's Hall, Newtownards, Co Down, promoted by Ards Choral Society, appearing with ACS Orchestra.
3.97 Queen's Hall, Newtownards, Co Down, promoted by ACS appearing with ACS Orchestra.
**AVAILABILITY:**
General.

## Ballinteer Male Singers *20/1995*

**Contact:** Mary Kelly
113, Broadford Rise
Ballinteer
Dublin 16
**Tel:** +353 1 4941874

## Ballyclare Male Choir *70/1933*

**Contact:** c/o Wross
12, Birchhill Avenue
Antrim BT41 1BT
Northern Ireland
**Tel:** +44 18494 63486

**MUSICAL/ARTISTIC DIRECTOR:**
William I. Thompson.
**AVAILABILITY:**
Evenings during September and May.

## Blackpool Church Choir

**Contact:** Ms Lorena Gillard
32, Brookdale
Broomfield, Mill Road
Midleton, Co Cork
**Mobile:** +353 87 448419

**KEY IRISH PERFORMANCES** (since January 1994):
12.12.96 Airport Church, Cork.
15.12.96 Cork City performance, promoted by the Mayfield Church Choirs.
**AVAILABILITY:**
Weekends, evenings and throughout the holiday period.

## Boys Brigade Centenary Choir *56/1988*

**Contact:** George Meneilly
**Tel:** +44 1247 853332

**MUSICAL/ARTISTIC DIRECTOR:**
William I. Thompson.
**AVAILABILITY:**
Evenings.

## Breffni Singers *40/1973*

**Contact:** Margaret Connolly
Concordia
Manorhamilton
Co Leitrim
**Tel:** +353 72 55563

**MUSICAL/ARTISTIC DIRECTOR:**
Margaret Connolly.
**AVAILABILITY:**
Weekends.

# Cantique

**Contact:** Hilly Dunford
22, Corbawn Close
Shankill
Co Dublin
**Tel/Fax:** +353 1 2821682 / +353 1 2821682
*See contemporary ensembles page 135.*

# Castlebar Choral Society *50/1972*

**Contact:** Ms Carol Greene
16, Waterville
Castlebar
Co Mayo
**Tel:** +353 94 21546

**GROUP MEMBERS:**
15 sopranos, 15 altos, 10 tenors, 6 basses, piano accompanist.
**KEY IRISH PERFORMANCES** (since January 1994):
95/97 Cork International Choral Festival, Cork.
**PRIZES/AWARDS/APPOINTMENTS:**
1982 Ist Prize, mixed choirs, Section 2, Cork International Choral Festival.
**TRAINING AND/OR QUALIFICATIONS:**
1996, Attended a weekend workshop with Dr Geoffrey Spratt, Cork School of Music.
**AVAILABILITY:**
Weekends.
**ADDITIONAL INFORMATION:**
Has been in existence for 25 years. Performs throughout County Mayo and generally sings to raise money for local charities.

# Christchurch Cathedral Choir *28/1492*

**Contact:** Ms Helen Roycroft
4, Orwell Park
Rathgar, Dublin 6
**Tel:** +353 1 4966740

*"Superb control of line, pitching, vocal colour and dynamics, including some luminous pianissimos of pin-dropping quietness"*
6.94 Irish Times (Martin Adams).

**MUSICAL/ARTISTIC DIRECTOR:**
Mark Duley.
**KEY IRISH PERFORMANCES** (since January 1994):
6.95 Lismore Cathedral, promoted by West Waterford Early Music Festival, appearing with Malcolm Proud (harpischord).
5.96 Christchurch Cathedral, Dublin International Organ and Choral Festival, accompanied by Ben Van Oosten (organ).
6.96 St James's Church, Durrus, Co Cork, promoted by West Cork Music.
7.96 Christchurch Cathedral, Dublin, promoted by Cathedral Arts, accompanied by Andrew Johnstone.
**KEY PERFORMANCES OUTSIDE IRELAND** (since January 1994):
8.95 Durham Cathedral, resident choir for one week, accompanied by Andrew Johnstone and Mark Duley.
8.95 Westminster Abbey, resident choir for one week, appearing with Andrew Johnstone.
**SELECTED BROADCASTS AND/OR RECORDED WORK:**
11.95 Sacred Music of CV Stanford Vol 3 for Priory Records, England.
12.9.96 Carol Service from Christchurch Cathedral for RTÉ, FM3.
5.96 Charpentier Mass for Double Choir, for RTÉ FM3.
**SELECTED REVIEWS** (since January 1994):
7.96 Irish Times (Michael Dervan).
5.96 Irish Times (Martin Adams).
**PRIZES/AWARDS/APPOINTMENTS:**
2.95 AIB Better Ireland Award winner (£5,000).
10.96 Friend of Cathedral Music, (£10,000).
**TRAINING AND/OR QUALIFICATIONS:**
Regular coaching with Margaret Humphrey - Clarke (Eton Choir School).
**AVAILABILITY:**
General.
**ADDITIONAL INFORMATION:**
A semi-professional ensemble of 24 adult singers. Have a vast repertoire covering five centuries and is heard regularly in the five choral services in the Cathedral every week. During summer of 1997 the choir travelled to Paris and Chartres.

# Cois Claddagh *25/1982*

**Contact:** Dr Brendan O'Connor
Oranswell
Galway
**Tel/Fax:** +353 91 756812 / +353 91 756888
**Email:** aquafact@iol.ie

**KEY IRISH PERFORMANCES** (since January 1994):
1995 Cork International Choral Festival.
19.8.95 Claremorris, Co Mayo promoted by the George Moore Society appearing with the National Symphony Orchestra of Ireland.
30.9.95 Corrib Great Southern Hotel, Galway, promoted by Rotary International.
15.10.95 St Ignatius Church, Galway.
**KEY PERFORMANCES OUTSIDE IRELAND** (since January 1994):
10.95 Boston, USA, promoted by George Moore Society.
**PRIZES/AWARDS/APPOINTMENTS:**
1985/86 National Choir Section winners at the Cork Choral Festival.
1993/94 National Chamber Choir winners at the Cork Choral Festival.
**AVAILABILITY:**
Weekends.
**ADDITIONAL INFORMATION:**
Members include traditional musicians. Repertoire includes a blend of choral music and traditional Irish song and dance music. Regularly commissions Irish composers such as Míchéal Ó Súilleabháin and John Buckley. Sings for enjoyment and always welcomes new singers.

# Cór na Mara *28/1991*

**Contact:** Sr Angela Lawless
Dominican Convent
Taylor's Hill
Galway
**Tel:** +353 91 522124 / +353 91 523975

**MUSICAL/ARTISTIC DIRECTOR:**
Sr Angela Lawless.
**SELECTED BROADCASTS AND/OR RECORDED WORK:**
1994, 1995, 1996 masses for Raidío na Gaeltachta.
**PRIZES/AWARDS/APPOINTMENTS:**
1994 2nd and 3rd Prize winners and Larkin Cup recipients in the Óireachtas competitions. 1995 2nd Prize winner and cup winners in the Óireachtas competitions. Received an EU grant under the NDW new opportunities scheme for women.
**TRAINING AND/OR QUALIFICATIONS:**
Workshops have been undertaken with Joan Hanrahan, from Maoin

Cheoil an Chláir, Co Clare, Michael Ó hEidhín, Cigire Scoile, and Carl Hession, B Mus.
**AVAILABILITY:**
General.

## Counterpoint *24/1950*

**Contact:** Mrs Rosalind McGrath
Leeward
Drumanphy Road
Portadown
Co Armagh BT62 1QX
Northern Ireland
**Tel/Fax:** +44 1762 852057

**MUSICAL/ARTISTIC DIRECTOR:**
Mr Harry Anderson.
**ADDITIONAL INFORMATION:**
Wide repertoire combining light classical, sacred and secular songs. Own soloists to complement programmes.

## Crosshaven Singers *35/1982*

**Contact:** Helen Colbert
38, Avondale Park
Ballintemple
Cork
**Tel:** +353 21 295269

**MUSICAL/ARTISTIC DIRECTOR:**
Helen Corbert.
**AVAILABILITY:**
General.

## Culwick Choral Society *130/1898*

**Contact:** Mrs Helen O'Colmain
Culwick Choral Society
Cnoc Alla
41, Hyde Park Avenue
Blackrock
Co Dublin
**Email:** magdalen.oconnell@nui.ie or cblock@indigo.ie

*"Singing of deep commitment, always purposeful, and often very beautiful in the delicacy of its shading"* Irish Times (Bach B minor mass).

**MUSICAL/ARTISTIC DIRECTOR:**
Colin Block.
**CHORUS MASTER:**
Malcolm Wisener.
**KEY IRISH PERFORMANCES** (since January 1994):
29.4.95 and 19.5.94 National Concert Hall, Dublin, performing Rossini's 'Petite Messe Solonnelle', appearing with Gillian Smith.
22.2.97 National Concert Hall, Dublin, in a performace of Haydn's 'Creation', appearing with with Orchestra of St Cecilia.
Annually in December, St Patrick's Cathedral, Dublin, performance of Handel's Messiah.
**SELECTED BROADCASTS AND/OR RECORDED WORK:**
Various recordings for RTÉ.
**SELECTED REVIEWS** (since January 1994):
19.5.94 Irish Times.
**ADDITIONAL INFORMATION:**
Works generally in the National Concert Hall with well known soloists, conductors and orchestras. Repertoire includes classical, operatic chorus and folk songs. Rehearsals take place on Thursday nights and learning tapes are provided for those who do not read music.

## Downshire Ladies Choir *30/1967*

**Contact:** Mr William I. Thompson
17, Irwin Drive
Belfast BT4 3AR
Northern Ireland
**Tel:** +44 1232 651611

**MUSICAL/ARTISTIC DIRECTOR:**
William I. Thompson.
**AVAILABILITY:**
General.

## Dublin County Choir *120/1975*

**Contact:** Mrs Bernadette McCarthy
31, Marley Lawn
Rathfarnham
Dublin 16
**Tel/Fax:** +353 1 4943921 / +353 1 8733521
**Email:** cblock@indigo.ie or bools@indigo.ie

*"Surely we have no better choir here at present: have we any to equal it?"* Irish Times.

**MUSICAL DIRECTOR:**
Colin Block.
**CHORUS MASTER:**
John Dexter.
**KEY IRISH PERFORMANCES** (since January 1994):
28.10.95 National Concert Hall, Dublin performing Vaughan Williams 'Sea Symphony'.
17.5.97 NCH performing Purcell's 'Didi and Aeneas'.
16.11.97 NCH, Dublin performing 'Good Vibrations- music of the 60's & 70's'.
**KEY PERFOMANCES OUTSIDE IRELAND** (since January 1994):
27.4.92 Wolfratshausen, Germany in a performance of Verdi's Requiem appearing with Munich Haydn Orchestra.
Have also appeared at the Llandudno Festival, Wales.
**SELECTED BROADCASTS AND/OR RECORDED WORK:**
8.96 Let the Bells Ring (Christmas CD) for Ambush Records.
Various recordings for RTÉ and Friday Night is Music Night for BBC.
**SELECTED REVIEWS:**
28.10.95 Irish Times.
**AVAILABILITY:**
General.
**ADDITIONAL INFORMATION:**
Normally appear at the National Concert Hall with distinguished soloists and orchestras. Wide repertoire from Bach to the Beatles, folk songs, operatic choruses, standards. Frequently appear as guests in charity concerts. Rehearsals are on Monday nights and learning tapes are provided for those who do not read music.

## Dublin Welsh Male Voice Choir *50+/1965*

**Contact:** Mr Keith Young
6 Gortnamona Drive
Foxrock, Dublin 18
**Tel:** +353 1 2894482
**Email:** kyoung@indigo.ie

**MUSICAL/ARTISTIC DIRECTOR:**
Keith Young.
**KEY IRISH PERFORMANCES** (since January 1994):
10.95 Ballina, Co Mayo, appearing with the Moy Singers, Ballina.
11.95 National Concert Hall, Dublin, promoted by Harry Perry.
5.97 Killaloe Cathedral, Co Clare.
5.97 Limerick Cathedral.
6.97 Castlecomer, Co Kilkenny, promoted by Castlecomer Male Voice Choir.
**KEY PERFORMANCES OUTSIDE IRELAND** (since January 1994):
11.94 Llandudno, North Wales, promoted by Llandudno Music Festival.
3.95 Pontarodulan, South Wales.
4.95 Atlanta, South Georgia, USA, promoted by South Georgia Tourist Board and Choir of the World.
2.97 St David's Hall, Cardiff, Wales, promoted by London Welsh Association.
**SELECTED BROADCASTS AND/OR RECORDED WORK:**
'Live at 3', 'Late, Late Show' and 'Mike Murphy Show', for RTÉ.
'Newsreels', 'Pre-International Rugby Games', for BBC (Wales).
Recordings for HTV (Wales).
**PRIZES/AWARDS/APPOINTMENTS:**
From 1970 to 1993, 1st Prize, awarded at the Pan Celtic Festival, Kerry.
From 1980 to 1992, 1st Prize, awarded at the Arklow and Navan Festivals.

# Dungannon Choral Society *40/1930's*

**Contact:** Miss Kathy Stephenson
71, Northland Village
Dungannon
Co Tyrone BT71 6JN
Northern Ireland
**Tel:** +44 1865 723344

**MUSICAL/ARTISTIC DIRECTOR:**
Frank Richardson.
**KEY IRISH PERFORMANCES** (since January 1994):
12.95 Dungannon, Co Tyrone, Christmas music performance.
3.96 and 1.97, Dungannon, Co Tyrone, light choral music performance.
3.97 Dungannon and Lisburn 'The Passion of Christ' by Arthur Somerville.

# Eblana *20/1996*

**Contact:** Miriam O'Sullivan
60, Merchant's Square
East Wall
Dublin 3
**Tel:** +353 1 8550891

**MUSICAL/ARTISTIC DIRECTOR:**
John O'Flynn.
**KEY IRISH PERFORMANCES** (since January 1994):
5.12.96 Ely House, Dublin.
2.21.3.97 St Mary's, Howth, Co Dublin promoted by Aoife Nolan Trust Fund (charity concert) appearing with Edel Sludds (organ).
10.4.97 Alliance Français, Dublin, promoted by the French Embassy, appearing with Edel O'Dwyer (cello), Elizabeth Keighary (piano).
20.6.97 Church of St Adam and Eve Merchant's Quay, appearing with Paul McKeever (organ).
**AVAILABILITY:**
General.
**ADDITIONAL INFORMATION:**
A chamber choir whose repertoire comprises, for the most part, of music from the 16th and 20th centuries. In addition to public concerts, has participated in sacred services at regular intervals. Following a commission from the French Embassy, has developed a specialised programme of French music ranging from Jannequin to Messiaen.

# Fermanagh Choral Society *50*

**Contact:** Ms Gillian Mayes
15a, Cooper Crescent
Enniskillen
Co Fermanagh
**Tel:** +44 1365 325475

**MUSICAL/ARTISTIC DIRECTOR:**
David Asater.
**AVAILABILITY:**
General.

# Galway Baroque Singers *65+/1983*

**Contact:** Joan Armitage (Secretary)
14, Montrose House
Whitestrand
Galway
Co Galway
**Tel:** +353 91 561712

**MUSICAL/ARTISTIC DIRECTOR:**
Audrey Corbett.
**KEY IRISH PERFORMANCES** (since January 1994):
11.94 Galway Cathedral, promoted by RTÉ appearing with the RTÉ Concert Orchestra, Ian Caddy and Ronan Tynan.
11.95 Leisureland, Galway promoted by RTÉ appearing with the RTÉCO.
4.96 Town Hall Theatre, Galway appearing with Doreen Curran, Emmanuel Lawlor and Philip Martin.
11.96 Galway Cathedral, promoted by RTÉ appearing with the RTÉCO, Mary Hegarty and Damien Smith.
**PRIZES/AWARDS/APPOINTMENTS:**
23.3.97 1st Prize, National Mixed Voice choir and Best Overall Choir of the Limerick Church Music Choral Festival.
3.5.97 1st Prize, national open competition for mixed voice choirs at the Cork International Choral Festival.

# Glens Choir *35/1970*

**Contact:** Christine McSparran
**Tel/Fax:** +44 12667 71411 / +44 12667 72112

**MUSICAL/ARTISTIC DIRECTOR:**
Christine McSparran.
**KEY IRISH PERFORMANCES** (since January 1994):
9.95 Dublin, promoted by the Voices of the World, appearing with the National Symphony Orchestra of Ireland.
12.95 Cushendall, Co Antrim, Interdenominational Carol Service.
8.96 Hearts of the Glen Festival, Cushendall, Co Antrim.
9.96 Life boat Launch, Cushendall, Co Antrim.

# Kenmare Chamber Choir *13/1993*

**Contact:** Dr Gordon Smith
Direenacallaha House
Dauros
Kenmare
Co Kerry
**Tel/Fax:** +353 64 41784 / +353 64 42073

**MUSICAL/ARTISTIC DIRECTOR:**
Dr Gordon Smith.

## Kerry Choral Union *75/1980*

**Contact:** Aidan Lynch
15, Hawthorn Avenue
Ballycasheen
Killarney
Co Kerry
**Tel/Fax:** +353 64 33749

*"The professionalism, stage presence, dress, discipline, and voice-blend, of this talented group ... deserved the applause that greeted them ..."*
14.12.95 Kerry's Eye (Padraig Kennelly).

**MUSICAL/ARTISTIC DIRECTOR:**
Aidan Lynch.
**KEY PERFORMANCES OUTSIDE IRELAND** (since January 1994):
3.95 New York, USA, appearing with Rena Fitzgibbon.
3.95 Boston, USA, appearing with Rena Fitzgibbon.
**SELECTED BROADCASTS AND/OR RECORDED WORK:**
12.95 'Sounds of the Season 1995' for Horizon Television.
12.96 'Sounds of the Season 1996' for Vitel Productions.

## Kings Chorale *70/1987*

**Contact:** Mrs Paula Trimble
10, Kimberly Road
Carnmoney
Co Antrim
Northern Ireland
**Tel:** +44 1232 836393

**MUSICAL/ARTISTIC DIRECTOR:**
William I. Thompson.
**AVAILABILITY:**
General.

## Limerick Choral Union *60/1967*

**Contact:** Mr Malcolm Green
Downside
South Circular Road
Limerick
**Tel:** +353 61 302148

**PRIZES/AWARDS/APPOINTMENTS:**
2.97 Best Limerick Choir, Limerick International Church Music Festival.
**AVAILABILITY:**
General.

## Lindsay Singers *30/1957*

**Contact:** Mrs Ethna Barror
87, Lindsay Road
Dublin 9
**Tel:** +353 1 8304320

*"The highlight of the performance was, without doubt, the singing of the Lindsay Singers as the angels in 'Elijah'"* 2.94 Irish Times.

**KEY IRISH PERFORMANCES** (since January 1994):
1994, Ist Prize winner, Sligo International Choral Festival.
1995/1996/1997 Choir of the Year, Sligo International Choral.
**AVAILABILITY:**
Evenings.

## Madrigal '75 *24/1975*

**Contact:** Dr Geoffrey Spratt
Director
Cork School of Music
Union Quay
Cork
**Tel/Fax:** +353 21 270076 / +353 21 276595

**KEY IRISH PERFORMANCES** (since January 1994):
Bantry House, Co Cork, promoted by West Cork Music, appearing with guest instrumentalists.
3.7.95 St Mary's Church, Pope's Quay, Cork, promoted by RTÉ, appearing with the RTÉ Vanbrugh Quartet and soloists.
**SELECTED BROADCASTS AND/OR RECORDED WORK:**
1988 'The Choral Music of Séamus de Barra' for Grapevine, London.
Since 1976 Numerous broadcasts for RTÉ.
**AVAILABILITY:**
Weekends.
**ADDITIONAL INFORMATION:**
Has premiéred many new works, particularly at the Cork International Choral Festival and has won numerous prizes in Irish and continental competitions. Performs frequently with the RTÉ Vanbrugh Quartet.

## Madrigallery *16/1992*

**Contact:** Kevin O'Carroll
Woodlands
Halfway House
Co Waterford
**Tel:** +353 51 876260

**MUSICAL/ARTISTIC DIRECTOR:**
Kevin O'Carroll.
**GROUP MEMBERS:**
5 sopranos, 4 altos, 3 tenors, 4 basses.
**KEY IRISH PERFORMANCES:**
5.97 Waterford City Hall, appearing Andreja Maliř and Malcolm Proud.
**AVAILABILITY:**
General.

## Mayo County Choir *30/1995*

**Contact:** Ms Niamh O'Kelly
The Old School House
Rossduane
Kilmeena
Westport, Co Mayo
**Tel/Fax:** +353 98 41030

**MUSICAL/ARTISTIC DIRECTOR:**
Niamh O'Kelly.
**KEY IRISH PERFORMANCES** (since January 1994):
9.2.97 Findlaters Church, Dublin promoted by Hibernian Insurance.
14.3.97 Ballintubber Abbey promoted by National Council for the Blind.
22.5.97 Welcome Inn, Castlebar, Co Mayo.
7.6.97 Taibhdhearc Theatre, Galway.
**SELECTED BROADCASTS AND/OR RECORDED WORK:**
9.6.96 and 20.12.96 'Nationwide' programme for RTÉ.
11.6.96 Performance on Raidió na Gaeltachta.
**AVAILABILITY:**
General.

# Moy Singers *40/1986*

**Contact:** Mrs Aileen Donagher McGowan
Emmet Street
Ballina
Co Mayo
**Tel/Fax:** +353 96 70669

**MUSICAL/ARTISTIC DIRECTOR:**
Aileen Donagher McGowan.
**KEY IRISH PERFORMANCES** (since January 1994):
1994 Ballina, Co Mayo, promoted by Mayo 5000, appearing with the RTÉ Concert Orchestra.
1995 Craigavon, promoted by Concordia, appearing with the Craigavon Chorale.
1995 Ballina, Co Mayo, appearing with Niamh Murray.
1996 Ballina, Co Mayo and Dublin, appearing with the Dublin Welsh Male Voice Choir.
**KEY PERFORMANCES OUTSIDE IRELAND** (since January 1994):
6.95 Vienna, Austria, appearing with Michaels Kammercor.
4.97 France, St Raphael and Monaco.
**PRIZES/AWARDS/APPOINTMENTS:**
1992 3rd Prize in the Cork International Choral Festival.
**AVAILABILITY:**
General.

# Newry Musical and Orchestral Society *80/1945*

**Contact:** Kate Carragher
6, Varriff Vale
Dublin Road
Newry
Co Down
Northern Ireland
**Tel:** +44 1693 60898

# Opus '96 *10/1996*

**Contact:** Aidan Lynch
15, Hawthorn Avenue
Ballycasheen
Killarney
Co Kerry
**Tel/Fax:** +353 64 33749

**KEY IRISH PERFOMANCES** (since January 1994):
4.5.97 Cork International Choral Festival.
**AVAILABILITY:**
General.

# Our Lady's Choral Society *120/1945*

**Contact:** Rev Patrick D. O'Donoghue
Holy Cross College
Clonliffe
Dublin 3
**Tel/Fax:** +353 1 8571648 / +353 1 8371474

**MUSICAL/ARTISTIC DIRECTOR:**
Proinnsias Ó Duinn.
**KEY IRISH PERFORMANCES** (since January 1994):
12.95 National Concert Hall, Dublin promoted by the Society appearing with the National Sinfonia.
12.5.96 NCH, promoted by the Society, appearing with the National Sinfonia.
6.12.96 National Gallery of Ireland, Dublin promoted by the Friend's of the National Gallery accompanied by Mary Scarletti (piano).
1.6.97 White Abbey, Kildare promoted by the Carmelite Fathers accompanied by Mary Scarletti (organ).
**SELECTED BROADCASTS AND/OR RECORDED WORK:**
25.12.95 Eurovision Christmas mass for RTÉ.
**AVAILABILITY:**
General.

# Pavane 10/1991

**Contact:** Brian Hunter
Director
12, Cabin Hill Park
Belfast BTS 7AL
Northern Ireland
**Tel:** +44 1232 653891

**MUSICAL DIRECTOR:**
Brian Hunter.
**KEY IRISH PERFORMANCES** (since January 1994):
3.94 Institute of Electrical Engineers, Antrim.
11.94 Belfast Festival at Queen's.
10.96 Bangor, promoted by Cinema Organ Society and appearing with Nigel Ogden (organ).
**SELECTED BROADCASTS AND/OR RECORDED WORK:**
From 1993 to 1995, Three appearances on the 'Classical Show' for BBC.
1995 and 1996, 'Music for a While' for BBC.
1995 'Songs of Praise' for BBC.
**AVAILABILITY:**
General.
**ADDITIONAL INFORMATION:**
Equally at home in classical, light classical, sacred recitals.

# Portadown Ladies Choir *40/1951*

**Contact:** Mrs Maureen McAdam
29, Old Rectory Park
Portadown, BT62 3QH
Northern Ireland
**Tel/Fax:** +44 1762 334 698 (h) +44 1762 337172 (w) / +44 1762 350950

**MUSICAL/ARTISTIC DIRECTOR:**
Gordon Speers.
**AVAILABILITY:**
Weekends.

# Portadown Male Voice Choir *45/1926*

**Contact:** Mr Everett Browne
1, Crawford Park
Portadown
Craigavon, BT62 3QW
Northern Ireland
**Tel:** +44 1762 330133

**MUSICAL/ARTISTIC DIRECTOR:**
Gordon Speers.
**AVAILABILITY:**
Weekends, evenings from September to April.

# RTÉ Chorus

**Contact:** Mr Simon Taylor
Music Department
RTÉ, Donnybrook
Dublin 4
**Tel/Fax:** +353 1 2082779 / +353 1 2082511

# RTÉ Philharmonic Choir

**Contact:** Mr Simon Taylor
Music Department
RTÉ, Donnybrook
Dublin 4
**Tel/Fax:** +353 1 2082779 / +353 1 2082511

# Renaissance *30/1976*

**Contact:** Brian Hunter, Director
12, Cabin Hill Park
Belfast BTS 7AL
**Tel:** +44 1232 653891

**MUSICAL/ARTISTIC DIRECTOR:**
Brian Hunter.
**KEY IRISH PERFORMANCES** (since January 1994):
2.96 St Anne's Cathedral, Belfast.
**PRIZES/AWARDS/APPOINTMENTS:**
1984 Winner of the BBC Sainsbury's Choir of the Year.
1991/92 Winner of the Belfast Telegraph EMA Award for classical ensemble.
**AVAILABILITY:**
General.
**ADDITIONAL INFORMATION:**
Mainly performs a classical, sacred repertoire. Can also provide a lighter programme when required.

# St Agnes' Choral Society *60/1957*

**Contact:** Mr Paul Anthony
8, Upper Malone Park
Belfast BT9 6PP
Northern Ireland
**Tel:** +44 1232 613109
**Email:** panthony@hotmail.com

**MUSICAL/ARTISTIC DIRECTOR:**
William Cairns.
**KEY IRISH PERFORMANCES** (since January 1994):
1994 Production of 'Oliver' in the Grand Opera House, Belfast.
1995 Production of 'My Fair Lady' in the GOH, Belfast.
1996 Production of 'South Pacific' in the GOH, Belfast.
1997 Production of 'Music Man' in the GOH, Belfast.
**PRIZES/AWARDS/APPOINTMENTS:**
1972 and 1973, 1st Prize winners at the Waterford International Festival of Light Opera.
**AVAILABILITY:**
General.
**ADDITIONAL INFORMATION:**
Largest choral society in Northern Ireland. Invited annually to present a show in the Grand Opera House, Belfast.

# St Cecilia Singers *20/1985*

**Contact:** Ms Sandra Ganly
10, Commons Road
Loughlinstown
Co Dublin
**Tel:** +353 1 2826796
**Email:** mikeg@iol.ie

**MUSICAL/ARTISTIC DIRECTOR:**
Sandra Ganly.
**KEY IRISH PERFORMANCES** (since January 1994):
11.94 Wesley House, Dublin appearing with Simon Taylor (guitar).
3.95 St Ann's Church, Dawson Street, Dublin appearing with St Ann's Boy's Choir.
5.95 St Flannan's Cathedral, Killaloe, Co Clare.
12.96 Wesley House, Dublin, appearing with the Dublin Boy Singers.

# St Columb's Cathedral Choir *28*

**Contact:** Mr Timothy Allen
2, St. Columb's Court
Londonderry, BT48 6PT
Northern Ireland
**Tel/Fax:** +44 1504 262412

**MUSICAL/ARTISTIC DIRECTOR:**
Timothy Allen.
**KEY IRISH PERFORMANCES** (since January 1994):
10/92 - 97 Two Cathedral's Festival, Derry, appearing with St Eugene's Cathedral Choir.
12.94 The Guildhall, Derry promoted by Derry City Council appearing with the Ulster Orchestra.
3.95 St Anne's Cathedral, Belfast promoted by the BBC appearing with the BBC Choral Broadcast.
7.95 Christchurch Cathedral Choir, Dublin.
**KEY PERFORMANCES OUTSIDE IRELAND** (since January 1994):
7.94 Abbate aux Hommes, Caen and Abbey of Bec. Hellouin.
**SELECTED BROADCASTS AND/OR RECORDED WORK:**
1996 Own cassette recording of music from St Columb's Cathedral.
**AVAILABILITY:**
General.
**ADDITIONAL INFORMATION:**
One of the four all-male cathedral choirs in Ireland.

# St George's Singers *40+/1985*

**Contact:** Mr Darcy Chillingworth
65, Whitehouse Park
Newtownabbey
Co Antrim BT37 9SH
Northern Ireland
**Tel:** +44 1232 852615

**MUSICAL/ARTISTIC DIRECTOR:**
Mr David Byers.
**AVAILABILITY:**
General.

## St Ignatius Parish Choir *25/1971*

**Contact:** Mr Edward J Lloyd
Sea Road
Galway
**Tel:** +353 91 523029

**MUSICAL/ARTISTIC DIRECTOR:**
Edward J Lloyd.
**ADDITIONAL INFORMATION:**
Blend music and singing with lively spirit of group.

## St Joseph's Church Choir *15/1990*

**Contact:** David Maxwell
6, Fairview Green
Fairview
Dublin 3
**Tel:** +353 1 8339159

## St Mary's Senior Church Choir *60/1939*

**Contact:** Jane Kennedy
Poulnagunogue
Mountain Road
Clonmel
Co Tipperary
**Tel:** +44 52 23053

## Scoil Mhuire Choir 65/1995

**Contact:** Alison Barry
3, Greenwood Estate
Lehenaghmore
Cork
**Tel:** +353 21 964370

## Setanta *60/1978*

**Contact:** Una Murphy
Dun Laurel
Ballymascanlon
Dundalk
Co Louth
**Tel:** +353 42 71709

## South Down Choral Society *45/1960*

**Contact:** Mrs Kathleen Chiswell
Cedar Wood
52, Ashgrove Road
Newry
Co Down BT34 1QN
Northern Ireland
**Tel:** +44 1963 63426

**ADDITIONAL INFORMATION:**
Wide repertoire but is dedicated to singing mainly oratorio. Sample of works performed include the Fauré Requiem, Luther Requiem and Mozart Requiem.

## South Kerry Choir *24/88*

**Contact:** Mr Pat Wiltshire
Ashgrove, Kenmare
Co Kerry
**Tel/Fax:** +353 64 41358
**Email:** tanamara@iol.ie

**MUSICAL/ARTISTIC DIRECTOR:**
Frederiek Laumans.
**KEY IRISH PERFORMANCES** (since January 1994):
16/18.6.95 Holy Cross Kenmare/The Friary, Killarney, promoted by Maudeen Seghers appearing with Kerry Chamber Choir and Kerry Orchestra.
26/27.4.96 Holy Cross, Kenmare/St John's Tralee, promoted by Maudeen Seghers appearing with Kerry Chamber Choir and Kerry Orchestra.
27.4.97 St Patrick's, Kenmare, promoted by Pat Wiltshire appearing with the Goethe Institute Choir and Limerick Choral Union.
**AVAILABILITY:**
General.
**ADDITIONAL INFORMATION:**
Community based choir formed by Hans Rosen in 1988, with members drawn from Kenmare to Waterville. Seven different nationalities are represented in the choir. Rehearse every Tuesday evening in Sneem from September to June.

## Sperrin Choir *45/1974*

**Contact:** George Johnston
50, Glenburn Park
Magherafelt BT45 5BJ
Northern Ireland
**Tel:** +44 1648 32854

**MUSICAL/ARTISTIC DIRECTOR:**
G.E. Johnston.
**GROUP MEMBERS:**
18 sopranos, 11 altos, 10 tenors, 11 basses.
**KEY IRISH PERFORMANCES** (since January 1994):
5.94 Antrim and Magherfelt promoted by the choir committee appearing with the Antrim Choral Society.
12.96 Antrim and Magherfelt promoted by the choir committee appearing with ACS.
**AVAILABILITY:**
General.

## The Belfast Phoenix Choir *50/1987*

**Contact:** Mrs Doreen Robinson
650, Antrim Road
Newtownabbey
Co Antrim BT36 4RG
Northern Ireland
**Tel:** +44 1232 832129

**KEY PERFORMANCES OUTSIDE IRELAND** (since January 1994):
1994 Ayr, Scotland, promoted by the Presbyterian Church in Ayr.
**AVAILABILITY:**
Weekends, evenings.

# The Lassus Scholars *20/1996*

**Contact:** Ms Ite O'Donovan
67, Rialto Cottages
Dublin 8
**Tel/Fax:** +353 1 4539663

*"In the closing Christmas carols, the technical polish of all the singing surpassed all that had gone on before"* 16.12.96 Irish Times.

**MUSICAL/ARTISTIC DIRECTOR:**
Ite O'Donovan.
**KEY IRISH PERFORMANCES** (since January 1994):
14.12.96 National Concert Hall, Dublin promoted by the Dublin Choral Foundation, appearing with the DIT Conservatory of Music and Drama Symphony Orchestra.
17.2.97 Royal Dublin Society, Dublin, promoted by the RDS Irish Artists Forum, accompanied by Celine Kelly (piano).
30.5.97 NCH, Dublin promoted by Absolute Music, appearing with Paul McKeever (organ).
30.3.97 Church of Adam and Eve, Dublin promoted by Dublin Choral Foundation and the Director of Music at the Church of Adam and Eve appearing with the Orlando Chamber Orchestra.
**KEY PERFORMANCES OUTSIDE IRELAND** (since January 1994):
23.3.97 Alvito Cathedral, Italy promoted by Eduardo Zapata, accompanied by the then Dublin String Ensemble (now called the Orlando Chamber Orchestra).
24.3.97 Sora Cathedral, Italy promoted by Eduardo Zapata, accompanied by the Orlando Chamber Orchestra.
**SELECTED BROADCASTS AND/OR RECORDED WORK:**
1.12.96 Cursaí Ealaine for RTÉ.
1.1.97 'Riverdance'/combined Irish music recording for Key Note Classics Ltd, England.
**SELECTED REVIEWS** (since January 1994):
3.6.97 Irish Times.
**AVAILABILITY:**
General.
**ADDITIONAL INFORMATION:**
Have become established as a versatile chamber choir since inaugural concert in the National Concert Hall 12.96. Though specialising in the 16th Century compositions of Lassus and his contemporaries, is equally at home in all musical styles.

# The Nás na Rí Singers *60*

**Contact:** Mr John Francis Murphy
17, Ailesbury Park
Newbridge
Co Kildare
**Tel:** +353 45 433727

**MUSICAL/ARTISTIC DIRECTOR:**
John Francis Murphy.
**AVAILABILITY:**
General.
**ADDITIONAL INFORMATION:**
Mixed voice choir and have been in existence over 25 years. Have performed and competed successfully both at home and abroad. Perform at least two major concerts annually with repertoire ranging from full choral works to part songs in many styles.

# The Park Singers *90/1970*

**Contact:** Mr Sean Creamer
34, Abbey View
Monkstown
Co Dublin
**Tel:** +353 1 2802064

**MUSICAL/ARTISTIC DIRECTOR:**
Sean Creamer.
**KEY PERFORMANCES OUTSIDE IRELAND** (since January 1994):
1-5.4.97 Oporto and Lisbon, Portugal promoted by the Festival di Gara.
**AVAILABILITY:**
General.

# Ulysses Choir *40/1993*

**Contact:** Fergus O'Carroll
362, South Circular Road
Dublin 8
**Tel:** +353 1 4544122

# University of Limerick Choral Society *60/1992*

**Contact:** Dr Gareth Cox
Music Department
Mary Immaculate College
South Circular Road
Limerick
**Tel/Fax:** +353 61 314588 / +353 61 313632

**MUSICAL/ARTISTIC DIRECTOR:**
Gareth Cox.
**KEY IRISH PERFOMANCES** (since January 1994):
St Michael's Church, Limerick appearing with Limerick Baroque Players. University Concert Hall, Limerick appearing with the University of Limerick Orchestra. Waterford Institute of Technology, appearing with Limerick Baroque Players and Waterford IT Choir.
**AVAILABILITY:**
General.

# Virginia Singers *25/1984*

**Contact:** Ms Mary Whelan
Kells Road
Virginia
Co Cavan
**Tel/Fax:** +353 49 47103

**MUSICAL/ARTISTIC DIRECTOR:**
Mary Whelan.
**ADDITIONAL INFORMATION:**
An amateur choral group. Hold annual concerts locally and in neighbouring towns. Have taken part in the "Voices of the World" Choral Festival.

# Wesley Choir *56/1988*

**Contact:** Mrs Ada Pauley
30, Brook Meadow
Doagh
Ballyclare BT39 OQF
Northern Ireland
**Tel:** +44 19603 22580

**MUSICAL/ARTISTIC DIRECTOR:**
William I. Thompson.
**AVAILABILITY:**
General.

# West Clare Singers *15/1990*

**Contact:** Peggy Lillis
Railway House
Kilkee
Co. Clare
**Tel:** +353 65 56045

# Section seven

## Conductors

# CHORAL CONDUCTORS

## Timothy Allen *Choral Conductor*

**Contact:** 2, St Columb's Court
Londonderry, BT48 6PT
Northern Ireland
**Tel/Fax:** +44 1504 262412

**TRAINING AND/OR QUALIFICATIONS:**
From 1981 to 1984, MA Degree, Cambridge University.
1991 FRCO From the Royal College of Organists.
**REGULARLY CONDUCTS WITH:**
St Columb's Cathedral Choir, Two Cathedral Festival Chorus.

## Colin Block *Choral Conductor*

**Contact:** Mr Colin Block
**Tel/Fax:** +353 1 2987794
**Email:** cblock@indigo.ie

*"A performance as wonderful as any I remember, even including Barbirolli's last in the Stadium"*

**KEY IRISH PERFORMANCES** (since January 1994):
Annually in December, a performance of Handel's 'Messiah' in St Patrick's Cathedral, Dublin with Culwick Choral Society and Orchestra of St Cecilia.
Annually in December, a performance of Vaughan William's 'Sea Symphony' appearing with Dublin County Choir and Orchestra of St Cecilia at the National Concert Hall, Dublin.
22.2.97 National Concert Hall, Dublin, in a performance of 'Haydn's Creation' appearing with Culwick Choral Society and Orchestra of St Cecilia.
30.6.96 St Anne's Church, Dawson Street, Dublin, appearing with Orchestra of St Cecilia.
**SELECTED BROADCASTS AND/OR RECORDED WORK:**
8.96 'Let the Bells Ring (Christmas CD)', for Ambush Records.
1.2.95 Bartok & Hindemith (Birth centenary recordings), for RTÉ.
'Jupiter Ensemble', with RTÉCO, Serenata, for RTÉ.
**SELECTED REVIEWS** (since January 1994):
28.10.95 Irish Times.
**TRAINING AND/OR QUALIFICATIONS:**
From 1961 to 1964, Royal Academy of Music, London, taught by Maurice Miles, Alan Bush and James Brown.
**REGULARLY CONDUCTS WITH:**
Dublin County Choir, Culwick Choral Society.
**REGULARLY GUESTS WITH:**
RTÉ Concert Orchestra, Orchestra of St Cecilia, Steadfast Band.
**ADDITIONAL INFORMATION:**
Conductor of both professional and amateur ensembles, with concert platform and recording studio experience in many areas of music, ie. musical comedy, light music, symphonic, opera, chamber ensemble, and choral. Has technical expertise with computers and keyboards. Arranger and composer.

## David Byers *Choral Conductor*

**Contact:** Mr David Byers
425, Beersbridge Road
Bloomfield, Belfast BT5 5DU
Northern Ireland
**Tel/Fax:** +44 1232 659706
**Email:** davidbyers@btinternet.com

*"Vast amount of choralism had been prepared by [David Byers] very thoroughly to provide a great impact in music like the exhilarating Hosanna for double choir"* 1.4.96 Belfast Telegraph

**KEY IRISH PERFORMANCES** (since January 1994):
4.94/97 St Anne's Cathedral, Belfast, conducting St George's Singers and Orchestra, performing Bach's 'St Matthew Passion'.
4.96 Whitla Hall, Queen's University, Belfast, conducting St George's Singers and Orchestra, performing Bach's 'B Minor Mass'.
4.95 Whitla Hall, Queen's University, Belfast, conducting St George's Singers and Orchestra, performing Handel's 'Judas Maccabaeus'.
10.95 St George's Church, Belfast, conducting St George's Singers, performing Rossini's 'Petite Messe Solennelle'.
**SELECTED BROADCASTS AND/OR RECORDED WORK:**
Editions of 'Songs of Praise', for BBC television.
**PRIZES/AWARDS/APPOINTMENTS:**
From 1968 to 1972, Manson Scholar at Royal Academy of Music, London.
1972 Belgian Government Scholarship.
1972 Macauley Fellowship.
1984 ARAM.
From 1971 to 1981, Conductor of New Belmont Consort.
From 1988 to 1993, Conductor for 'Songs of Praise', for the BBC.
At present conductor of St George's Singers and Orchestra.
**TRAINING AND/OR QUALIFICATIONS:**
From 1969 to 1972, Conductor of Belmont Consort for ILEA at Marylebone Institute.
Training as composer and organist at Royal Academy of Music, London, obtaining GRSM, LRAM, ARCO.
Professional Cert in Composition, from Royal Academy of Music, London.
**AVAILABILITY:**
General.
*See also page 180.*

## Fergal Carroll *Choral Conductor*

**Contact:** Mr Fergal Carroll
5 Silversprings
Clonmel, Co Tipperary
**Tel:** +353 52 22858

*"... An unquestionable triumph for the musical director and conductor, [Fergal Carroll]"*
5.96 The Nationalist, Clonmel

**KEY IRISH PERFORMANCES** (since January 1994):
5.96 White Memorial Theatre, Clonmel, in a production of 'The Gypsy Baron' appearing with St Mary's Choral Society.
12.96 Waterford Institute of Technology appearing with WIT Symphony Orchestra.
3.97 University Concert Hall, Limerick, promoted by Limerick. International Band Competition, appearing with Banna Chluain Meala.
4.97 White Memorial Theatre, Clonmel 'The King and I' appearing with St Mary's Choral Society.
**SELECTED BROADCASTS AND/OR RECORDED WORK:**
8.95 'Theatre Nights' for RTÉ.
2.96 'Live at 3' for RTÉ.
**SELECTED REVIEWS** (since January 1994):
5.97 The Nationalist (Clonmel).
5.96 South Tipp Today.
**TRAINING AND/OR QUALIFICATIONS:**
From 1993 to 1997, BA Music from Waterford Institute of Technology.
From 2.96 to 11.96, Masterclass with Robert Houlihan.
**AVAILABILITY:**
General.

**ADDITIONAL INFORMATION:**
Works extensively at musical arranging and orchestration. A number of these arrangements have been used by the 'The Late Late Show' and 'Theatre Nights' for RTÉ.

## Séan Creamer *Choral Conductor*

**Contact:** Mr Séan Creamer
34, Abbey View
Monkstown
Co Dublin
**Tel:** +353 1 2802064

**KEY IRISH PERFORMANCES** (since January 1994):
12.96 Amharchlann Naithí, conducted the Park Singers.
1.97 National Concert Hall, Dublin appearing with the Dublin Secondary Schoolgirl's Choir.
6.97 NCH appearing with the National Children's Choir.
**KEY PERFORMANCES OUTSIDE IRELAND** (since January 1994):
1/5.4.97 Oporto and Lisbon, Portugal promoted by the Festival di Gara, appearing with the Park Singers.
**TRAINING AND/OR QUALIFICATIONS:**
1954, B Mus from University College, Dublin.
**REGULARLY CONDUCTS WITH:**
Dublin Secondary Schoolgirls Choir, The National Children's Choir, The Park Singers.
**AVAILABILITY:**
General.

## Mark Duley *Choral Conductor*

**Contact:** Mark Duley
22, St. Alban's Road
Dublin 8
**Tel/Fax:** +353 1 4538696 / +353 1 6798991
**Email:** cccdub@indigo.ie

**ADDITIONAL INFORMATION:**
Organist and Director of Music at Christchurch Cathedral, Dublin.

## Lorena Gillard *Choral Conductor*

**Contact:** Ms Lorena Gillard
32, Brookedale
Broomfield, Mill Road
Midleton, Co Cork
**Mobile:** +353 87 448419

**KEY IRISH PERFORMANCES** (since January 1994):
12.12.96 Airport Church, Cork, appearing with the Blackpool Church Choir.
15.12.96 Cork promoted by the Mayfield Church Choirs, appearing with the Blackpool Church Choir.
**TRAINING AND/OR QUALIFICATIONS:**
From 1990 to 1994, B Religious Studies (Music) Mater Dei Institute of Education.
1995 Certificate received from the International Summer School of Institute Kodaly.
1996 Certificate received from the Cork Summer School for Conductors, Cork School of Music.
**REGULARLY CONDUCTS WITH:**
Blackpool Church Choir (principal conductor), St Aloysius' College School Choir (principal conductor).
**REGULARLY GUESTS WITH:**
Carrigtwohill Folk Group.
**AVAILABILITY:**
Weekends, evenings and throughout the holiday seasons.

## Edward Holly *Choral Conductor*

**Contact:** Mr Edward Holly
40, Glenmore Drive
Drogheda, Co Louth
**Tel:** +353 41 38000
*See piano page 39.*

## Séamas Ludden Choral Conductor

**Contact:** Mr Séamas Ludden
96, Millview Lawns
Malahide, Co Dublin
**Tel:** +353 1 8452182 / +353 1 8450107
*See Baritone page 114.*

## Aidan Lynch *Choral Conductor*

**Contact:** Mr Aidan Lynch
15, Hawthorn Avenue
Ballycasheen
Killarney, Co Kerry
**Tel/Fax:** +353 64 33749
**Instruments:** Trumpet, piano, keyboard, tenor horn, euphonium, tuba.

**KEY IRISH PERFORMANCES** (since January 1994):
95/96 Tralee, Holy Cross Church, appearing with Kerry Choral Union and Killarney Concert Band.
**KEY PERFORMANCES OUTSIDE IRELAND** (since January 1994):
1995 St Patrick's Cathedral, New York, appearing with Kerry Choral Union.
**SELECTED BROADCASTS AND/OR RECORDED WORK:**
12.95 'Sounds of the season 1995' for Kerry TV and Radio Kerry.
**PRIZES/AWARDS/APPOINTMENTS:**
1987 Fleischmann Prize, awarded by University College Cork.
1988 Certificate of merit, awarded by Kilkenny UDC.
**TRAINING AND/OR QUALIFICATIONS:**
From 1977 to 1980, B Mus from University College, Cork.
From 1982 to 1983, H Dip from UCC.
**REGULARLY PERFORMS WITH:**
Brass-O!, Opus '96, Killarney Concert Band.
**REGULARLY CONDUCTS WITH:**
Kerry Choral Union, Killarney Concert Band.
**REGULARLY GUESTS WITH:**
Glen Eagle Concert Band, Opus 96.
**AVAILABILITY:**
General.
**ADDITIONAL INFORMATION:**
Actively involved in promoting music in the Kerry area and holds small concerts in his studio in Killarney. Helps to promote other events in the town.
*See trumpet page 54.*

## Michael McGlynn *Choral Conductor*

**Contact:** Mr Michael McGlynn
PO Box 4468
Churchtown
Dublin 14
**Tel/Fax:** +353 1 2835533
**Email:** info@anuna.ie
**WWW:** http://www.anuna.ie

**REGULARLY CONDUCTS WITH:**
Anúna.

## Colin Mawby *Choral Conductor*

**Contact:** Mr Colin Mawby
Gerrardstown
Garlow Cross
Navan, Co Meath
**Tel/Fax:** +353 46 29394

**AVAILABILITY:**
Subject to negotiation.
**REGULARLY CONDUCTS WITH:**
National Chamber Choir.

## Blánaid Murphy *Choral Conductor*

**Contact:** Blánaid Murphy
16, Westgate
St Augustine Street
Dublin 8
**Tel/Fax:** +353 1 6773712

**REGULARLY CONDUCTS WITH:**
Cantique, Cor na n-Óg, Polyphonia, Irish Philharmonic Chorus, Canzona.

## Mary Nugent *Choral Conductor*

**Contact:** Ms Mary Nugent
9, Gledswood Park
Clonskeagh
Dublin 14
**Tel:** +353 1 2693956

**ADDITIONAL INFORMATION:**
Conducting experience includes: 'Ceiliúradh' (with Luke Tobin and Aedín Halpin) in St Mary's Church, Dublin, 'An Evening of Early and Baroque Music', 'A Spring Sequence, with the Queen's Consort and Friends all in the Harty Room, Belfast. Has a special interest in children's performance, and has conducted a number of children's choirs, string orchestras and has co-ordinated traditional groups in Dublin and Belfast.
*See traditional flute page 218.*

## Kevin O'Carroll *Choral Conductor*

**Contact:** Mr Kevin O'Carroll
Woodlands
Halfway House
Co Waterford
**Tel:** +353 51 876260

**KEY IRISH PERFORMANCES** (since January 1994):
12.96 Trinity Cathedral, Waterford and St Mary's, Dungarvan, promoted by the Lions Club, appearing with Cathedral Choir, Madrigallery and orchestra.
5.97 Waterford City Hall, promoted by Madrigallery, appearing with Madrigallery and ensemble.
**SELECTED BROADCASTS AND/OR RECORDED WORK:**
5.97 Concert recording for SLR FM, Waterford.
**TRAINING AND/OR QUALIFICATIONS:**
From 1972 to 1979, Schola Cantorum, Mullingar. From 1979 to 1981, University College, Dublin.
**REGULARLY CONDUCTS WITH:**
Madrigallery.
**REGULARLY GUESTS WITH:**
Waterford Cathedral Choir, Edmund Rice Choral and Musical Society, De la Salle Musical Society.
**AVAILABILITY:**
Evenings.
**ADDITIONAL INFORMATION:**
Specialises in three areas, madrigals, church music and musical theatre (light opera and musicals).

## Ite O'Donovan *Choral Conductor*

**Contact:** Ms Ite O'Donovan
67, Rialto Cottage
Dublin 8
**Tel/Fax:** +353 1 453 9663

*"There was a palpable sense of joy [throughout the cathedral] at an artistically stunning and spiritually moving occasion."* 8.4.94 Irish Times
(Palestrina Choir and Chamber Orchestra)

**KEY IRISH PERFORMANCES** (since January 1994):
9.12.95 National Concert Hall, Dublin, appearing with the Palestrina Choir and DIT Conservatory of Music and Drama Symphony Orchestra.
24.4.96 and 15.4.97 Irish Museum of Modern Art, Dublin, appearing with DIT CMDSO.
14.12.96 NCH, promoted by the Dublin Choral Foundation, appearing with the Lassus Scholars and DIT CMDSO.
**KEY PERFORMANCES OUTSIDE IRELAND** (since January 1994):
5.7.95 St Patrick's Cathedral, New York, promoted by the Palestrina Choir/St Patrick's Cathedral, appearing with the Palestrina Choir.
8.96 Zlin, Czech Republic, promoted by Symphonic Workshops, appearing with Bohuslav Martinu Philharmonic.
23.3.97 Alvito Cathedral, Italy, promoted by Eduardo Zapata, appearing with the Lassus Scholars and the Dublin String Ensemble (now the Orlando Chamber Orchestra).
24.3.97 Sora Cathedral, promoted by Eduardo Zapata, appearing with the Lassus Scholars and the OCO.
**SELECTED BROADCASTS AND/OR RECORDED WORK:**
11.95 National Chamber Choir, for RTÉ.
12.95 'Crosscurrents' (documentary) for RTÉ.
1.97 'Irish Selection' for Keynote Classics Limited, England.
**SELECTED REVIEWS** (since January 1994):
19.10.95 Irish Times.
15.12.95 Evening Herald.
**PRIZES/AWARDS/APPOINTMENTS:**
From 1982 to 1995, Director of the Palestrina Choir, Pro-Cathedral, Dublin.
1986 National President of the International Federation of Pueri Cantores, Irish Episcopal Conference.
**TRAINING AND/OR QUALIFICATIONS:**
From 9.90 to 5.91, Studied with James Cavanagh at the Royal Irish Academy of Music.
From 7.96 to 8.96, Symphonic workshops with Victor Feldbrill.
**REGULARLY CONDUCTS WITH:**
DIT Conservatory of Music and Drama Symphony Orchestra, Lassus Scholars (and Piccolo Lasso junior choir), The Orlando Chamber Orchestra.
**REGULARLY GUESTS WITH:**
Cantichorus - 6 European Choirs, Antwerp (1993), National Chamber Choir (1995), 1995, 1996, 1997, Young Dublin Sinfonia Youth Orchestra
**AVAILABILITY:**
General but subject to teaching schedule during the academic year.
**ADDITIONAL INFORMATION:**
Established in Ireland for many years as a choral conductor. Has also developed skills as an orchestral conductor having received tuition from two American conductors (Tsung Yeh and Kirk Trevor) at the International Symphonic Workshops in the Czech Republic. Has conducted ensembles ranging from string and chamber orchestras to symphony and philharmonic orchestras. Wide repertoire from Bach to Britten.

# John O'Flynn *Choral Conductor*

**Contact:** Mr John O'Flynn
91, Connaught Street
Dublin 7
**Tel:** +353 1 8388744

**KEY IRISH PERFORMANCES** (since January 1994):
31.10.96 Castlebar Church, Co Mayo, promoted by the Arts Festival, Castlebar, appearing with the Italian Institute Choir and Doreen Curran.
10.4.97 Alliance Francaise, appearing with Eblana.
21.4.97 Stann's Dawson Street, promoted by the Italian Cultural Institute, appearing with the Italian Choir, soloists and strings.
15.6.97 St Mary's Church, Dublin 4, appearing with Ceiliuradh.
**TRAINING AND/OR QUALIFICATIONS:**
From 1983 to 1985, Advanced Diploma from the Kodaly Institute, Hungary (teachers Ildikó Herbóly-Koscar and Peter Erdei).
**REGULARLY CONDUCTS WITH:**
Eblana, Italian Cultural Institute Choir, Ceiliuradh.
**REGULARLY GUESTS WITH:**
Cantique.
**AVAILABILITY:**
General.
**ADDITIONAL INFORMATION:**
Has worked as a conductor of adult groups since 1995. Is involved with a number of Dublin-based choirs. These range in size and style from Eblana, an a capella chamber group specializing in 16th and 20th Century music, to the chorus of the Italian Cultural Institute whose repertoire mostly consists of 18th and 19th Century operatic and sacred music. Also has considerable experience with children's choirs.

# Niamh O'Kelly *Choral Conductor*

**Contact:** Ms Niamh O'Kelly
The Old School House
Rossduane
Kilmeena
Westport
Co Mayo
**Tel/Fax:** +353 98 41030

**KEY IRISH PERFORMANCES** (since January 1994):
6.96 The Joe Mooney Summer School, Drumshanbo, Co Leitrim, appearing with the Bells of Mayo.
8.96 Athenry Festival, Co Galway appearing with the Bells of Mayo.
7.6.97 Taibhearc Theatre, Galway appearing with the Bells of Mayo and Mayo County Choir.
9.2.97 Findlaters Church, Dublin, appearing with the Bells of Mayo and Mayo County Choir.
**SELECTED BROADCASTS AND/OR RECORDED WORK:**
9.6.96 'Nationwide' for RTÉ.
11.6.96 Performance on Raidió na Gaeltachta.
20.12.96 'Nationwide' for RTÉ.
**PRIZES/AWARDS/APPOINTMENTS:**
1979 Golden Voice of Ireland. Arts Council Scholarship.
From 1981 to 1994, Appointed Principal Conductor with the US Army Choirs in Augsburg, Germany.
**TRAINING AND/OR QUALIFICATIONS:**
From 1971 to 1974, ALCM from the DIT Conservatory of Music and Drama, Dublin.
From 1974 to 1975, Postgraduate course from the Royal College of Music, London.
From 1979 to 1982, Studies undertaken at the Leopold Mozart Conservatorium, Augsburg, Germany.
**REGULARLY CONDUCTS WITH:**
The Bells of Mayo, Mayo County Choir and Cantoraí Umhaill (principal conductor). Erris Male Voice Choir, Cois Cladaigh Chamber Choir, Galway and the Moy Singers, Ballina, Co Mayo.
**AVAILABILITY:**
General.
**ADDITIONAL INFORMATION:**
Own choral music is published by GIA Incorporated in the USA. Has experience as a choral and vocal adjucator and as an arranger. Available for choral and bell workshops.

# Andrew Purcell *Choral Conductor*

**Contact:** Mr Andrew Purcell
The King's Hospital
Palmerstown
Dublin 20
**Mobile:** +353 87 2322400

**KEY IRISH PERFORMANCES** (since January 1994):
4.95/96 VEC Hall, Inchicore, Dublin, appearing with St Michael's Musical Society.
**KEY PERFORMANCES OUTSIDE IRELAND** (since January 1994):
2.97 Zaccaria Church, Venice, Italy, promoted by Club Europe Concert Tours, appearing with The King's Hospital Senior Choir.
2.97 Bad Deutsch, Altanberg, Vienna, Austria, promoted by Club Europe Concert Tours, appearing with The King's Hospital Senior Choir.
**SELECTED BROADCASTS AND/OR RECORDED WORK:**
12.94 Christmas Day Morning Service for RTÉ.
3.97 Morning Service for RTÉ.
**SELECTED REVIEWS** (since January 1994):
4.96 Association of Irish Musical Societies review of 'Anything Goes'.
**PRIZES/AWARDS/APPOINTMENTS:**
6.91 BA Music (Hons) from National Council for Educational Awards/ Waterford Institute of Technology.
7.93 Appointed Choirmaster of chapel choir by The King's Hospital Church of Ireland School, Dublin 20.
**TRAINING AND/OR QUALIFICATIONS:**
From 1988 to 1991, BA Music (2.1 Hons) from NCEA/Waterford Institute of Technology.
From 1991 to 1992, Higher Diploma in Education from Trinity College Dublin.
From 1993 to 1994, RIAM conducting course.
7.94 Choral conducting course, with Cork School of Music.
**REGULARLY CONDUCTS WITH:**
The King's Hospital Chapel Choir, The King's Hospital Chamber Choir.
**REGULARLY GUESTS WITH:**
The King's Hospital Musical Society, COTA Singers, Ballybrack, Co Dublin.
St Michael's Musical Society, Inchicore.
**AVAILABILITY:**
Weekends, evenings, June to the end of August.

# Doreen Robinson *Choral Conductor*

**Contact:** Ms Doreen Robinson
650, Antrim Road
Newtownabbey
Co Antrim BT36 4RG
Northern Ireland
**Tel:** +353 1232 832129

**PRIZES/AWARDS/APPOINTMENTS:**
1975 BBC runner up in the international choral competition 'Let the People Sing' (large choirs section), representing the United Kingdom.
**TRAINING AND/OR QUALIFICATIONS:**
LRSM from the Associated Board of the Royal School of Music.
FLCM from the London College of Music.
FTCL from Trinity College of Music, London.
BA (Hons) Music from the Open University.
**REGULARLY CONDUCTS WITH:**
The Belfast Phoenix Choir.
**REGULARLY GUESTS WITH:**
Various church choirs in Holywood, Co Down.
**AVAILABILITY:**
General.

## Bernie Sherlock *Choral Conductor*

**Contact:** Ms Bernie Sherlock
41, Cliftonville Road
Glasnevin
Dublin 9
**Tel/Fax:** +353 1 8305944
**Email:** mdandbs@iol.ie

*"Clean tone and accurate pitching were well sustained throughout the concert"*

19.12.97 Irish Times (ref: DIT Choral Society performance).

**KEY IRISH PERFORMANCES** (since January 1994):
1.5.96 Christchurch Cathedral, Dublin, promoted by College of Music, conducting College of Music Choral Society.
18.12.96 Christchurch Cathedral, Dublin, promoted by Sally-Anne Fisher, conducting Dublin Institute of Technology Choral Society.
28.4.97 Adam and Eve Church, Dublin, promoted by DIT, conducting DIT Choral Society.
6.5.97 Bank of Ireland Arts Centre, Dublin, promoted by Ellen Lynch, conducting DIT Chamber Choir.
**TRAINING AND/OR QUALIFICATIONS:**
From 1980 to 1985, BA Mod (Hons) and H Dip Ed (Hons), from Trinity College Dublin.
1983 ARIAM, from Royal Irish Academy of Music, Dublin.
1986 LTCL, from Trinity College London.
From 1986 to 1988 Advanced Diploma and Advanced Post Diploma Certificate, from Kódaly Institute, Hungary.
**SELECTED BROADCASTS AND/OR RECORDED WORK:**
5.10.97 Sunday Tribune.
**PRINCIPAL CONDUCTOR WITH:**
DIT Choral Society, DIT Chamber Choir and DIT Youth Choirs.
**GROUPS GUESTED WITH** (since January 1994):
Portmarnock Singers and Dublin County Choir.
**AVAILABILITY:**
General.
**ADDITIONAL INFORMATION:**
Director of choirs in Dublin Institute of Technology of Music and Drama. Choirs have won many prizes in national competitions including Arklow, New Ross, Navan, Dundalk, Kilcoole, Feis Ceoil, Carrickmacross. Have also received second and third prizes in the North Wales Choral Festival.

## William I. Thompson *Choral Conductor*

**Contact:** Mr William Thompson
17, Irwin Drive
Belfast BT4 3AR
Northern Ireland
**Tel:** +44 1232 651611

**REGULARLY CONDUCTS WITH:**
Ballyclare Male Choir.
Downshire Ladies Choir.

## Declan Townsend *Choral Conductor*

**Contact:** Dr Declan Townsend
Na Feidleachain
Ballynalouhy
Ballinhassig
Co Cork
**Tel:** +353 21 771660

**AVAILABILITY:**
General.
**ADDITIONAL INFORMATION:**
Has conducted light opera in Cork, Clonmel and Limerick. Conducts variety of choral groups from two-part children's choirs to oratorio and from percussion, string, youth, chamber orchestra to symphony orchestras. Has also arranged pieces for ensembles and composed music for solo voice, voice and piano, voice and strings, choirs, chamber groups, orchestral music and wind orchestra. Has been an adjudicator at Feiseanna, and has worked as an examiner for various bodies. Music reviewer for The Examiner publication, Cork.

## Keith Young *Choral Conductor*

**Contact:** Mr Keith Young
6, Gortnamona Drive
Foxrock
Dublin 18
**Tel:** +353 1 2894482
**Email:** kyoung@indigo.ie

**REGULARLY CONDUCTS WITH:**
Dublin Welsh Male Voice Choir.
**REGULARLY GUESTS WITH:**
Treharris Male Voice Choir, Castlecomer Male Voice Choir, Moy Singers.
**AVAILABILITY:**
General.

# ORCHESTRAL CONDUCTORS

## Mark Armstrong *Orchestral Conductor*

**Contact:** Mr Mark Armstrong
35, Scholarstown Park
Rathfarnham
Dublin 16
**Mobile/Fax:** +353 87 635260 / +353 1 4938786

*"... Conducted with skill and sympathy ..."*

24.11.92 Belfast Telegraph.

**KEY IRISH PERFORMANCES** (since January 1994):
9.4.94 National Concert Hall, Dublin, promoted by Dún Laoghaire Choral Society, appearing with Dún Laoghaire Choral Society and the Irish Chamber Orchestra.
4.8.95 NCH, Dublin appearing with the RTÉ Concert Orchestra/Culwick Choral Society.
5.4.96 St Patrick's Cathedral, Dublin, appearing with the Goethe Institute Choir and the Hibernian Chamber Orchestra.
28.7.97 NCH appearing with the Irish Youth Wind Ensemble.
**KEY PERFORMANCES OUTSIDE IRELAND** (since January 1994):
1994 Palace Theatre, London appearing with Opera Theatre Company Orchestra and soloists.
1997 Solihull, England, appearing with Solihull Chandos Choir.
1997 Aberdeen, Scotland, appearing with the Irish Youth Wind Ensemble.
**SELECTED BROADCASTS AND/OR RECORDED WORK:**
1993 'O Holy Night' with RTÉ Concert Orchestra and Cor Na nÓg, for RTÉ/Lunar Records.
1994 'A Fairer Paradise' with Niamh Murray and the Irish Chamber Orchestra for Sony.
1995' Riverdance the album' (Seolta) for Celtic Heartbeat.
**SELECTED REVIEWS** (since January 1994):
9.4.96 Irish Times.
28.1.97 Irish Times.

**TRAINING AND/OR QUALIFICATIONS:**
From 1985 to 1988, BA (Hons) Music from Trinity College, Dublin.
**REGULARLY CONDUCTS WITH:**
Band of the Curragh Command, Dún Laoghaire Choral Society, Seolta.
**REGULARLY GUESTS WITH:**
RTÉ Concert Orchestra, Irish Chamber Orchestra, National Chamber Choir, RTÉ Cor na nÓg, Hibernian Chamber Orchestra, Irish Youth Wind Ensemble.
**ADDITIONAL INFORMATION:**
Combines a career as an army band conductor with a range of other musical activities i.e. (keyboard player, arranger and adjudicator). Happy to perform a varied repertoire. Own choral group 'Seolta' have performed on 5 CD's to date.

## Iosef Calef *Orchestral Conductor*

**Contact:** Iosef Calef
c/o The Cork School of Music
Union Quay
Cork
**Tel/Fax:** +353 21 270076 / +353 21 276595

**REGULARLY CONDUCTS WITH:**
University of Limerick Chamber Orchestra.
*See cello page 68.*

## James Cavanagh *Orchestral Conductor*

**Contact:** Mr James Cavanagh
17, Mannix Road
Drumcondra
Dublin 9
**Tel:** +353 1 8372216

*"James Cavanagh is a superb orchestral trainer as the standard of playing demonstrated"*
18.8.95 Sunday Tribune.

**KEY IRISH PERFORMANCES** (since January 1994):
2.96 National Concert Hall, Dublin, promoted by RTÉ, appearing with the National Symphony Orchestra of Ireland.
8.96 NCH promoted by RTÉ, appearing with the RTÉ Concert Orchestra.
12.96 O'Reilly Hall, UCD, Dublin, promoted by RTÉ, appearing with the RTÉCO.
2.97 NCH, promoted by Royal Irish Academy of Music, appearing with the RIAM Orchestras.
**KEY PERFORMANCES OUTSIDE IRELAND** (since January 1994):
8.95 Aberdeen, promoted by Aberdeen Music Festival.
12.95 Tokyo, promoted by Inel Baskerville, appearing New Japanese Philharmonic.
4.97 St Laurenti Itzehoe, promoted Marie Schmid, appearing with RIAM Orchestra.
**SELECTED BROADCASTS AND/OR RECORDED WORK:**
9.92 'Messiah' recording.
12.95 'Messiah' recording.
1.96 Irish Youth Wind Ensemble recording for BBC.
**SELECTED REVIEWS** (since January 1994):
8.94 Evening Press.
**PRIZES/AWARDS/APPOINTMENTS:**
1985 Appointed director of the Irish Youth Wind Ensemble.
1988 Appointed conductor of RIAM Orchestras.
**TRAINING AND/OR QUALIFICATIONS:**
From 1985 to 1990, Studied with Janos Furst.
From 1988 to 1990, Studied with George Hurst.
**REGULARLY CONDUCTS WITH:**
RIAM Symphony Orchestra.
**REGULARLY GUESTS WITH:**
RTÉCO, NSOI, Orchestra of St Cecilia, New Japan Philharmonic.
**AVAILABILITY:**
Subject to schedule.
**ADDITIONAL INFORMATION:**
Known choral trainer (Tallaght Choral Society 1985-1995). Has directed orchestras, choirs and wind ensembles and is Musical Director of the Gay Byrne Radio Show for RTÉ. Also lectures in conducting at the Royal Irish Academy of Music.

## Ciaran Crilly *Orchestral Conductor*

**Contact:** Ciaran Crilly
5, Gransha Park
Belfast BT11 8AT
Northern Ireland
**Tel:** +44 1232 613937

*"Conducting of great vibrancy and technical assurance"* 6.93 London Student.

**KEY PERFORMANCES** (since January 1994):
4.6.95 Whitla Hall, Belfast, promoted by NB Productions, appearing with Dublin Screen Orchestra.
**KEY PERFORMANCES OUTSIDE IRELAND** (since January 1994):
12.7.95 Bartók Hall, Szombathely, Hungary, promoted by Bartók Festival, appearing with Savaria String Orchestra.
**PRIZES/AWARDS/APPOINTMENTS:**
From 1991 to 1993, Appointed Music Director of King's Players Theatre Company.
1994 Appointed Music Director, Tupenny Truth Productions.
1994 Appointed Artistic Director of Dublin Screen Orchestra.
**TRAINING AND/OR QUALIFICATIONS:**
From 10.89 to 6.93, B Mus, from King's College London.
Has also studied at the Guildhall School of Music and Drama, London.
Has attended masterclasses with Dominique Rouits at the Bartók Festival in Hungary.
**AVAILABILITY:**
General.
**ADDITIONAL INFORMATION:**
Particularly interested in 20th Century Music. Invitation to conduct the inaugural concert of the Sibin Chamger, Romania. Violinist with Pim String Quartet and Les Maubles jazz ensemble.
*See page 59.*

## John Finucane *Orchestral Conductor*

**Contact:** Mr John Finucane
23, Belgrave Square
Monkstown
Co Dublin
**Tel/Mobile:** +353 1 2809393 / +353 87 447203

**KEY IRISH PERFORMANCES** (since January 1994):
7.96 National Concert Hall, Dublin, conducted with National Symphony Orchestra of Ireland.
3.97 NCH, Dublin, conducted with NSOI.
19.8.97 NCH, Dublin, conducted with RTÉ Chamber Orchestra.
1995 Tour of Northern Ireland with Ulster Orchestra.
**REGULARLY CONDUCTS WITH:**
Dublin Youth Symphony Orchestra, Hibernian Chamber Orchestra.
**REGULARLY GUESTS WITH:**
Surrey Sinfoniella, Goethe Institute Choir.
**AVAILABILITY:**
Subject to schedule.
*See clarinet, page 3.*

# Liam Fitzgerald *Orchestral Conductor*

**Contact:** Mr Liam Fitzgerald
52, Highfield Road
Rathgar
Dublin 6
**Tel:** +353 1 4970350

**REGULARLY CONDUCTS WITH:**
Dublin Baroque Players.

# James Galway *Orchestral Conductor*

**Contact:** Mr James Galway
c/o Kathryn Enticott
IMG Artists
Media House
3, Burlington Lane
Chiswick
London W4 2TH
England
**Tel/Fax:** +44 181 2335800 / +44 181 2335801
*See flute page 14.*

# Eoin Gillen *Orchestral Conductor* 

**Contact:** Eoin Gillen
1, Southwood Park
Blackrock, Co Dublin
**Tel:** +353 1 2880880
**Email:** ggillen@homenet.ie

*"The excellent quality of the concert was not really any surprise"* Varsity, 22.11.96
*See French horn page 23.*

# Gareth Hudson *Orchestral Conductor*

**Contact:** Mr Gareth Hudson
50, Orpen Green
Blackrock
Co Dublin
**Tel/Fax:** +353 1 2082779 / +353 1 2082511

**KEY IRISH PERFORMANCES** (since January 1994):
From 1994 to 1997, National Concert Hall, Dublin, the RDS, Dublin, and on tour in Ireland (Galway, Cork, Limerick) promoted by RTÉ, appearing with the RTÉ Concert Orchestra.
**KEY PERFORMANCES OUTSIDE IRELAND** (since January 1994):
From 1994 to 1997, Tour of Scotland, appearing with BBC Scottish Symphony Orchestra.
**SELECTED BROADCASTS AND/OR RECORDED WORK:**
From 1994 to 1997, Various works for RTÉ.
From 1994 to 1997, Various works for BBC Radio 3 and Radio Scotland.
1996 'Phantom of the Opera' for Polydor.
**PRIZES/AWARDS/APPOINTMENTS:**
1987 Outstanding Contribution to Music in Ireland, awarded by Irish Life Building Society.
**TRAINING AND/OR QUALIFICATIONS:**
From 1972 to 1973, LRAM, LGSM Diplomas from City of Leeds, College of Music.
From 1973 to 1976, BA (Hons) Degree in music, ARCM diploma from University of Liverpool.
**REGULARLY CONDUCTS WITH:**
Musical Theatre, Basel, Switzerland.
**REGULARLY GUESTS WITH:**
RTÉCO, BBC Scottish Symphony Orchestra.
**AVAILABILITY:**
General.
**ADDITIONAL INFORMATION:**
Wide range of musical direction and conducting experience, chiefly in the field of music theatre, film music and broadcasting. International examiner for the Royal Schools of Music and also adjudicates festivals and competitions. Planning consultant for concerts and programmes.

# Noel Kelehan *Orchestral Conductor*

**Contact:** Mr Noel Kelehan
40, Anne Devlin Road
Dublin 14
**Tel/Fax:** +353 1 4945396 / +353 1 2082511

**REGULARLY CONDUCTS WITH:**
RTÉ performing groups.
**REGULARLY GUESTS WITH:**
Has worked with various orchestras throughout Europe over a 30 year period.
**AVAILABILITY:**
General.
*See jazz piano page 281.*

# Brian MacKay *Orchestral Conductor*

**Contact:** Mr Brian MacKay
Front Flat
8, Kenilworth Road
Dublin 6
**Tel/Fax:** +353 1 4974812 / +353 1 4902822

**KEY IRISH PERFORMANCES** (since January 1994):
3.97 National Concert Hall, Dublin, conducting The Cameron Singers.
**KEY PERFORMANCES OUTSIDE IRELAND** (since January 1994):
11.95 Nairobi, appearing with the Nairobi Symphony Orchestra.
11.96 Nairobi, appearing with the Nairobi SO and Chorus.
8.97 Hereford, UK appearing with the 'Philodi' Choir at the Three Choirs Festival.
**SELECTED BROADCASTS AND/OR RECORDED WORK:**
1987, With the Guildhall Chamber Orchestra for BBC Northern Ireland.
8.91 and 8.93, With the Essex Chamber Orchestra for BBC Radio Essex.
**TRAINING AND/OR QUALIFICATIONS:**
From 1980 to 1984, Studied at the Royal College of Music, London.
1985, Masterclasses with Janos Furst and the Irish Chamber Orchestra in Dublin.
From 1990 to 1992, Studied at the Kodály Institute.
**REGULARLY CONDUCTS WITH:**
BBC Club Choir, Essex Chamber Orchestra, Guildhall Chamber Orchestra.
**REGULARLY GUESTS WITH:**
The Nairobi Symphony Orchestra, Summer Music Orchestra and Choir, Essex Chamber Orchestra, The Cameron Singers (Dublin), Nairobi Music Society Chorus, 'Philodi' Summer School Choir.
**AVAILABILITY:**
General.
**ADDITIONAL INFORMATION:**
Has been working as a pianist, conductor, harpsichordist and vocal coach since moving to Dublin in 1993. Performs, conducts and teaches in England, Europe and Africa, which he has visited regularly with many Irish and British singers and instrumentalists.
*See piano page 43.*

# Hugh Maguire *Orchestral Conductor*

**Contact:** Dr Hugh Maguire
Manor Farm
Benhall Green
Suffolk IP17 IHN
England
**Tel/Fax:** +44 1728 603245

**AVAILABILITY:**
General.

# Julian G. Maunder
## *Orchestral Conductor*

**Contact:** Mr Julian G. Maunder
129, Belmont Road
Belfast BT4 2AD
Northern Ireland
**Tel:** +44 1232 673326

*"... I came away impressed ... a real sense of musical dialogue and genuine ensemble"*

17.11.96 Irish News

**KEY IRISH PERFORMANCES** (since January 1994):
5.94 St George's Church, Belfast, appearing with St George's Orchestra.
10.95 Elmwood Hall, Belfast, appearing with Belfast Studio Symphony Orchestra.
5.96 St Anne's Cathedral, promoted by Belfast Cathedral Summer Recital Series, appearing with City of Belfast Sinfonia.
11.96 Elmwood Hall, Belfast, promoted by Belfast Festival at Queen's, appearing with City of Belfast Sinfonia and George Zukerman.
**SELECTED BROADCASTS AND/OR RECORDED WORK:**
Spring 1993 Chamber Orchestra Recital, for ITACA Produciones, Sevilla, Spain/Canal sur SA.
5.96 Concert at Belfast Cathedral, own recording.
**SELECTED REVIEWS** (since January 1994):
17.5.96 Belfast Telegraph.
17.11.96 Irish Times.
**TRAINING AND/OR QUALIFICATIONS:**
From 1985 to 1988, BA (Hons) Music from CCAT Cambridge.
1987 Canford Summer School, studied with George Hurst and Adrian Leaper.
From 1988 to 1990, LRAM and Certificate of Advanced Studies, RAM from Royal Academy of Music, London.
8.96 SNK Utrecht, Holland, studied with Jaques Van Steen and Dane Wierdsma.
**REGULARLY CONDUCTS WITH:**
City of Belfast Sinfonia.
**REGULARLY GUESTS WITH:**
Belfast Studio Symphony Orchestra (Hon. Associate Conductor), St George's Orchestra, Belfast, Choir and Orchestra, of Queen's University Music Society.
**AVAILABILITY:**
General.
**ADDITIONAL INFORMATION:**
Although specific training is in conducting, has also experience as a professional orchestral player and chamber musician. Has sung in, and directed choirs, and also enjoys regular work with local youth orchestras.

# Colin Nicholls *Orchestral Conductor*

**Contact:** Mr Colin Nicholls
8, Dean Street
Cork
**Tel:** +353 21 963433

*"... [Colin Nicholls, East Cork Choral Society, etc] ... are to be congratulated on bringing us this musical and devotional gem"*

27.3.95 The Examiner (Tomás Ó Canáinn)

**KEY IRISH PERFORMANCES** (since January 1994):
3.95 City Hall, Cork, directing the East Cork Choral Society with the Cork Symphony Orchestra in a production of Elgar's 'Dream of Gerontius'.
12.95 St Fin Barr's Cathedral, Cork, directing the East Cork Choral Society in a production of the Messiah.
11.96 St Fin Barre's, Cork, directing the ECCS in Mozart's Requiem.
4.97 St Luke's, Cork and Kilkenny Cathedral, directing the ECCS with Saintwicks Choir performing works by Vivaldi, Bach and Schütz.
**KEY PERFORMANCES OUTSIDE IRELAND** (since January 1994):
9.95 Hereford Cathedral, directing St Fin Barr's Cathedral Choir.
**SELECTED BROADCASTS AND/OR RECORDED WORK:**
9.94 Broadcast from St Fin Barr's Cathedral, Cork, for RTÉ.
4.96 Good Friday and Easter Day Services, for RTÉ.
**PRIZES/AWARDS/APPOINTMENTS:**
4.84 Appointed conductor of East Cork Choral Society.
4.84 Appointed Musical Director of St Fin Barr's Cathedral.
**TRAINING AND/OR QUALIFICATIONS:**
From 1962 to 1965, GTCL and LTCL Mus Ed from Trinity College, London.
1969 LRAM (piano) from the Royal Academy of Music.
1978, FRCO from the Royal College of Organists, London.
1979 Choirmaster Diploma from the Royal College of Organists, London.
**REGULARLY CONDUCTS WITH:**
St Fin Barr's Cathedral Choir, East Cork Choral Society.
**REGULARLY GUESTS WITH:**
Cantairí Mhuscraí, Lismore Choir, Cork Symphony Orchestra.
**AVAILABILITY:**
General.
**ADDITIONAL INFORMATION:**
Organ tutor for the VEC Cork School of Music. Part-time lecturer in harmony, University College, Cork. Available as organist, accompanist on piano/organ.
*See organ page 29.*

# Proinnsías Ó Duinn
## *Orchestral Conductor*

**Contact:** Proinnsías Ó Duinn
c/o Morgan Enterprises Limited
28, Wilson Road
Mount Merrion, Co Dublin
**Tel/Fax:** +353 1 2836343 / +353 1 2836342

**REGULARLY CONDUCTS WITH:**
RTÉ performing groups, Our Lady's Choral Society, Orquesta Sinfonica Nacional Del Ecuador.
**REGULARLY GUESTS WITH:**
National Symphony Orchestra of Ireland, Irish Chamber Orchestra, National Sinfonia.
**PRIZES/AWARDS/APPOINTMENTS:**
Fellowship, awarded by the Arts Council.
Awarded the Jacob's Music Critic Award for work with RTÉ Singers.
**TRAINING AND/OR QUALIFICATIONS:**
From 1961 to 1962, Studied with Pierre Monteau.
From 1963 to 1965, Studied with Leopold Stodowski.

**SELECTED BROADCASTS AND/OR RECORDED WORK:**
'Maritana' (the complete opera), for Naxos Records.
'Mozart Horn Concertos', for EMI Records.
'Romantic Ireland', for Naxos Records.
**AVAILABILITY:**
Subject to RTÉCO schedule.
**ADDITIONAL INFORMATION:**
Principal Conductor with the RTÉ Concert Orchestra.

# David G. Openshaw

## *Orchestral Conductor*

**Contact:** Mr David G. Openshaw
183, Cavehill Road
Belfast BT15 5BP
Northern Ireland
**Tel:** +44 1232 771209

*"Again proved himself a totally reliable ... an unflappable conductor"* 3.3.97 Irish News

**KEY IRISH PERFORMANCES** (since January 1994):
5.96 Larne Auditorium, promoted by 'The Music Co' and Larne and District Arts, appearing with the Ulster Orchestra.
10.96 Members Rooms, Belfast, promoted by 'The Music Co', promoted by the Ulster Orchestra.
2.97 Dublin Airport (Festival), promoted by 'The Music Co', appearing with the Ulster Orchestra.
**TRAINING AND/OR QUALIFICATIONS:**
During 1980's, Studied with George Hurst (Canford Conductors Course).
**REGULARLY CONDUCTS WITH:**
Studio Symphony Orchestra.
**REGULARLY GUESTS WITH:**
Ulster Orchestra.
**AVAILABILITY:**
General.
**ADDITIONAL INFORMATION:**
Has had approx. 35 premieres in Northern Ireland with the Studio Symphony Orchestra including Saint-Saens Symphony No. 3, Prokofiev Piano Concerto No. 1, Ravel's 'Bolero', Vaughan Williams Symphonies No. 2 and 7 'Antarctica', Shostakovich Symphonies No. 6, and 12, R. Schumann 'Contzertstuck' for 4 horns, and other works by Beethoven.

# Mícheál Ó Súilleabháin

## *Orchestral Conductor*

**Contact:** Prof Mícheál Ó Súilleabháin
Irish World Music Centre
University of Limerick
Co Limerick
**Tel:** +353 61 202065
*See traditional piano page 222.*

# John Page *Orchestral Conductor*

**Contact:** Mr John Page
3, Mountvernon
Culmore
Derry
Northern Ireland
**Tel:** +44 1524 359712

**KEY IRISH PERFORMANCES** (since January 1994):
4.94 National Concert Hall, Dublin, appearing with Northern Ireland Symphony Orchestra.
4.95 Elmwood Hall, Belfast, appearing with Northern Ireland Symphony Orchestra.
7.94 St John's, Sligo, appearing with NISO.
7.94 Public Library, Dundalk, appearing with NISO.
**KEY PERFORMANCES OUTSIDE IRELAND** (since January 1994):
8.95 Kleinhans Hall, Buffalo, New York, appearing with Western New York Sinfonia.
**PRIZES/AWARDS/APPOINTMENTS:**
From 1990 to 1992, Musical Director of the Opera Society, Kings College, London.
From 1990 to 1993, Conductor of KCL/RAM symphony orchestra, Kings College, London.
From 1994 to 1995, Conductor of Northern Ireland Symphony.
**TRAINING AND/OR QUALIFICATIONS:**
From 1989 to 1993 B Mus (Hons), Kings College London/Royal Academy of Music.
From 1994 to 1995 MA, in Musicology, University College, Dublin.
**AVAILABILITY:**
General.
**ADDITIONAL INFORMATION:**
Also works as repetiteur for opera companies.

# Colman Pearce *Orchestral Conductor*

**Contact:** Mr Colman Pearce
c/o National Symphony Orchestra of Ireland
RTÉ, Dublin 4
**Tel/Fax:** +353 1 2082151 / +353 1 2082511

*"Colman Pearce is a most brilliant musician and a conductor of the greatest excellence"*
Malcolm Arnold

**PRIZES/AWARDS/APPOINTMENTS:**
1978 Co-Principal Conductor of the then RTÉ Symphony Orchestra, becoming Principal Conductor in 1981 and subsequently Senior Staff Conductor.
From 1984 to 1987, appointed Principal Guest Conductor with Bilbao Symphony Orchestra.
From 1987 to present, appointed Principal Conductor and Music Director of the Mississippi Symphony Orchestra.
**TRAINING AND/OR QUALIFICATIONS:**
Trained at National University of Ireland, Dublin, B Mus (Hons). Studied conducting with Franco Ferrara in Hilversum and Hans Swarowsky in Vienna.
**SELECTED BROADCASTS AND/OR RECORDED WORK:**
Recordings of the works of Victory, Boydell and Stanford released on the Naxos label. CD 'The Memory is a living thing' released in the USA contains a number of songs.
CD's of works by Deane, Corcoran, Wilson and Buckley (due for imminent release).
**ADDITIONAL INFORMATION:**
As Guest Conductor has directed concerts in North and South America, Britain and throughout Europe. Has a particular interest in contemporary music and has conducted many first performances in Ireland of works by international and Irish composers. Premiéred his own song cycle 'Summerfest' (poems by Michéal Ó Siadhail) with Bernadette Greevy at the National Gallery of Ireland in 1993.

# Adrian Petcu *Orchestral Conductor*

**Contact:** Mr Adrian Petcu
7, Grosvenor Place
Wellington Road
Cork
**Tel/Fax:** +353 21 505153
*See violin page 65.*

# John Reidy *Orchestral Conductor*

**Contact:** Dr John Reidy
45, Lower Kimmage Road
Dublin 6w
**Tel:** +353 1 4922513

*"Reidy had that conductors knack of producing glowing choral resonances"*
12.93 Irish Times (Michael Dervan)

**KEY IRISH PERFORMANCES** (since January 1994):
1994 St Patrick's Cathedral, Dublin appearing Musica Sacra and the Irish Chamber Orchestra.
**SELECTED BROADCASTS AND/OR RECORDED WORK:**
1994 Own professional video recording of Musica Sacra and the Irish Chamber Orchestra.
1994 National Chamber Choir recording for RTÉ FM3.
1995 NCC recording for RTÉ FM3.
**TRAINING AND/OR QUALIFICATIONS:**
From 1987 to 1988, Studied with Lawrence Leonard at the Morley College, London.
1990 Studied with Frantisek Vajnar at the Dublin Masterclasses Summer School.
1991 Studied with George Hurst at the Canford Summer School.
1992 Studied with Theodor Bilek.
**AVAILABILITY:**
Tuesday, Wednesday and Thursday evenings.
**ADDITIONAL INFORMATION:**
Has worked extensively with amateur and professional ensembles in Ireland and abroad including the Irish Chamber Orchestra, the RTÉ Concert Orchestra, the Ulster Orchestra, the Martinn Philharmonic, Musica Sacra, and the Orchestra of St Cecilia. Worked with the The National Chamber Choir from 1994 and 1995.

# Fergus Sheil *Orchestral Conductor*

**Contact:** Mr Fergus Sheil
15, Blackheath Park
Clontarf, Dublin 3
**Mobile:** +353 87 495759

*"... The point and pace of his conducting quite outclassed what was heard on the opening night"* 3.1.97 Irish Times (Michael Dervan) in a production of 'L'Elisir d'amore' by Donizetti.

**KEY IRISH PERFORMANCES** (since January 1994):
23.6.96 St Ann's Church, Dawson Street, Dublin appearing with the Orchestra of St Cecilia.
13.8.96 National Concert Hall, Dublin, appearing with the RTÉ Concert Orchestra.
8.12.96 Gaiety Theatre, promoted by Opera Ireland, conducting Donizetti's 'L'Elisir d'Amore'.
20.4.97 National Concert Hall, Dublin, promoted by the Irish Chamber Orchestra, appearing with the RTÉ Concert Orchestra.
**KEY PERFORMANCES OUTSIDE IRELAND** (since January 1994):
16.3.96 Durham, UK, promoted by Northern Sinfonia, appearing with Northern Sinfonia, Newcastle.
**SELECTED BROADCASTS AND/OR RECORDED WORK:**
1.3.95 RTÉ Concert Orchestra, Young Irish composers works for RTÉ.
9.1.96 Haydn Symphony No 73 with RTÉ Concert Orchestra for RTÉ
**SELECTED REVIEWS** (since January 1994):
22.4.97 Irish Times
**PRIZES/AWARDS/APPOINTMENTS:**
1995 BRI Conductors Prize awarded by the National Association of Youth Orchestras (UK).
1996 1st Conductors Award awarded by The Arts Council.
1996 Appointed Chorus Master/Head of Music by Opera Ireland.
1996 Appointed Stage Musical Director by the Wexford Festival Opera.
**TRAINING AND/OR QUALIFICATIONS:**
From 1988 to 1992, BA Mod (Music) from TCD.
From 1994 to 1995 studied at the Accademia Musicale Chigiana (Siena).
1994 Studied at the Internationale Bachakademie Stuttgart.
From 1993 to 1996, studied privately with Leon Barzin.
**REGULARLY CONDUCTS WITH:**
Opera Ireland Chorus, Wexford Sinfonia, Dublin Orchestral Players.
**REGULARLY GUESTS WITH:**
RTÉ Concert Orchestra, Irish Chamber Orchestra, Opera Ireland, Northern Sinfonia (Newcastle).
**AVAILABILITY:**
General.
**ADDITIONAL INFORMATION:**
Since embarking on career in 1993, has been engaged by most professional opera companies and orchestras in the Republic (Wexford Festival Opera, Opera Ireland, Opera Theatre Company, Orchestra of St Cecilia, RTÉ Concert Orchestra and the Irish Chamber Orchestra. Has performed throughout the country and represented RTÉ at the European conductors competition - 'Pedro de Freitas Branco' organised by Radio Portugal in 1997.

# Geoffrey Spratt *Orchestral Conductor*

**Contact:** Dr Geoffrey Spratt
Director
Cork School of Music
Union Quay
Cork
**Tel/Fax:** +353 21 270076 / +353 21 276595
**Instruments:** Flute, viola, tenor.

**KEY IRISH PERFORMANCES** (since January 1994):
10.6.95 St Anne's Church, Dawson Street, Dublin, appearing with the Orchestra of St Cecilia.
3.7.95 St Mary's Church, Pope's Quay, Cork, appearing with Madrigal '75, The RTÉ Vanbrugh Quartet and soloists, promoted by RTÉ.
24.8.95 St Canices's Cathedral, Kilkenny, appearing with Irish Youth Choir, RTÉCO and soloists, promoted by Kilkenny Arts Week.
25.8.95 National Concert Hall, Dublin, appearing with Irish Youth Choir, RTÉCO and soloists, promoted by RTÉ.
**KEY PERFORMANCES OUTSIDE IRELAND** (since January 1994):
19.12.94 Redmond, Oregon, USA, appearing with the Choir and Orchestra of the Central Oregon Community College, USA.
21.12.94 Bend, Oregon, USA, appearing with the Choir and Orchestra of the Central Oregon Community College.
**SELECTED BROADCASTS AND/OR RECORDED WORK:**
Since 1980 radio and television broadcasts for RTÉ.
1988 'The Choral Music of Séamas de Barra' for Grapevine Records, London.
**PRIZES/AWARDS/APPOINTMENTS:**
From 1976 to 1992, Lecturer in Music, University College Cork, and Founder/Conductor of the UCC Choir, UCC Orchestra, and Conductor of UCC Choral Society.
Since 1982, Founder/Conductor of the Irish Youth Choir.
Since 1985, Conductor of Madrigal '75.
Since 1992, Director of the Cork School of Music and Founder/ Conductor of the Fleischmann Choir.
**TRAINING AND/OR QUALIFICATIONS:**
From 1970 to 1976, BA Music (Hons) and Ph D, awarded by Bristol University.
**AVAILABILITY:**
General.
**ADDITIONAL INFORMATION:**
Choral conductor for both acappella and large-scale choral/orchestral repertoires. Background as a professional instrumentalist has resulted in symphonic work with orchestras such as the NSOI, RTÉCO and the Orchestra of St Cecilia.

# Andrew Synnott *Orchestral Conductor*

**Contact:** Mr Andrew Synnott
98 Wilfield Road
Sandymount
Dublin 4
**Tel:** +353 1 2696023
**Instruments:** Piano, organ, harpsichord, voice, composer.

*"Andrew Synnott conducts with style and brio"*

2.97 Sunday Tribune

**KEY PERFORMANCES OUTSIDE IRELAND** (since January 1994):
1995 Huddersfield Contemporary Music Festival, appearing with the Opera Theatre Company.
1997 Buxton Opera Festival, appearing with Opera Theatre Company and the Northern Sinfonia.
**REGULARLY GUESTS WITH:**
Opera Theatre Company, Northern Sinfonia (Manchester).
**AVAILABILITY:**
General.
**ADDITIONAL INFORMATION:**
Has worked for all of Ireland's leading performing groups including the National Symphony Orchestra of Ireland, RTÉ Concert Orchestra, the National Chamber Choir, Opera Ireland, and Opera Northern Ireland. Also composes and arranged Mozart's 'Magic Flute' for Opera Theatre Company.
*See piano page 50.*

# Brendan Townsend
## *Orchestral Conductor*

**Contact:** Mr Brendan Townsend
Tollisstraat 12
6443 EH Brunssum
Netherlands
**Tel/Fax:** +31 45 5251901
**Email:** townsend@cobweb.nl
**Instruments:** Cello

*"Brendan Townsend weaved a magical spell over the orchestra and audience alike"*
15.9.96 De Volkskrant

**KEY IRISH PERFORMANCES** (since January 1994):
4.5.95 City Hall, Cork, promoted by Cork School of Music, appearing with CSM Symphony Orchestra.
**KEY PERFORMANCES OUTSIDE IRELAND** (since January 1994):
17.12.94 Beurs Van Berlage, Amsterdam, appearing with Amsterdams Promenade Orchestra.
5.8.95 Siena, Italy, promoted by Academia Chigiana, appearing with Sofia Symphony Orchestra.
13.9.96 Concertgeboun, promoted by National Radio Netherlands, appearing with Radio Symphony Orchestra.
13.6.97 Geleen, Netherlands, promoted by BrenGer Music, appearing with Sinfonietta Geleen.
**TRAINING AND/OR QUALIFICATIONS:**
From 1.9.86 to 1.9.89, Dip CSM and LTCL from Cork School of Music.
From 1.9.90 to 30.6.94, UM (conducting) DM (cello) from the Conservatorium voor Muziek, Maastricht.
From 1.7.95 to 30.8.95, Studied at the Accademia Musicale, Siena, Italy with Yuri Termikanov.
**REGULARLY CONDUCTS WITH:**
Sinfonietta Geleen, Ars Antiqu et Nova, Jeker kamer Orkest.
**REGULARLY GUESTS WITH:**
Amsterdam Promenade Orkest, Venlo Symphony Orchestra, Pittsburgh Symphony Orchestra, USA, Radio Symphony Orchestra, NL. Amsterdam Promenade Orkest.
**AVAILABILITY:**
General.
**ADDITIONAL INFORMATION:**
A recent finalist for a position with the Pittsburgh Symphony Orchestra.
*See cello page 71.*

# Philip Walton *Orchestral Conductor*

**Contact:** Mr Philip Walton
c/o Karen Durant Management
298, Nelson Road
Whitton
Twickenham
Middlesex , TW2 78W
**Tel/Fax:** +44 181 893 3172 / +44 181 893 8090

*"The winds of the Ulster Orchestra reinforced their already high reputation under Philip Walton"* 11.93 Belfast Telegraph

**KEY IRISH PERFORMANCES** (since January 1994):
11.94 Elmwood Hall, Belfast, promoted by Belfast Festival at Queen's, appearing with Ulster Camerata.
21.10.95 Omagh Leisure Centre, promoted by Omagh Festival, appearing with Ulster Camerata.
**SELECTED REVIEWS** (since January 1994):
11.94 Belfast Telegraph.
11.94 Ulster Newsletter.
**PRIZES/AWARDS/APPOINTMENTS:**
1991 Studied with Frantisek Vajnar (conductor), as part of an award recieved by the Arts Council, Northern Ireland.
**TRAINING AND/OR QUALIFICATIONS:**
From 10.75 to 7.78, B Mus, awarded from Sheffield University.
From 9.81 to 7.82, Dip Ncos, from the Goldsmith's College, London.
**ADDITIONAL INFORMATION:**
Particularly interested in education and has produced a high standard of performance in classical symphonies with school orchestras. Large repertoire available.

# John Christie Willot
## *Orchestral Conductor*

**Contact:** Mr John Christie Willot
Scobain
Castletownshend
Co Cork
**Tel/Fax:** +353 28 36105

**KEY PERFORMANCES OUTSIDE IRELAND** (since January 1994):
8.9.96 Mannheim, Germany, promoted by the Reiss Museum, Mannheim, appearing with a small ensemble.
From 24.3.97 to 18.5.97, State Opera Mainz, Germany, conducting State Opera Mainz.
25.6.97 Freiburg, Germany, conducting the Profectio Ensemble.
1997 Craiova, Rumania, conducting the Rumanian State Symphony Orchestra.
**SELECTED BROADCASTS AND/OR RECORDED WORK:**
25.6.96 'Work in Progress' by J.C. Willot for Scobaun Music.
**TRAINING AND/OR QUALIFICATIONS:**
From 1983 to 1986 studied musicology and ethnomusicology at University of Basel, Switzerland (teachers H.H. Eggebrecht and H. Oesch).
From 1986 to 1991, Composition at State Music Academy, Stuttgart, Germany (studying under M Kelemen).
**REGULARLY CONDUCTS WITH:**
Profectio Ensemble, Germany.

**GUESTS WITH:**
Rumanian State Symphony Orchestra.
State Opera Mainz.
**AVAILABILITY:**
General.
**ADDITIONAL INFORMATION:**
Conductor and composer, JC Willot also works in the area of music and electronics.

# BAND CONDUCTORS

## Fergal Carroll *Band Conductor*

**Contact:** Mr Fergal Carroll
5, Silversprings
Clonmel
Co Tipperary
**Tel:** +353 52 22858
*See page 165.*

## John Clancy *Band Conductor*

**Contact:** Mr John Clancy
22, Pinewood Estate
Wexford
Co Wexford
**Tel:** +353 53 45630

**KEY IRISH PERFORMANCES** (since January 1994):
94/95/96 Performances in Wexford town, Enniscorthy, Waterford and Dublin.
**KEY PERFORMANCES OUTSIDE IRELAND** (since January 1994):
1994 Fishguard, Wales promoted by Goodwick Brass Band.
1994 Zurich promoted by ABS Pumps Limited.
1997 London promoted by the European Bands Association.
**SELECTED BROADCASTS AND/OR RECORDED WORK:**
1983 'In the Spotlight' for Dogen Recordings.
1988 'Bandstand'for RTÉ.
1991 'Songs of Praise' for BBC.
**PRIZES/AWARDS/APPOINTMENTS:**
1997 Conductor of Loc Garman band which won the 2nd prize winner with the European Brass Band Association.
From 1989 to 1996, Conductor of the Irish national and regional championships winning band (Loc Garman) with the Irish Association of Brass and Concert Bands.
**REGULARLY CONDUCTS WITH:**
Loc Garman Band.
**REGULARLY GUESTS WITH:**
Goodwick Brass Band.
**AVAILABILITY:**
General.

## Kenneth Crann *Band Conductor*

**Contact:** Mr Kenneth Crann
Beechgrove
Dublin Road
Mullingar
Co Westmeath
**Tel:** +353 44 43110

**TRAINING AND/OR QUALIFICATIONS:**
From 1992 to 1993, Diploma in Music, from Victoria College of Music, London.
From 1993 to 1997, BA in Music, from the National University of Ireland, Maynooth.
**REGULARLY CONDUCTS WITH:**
Tullamore Town Band, Mullingar Town Band (assistant conductor).
**AVAILABILITY:**
General.
**ADDITIONAL INFORMATION:**
Heavily involved in the concert band movement in Ireland, for the past seventeen years.

## Michael Fottrell *Band Conductor*

**Contact:** Mr Michael Fottrell
69, Michael Street
New Ross
Co Wexford
**Tel/Fax:** +353 51 422918 / +353 51 422326

*"... [The New Ross Silver Band] won at Clonakilty and impressed the judges by their youth and vitality"* 1986 New Ross Standard

**KEY IRISH PERFORMANCES** (since January 1994):
7.94 South of Ireland Band Championships, Clonakilty, Co Cork, promoted by the West Cork Festival Committee, appearing with Silver Sounds.
4.95 National Band Championships, Crumlin, Dublin, promoted by Irish Association of Brass and Concert Bands, appearing with Silver Sounds.
4.96/97 NBC Dundrum, Dublin, promoted by the Irish Association of Brass and Concert Bands, appearing with Silver Sounds.
**SELECTED BROADCASTS AND/OR RECORDED WORK:**
10.86 Silver Sounds, own recording.
8.87/88 'Hands' for RTÉ.
9.90 'Good as Gold' own recording at Windmill Lane Studios.
**PRIZES/AWARDS/APPOINTMENTS:**
1.4.89 and 5.4.97 Prizes awarded by the Irish Association of Brass and Concert Bands.
5.4.97 Prize awarded by the IABCB.
**REGULARLY CONDUCTS WITH:**
Silver Sounds, The New Ross Band, The New Ross Singers, St Mary and Michael's Parish Choir, New Ross.
**REGULARLY GUESTS WITH:**
New Ross Musical Society, Ros Ponte Singers, Waterford City Brass, Enniscorthy Brass Band, HFC Silver and Woodwind, Wexford. Craig na Managh Brass Band.
**AVAILABILITY:**
General.
**ADDITIONAL INFORMATION:**
Is dedicated to the opportunity of presenting young people with a choice of music making at minimal cost.

## Vincent Kennedy *Band Conductor*

**Contact:** Ms Vincent Kennedy
18, Carriglea Drive
Firhouse
Dublin 24
**Tel:** +353 1 4525580

**REGULARLY CONDUCTS WITH:**
Notre Dame Des Missions Choirs.
**REGULARLY GUESTS WITH:**
Notre Dame Des Missions and Third Day Chorale.

**PRINCIPAL CONDUCTOR WITH:**
Rathfarnham Concert Band.
**ADDITIONAL INFORMATION:**
Composer and plays the trumpet.

## Andrew Rowan *Band Conductor*

**Contact:** Mr Andrew Rowan
10, Galbraith Gardens
Waringstown BT 66 7QN
Northern Ireland
**Tel:** +44 1762 881097

**TRAINING AND/OR QUALIFICATIONS:**
FLCM, LLCM, ALCM.
*See flute page 19.*

# Section eight

## Composer Listings

This section was compiled with the kind assistance of the following organisations:

**Contemporary Music Centre, 95, Lower Baggot Street, Dublin 2**
**Contact: Eve O'Kelly**
**Tel/Fax: +353 1 6612105 / +353 1 6762639.**
**Email: info@cmc.ie**
All-Ireland archive and resource centre which promotes and documents the music of modern Irish classical music composers. Services include a major library of scores and information materials, a sound archive and information service.

**Association of Irish Composers, Copyright House, Pembroke Row, Dublin 2**
**Contact: Maura Eaton**
**Tel/Fax: +353 1 4942880.**
The representative body of composers of contemporary music in Ireland. Aims to improve standard of compositions and to obtain support and recognition for composers and their work at home and abroad.

**Composers Ink, 18, Fitzwilliam Square, Dublin 2**
**Contact: Ruth Hickey**
**Tel/Fax: +353 1 6615605.**
Composers Ink is an agency set up in July 1997 to represent Irish composers to publishers, broadcasting companies, record labels, concert promoters, film producers, etc. It is the intention of Composers Ink to raise the profile and alter, for the better, public perception of the work of Irish composers.

# COMPOSER LISTINGS

## Elaine Agnew *Composer*

**Contact:** Ms Elaine Agnew
Brownhill Farm
17, Deerpark Road
Kilwaughter
Larne
Co Antrim BT40 2PW
Northern Ireland
**Tel:** +44 1574 277566

**TYPE OF MUSIC:** Classical.

## Michael Alcorn *Composer*

**Contact:** Dr Michael Alcorn
School of Music
Queen's University
Belfast BT7 1NN
Northern Ireland
**Tel/Fax:** +44 1232 335105 / +44 1232 238484
**Email:** alcorn@soundin.dnet.co.uk

**TYPE OF MUSIC:** Classical (including electro-acoustic music).

## Fergal Andrews *Composer*

**Contact:** Mr Fergal Andrews
28, The Strand
Donabate
Co Dublin
**Tel:** +353 1 8435267

**TYPE OF MUSIC:** Electro-acoustic.

## Michael Ball *Composer*

**Contact:** Mr Michael Ball
31, Sefton
Rochestown Avenue
Dún Laoghaire
Co Dublin
**Tel/Fax:** +353 1 2350747 / +353 1 2350775

**TYPE OF MUSIC:** Classical.

## Gerald Barry *Composer*

**Contact:** Mr Gerald Barry
2, Rosemount Terrace
Arbour Hill
Dublin 7
**Tel/Fax:** +353 1 6712899

**TYPE OF MUSIC:** Classical.

## Derek Bell *Composer*

**Contact:** Dr Derek Bell
74, Bryansburn Road
Bangor, Co Down
Northern Ireland, BT20 3SB
**Tel:** +44 1247 457923

*See traditional harp page 226.*

## Séoirse Bodley *Composer*

**Contact:** Prof Séoirse Bodley
13, Cloister Green
The Cloisters
Carysfort Avenue
Blackrock
**Tel/Fax:** +353 1 2781172
**Email:** 100703.1112@compuserve.com

**TYPE OF MUSIC:** Classical.

## Brian Boydell *Composer*

**Contact:** Dr Brian Boydell
'Dermalogue'
Baily, Howth
Co Dublin
**Tel/Fax:** +353 1 8322021

**TYPE OF MUSIC:** Classical.

## John Wolf Brennan *Composer*

**Contact:** Mr John Wolf Brennan
Luzernerstr 8
CH 6353
Weggis, Switzerland
**Tel/Fax:** +41 41 3902777 / +41 41 3902761

**TYPE OF MUSIC:** Contemporary.
*See piano page 32.*

## Melanie Brown *Composer*

**Contact:** Melanie Brown
88, Bushy Park Road
Terenure, Dublin 6
**Tel/Fax:** +353 1 4903366 / +353 1 4903251

**TYPE OF MUSIC:** Classical

## John Browne *Composer*

**Contact:** Mr John Browne
31, Alconbury Road
London E5 8RG
England
**Tel/Fax:** +44 181 8069395

**TYPE OF MUSIC:** Music for theatre, opera and children.

## John Buckley *Composer*

**Contact:** Mr John Buckley
4, Ayrefield Grove
Malahide Road, Dublin 13
**Tel:** +353 1 8475042

**TYPE OF MUSIC:** Contemporary classical.

## David Byers *Composer*

**Contact:** Mr David Byers
c/o BBC Northern Ireland
Broadcasting House
Ormeau Avenue
Belfast BT2 8HQ
Northern Ireland
**Tel/Fax:** +44 1232 338292 or +44 1232 338241 / +44 1232 33807

**TYPE OF MUSIC:** Classical.
*See also page 165.*

## William Campbell *Composer*

**Contact:** Mr William Campbell
1, Railway Cottages
Greenisland
Carrickfergus, Co Antrim
Northern Ireland
**Tel:** +44 1232 364569

**TYPE OF MUSIC:** Contemporary classical.

## David Catherwood *Composer*

**Contact:** David Catherwood
55, Schoenberg Avenue
Belfast BT4 2JR
Northern Ireland.
**Tel/Fax:** +44 1232 761610 / +44 1232 761156

**TYPE OF MUSIC:** Choral, instrumental, band.

## Rhona Clarke *Composer*

**Contact:** Dr Rhona Clarke
7, Fortfield Gardens
Rathmines, Dublin 6
**Tel:** +353 1 4972721

**TYPE OF MUSIC:** Classical.

## Siobhán Cleary *Composer*

**Contact:** Ms Siobhán Cleary
20, Mount Temple Road
Stoneybatter, Dublin 7
**Tel/Fax:** +353 1 6715196

**TYPE OF MUSIC:** Classical.

## Aidan Coleman *Composer*

**Contact:** Mr Aidan Coleman
28, Lisalea
Frascati Park
Blackrock
Co Dublin
**Tel:** +353 1 2835117

*See singers page 112.*

## Frank Corcoran *Composer*

**Contact:** Prof Frank Corcoran
Lenhassz, Strasse 8
20249 Hamburg
Germany
**Tel/Fax:** +49 40 463566

**TYPE OF MUSIC:** Contemporary classical.

## David Cox *Composer*

**Contact:** Dr David Cox
Department of Music
University College Cork
Western Road, Cork
**Tel/Fax:** +353 21 276871 / +353 21 271595

**TYPE OF MUSIC:** Classical.

## Ellen Cranitch *Composer*

**Contact:** Ms Ellen Cranitch
33, Westfield Road
Harold's Cross
Dublin 6w
**Tel/Fax:** + 353 1 4923486

**TYPE OF MUSIC:** Compositions for film, television, theatre.
*See flute page 271.*

## Tom Cullivan *Composer*

**Contact:** Mr Tom Cullivan
Knocknavoddy
Furbo, Spiddal
Co Galway
**Tel/Fax:** +353 91 590796

**TYPE OF MUSIC:** Classical.

## Séamas de Barra *Composer*

**Contact:** Mr Séamas de Barra
c/o Cork School of Music
Union Quay, Cork
**Tel/Fax:** +353 21 270076 / +353 21 276595

**TYPE OF MUSIC:** Contemporary classical.

## Jerome de Bromhead *Composer*

**Contact:** Mr Jerome de Bromhead
Martello Cottage
Strand Road, Killiney
Co Dublin
**Tel:** +353 1 2825948

**TYPE OF MUSIC:** Contemporary classical.

## Raymond Deane *Composer*

**Contact:** Mr Raymond Deane
c/o The Contemporary Music Centre
95, Lower Baggot Street
Dublin 2
**Tel/Fax:** +353 1 6612105 / +353 1 6762639
**Email:** info@cmc.ie
or
c/o Composers Ink
18, Fitzwilliam Square
Dublin 2
**Tel/Fax:** +353 1 6615605

**TYPE OF MUSIC:** Classical contemporary.
*See piano page 36.*

## Donnacha Dennehy *Composer*

**Contact:** Mr Donnacha Dennehy
c/o The Contemporary Music Centre
95, Lower Baggot Street
Dublin 2
**Tel/Fax:** +353 1 6612105 / +353 1 6762639
**Email:** info@cmc.ie
or
c/o Composers Ink
18, Fitzwilliam Square
Dublin 2
**Tel/Fax:** +353 1 6615605
**Email:** ddennehy@tcd.ie

**TYPE OF MUSIC:** Contemporary.
*See Crash Ensemble page 136.*

## Roger Doyle *Composer*

**Contact:** Mr Roger Doyle
Rynville News
Killarney Road
Bray
Co Wicklow
**Tel/Fax:** +353 1 6612105 / +353 1 6762639
**Email:** info@cmc.ie

**TYPE OF MUSIC:** Electro-acoustic.

## Benjamin Dwyer *Composer*

**Contact:** Benjamin Dwyer
c/o The Contemporary Music Centre
95, Lower Baggot Street
Dublin 2
**Tel/Fax:** +353 1 6612105 / +353 1 6762639
**Email:** info@cmc.ie
or
c/o Composers Ink
18, Fitzwilliam Square
Dublin 2
**Tel/Fax:** +353 1 6615605
**Email:** bdwyer@indigo.ie

**TYPE OF MUSIC:** Contemporary.
*See guitar page 20.*

## Maura Eaton *Composer*

**Contact:** Ms Maura Eaton
8, Ashton Avenue
Knocklyon
Dublin 16
**Tel:** +353 1 4942880

**TYPE OF MUSIC:** Classical.

## Eibhlis Farrell *Composer*

**Contact:** Dr Eibhlis Farrell
c/o The Contemporary Music Centre
95, Lower Baggot Street
Dublin 2
**Tel/Fax:** +353 1 6612105 / +353 1 6762639
**Email:** info@cmc.ie

**TYPE OF MUSIC:** Contemporary classical.

## Philip Flood *Composer*

**Contact:** Mr Philip Flood
39, Kynaston Road
Stoke Newington
London N16 OEA
England
**Tel:** +44 171 2497208

**TYPE OF MUSIC:** Classical.

## Stephen Gardner *Composer*

**Contact:** Mr Stephen Gardner
c/o The Contemporary Music Centre
95, Lower Baggot Street
Dublin 2
**Tel:** +353 1 6612105 / +353 1 6762639
**Email:** info@cmc.ie

**TYPE OF MUSIC:** Contemporary classical.

## Bernard Geary *Composer*

**Contact:** Bernard Geary
c/o The Contemporary Music Centre
95, Lower Baggot Street
Dublin 2
**Tel/Fax:** +353 1 6612105 / +353 1 6762639
**Email:** info@cmc.ie

**TYPE OF MUSIC:** Classical.

## John Gibson *Composer*

**Contact:** Mr John Gibson
41, Cloverhill Estate
Blackrock
Co Cork
**Tel:** +353 21 357676

**MUSIC TYPE:** Classical.
*See piano page 38.*

## Deirdre Gribbin *Composer*

**Contact:** Ms Deirdre Gribbin
11, March Terrace
Dinnington
Newcastle-Upon-Tyne, NE13 7AF
England
**Tel/Fax:** +44 1661 821270 / +44 191 2225242

**TYPE OF MUSIC:** Classical, traditional.

## Ronan Guilfoyle *Composer*

**Contact:** Mr Ronan Guilfoyle
10, O'Rourke Park
Sallynoggin
Co Dublin
**Tel:** +353 1 2853497

**MUSIC TYPE:** Contemporary.
*See guitar jazz page 273.*

## Douglas Gunn *Composer*

**Contact:** Mr Douglas Gunn
Ballaghmore Castle
Borris-in-Ossory
Co Laois
**Tel:** +353 505 23093
**Email:** dgunn@iol.ie
**WWW:** //ww.iol.ie/dgunn/

**TYPE OF MUSIC:** Classical.
*See Douglas Gunn Ensemble page 128.*

## Barry Guy *Composer*

**Contact:** Mr Barry Guy
Carrickmourne
Thomastown
Co Kilkenny
**Tel/Fax:** +353 56 58708 / +353 56 58709
**Email:** maya@tinet.ie

*See double bass page 295.*

## Philip Hammond *Composer*

**Contact:** Mr Philip Hammond
390, Beersbridge Road
Belfast BTS 5EA
Northern Ireland
**Tel/Fax:** +81 3 34074318

**TYPE OF MUSIC:** Classical.

## Paul Hayes *Composer*

**Contact:** Mr Paul Hayes
Hirro Heights, No 208, 5-1-14
Hirro
Shibuya-Ku
Tokyo 150
Japan
**Tel:** +0081 3-3407 4318

**TYPE OF MUSIC:** *Contemporary classical.*

## Ann Hoban *Composer*

**Contact:** Ms Ann Hoban
26, Cowper Village
Rathmines
Dublin 6
**Tel:** +353 1 4970818

**TYPE OF MUSIC:** Contemporary classical.

## Michael Holohan *Composer*

**Contact:** Mr Michael Holohan
Listoke Lodge
Listoke
Ballymakenny
Drogheda
Co Louth
**Tel/Fax:** +353 41 34853

**TYPE OF MUSIC:** Contemporary, classical and traditional.

## Maya Homburger *Composer*

**Contact:** Ms Maya Homburger
Carrickmourne
Thomastown
Co Kilkenny
**Tel/Fax:** +353 56 58708 / +353 56 58709

**TYPE OF MUSIC:** Classical.
*See baroque violin page 119.*

## Michael Howard *Composer*

**Contact:** Mr Michael Howard
53, Balkill Park
Howth
Co Dublin
**Tel:** +353 1 8323475
**Email:** howmac@indigo.ie

**TYPE OF MUSIC:** Classical, traditional.
*See classical guitar page 21.*

## William Hughes *Composer*

**Contact:** Mr William Hughes
6, Charter House
Maynooth
Co Kildare
**Mobile:** +353 87 447847

**TYPE OF MUSIC:** Classical, commercial.

## Donal Hurley *Composer*

**Contact:** Mr Donal Hurley
c/o The Contemporary Music Centre
95, Lower Baggot Street
Dublin 2
**Tel/Fax:** +353 1 6612105 / +353 1 6762639
**Email:** info@cmc.ie

**TYPE OF MUSIC:** Contemporary.

## Marion Ingoldsby *Composer*

**Contact:** Ms Marion Ingoldsby
37, St Nicholas Park
Carrick-on-Suir
Co Tipperary
or
c/o Music Department
University of York
York YO1 5DD
England (until June 1998)
**Tel/Fax:** +353 51 641222 or +44 1904 432446 / +44 1904 432450

**TYPE OF MUSIC:** Classical.

## Fergus Johnston *Composer*

**Contact:** Fergus Johnston
c/o The Contemporary Music Centre
95, Lower Baggot Street
Dublin 2
**Tel/Fax:** +353 1 6612105 / +353 1 6762639
**Email:** info@cmc.ie
or
c/o Composers Ink
18, Fitzwilliam Square
Dublin 2
**Tel/Fax:** +353 1 6615605

**TYPE OF MUSIC:** Contemporary classical.

## Denise Kelly *Composer*

**Contact:** Denise Kelly
66, Dartmouth Square
Ranelagh
Dublin 6
**Tel:** +353 1 6689366

**TYPE OF MUSIC:** Contemporary music for harp.
*See concert harp page 7.*

## Mary Kelly *Composer*

**Contact:** Ms Mary Kelly
c/o The Contemporary Music Centre
95, Lower Baggot Street
Dublin 2
**Tel/Fax:** +353 1 6612105 / +353 1 6762639
**Email:** info@cmc.ie

**TYPE OF MUSIC:** Contemporary classical.

## Vincent Kennedy *Composer*

**Contact:** Mr Vincent Kennedy
18, Carriglea Drive
Firhouse
Dublin 24
**Tel:** +353 1 4525580

**TYPE OF MUSIC:** Classical, symphonic band music.
*See conductors page 176.*

## John Kinsella *Composer*

**Contact:** Mr John Kinsella
7, Marley Rise
Rathfarnham
Dublin 16
**Tel:** +353 1 4936492

**TYPE OF MUSIC:** Contemporary classical.

## Mary S McAuliffe *Composer*

**Contact:** Ms Mary S McAuliffe
124, Applewood Heights
Greystones
Co Wicklow
**Tel/Fax:** +353 1 2876800 / +353 1 2984806
**WWW:** http://www.anuna.ie

**TYPE OF MUSIC:** Traditional, classical, film music, opera, music for children, choral music.

## Michael McGlynn *Composer*

**Contact:** Michael McGlynn
5, Lakelands Lawn
Stillorgan
Co Dublin
**Tel:** +353 1 2835533
**Email:** info@anuna.ie

**TYPE OF MUSIC:** Classical.
*See Anúna page 153.*

## John McLachlan *Composer*

**Contact:** Mr John McLachlan
11, Belgrave Road
Rathmines
Dublin 6
**Tel:** +353 1 4961484
**Email:** mclachlj@tcd.ie

**TYPE OF MUSIC:** Classical.

## Philip Martin *Composer*

**Contact:** Mr Philip Martin
Chapel House
Theobald's Green
Calstone
Calne
Wilts SN11 8QE
England
**Tel/Fax:** +44 1249 812508

**TYPE OF MUSIC:** Contemporary.
*See piano page 44.*

## Colin Mawby *Composer*

**Contact:** Mr Colin Mawby
Gerrardstown
Garlow Cross
Navan
Co Meath
**Tel:** +353 46 29394

**TYPE OF MUSIC:** Contemporary classical.
*See National Chamber Choir page 153.*

## Alan Mills *Composer*

**Contact:** Mr Alan Mills
87, Palmerstown Road
Wood Green
London N22 4QS
England
**Tel/Fax:** +44 181 8888214

**TYPE OF MUSIC:** Classical.

## David Morris *Composer*

**Contact:** Dr David Morris
Music Department
University of Ulster Jordanstown
Newtownabbey
Co Antrim BT37 0QB
**Tel/Fax:** +44 1232 365131 (ext 6690) / +44 1232 362810

**TYPE OF MUSIC:** Classical.

## Gráinne Mulvey *Composer*

**Contact:** Ms Gráinne Mulvey
Church Street
Leighlinbridge
Co Carlow
**Tel:** +353 503 21403

**TYPE OF MUSIC:** Classical.

## Gerard Murphy *Composer*

**Contact:** Gerard Murphy
15, Cullenswood Gardens
Ranelagh
Dublin 6
**Tel:** +353 1 4973929

**TYPE OF MUSIC:** Classical, opera.

## Kevin O'Connell *Composer*

**Contact:** Mr Kevin O'Connell
38, Rose Park
Dún Laoghaire
Co Dublin
**Tel:** +353 1 2807992

**TYPE OF MUSIC:** Classical, opera.

## Fergus O'Duffy *Composer*

**Contact:** Mr Fergus O'Duffy
56, Wainsfort Park,
Terenure, Dublin 6
**Tel:** +353 1 4909813

**TYPE OF MUSIC:** Classical, jazz.

## Jane O'Leary *Composer*

**Contact:** Dr Jane O'Leary
c/o The Contemporary Music Centre
95, Lower Baggot Street
Dublin 2
**Tel/Fax:** +353 1 6612105 / +353 1 6762639
**Email:** info@cmc.ie

**TYPE OF MUSIC:** Contemporary.
*See Concorde page 136.*

## Martin O'Leary *Composer*

**Contact:** Mr Martin O'Leary
c/o The Contemporary Music Centre
95, Lower Baggot Street
Dublin 2
**Tel/Fax:** +353 1 6612105 / +353 1 6762639

**TYPE OF MUSIC:** Contemporary classical.

## Mícheál Ó Súilleabháin *Composer*

**Contact:** Prof Mícheál Ó Súilleabháin
Irish World Music Centre
University of Limerick
Plassey Park, Co Limerick
**Tel.:** +353 61 202065

**TYPE OF MUSIC:** Classical, traditional.
*See piano page 234.*

## Brent Parker *Composer*

**Contact:** Mr Brent Parker
40, James Everett Park
Bray, Co Wicklow
**Tel:** +353 1 2865483

**TYPE OF MUSIC:** Classical.

## Charles Stephen Lawrence Parker *Composer*

**Contact:** Mr Stephen Parker
19, Raglan House
Ballsbridge Court
Ballsbridge, Dublin 4
**Tel:** +353 1 6603557
*See piano page 49.*

## Bernard Reilly *Composer*

**Contact:** Mr Bernard Reilly
26, Sandyford Downs
Dublin 13
**Tel:** +353 1 2958742
**Email:** breilly@tinet.ie

**TYPE OF MUSIC:** Jazz.
*See percussion jazz page 279.*

## Michael Seaver *Composer*

**Contact:** Michael Seaver
Cross Cool Harbour, (off Red Lane)
Blessington
Co Wicklow
**Tel:** +353 45 520264

**TYPE OF MUSIC:** Dance, contemporary.
*See clarinet page 5.*

## Eric Sweeney *Composer*

**Contact:** Dr Eric Sweeney
Music Department
Waterford Institute of Technology
Cork Road
Waterford
**Tel/Fax:** +353 51 75934 / +353 51 78292

**TYPE OF MUSIC:** Classical.

## Andrew Synott *Composer*

**Contact:** Mr Andrew Synott
98, Wilfield Road
Sandymount
Dublin 4
**Tel:** +353 1 2696023

**TYPE OF MUSIC:** Contemporary classical.
*See piano page 50.*

## Richard Thomas *Composer*

**Contact:** Mr Richard Thomas
PO Box 5450
Dublin 6
**Email:** rthom@tinet.ie

**TYPE OF MUSIC:** Classical.

## Fiachra Trench *Composer*

**Contact:** Mr Fiachra Trench
Easton House
Delgany, Co Wicklow
**Tel/Fax:** +353 1 2875972 / +353 1 2873852

**TYPE OF MUSIC:** Music for film and television.

## Joan Trimble *Composer*

**Contact:** Ms Joan Trimble
c/o The Contemporary Music Centre
95, Lower Baggot Street
Dublin 2
**Tel/Fax:** +353 1 6612105 / +353 1 6762639

**TYPE OF MUSIC:** Classical.

# Kevin Volans *Composer*

**Contact:** Kevin Volans
c/o Catherine Manners
Chester Music
Newmarket Road
Bury
St Edmunds, IP33 3YB
Suffolk
England

**TYPE OF MUSIC:** Classical.

# John Christie Willot *Composer*

**Contact:** Mr John Christie Willot
Scobain
Castletownshend
Co Cork
**Tel/Fax:** +353 28 36105

**TYPE OF MUSIC:** Contemporary classical.
*See conductors page 175.*

# James Wilson *Composer*

**Contact:** Mr James Wilson
10a, Wyvern
Killiney
Co Dublin
**Tel:** +353 1 2850786
**Email:** jwilson@iol.ie

**TYPE OF MUSIC:** Classical.

# Ian Wilson *Composer*

**Contact:** Dr Ian Wilson
36, Rathgar Street
Belfast BT9 79D
Northern Ireland
**Tel/Fax:** +44 1232 201383

**TYPE OF MUSIC:** Classical.

# Patrick Zuk *Composer*

**Contact:** Mr Patrick Zuk
c/o Cork School of Music
Union Quay
Cork
**Tel/Fax:** +353 21 270076 / +353 21 276595

**TYPE OF MUSIC:** Contemporary classical.
*See piano page 52.*

# Section nine

## Traditional Musicians and Groups



**Please note that throughout this section of the book, Comhaltás Ceoltoirí Éireann, the organisation established in 1951 to promote Irish traditional music, song and dance, is referred to as CCÉ.**
**The qualification awarded by CCÉ, (Teastas i dTeagasc Ceolta Tíre), is abbreviated to TTCT**

# ACCORDIONS

**The standard two-row button accordion is the instrument generally used in playing traditional Irish music. The melodeon and piano accordion are also used.**

## Eilín Begley *Accordion*

**Contact:** Ms Eilín Begley
Loughlane
Caulstown
Dunboyne
Co Meath
**Tel/Fax:** +353 1 8256337
*See traditional groups page 256.*

## Séamus Begley *Accordion*

**Contact:** Mr Séamus Begley
Baile na bPúc
Baile na nGall
Tralee
Co Kerry
**Tel:** +353 66 55155

**REGULARLY PERFORMS WITH:**
Steve Cooney.

## Dan Brouder *Button Accordion*

**Contact:** Mr Dan Brouder
'Camas'
Monagae
Newcastle
Co Limerick
**Tel:** +353 69 72215

**KEY IRISH PERFORMANCES** (since January 1994):
7.95 University of Limerick, promoted by UL Archives, appearing with Francis O'Connor and Máire O'Keefe.
6.96 Dan Conell's Bar, Knocknagree, Co Cork, promoted by the RTÉ ('High Reel'), appearing with Johnny O'Leary, Joe Sullivan and Tim Kiely.
9.96 Irish Centre, Cork City, promoted by TnaG, appearing with Francis O'Connor and Gerry Murphy.
2.97 Doolin Church, Co Clare, promoted by the Miko Russell Festival Committee, appearing with Noel O'Donoghue, Tony Connell, Liam Lewis and Cyril O'Donoghue.
**KEY PERFORMANCES OUTSIDE IRELAND** (since January 1994):
7.94 Newstadt, promoted by the Festival Committee Newstadt, appearing with a group of musicians and dancers.
7.96 Italy, promoted by Benny Carroll Promotions, appearing with Eamonn Coyne, Gerry McNamara and Benny Carroll.
3.97 Italy, promoted by Benny Carroll Promotions, appearing with Francis O'Connor, Áine O'Connell and Benny Carroll.
**SELECTED BROADCASTS AND/OR RECORDED WORK:**
1994 'Céilí House' for RTÉ.
6.96 'High Reel' for RTÉ.
9.96 'Geantraí' for TNaG.
**PRIZES/AWARDS/APPOINTMENTS:**
1989 2nd Prize at the Macra Na Feirme National Talent Competition.
1991 1st Prize in the Munster Senior Competition, Munster Fleadh Cheoil.
**TRAINING AND/OR QUALIFICATIONS:**
Taught by Timmy Collins, Donall De Barra, Willie Fogarty (Kilfinane Education Centre, Co Limerick) P.J. Hernon (Scoil Éigse, Fleadh Cheoil na hÉireann).
**REGULARLY PERFORMS WITH:**
Francis O'Connor (flute) and various other musicians.
**AVAILABILITY:**
General.

## Joe Burke *Accordion*

**Contact:** Joe Burke
Tinageeragh
Kilnadeema
Loughrea
Co Galway
**Tel/Fax:** +353 91 842419
**Other instruments:** Flute.

*"Joe Burke had elevated the accordion to the status it deserves and has paved the way for a whole generation of virtuoso musicians"*
1980's Washington Post.

**KEY IRISH PERFORMANCES** (since January 1994):
15.2.97 Kinnity Castle, Birr, Co Offaly, promoted by Séan Ryan, appearing with Anne Conroy Burke.
31.3.97 Town Hall Theatre, Galway, promoted by the AIB appearing with Anne Conroy-Burke.
21.6.97 Stray Leaf Folk Club, Mullaghbawn, Co Monaghan appearing with Anne Conroy Burke.
28.6.97 National Concert Hall, Dublin, promoted by Hugh Hardy appearing with Anne Conroy Burke.
**KEY PERFORMANCES OUTSIDE IRELAND** (since January 1994):
6.4.96 Edinburgh Folk Festival, promoted by John Barrow, appearing with Anne Conroy Burke.
9.3.97 San Francisco Irish Festival, promoted by Peter O'Neill and Eddie Stack appearing with Anne Conroy Burke.
30.3.97 Anchorage, Alaska, USA, promoted by John Walshe appearing with Anne Conroy Burke.
4.6.97 Feestival 2002 Gooek, Belgium, appearing with Anne Conroy Burke.
**SELECTED BROADCASTS AND/OR RECORDED WORK:**
1973 'Traditional Music of Ireland' for Green Linnet Records.
1986 'Tailor's Choice' for Green Linnet Records.
1997 'Bucks of Oranmore' for Green Linnet Records.
**SELECTED REVIEWS** (since January 1994):
10.1.97 Irish Times.
2.97 Irish Music.
3.97 Irish America.
**PRIZES/AWARDS/APPOINTMENTS:**
8.90 Included in Hall of Fame, Rostrevor, Co Down.
31.3.97 Recipient of the Allied Irish Bank Traditional Music Award.
**REGULARLY PERFORMS WITH:**
Anne Conroy Burke (guitar, accordion).
**AVAILABILITY:**
General.
**ADDITIONAL INFORMATION:**
Has been performing for forty years and has made many recordings for various companies. Performs annually at major festivals at home and abroad. Has given masterclasses and workshops on the accordion at home and in France (Paris), and the USA (Dallas and Alaska).

# Adèle Commins *Accordion*

**Contact:** Ms Adèle Commins
Rathbrist
Tallanstown
Dundalk, Co Louth
**Tel:** +353 42 74272
**Other instruments:** Piano, fiddle, tin whistle, singing.

**KEY IRISH PERFORMANCES** (since January 1994):
1.96 Olympia Theatre, Dublin, promoted by Scór na nÓg, appearing with Dónal O'Connor.
6.96 Castlebellingham, promoted by Bord Chontae Lú, appearing with Brendan Needham.
9.96 Dundalk Town Hall, promoted by CCÉ and J.J. Gardiner.
5.97 Hotel Imperial, Dundalk, promoted by the Maytime Festival.
**SELECTED BROADCASTS AND/OR RECORDED WORK:**
1993 'Our Village' (video) for Ben Corcoran Studios.
9.96 'A Tribute to Rory Kennedy' (video) for Ben Corcoran Studios.
5.97 'Ray Stone Show' for LMFM radio.
**PRIZES/AWARDS/APPOINTMENTS:**
1991 1st Prize at Fleadh Cheoil na hÉireann.
1991 to 1996, Ist Prize at Fleadh Laighean.
**TRAINING AND/OR QUALIFICATIONS:**
From 1989 to 1993, Accordion studies with All-Ireland title holder, Rory Kennedy, CCÉ.
From 1990 to 1995, Grade 1-8 (Distinction) from Royal Irish Academy of Music, Dublin.
From 1994 to 1997, Piano studies with Leinster title holder, Siobhán Kennedy.
**REGULARLY PERFORMS WITH:**
J.J. Gardiner, CCÉ, Dún Dealgan
**AVAILABILITY:**
Weekends.
**ADDITIONAL INFORMATION:**
Has been playing music for 9 years and holds 13 Louth and 8 Leinster titles for accordion and piano. Has also been placed 1st and 2nd in All-Ireland accordion competitions. Winner of the Willie McSherry Cup (most promising player) at the Forkhill Feis in 1992 and 1994.

# Anne Conroy Burke *Accordion*

**Contact:** Anne Conroy Burke
Tinageeragh
Kilnadeema
Loughrea
Co Galway
**Tel/Fax:** +353 91 842419
**Other instruments:** Guitar.

*"We got unbeliefly [sic] good reactions from the spectators and the press"* 15.7.97 Letter from the Festival Committee 2002, Belgium *(see key performances outside Ireland).*

**KEY IRISH PERFORMANCES** (since January 1994):
15.2.97 Kinnity Castle, Birr, Co Offaly promoted by Séan Ryan appearing with Joe Burke.
31.3.97 Town Hall Theatre, Galway, promoted by the Allied Irish Bank appearing with Joe Burke.
21.6.97 Stray Leaf Folk Club, Mullaghban, Co Monaghan appearing with Joe Burke.
28.6.97 National Concert Hall, Dublin, promoted by Hugh Hardy appearing with Joe Burke.
**KEY PERFORMANCES OUTSIDE IRELAND** (since January 1994):
6.4.96 Edinburgh Folk Festival, promoted by John Barrow, appearing with Joe Burke.
9.3.97 San Francisco Irish Festival, promoted by Peter O'Neill and Eddie Stack, appearing with Joe Burke.
30.3.97 Anchorage, Alaska, USA promoted by John Walshe appearing with Joe Burke.
4.6.97 Feestival 2002 Gooek, Belgium, appearing with Joe Burke.
**SELECTED BROADCASTS AND/OR RECORDED WORK:**
1981 'The Jeannie C' with the group Oisín for Tara records.
1985 'Winds of Change' with Geraldine McGowan for Tara Records.
15.7.97 'High Reel' for RTÉ.
**PRIZES/AWARDS/APPOINTMENTS:**
1977 and 1978, All-Ireland Senior Accordion Champion winner with Slógadh.
**REGULARLY PERFORMS WITH:**
Joe Burke (accordion).
**AVAILABILITY:**
General.
**ADDITIONAL INFORMATION:**
Performances with Joe Burke feature her solo accordion playing as well as guitar. Has worked with other musicians i.e. Máire Breatnach, Kevin Burke, Donal Lunny and Davy Spillane. Tours include USA and the 1992 'Accordions That Shook The World' tour. Gives masterclasses at various summer schools.

# Christopher Cronin *Piano Accordion* 

**Contact:** Mr Christopher Cronin
Killyfad, Aughamore
Carrick-on-Shannon
Co Leitrim
**Tel:** +353 78 24685
*See page 222.*

# Mary Crowley *Piano Accordion*

**Contact:** Ms Mary Crowley
Fastnet View
Hollyhill, Skibbereen
Co Cork
**Tel/Mobile:** +353 28 38175 / +353 87 2349780

**KEY IRISH PERFORMANCES** (since January 1994):
8.95 All-Ireland Fleadh Cheoil na hÉireann, Listowel, Co Kerry, promoted by Scoil Éigse concerts, appearing with Pat Bass.
7.96 Phil Murphy weekend, Carrig-on-Bannow, Co Wexford, promoted by John Murphy, apppearing with Éibhlín de Paor.
8.96 All-Ireland Fleadh Cheoil na hÉireann, Listowel, Co Kerry, promoted by Scoil Éigse concerts, accompanied by Micheál Ó Runaí.
7.97 Phil Murphy weekend, Carrig-on-Bannow, Co Waterford, promoted by John Murphy, appearing with Mick Brown.
**KEY PERFORMANCES OUTSIDE IRELAND** (since January 1994):
8.93/94/95 Festival Interceltique Lorient, Brittany, France.
**SSELECTED BROADCASTS AND/OR RECORDED WORK:**
From 8.95 to 8.96, All-Ireland Fleadh Cheoil na hÉireann for RTÉ.
Also 'Céilí House and Fáilte Isteach' for RTÉ.
**PRIZES/AWARDS/APPOINTMENTS:**
From 1980 to 1987, County, Provincial and All-Ireland awards at Fleadhanna Cheoil, awarded by CCÉ.
**TRAINING AND/OR QUALIFICATIONS:**
7.88 TTCT from CCÉ.
From 10.88 to 6.91, BA Music and French from University College, Cork.
From 9.91 to 6.92, H Dip (Hons), from University College, Cork.
**AVAILABILITY:**
Weekends, evenings and during school holidays.
**ADDITIONAL INFORMATION:**
Has given workshops for CCÉ, Scoil Eigse and at the Phil Murphy Weekend in recent years. Adjudicator at all levels of competitions including All-Ireland and All-Britain events. Since 1992, lectures on the CCÉ TTCT course.

## Jackie Daly *Button Accordion*

**Contact:** Mr Jackie Daly
Doorus Mill
Kinvara
Co Galway
**Tel:** +353 91 637467

**KEY IRISH PERFORMANCES** (since January 1994):
6.9.96 Cork Folk Festival, appearing with Máire O'Keeffe.
18.10.96 Waterville, Co Kerry, promoted by Music Network, appearing with Máire O'Keeffe.
26.10.96 Castleisland Festival, Co Kerry appearing with Máire O'Keefe.
**KEY PERFORMANCES OUTSIDE IRELAND** (since January 1994):
From 19.12.95 to 10.2.96, Tour of Australia, appearing with Máire O'Keeffe.
From 2.4.96 to 27.4.96, Tour of England, appearing with Patrick Street.
**SELECTED BROADCASTS AND/OR RECORDED WORK:**
1995 'Many a Wild Night' for Gael-Linn.
**PRIZES/AWARDS/APPOINTMENTS:**
1974 1st Prize in All-Ireland, Fleadh Cheoil na hÉireann, Listowel, Co Kerry.
**REGULARLY PERFORMS WITH:**
Máire O'Keeffe.
**AVAILABILITY:**
General.
**ADDITIONAL INFORMATION:**
Tutor at various summer schools i.e, 1996 Willy Clancy Summer School, Co Clare.

## Martin Donohoe *Accordion*

**Contact:** Mr Martin Donohoe
Swellan Upper
Cavan Town
**Tel:** +353 87 2342270

*"Unique sound ... one of that rare breed of virtuoso Irish two-row accordionists".*
10.95 Shetland Times

**KEY IRISH PERFORMANCES** (since January 1994):
9.96 Mullagh Heritage Centre, promoted by the Local Authority Arts Officer, appearing with Fintan McManus (bouzouki).
10.96 Gort (Cooley weekend), Galway, promoted by local committee, appearing with Fintan McManus (bouzouki).
**KEY PERFORMANCES OUTSIDE IRELAND** (since January 1994):
1994 Shetland Folk Festival, promoted by Wilson Hunter.
2.97 Tour of Britain, promoted by CCÉ, appearing with 15 piece ensemble.
**SELECTED BROADCASTS AND/OR RECORDED WORK:**
1990 'Free spirit', for Cló Iar Chonnachta, Galway.
1990 'Corner House', for UTV and RTÉ.
**PRIZES/AWARDS/APPOINTMENTS:**
8.89 3rd Prize Fleadh Cheoil na hÉireann.
**TRAINING AND/OR QUALIFICATIONS:**
1985 TTCT from CCÉ.
**REGULARLY PERFORMS WITH:**
Group 'No Folking Compromise' and duo with Fintan McManus (guitar, bouzouki).
**AVAILABILITY:**
General.

## Bobby Gardiner *Button Accordion*

**Contact:** Bobby Patrick Gardiner
Burncourt, Cahir
Co Tipperary
**Tel:** +353 52 67235
**Other instruments:** Melodeon.

**KEY PERFORMANCES OUTSIDE IRELAND** (since January 1994):
10.95 Newcastle University, appearing with the Bru-Boru Group.
**SELECTED BROADCASTS AND/OR RECORDED WORK:**
1979 'Bobby Gardiner at Home' for Release Records.
1982 'The Best of Bobby Gardiner' for CCÉ.
1989 'The Master's Choice' for Ossian Publications.
**REGULARLY PERFORMS WITH:**
The Gardiner Trio (concertina, keyboard, accordion).
**AVAILABILITY:**
Weekends.
**ADDITIONAL INFORMATION:**
Has performed and recorded with the Bru-Boru Group at concerts in Japan, USA, Canada, Spain and other countries. Teaches traditional accordion and other instruments. Has recorded for television.

## P.J. Hernon *Button Accordion*

**Contact:** Mr P.J. Hernon
Rathmadder
Gurteen, Ballymote
Co Sligo
**Tel:** +353 71 82449
**Other instruments:** Concertina.

*"Simplicity is the hallmark of the master"*
1978 Irish Times.

**KEY IRISH PERFORMANCES** (since January 1994):
9.2.95 Stray Leaf Folk Club, Forkhill, Newry, promoted by Michael Quinn, appearing with Josephine Keegan (piano/fiddle).
2.7.95 Miltown Malbay, Co Clare, promoted by Muiris Ó Róchaín.
26.5.95 Cois na hAbhanna, Ennis, Co Clare, promoted by CCÉ, appearing with Swallows Tail.
**KEY PERFORMANCES OUTSIDE IRELAND** (since January 1994):
3-12.3.95 Chicago, Detroit, Boston, New York, promoted by Friends of Coleman Group, Harry Bradshaw and appearing with Charlie Lennon.
**SELECTED BROADCASTS AND/OR RECORDED WORK:**
1985 Tour of Europe for CCÉ.
1989 'Béal na Mhúrla'.
1997 'Swallows Tail' for Sound Records, Sligo.
**PRIZES/AWARDS/APPOINTMENTS:**
8.89 All-Ireland Duet Champion from CCÉ.
1989 All-Ireland Trio Champion from CCÉ.
**TRAINING AND/OR QUALIFICATIONS:**
From 1971 to 1973, BA from University College, Galway.
1983 TTCT from CCÉ.
**REGULARLY PERFORMS WITH:**
Marcus Hernon (flute, tin whistle), Swallows Tail Group.
**AVAILABILITY:**
General.
**ADDITIONAL INFORMATION:**
Has given workshops at An Scoil Samhraidh Willie Clancy, the South Sligo Summer School and Scoil Éigse for the last 10 years. Has been involved as both a producer and musician for various tapes, LPs and CDs. Presenter of own programme on Raidió na Gaeltachta and has presented 'Geantraí' for TnaG. Researcher for the Coleman Heritage Centre, Co Sligo. Has toured England, Scotland and Wales. Welcomes any opportunity to perform in Arts/Folk Festivals.

## Derek Hickey *Accordion*

**Contact:** Mr Derek Hickey
Drehidtrasna House
Adare
Co Limerick
**Tel:** +353 61 396131

**KEY IRISH PERFORMANCES** (since January 1994):
22.7.95 Big Top, Galway, promoted by Galway Arts Festival, appearing with De Dannan.
6.9.95 National Concert Hall, Dublin, promoted by The Famine commemoration, appearing with De Dannan.
9.9.95 Metropole Hotel, Cork, promoted by the Cork Folk Festival, appearing with Tommy O'Sullivan.
13.9.95 Quay's Bar, Galway, promoted by Quay's Folk Club, appearing with Frankie Gavin and Carl Hession.
**KEY PERFORMANCES OUTSIDE IRELAND** (since January 1994):
3.95 Germany, promoted by Petr Pandula, appearing with Cian and Tommy O Sullivan.
5.95 Skagen, Denmark, appearing with De Danann.
9/10.95 Helsinki, Finland, promoted by Olli Pellikka, appearing with Fintan Vallely, Liz Doherty and Maighread Ní Dhomhnaill.
24.10.95 Mulhouse, France, appearing with De Dannan.
**SELECTED BROADCASTS AND/OR RECORDED WORK:**
2.94 Raidió Na Gaeltachta.
5.94 'Mist Covered Mountain', for Clare FM.
6.95 'Late Late Show' for RTÉ.
**SELECTED REVIEWS** (since January 1994):
7.95 Irish Times.
**REGULARLY PERFORMS WITH:**
De Danann, Liz Doherty (fiddle), Tommy O'Sullivan (guitar and vocals).

## Conor Keane *Accordion*

**Contact:** Mr Conor Keane
Coore
Mullagh
Co Clare
**Tel:** +353 65 87159

*"Master of the Irish accordion"*
1993 Irish Times (Nuala O'Connor).

**KEY IRISH PERFORMANCES** (since January 1994):
7.93 City Hall, Belfast, appearing with Four Men and a Dog.
**KEY PERFORMANCES OUTSIDE IRELAND** (since January 1994):
15.8.95 Calgary, Canada, promoted by Herschal Freeman, appearing with Arcady.
23.8.95 Milwalkee, USA, promoted by Hershal Freeman, appearing with Arcady and the Voice Squad.
**SELECTED BROADCASTS AND/OR RECORDED WORK:**
1992 'Shifting Gravel' (Four Men and a Dog), for CBM.
1993 'Cooleys House' solo CD.
1995 'Many Happy Returns' for Shanachie.
**SELECTED REVIEWS:**
1993 Irish Times.
**REGULARLY PERFORMS WITH:**
Junior Crehan, Peter O'Loughlin and Shaskeen.
**AVAILABILITY:**
General.
**ADDITIONAL INFORMATION:**
Has performed in Hong Kong, Bagdad, Canada and USA.

## Gerard Lappin *Button Accordion*

**Contact:** Mr Gerard Lappin
24, Greenisland Road
Derrinran
Portadown
Co Armagh
Northern Ireland
**Tel:** +44 1762 851489
**Other instruments:** Tin whistle, fiddle.

**KEY IRISH PERFORMANCES** (since January 1994):
9.95 Sligo, promoted by Stephen Oates and Heineken Pub Sessions, appearing with Martin McGinley.
9.96 Sligo, promoted by Stephen Oates and Heineken, appearing with Séamus O'Kane.
3.97 Derry, promoted by St Patrick's weekend festival, appearing with Maurice Bradley.
5.97 Monaghan, promoted by the Fiddler of Oriel Festival, appearing with Brian Lavery and Séamus O'Kane.
**KEY PERFORMANCES OUTSIDE IRELAND** (since January 1994):
10.94 Shetland Islands, promoted by the Shetland Folk Festival.
**SELECTED BROADCASTS AND/OR RECORDED WORK:**
1994 'Scór' Finals (music for sets) for RTÉ.
**PRIZES/AWARDS/APPOINTMENTS:**
1978 1st Prize at the CCÉ Ulster Fleadh Cheoil for Solo Accordion.
1995 2nd prize in CCÉ Fleadh Cheoil na hÉireann (Senior Duet).
**REGULARLY PERFORMS WITH:**
Maurice Bradley (fiddle), Shane McAleer (fiddle), Gerry McCullagh (banjo).
**AVAILABILITY:**
Weekends, evenings, school holidays.
**ADDITIONAL INFORMATION:**
Has been teaching both groups and individuals on a variety of instruments since 1977. Has adjudicated and taken part in many fleadhanna both in Ireland and overseas.

## John Lyons *Accordion*

**Contact:** Mr John Lyons
Ryans Cross
Ralahine South
Newmarket-on-Fergus
Co Clare
**Tel:** +353 61 368720
**Other instruments:** Singer

**SELECTED BROADCASTS AND/OR RECORDED WORK:**
1970 'May Morning Dew' for Topic Records.
1992 'Troubled Man' for Celtic Records.
**PRIZES/AWARDS/APPOINTMENTS:**
1960/66 Prizewinner at many Fleadhanna.
**REGULARLY PERFORMS WITH:**
Pat Comber (pipes), Kieran Dunne (flute), Pat Mullins (fiddle).
**AVAILABILITY:**
General.
**ADDITIONAL INFORMATION:**
Performs around Clare and Limerick, playing for set dancing groups and singers. Sings with the Ennis Singing Club, the Cork Singing Club as well as occasional singing spots in English Folk clubs. Since 1985, has been toured throughout France.

## Eddie McGinley *Button Accordion*

**Contact:** Eddie McGinley
14, Park Drive Green
Castleknock
Dublin 15
**Tel:** +353 1 8203690
*See guitar page 233.*

## Éamon McGivney *Accordion*

**Contact:** Mr Éamon McGivney
Mullach, Co Clare
**Tel:** +353 65 87417
*See fiddle page 209.*

## Tony MacMahon *Accordion*

**Contact:** Tony MacMahon
6, Elton Park
Sandycove
Co Dublin
**Tel/Fax:** +353 1 2804506

**KEY IRISH PERFORMANCES** (since January 1994):
1994 Amharclann Náithi, Dublin, promoted by RTÉ, appearing with Iarla Ó Lionaird.
1994 Dublin Castle, promoted by the Department of Foreign Affairs, appearing with Noel Hill.
1995 West Belfast Community Arts Festival, promoted by RTÉ.
**KEY PERFORMANCES OUSIDE IRELAND** (since 1994):
10.95 Bremen, Germany, promoted by Radio Bremen.
9.96 Tour of Germany, promoted by Florian Furst and Musikbüro, appearing with Séamas Tansey and Tommy Keane.
**SELECTED BROADCASTS AND/OR RECORDED WORK:**
1994 'Music of Dreams', for Gael-Linn and RTÉ.
1995 'Caravaggio', for RTÉ.
**PRIZES/AWARDS/APPOINTMENTS:**
From 1955, 1st Prizes in the All-Ireland Fleadhanna (category 14 to 18 yrs), awarded by CCÉ.
**REGULARLY PERFORMS WITH:**
Noel Hill (concertina).
**AVAILABILITY:**
General.

## Mary MacNamara *Accordion*

**Contact:** Ms Mary MacNamara
Main Street
Tulla, Co Clare
**Tel:** +353 65 35314
*See concertina page 202.*

## Josephine Marsh *Button Accordion*

**Contact:** Ms Josephine Marsh
11a, Abbey Street
Ennis, Co Clare
**Tel/Fax:** +353 65 41782 / +353 65 24783
**Other instruments:** Concertina, tin whistle, fiddle.

*"The lyric beauty she brings from the accordion is hair-bristling stuff!"*
1995 National Folk Festival, Geelong, Australia.

**KEY IRISH PERFORMANCES** (since January 1994):
4.96 Irish Film Centre, Dublin, promoted by 'Sult' for TnaG, appearing with Donal Lunny and Steve Cooney.
7.96 Galway Arts Festival, promoted by the Druid Theatre, appearing with Pat Marsh and Declan Corey.
12.96 MacNamaras, Scariff, Co Clare, promoted by 'Nationwide' for RTÉ, appearing with De Dannan.
9.97 Tour of Ireland.
**KEY PERFORMANCES OUTSIDE IRELAND** (since January 1994):
3.95 Port Fairy Festival, Australia, appearing with Mick McMahon (guitar).
4.95 National Folk Festival, Canberra, Australia, appearing with Mick McMahon.
4.96 Brittany Festival, promoted by 'Printemps de Chateau Neuf', appearing with Bernard Bizien.
7-8.97 Tour of France.
**SELECTED BROADCASTS AND/OR RECORDED WORK:**
4.94 'Sanctuary Sesiúns' CD for Cruises Pub.
1.96 'Josephine Marsh' for own label.
4.96 'Sult' for TnaG.
**SELECTED REVIEWS** (since January 1994):
1.96 Irish Times (Nuala O'Connor).
3.96 Hot Press (Bill Graham).
2.97 Irish Echo (Earle Hitchner).
**PRIZES/AWARDS/APPOINTMENTS:**
1982 Slógadh All-Ireland title (under 15).
1985 An tÓireachtas All-Ireland titles (Under 18 and senior).
**REGULARLY PERFORMS WITH:**
Josephine Marsh Band, Declan Corey, Bernard Bizien.
**AVAILABILITY:**
General.
**ADDITIONAL INFORMATION:**
Also a traditional music teacher and has given workshops in Australia and France. Featured on 3 new albums released in 1997. Has composed over thirty pieces of music.

## Tríona Ní Dhomhnaill *Accordion* 

**Contact:** Agent: Al Evers
A Train Management
PO Box 29242
Oakland
California 94604
USA
c/o Mrs Bríd O'Donnell
7, Ashgrove Court
Dundrum
Dublin 14
**Tel/Fax:** +1 510 893 4705 or + 353 1 2982413 / +1 510 893 4807
*See piano page 233.*

## Breanndán Ó Beaglaoich
*Button Accordion*

**Contact:** Breanndán Ó Beaglaoich
Cuas
Baile na nGall
Trá Lí
Cho Chiarraí
**Tel:** +353 66 55399
**Other instruments:** Melodeon, singing.

*"It took Begley's presence and the traditional love of polkas to add the spark, making the music dangerous"* 1.9.94 The Scotsman (Norman Chambers).

**KEY IRISH PERFORMANCES** (since January 1994):
2.6.94 Queen's University, Belfast, promoted by Mary Fox, appearing with Paul McGrattan, Mary McNamara and M. Willis.
10.9.94 Swatra, Co Derry, promoted by Brendan Boylan.
13.5.95 Ashley Hall, Belfast, promoted by Mary Fox, appearing with Dermot McLaughlin and Mick Mulkerrins.
20.5.95 'Stray Leaf Folk Club', Mullaghbawn, promoted by Jerry O'Hanlon, appearing with Fran McPhail.
**KEY PERFORMANCES OUTSIDE IRELAND** (since January 1994):
8.94 Edinburgh Festival, promoted by Dave Richardson, appearing with the Boys of the Lough.
10.94 Shetland Folk Festival, promoted by Eileen Hunter.
5.96 Cologne, Germany, appearing on Lindenstrasse.
9.96 Tour of Germany - Cologne, Hamburg, Berlin, Dresden, Munich and Frankfurt.
**SELECTED BROADCASTS AND/OR RECORDED WORK:**
5.94 'Long Black Veil' with The Chieftains.
14.1.95 'Late Late Show' for RTÉ.
1996 'We Won't go home till Morning' for Kells Records, New York.
**SELECTED REVIEWS** (since January 1994):
9.94 Edinburgh Festival Review.
17.11.95 Irish Times (Joe Jackson).
**PRIZES/AWARDS/APPOINTMENTS:**
1983 1st in All-Ireland Fleadh Cheoil (melodeon) with CCÉ.
1983 1st in All-Ireland Trio competition with Scór.
**REGULARLY PERFORMS WITH:**
Duo with Seán Garvey, trio with Frankie Lane and Dermot McLaughlin, trio with Noel O'Grady and Paul O'Shaughnessy and Samhain with Paul McGrattan.
**AVAILABILITY:**
General.
**ADDITIONAL INFORMATION:**
Has travelled extensively throughout Europe, Ireland and England. Toured for 6 weeks in USA and Canada with Boys of the Lough. Has performed with a number of groups including Na Casadaigh and Stockton's Wing. Presenter of traditional programmes on TnaG, ('Geantraí' and another forthcoming series).

## Paddy O'Brien *2 Row Button Accordion*

**Contact:** Mr Paddy O'Brien
3441, 23rd Avenue South
Minneapolis
MN 55407, USA
**Tel:** +1 612 721 7452
**Email:** paddyob@mci2000.com

*"... All of these tunes ... and Paddy's way of playing them have great depth and dignity"*
22.8.95 Mark Bickford, posting to the IRTRAD Newsgroup on the Internet.

**KEY IRISH PERFORMANCES** (since January 1994):
7.94 An Scoil Samhraidh Willie Clancy, Co Clare.
7.94 Mother Redcap's, Dublin, promoted by Eilís Moore.
**KEY PERFORMANCES OUTSIDE IRELAND** (since January 1994):
9.95 Cincinnati Celtic Festival, promoted by Cincinnati Folklife Incorporated, appearing with Joseph Smith (guitar).
10.96 Kentuck Festival of the Arts, Tuscaloosa, Alabama, appearing with Chulrua.
3.97 Irish Music Academy of Cleveland, Ohio, appearing with Michael Cooney (pipes).
4.97 Irish Arts Center, New York, appearing with Chulrua.
**SELECTED BROADCASTS AND/OR RECORDED WORK:**
1988 'Stranger at the Gate' for Green Linnet (SIF 091).
1992 'The Pure Drop' for RTÉ.
1995 'Paddy O'Brien Tune Collection' (self-produced collection of 500 reels and jigs).
**SELECTED REVIEWS** (since January 1994):
3.95 Saint Paul Pioneer Press.
9.96 An Nuaidheacht (newsletter of Conradh na Gaeilge, Washington DC).
**PRIZES/AWARDS/APPOINTMENTS:**
1973 1st Prize (Solo Accordion) An tóireachtas Competition.
1975 1st Prize (Senior Accordion Championship) at a CCÉ All-Ireland Fleadh Cheoil.
**AVAILABILITY:**
General, with 2 months notice.
**ADDITIONAL INFORMATION:**
1997 toured extensively in the USA with Chulrua. Collector of more than 3,000 traditional compositions, including the many rare and unusual tunes, which were included in Breandán Breathnach's 'Ceol Rince na hÉireann'. 1994, ran a week-long workshop at An Scoil Samhraidh Willie Clancy, Co Clare.

## Charles O'Connor *Piano Accordion* 

**Contact:** Mr Charles O'Connor
'St Gabriel's'
Magheraboy Road
Sligo
**Tel:** +353 71 45722
**Other instruments:** Piano accordion.
*See piano page 233.*

## Máirtin O'Connor *Accordion*

**Contact:** Mr Máirtin O'Connor
Annaghdown Pier
Annaghdown
Co Galway
**Tel:** +353 91 791474

*"Unique among traditional box players, Máirtin O Connor unashamedly allows his instrument to seduce him into the most blissful edens of Latin style ..."* Irish Times (Fintan Vallely).

**KEY IRISH PERFORMANCES** (since January 1994):
27.9.95 Watergate Theatre, Kilkenny, promoted by Michael Hannigan, appearing with Máirtin O'Connor Band.
**KEY PERFORMACES OUTSIDE IRELAND** (since January 1994):
15.7.95 Miles Davis Hall, Montreux, promoted by Emmanul Zota, appearing with Máirtin O'Connor Band.
**SELECTED BROADCASTS AND/OR RECORDED WORK:**
'The Connachtman's Rambles', recorded by Mulligan Records. 'Perpetual Motion', recorded by Claddagh Records. 'Chatterbox', recorded by Dara Records.
**SELECTED REVIEWS** (since January 1994):
19.4.94 Belfast Telegraph (Neil Johnston).
9.10.95 News Letter (Ian Wilson).
10.10.95 Belfast Telegraph (Rathcol).
**PRIZES/AWARDS/APPOINTMENTS:**
1995 AIB Traditional Musician of the Year in association with Galway Chamber of Commerce.
**ADDITIONAL INFORMATION:**
Music touches on Irish/French/Turkish semi-classical leanings. Has worked with Dé Dannan, Tommy Hayes, Steve Cooney, Máire Breathnach, Keith Donald and many more.

## Con Ó Driscеoil *Accordion*

**Contact:** Mr Con Ó Drisceoil
61, Maryborough Avenue
Douglas
Co Cork
**Tel:** +353 21 362878
**Other instruments:** Singer, piano.

**KEY IRISH PERFORMANCES** (since January 1994):
1.95 Tour of Ireland, promoted by Music Network, appearing with Dermot Diamond, Fintan Vallely and M. Ní Dhomhnaill.
11.95 National Concert Hall, Dublin, promoted by Na Píobairí Uilleann, appearing with the Four Star Trio.
7.96 Miltown Malbay, Co Clare, promoted by An Scoil Samhraidh Willie Clancy.
**KEY PERFORMANCES OUTSIDE IRELAND** (since January 1994):
8.94 Wadebridge, Cornwall, promoted by the Wadebridge Folk Festival, appearing with the Four Star Trio.
3.96 Jakarta, Indonesia, promoted by St Patrick's Society of Indonesia, appearing with a large music and dance group.
7.96 Tocane St Apre, Dordogne, France, promoted by Rencontre Musicale.
**SELECTED BROADCASTS AND/OR RECORDED WORK:**
6.96 'High Reel' for RTÉ.
9.96 'Geantraí' for TnaG.
7.97 CD for Craft Recordings, 11, Merton Avenue, Dublin 8.
**REGULARLY PERFORMS WITH:**
The Four Star Trio (accordion, fiddle, guitar, vocals).
**AVAILABILITY:**
Weekends and during school holidays.
**ADDITIONAL INFORMATION:**
Composer of comic songs in traditional style, i.e. 'The Pool Song' (recorded by Jimmy Crowley and The Dubliners), 'The Miltown Cockroach' and 'a Hymn to St Finbarr' (recorded by The Four Star Trio) (CRCD02).

## Séan O'Driscoll *Accordion* 

**Contact:** Mr Séan O'Driscoll
Castle View
Blarney
Co Cork
**Tel:** +353 21 385386
*See tenor banjo page 196.*

## Colette O'Leary *Piano Accordion*

**Contact:** Ms Colette O'Leary
7, Rathgar Avenue
Rathgar
Dublin 6
**Tel:** +353 1 4905480
**Other instruments:** Tin whistle.

**KEY IRISH PERFORMANCES** (since January 1994):
3.5.97 Fiddler of Oriel, Monaghan, promoted by Brendan O'Duffy, appearing with the Bumblebees.
28.5.97 Róisín Dubh, Galway, promoted by John Mannion, appearing with the Bumblebees, Donogh Hennessy and Sharon Shannon.
13.6.97 Sandymount Green, Dublin, promoted by John Dunford, appearing with the Bumblebees and Scullion.
14.6.97 Ionad Cois Locha, Donegal, promoted by Micheál Ferry, appearing with the Bumblebees.
**KEY PERFORMANCES OUTSIDE IRELAND** (since January 1994):
4-13.4.97 Barbican, London, promoted by Philip King, and John Dunford, appearing with the Bumblebees, Donogh Hennessy, Donal Lunny and Sharon Shannon.
**SELECTED BROADCASTS AND/OR RECORDED WORK:**
26.2.97 'Sult' for Hummingbird Productions/TnaG.
24.5.97 'Celtic Reel' for Radio Ireland.
9.6.97 'Coppers and Brass' for Midlands Radio 3, Tullamore.
**PRIZES/AWARDS/APPOINTMENTS:**
1985 All-Ireland Fleadh Cheoil na hÉireann Champion (Under-18) from CCÉ.
1986 All-Ireland Fleadh Cheoil na hÉireann Champion (Over 18) from CCÉ.
**TRAINING AND/OR QUALIFICATIONS:**
1986 TTCT from CCÉ.
From 8.88 to 8.91, Attended Scoil Éigse.
8.94 Attended the Paddy O'Brien Summer School.
**REGULARLY PERFORMS WITH:**
Bumblebees.
**AVAILABILITY:**
General.
**ADDITIONAL INFORMATION:**
Has worked as a primary school teacher and arts administrator but now plays music full-time. A member of newly formed traditional group, Bumblebees, who launched their debut CD in May 1997.

## Annette Owens *Button Accordion*

**Contact:** Ms Annette Owens
74, Glenn Road
Tempo
Co Fermanagh, BT94 3JW
Northern Ireland
**Tel:** +44 13655 41498
**Other instruments:** Concertina, piano.

*"Plays music from the heart that is infectious in its tempo of jigs and reels and subtle in the playing of the slower pieces"* 29.11.95 Down Recorder.

**KEY IRISH PERFORMANCES** (since January 1994):
1995 Folk Club, Downpatrick, Co Down, promoted by K Mackle, appearing with G McMahon.
1997 Hill Bar, Loughrea, Co Galway, promoted by G Mallony, appearing with G. McMahon.
**KEY PERFORMANCES OUTSIDE IRELAND** (since January 1994):
1994 Glasgow, Scotland, promoted by J McHugh.
1996 Bielefield, Germany, promoted by Fermanagh District Council, appearing with J McGrath, C Kennedy.
**SELECTED BROADCASTS AND/OR RECORDED WORK:**
1991/92 'Ronan on the Road' for UTV.
1996 'Holiday Ireland' and 'Wish you were Here' for UTV.
**PRIZES/AWARDS/APPOINTMENTS:**
1988 1st Prize at CCÉ All-Ireland Fleadh Cheoil na hÉireann under 12 piano.
1989 1st Prize at CCÉ All-Ireland Fleadh Cheoil na hÉireann (age category 12-15) concertina.
**REGULARLY PERFORMS WITH:**
J McGrath (guitar), G McMahon (guitar).
**AVAILABILITY:**
General.
**ADDITIONAL INFORMATION:**
Has played Irish traditional music from the age of seven. Progressed from button accordion to the concertina and piano and has won All-Ireland titles in both. Performs throughout Ireland and abroad.

# Charlie Piggott *Accordion*

**Contact:** Charlie Piggott
Mountscribe
Kinvara
Co Galway
**Tel:** +353 91 637499
**Other instruments:** Banjo, tin whistle.

*"... An unhurried elegance and a captivating, uplifting swing"* 19.4.96 Irish Times.

**KEY IRISH PERFORMANCES** (since January 1994):
7.95 Galway Arts Festival, in the De Dannan 21st Birthday Celebration concert.
10.95 Séamus Ennis Festival, Finglas, Dublin promoted by Gerard Griffin.
1996 Joyce Summer School, Kilfinane, promoted by Donal O'Connor, appearing with, Thomás O'Réilan (bodhrán).
4.97 Cúirt Galway International Poetry Festival, appearing with the Lonely Stranded Band.
**KEY PERFORMANCES OUTSIDE IRELAND** (since January 1994):
3.94 3rd Celtic Music Festival, San Francisco, USA, promoted by Eddie Stack.
3.96 5th Celtic Music Festival, San Francisco, USA, promoted by Eddie Stack, appearing with the Lonely Stranded Band.
5.96 Brighton Arts Festival, England, promoted by Rodger Leach, appearing with the LSB.
10.96 4th Celtic Music Festival, Monticello, New York, USA, appearing with the LSB.
**SELECTED BROADCASTS AND/OR RECORDED WORK:**
1976 'Mist Covered Mountain' with De Danann for Gael-Linn.
1977 Selected jigs, reels and hornpipes with De Danann, for Sheannachi.
1996 'Lonely Stranded Band' for Cló-Iar Chonnachta (116).
**SELECTED REVIEWS** (since January 1994):
5.96 Irish Music.
9.96 Irish Music.
**PRIZES/AWARDS/APPOINTMENTS:**
1976 Certificate awarded for significant cultural contribution from the Smithsonian Institution (USA).
1978 Made Honourary Citizen of Louisville, Kentucky by the Ancient Order of Hibernians (USA).
**REGULARLY PERFORMS WITH:**
The Lonely Stranded Band.
**AVAILABILITY:**
General.

# John Regan *Accordion*

**Contact:** Mr John Regan
8, Carrickhill Road
Portmarnock
Co Dublin
**Tel:** +353 1 8461903

*"My favourite accordion players are Joe Burke and John Regan"* 1.97 Irish Music Magazine (P.J. Hayes).

**KEY IRISH PERFORMANCES** (since January 1994):
9.95 Town Hall, Sligo, Fiddler of Mooney Celebration Concert, appearing with Brendan McGlinchey, Jim McKillopp.
9.95 Gurteen, Co Sligo, Coleman Memorial Concert, appearing with Séamus Tansey, P.J. Hernon and Marcus Hernon.
5.96 Forkhill, Co Armagh, promoted by CCÉ, appearing with Siamsa Céilí Band and Paddy Glackin.
6.96 Townhall, Riverstown, Co Sligo, promoted by James Morrison Committee, appearing with Joe Burke and Brendan McGlinchey.
**KEY PERFORMANCES OUTSIDE IRELAND** (since January 1994):
CCÉ Tours of England, USA and Canada.
**SELECTED BROADCASTS AND/OR RECORDED WORK:**
6.94 'Seisiún' ('Humours of Donnybrook') for RTÉ.
1995 'Up for the Fleadh' for RTÉ.
1996 'Fleadh Cheoil na hÉireann' for RTÉ.
**PRIZES/AWARDS/APPOINTMENTS:**
8.70 1st Prize at CCÉ All-Ireland Fleadh Ceoil Senior Accordion competition.
8.72 1st Prize at CCÉ All-Ireland Fleadh Ceoil Senior Duet competition with Paddy Glackin.
**AVAILABILITY:**
General.
**ADDITIONAL INFORMATION:**
Particular interest in music of East Galway (Paddy Fahy, Paddy Carty and Aggy White). Has taught in the Scoileanna Éigse in Kilkenny, Clonmel, Sligo and Listowel.

# Tanya Vassilevich
***Bayan (Byelorussian/Russian button accordion)***

**Contact:** Ms Tanya Vassilevich
2, Dominic Street Court
Dominic Street
Cork
**Tel/Fax:** +353 21 398475 / +353 21 272103
**Other instruments:** Tsimbali

*"... Byelorussian bayan exile, opened a challenging curtain on the Eastern European landscape, in the magic garden of exotic sound"* 11.9.95 Irish Times.

**KEY IRISH PERFORMANCES** (since January 1994):
8.9.95 Everyman Palace, Cork, promoted by Cork Folk Festival, appearing with Cafe Orchestra and Loyko.
**SELECTED BROADCASTS AND/OR RECORDED WORK:**
8.6.87 'Folk Music in Belarus', for Republic Youth Radio, Minsk, Belarus.
26.11.91 'Choral programme', for Republic Television Company, Minsk, Belarus.
**PRIZES/AWARDS/APPOINTMENTS:**
25.4.80 Solo Diploma winner, awarded by Department of Culture, Brest, Belarus, at the Republic Music Teachers Competition.
**TRAINING AND/OR QUALIFICATIONS:**
From 9.74 to 7.79, BA Degree, College of Music, Baranovichi, Belarus.
From 9.84 to 6.89, MA, University of Culture, Minsk, Belarus.
**AVAILABILITY:**
General.
**ADDITIONAL INFORMATION:**
Was director of folk groups 'Kirmash', 'Tuteishiya' at the College of Music, Baravovichi, Belarus.
*See tsimbali page 299.*

## BANJO

# John Carty *Banjo*

**Contact:** John Carty
Knockroe
Boyle
Co Roscommon
**Tel/Fax:** +353 79 68063
*See fiddle page 204.*

## Kieran Hanrahan *Tenor Banjo*

**Contact:** Mr Kieran Hanrahan
4, The Rise
Woodpark
Ballinteer
Dubin 16
**Tel:** +353 1 2988650

**KEY IRISH PERFORMANCES** (since January 1994):
3.95 Killarney, promoted by John O'Shea.
6.95 Harcourt Hotel, promoted by Mary Cashin.
7.95 Miltown Malbay, promoted by John Burke, appearing with the Temple House Ceili Band.
**SELECTED BROADCASTS AND/OR RECORDED WORK:**
From 1979 to 1990, various recordings with 'Stocktons Wing'.
1994 'The Long Black Veil' (The Chieftains) for BMG.
**PRIZES/AWARDS/APPOINTMENTS:**
1977 All-Ireland Senior Tenor Banjo Champion, awarded by CCÉ.
**REGULARLY PERFORMS WITH:**
Kieran Hanrahan Trio (banjo, accordian, guitar) Temple House Ceili Band.
**ADDITIONAL INFORMATION:**
Has recorded and performed with The Chieftains, Stocktons Wing and Sammy Davis Junior. Arranged traditional music for Irish film "The Field", and has taught traditional music technique to leading musicians in other musical fields.

## Catherine McLaughlin *Banjo* 

**Contact:** Mrs Catherine McLaughlin
Dooish Crossoads
Drumquin
Co Tyrone BT78 4KE
Northern Ireland
**Tel:** +44 1662 831713
*See singers page 248.*

## Sandi Miller *Banjo*

**Contact:** c/o Mr Bill Whelan
39, Fairview Gardens
Dublin 3
**Tel:** +353 1 8331920
*See fiddle page 297.*

## Pádraig Morrell *Tenor Banjo*

**Contact:** Pádraig Morrell
Carraun, Corballa
Ballina, Co Mayo
**Tel:** +353 96 70383

**KEY IRISH PERFORMANCES** (since January 1994):
3/4.94 Joe Cooley weekend, Gort, Co Galway, appearing with P and B Gallagher.
8.95 Feakle Festival, Co Clare, appearing with P Gallagher and John Murphy.
9.95 Sligo Traditional Music Festival, appearing with P Gallagher and Tom Mc Donagh.
5.96 Feile na nDéise, Dungarvan, Co Waterford, appearing with P and B Gallagher and P Doyle.
**SELECTED BROADCASTS AND/OR RECORDED WORK:**
20.1.92 'Corner House' for RTÉ.
12.6.96 'The High Reel' for RTÉ.
14.9.96 'Ceili House' at St Vincent's GAA club for RTÉ.
**PRIZES/AWARDS/APPOINTMENTS:**
91/92 Banjo tutor for the South Sligo Summer School.
**REGULARLY PERFORMS WITH:**
Peter Gallagher (box), Brian Gallagher (pipes) Paul Doyle (guitar).
**AVAILABILITY:**
General.

## Johnny Murgrew *Banjo*

**Contact:** Mr Johnny Murgrew
112, Shanreagh Park
Limavady, Co Derry
**Tel:** +44 15047 64820
*See guitar page 223.*

## Gerry O'Connor *Banjo*

**Contact:** c/o Myriad Media Management
23, Monastery Gate Green
Clondalkin
Dublin 22
**Tel/Fax:** +353 1 4640094

*"... May be the single best four string banjoist in the history of Ireland. His phenomenal technique fully justifies it"* 9.7.97 Celtic Music (Earl Hitchner).

**SELECTED BROADCASTS AND/OR RECORDED WORK:**
1991 'Time to Time', recorded by Mulligan Records.
**REGULARLY PERFORMS WITH:**
Four Men and a Dog, Wild Geese, Arcady, Manus Lunny, Vinnie Kilduff, Steve Cooney.

## Séan O'Driscoll *Tenor Banjo*

**Contact:** Mr Séan O'Driscoll
Castle View
Blarney
Co Cork
**Tel:** +353 21 385386
**Other instruments:** Accordion, guitar, cittern, mandolin, singer.

**KEY IRISH PERFORMANCES** (since January 1994):
1996 Feakle Festival, Co Clare, appearing with Laurence Nugent.
1996 Lobby Bar, Cork, appearing with Laurence Nugent.
1996 McCarthys, Baltimore, Cork, appearing with Laurence Nugent.
1996 Cork Folk Festival, appearing with Mary O'Driscoll.
**KEY PERFORMANCES OUTSIDE IRELAND** (since January 1994):
1996 North Texas Festival, appearing with James Keane.
1996 Alaskan Folk Festival, appearing with Laurence Nugent.
1996 Cleveland Folk Festival, appearing with Laurence Nugent and Liz Carroll.
1996 St Paul's Irish Festival, appearing with Mary O'Driscoll.
**SELECTED BROADCASTS AND/OR RECORDED WORK:**
'Up the Airy Mountain' for Green Linnet.
'Hill 16' for Shanachie.
'Séan O'Driscoll' own recording.
**REGULARLY PERFORMS WITH:**
Laurence Nugent (flute) Paddy O'Brien (accordion), Mary O'Driscoll (fiddle).
**AVAILABILITY:**
General.
**ADDITIONAL INFORMATION:**
Has given master classes in banjo, accordion and guitar.

## Brendan O'Dwyer *Banjo*

**Contact:** Mr Brendan O'Dwyer
Ruan
Bansha, Co Tipperary
or
48, Perth Road
Finsbury Park
London N4 3HB, England
**Tel:** +353 62 54534 / +44 171 2636686
**Other instruments:** Bones, guitar, bass guitar and tin whistle.

**KEY IRISH PERFORMANCES** (since January 1994):
4.94 Coachman, Clonmel, Co Tipperary, promoted by Coachman Promotions, appearing with local musicians.
6.95 Cashel, Co Tipperary, promoted by Traditional Pub Promotions, appearing with local musicians.
8.96 Looby's, Co Tipperary, promoted by Looby Promotions, appearing with local musicians.
12.96 The Foot, Co Tipperary, appearing with local musicians.
**KEY PERFORMANCES OUTSIDE IRELAND** (since January 1994):
7.8.94 George Robey, London, promoted by Robey Promotions, appearing with Shrug.
15.6.96 Póitin Stil, London appearing with Bang on the Ear.
22.11.96 The New Fountain, London, appearing with Doc Carroll and his Band.
10.5.97 The Dolphin, London, promoted by Dolphin Promotions, appearing with The Galtee Rangers.
**SELECTED BROADCASTS AND/OR RECORDED WORK:**
12.1.97 'PM' program for BBC Radio 4.
**TRAINING AND/OR QUALIFICATIONS:**
Since 9.96 Meitheal Cheol, (teacher Karen Ryan), Year 3 intermediate (banjo).
Since 9.96 Meitheal Cheol, (teacher Kathy Walton), Year 2 (whistle).
4.97 Barbican Centre, London, fiddle workshop (Donegal style).
5.97 Barbican Centre, London, flute workshop (teacher James Galway).
**REGULARLY PERFORMS WITH:**
The Galtee Rangers, Meitheal Cheol.
**AVAILABILITY:**
General.
**ADDITIONAL INFORMATION:**
Has a broad background in performance and appreciation of music coming from a strong musical family tradition. Available for all types of projects.

## Charlie Piggott *Banjo*

**Contact:** Charlie Piggott
Mountscribe
Kinvara, Co Galway
**Tel:** +353 91 637499
*See accordion, page 195.*

# BODHRÁN, BONES AND OTHER PERCUSSION

## Lloyd Byrne *Percussion*

**Contact:** Mr Lloyd Byrne
c/o 46, Loreto Avenue
Rathfarnham,Dublin 14
**Tel/Mobile:** +353 1 495 0103 / +353 87 2390961
*See classical percussion page 30.*

## Noel Carberry *Bodhrán*

**Contact:** Mr Noel Carberry
1, Derryhawn
Kenagh, Co Longford
**Tel:** +353 43 25194
*See uilleann pipes page 235.*

## Morgan Crowley *Bodhrán*

**Contact:** Morgan Crowley
259, Howth Road
Dublin 5 (h)
c/o Hilary Gagan Associates
Caprice House
3, New Burlington Street
London W1X 1FE
England (a)
**Tel:** +353 1 8335805
**Email:** morganstar@compuserve.com
*See singers page 112.*

## Steve Dunford *Bodhrán*

**Contact:** Mr Steve Dunford
6, The Avenue
Boden Park, Rathfarnham
Dublin 16
**Tel/Fax:** +353 1 4947615 or +353 1 49323358 / +353 1 4931707

**REGULARLY PERFORMS WITH:**
Máire Breatnach Band.

## Brian Dunning *Bodhrán and Bones*

**Contact:** Mr Brian Dunning
72, Moyglare Village
Maynooth, Co Kildare
**Tel/Fax:** +353 1 6285678
*See flute page 271.*

## Séamas Fogarty *Bones*

**Contact:** Mr Seamas Fogarty
54, Woodlawn Park
Churchtown, Dublin 14
**Tel/Fax:** +353 1 2983028 / +353 1 6763900
*See concertina page 201.*

## Michael Howard *Bodhrán*

**Contact:** Mr Michael Howard
53, Balkill Park
Howth, Co Dublin
**Tel:** +353 1 8323475
**Email:** howmac@indigo.ie
*See guitar classical page 21.*

## Barry Kerr *Bodhrán*

**Contact:** Mr Barry Kerr
25, Island View Lane
Kinnego, Lurgan
Co Armagh, BT67 9JF
Northern Ireland
**Tel/Fax:** +44 1762 321730 or +44 1762 324660 /
+44 1762 324449
*See flute page 216.*

## Neill Lyons *Bodhrán*

**Contact:** Neill Lyons
22, Verbena Grove
Sutton
Dubin 13
**Tel:** +353 1 8390032

**KEY IRISH PERFORMANCES** (since January 1994):
7.96 Harcourt Hotel, Dublin, appearing with Délos.
3.97 Queen's Hotel, Ennis, appearing with Turas.
4.97 Mean Fiddler, Dublin, promoted by Earthwatch, appearing with Délos.
5.97 National Concert Hall, Dublin, promoted by An tÓireachtas, appearing with Délos, Frankie Gavin and Noel Hill.
**KEY PERFORMANCES OUTSIDE IRELAND** (since January 1994):
Festival Interceltique Lorient, Brittany France, appearing with Délos.
**SELECTED BROADCASTS AND/OR RECORDED WORK:**
1.94 For RTÉ 1.
6.96 Délos CD for Délos records.
**PRIZES/AWARDS/APPOINTMENTS:**
8.94 All-Ireland (under 18) Bodhrán Champion, awarded by CCÉ, Clonmel.
10.96 Senior Bodhrán Champion, awarded by An tÓireachtas, Donegal.
**REGULARLY APPEARS WITH:**
Daire Bracken (fiddle), Eamonn de Barra (flute) and the group Délos, Peter Molloy (flute).
**AVAILABILITY:**
General.

## Tim Lyons *Bodhrán*

**Contact:** Mr Tim Lyons
Roshill Road
Roscam
Galway
**Tel:** +353 91 752180
*See singers page 247.*

## Mel Mercier *Bodhrán and Bones*

**Contact:** Mr Mel Mercier
Music Department
University College Cork
Cork
**Tel/Fax:** +353 21 902271 / +353 21 271595
**Other instruments:** Various African and Indian percussion instruments, Japanese gamelan.

*"Mel Mercier's 'dance' displays his mighty command of percussion idioms"* Irish Times.

**KEY IRISH PERFORMANCES** (since January 1994):
1996 Point Depot, Dublin appearing in Riverdance.
11.96 University of Limerick, promoted by the Irish World Music Centre (Sionna Festival), appearing with Pulsus.
3.97 Temple Bar Music Centre, Dublin appearing with the University College, Cork Japanese Gamelan.
**KEY PERFORMANCES OUTSIDE IRELAND** (since January 1994):
1-2.97 Tour of Spain and France with Liam O'Flynn.
3.97 Barbican Centre, London, appearing with UCC traditional musicians.
**SELECTED BROADCASTS AND/OR RECORDED WORK:**
'Pulsus' for the 'River Of Sound' TV series for Hummingbird productions.
Dance piece on Volume CD recorded at the Crawford Gallery, Cork.
Track 'Crispy Must be More' co-composed with M Ó Súilleabháin, on the 'Gaiseadh' for Virgin/Venture.
**SELECTED REVIEWS** (since January 1994):
5.11.96 Irish Times.
**TRAINING AND OR QUALIFICATIONS:**
From 1986 to 1989, B Mus from University College, Cork.
1989 to 1991, MA in World Music from the California Institute of the Arts.
**REGULARLY PERFORMS WITH:**
Prof Míchéal Ó Sulleabháin (piano), Pulsus (percussion group) and Liam O'Flynn.
**AVAILABILITY:**
Subject to schedule.

## John Moulden *Bodhrán, Spoons*

**Contact:** Mr John Moulden
10, Apollo Walk
Portrush
Co Antrim, BT56 8HQ
Northern Ireland
**Tel:** +44 1265 825080
**Email:** jmoul81075@aol.com
*See singers page 249.*

## Colm Murphy *Bodhrán*

**Contact:** Mr Colm Murphy
Kilcronan
Bantry
Co Cork
**Tel:** +353 27 67254

*"... Matchless bodhrán playing bonds the lot together"* 1996 The Examiner (Pat Ahern).

**KEY IRISH PERFORMANCES** (since January 1994):
1996 Royal Dublin Society, RTÉ Proms, appearing with De Dannan.
1995 Áras án Uachtarain, Dublin, appearing with De Dannan.
Various appearances at the National Concert Hall, Dublin, i.e The Famine Commemoration Concert, Amnesty International Concert, An Taisce concert etc.
**KEY PERFORMANCES OUTSIDE IRELAND** (since January 1994):
1994 Yokohama, Japan promoted by Nomad, appearing with De Dannan.
1996 Theatre du Ville, Paris, promoted by Imaginaire Irlandais, appearing with De Dannan.
1995 Moscow, promoted by Aer Rianta/Department of Foreign Affairs, appearing with Moscow Youth Orchestra/Island Neddy.
1997 Hong Kong/Beijing, tour appearing with De Dannan.
**SELECTED BROADCASTS AND/OR RECORDED WORK:**
1993 Performances on 'Dolphin's Way' composed by Michéal Ó Suillebháin for Virgin.
1996 'An Bodhrán'/'The Irish Drum' for Gael-Linn records.
1996 Recording of 'Hibernian Rhapsody' for Bees/Knees records.

**SELECTED REVIEWS** (since January 1994):
1994 Melody Maker.
1996 The Examiner, (Pat Ahern).
**PRIZES/AWARDS/APPOINTMENTS:**
From 1994 to 1996, Bodhrán tutor, Music Department, University College, Cork.
**AVAILABILITY:**
General.
**REGULARLY PERFORMS WITH:**
De Dannan.
**ADDITIONAL INFORMATION:**
Has performed on numerous recordings since the seventies, playing on classic albums by De Dannan, Áltan, Jackie Daly, Máirtin O'Connor, Séan Ryan, Michéal Ó Suillebháin, Cáthal McConnell and others.

## Fergal O'Brien *Bodhrán*

**Contact:** Fergal O'Brien
Tulymacrieve Road
Mullaghbawn
Newry
Co Down
Northern Ireland, BT35 9RE
**Tel:** +44 1693 888066
**Other instruments:** Concertina and piano.

*"Last years appearance was a highly memorable event for all of those present"*
8.2.97 Stray Leaf Folk Club, Newsletter (ref: perf on 25.5.96).

**KEY IRISH PERFORMANCES** (since January 1994):
25.5.96 O'Hanlons, Mullaghbawn, promoted by the Stray Leaf Folk Club, appearing with the Conway Family.
6.96 Queen's University, Belfast, promoted by the the Beat Initiative, appearing with Terry Conlon and Jacky McPeake.
8.6.96 Visitors Centre, Scarva, promoted by Scarva 800 committee, appearing with Lambeg players.
8.2.97 O'Hanlons, Mullaghbawn, promoted by Stray Leaf Folk Club, appearing with the Conway Family
**KEY PERFORMANCES OUTSIDE IRELAND** (since January 1994):
5.4.97 Palma de Mallorca, promoted by Pedro Pascual Fullana, appearing with Seven Towers Dancing Club, Ballymena.
**SELECTED BROADCASTS AND/OR RECORDED WORK:**
8.2.97 'Wham Bam Strawberry Jam', recorded by BBC (children's programme featuring traditional music and poetry).
3.97 'The High Reel', for RTÉ.
**PRIZES/AWARDS/APPOINTMENTS:**
1980 All-Ireland Grúpa Cheoil champions, awarded by Slogadh.
1997 3er Premio Especial Danza, awarded by Jurado International Festival, Palma, Spain.
**TRAINING AND/OR QUALIFICATIONS:**
From 1976 to 1977, 'O' level music.
1977 Grade 5 theory, from Trinity College of Music, London.
6.97 Masterclass in concertina, Chulainn, Mullaghbawn, (teacher Michael O'Halmháin).
1978 Grade 8 piano, from Trinity College of Music, London.
**REGULARLY PERFORMS WITH:**
Terry Conlon (accordion), Conway family (Dundalk) and Pádraig O'Brien (fiddle).
**AVAILABILITY:**
General.
**ADDITIONAL INFORMATION:**
Has attended numerous festivals in Ireland and on the continent. Has made several television appearances. Comes from a strong family music tradition.

## Brendan O'Dwyer *Bones*

**Contact:** Mr Brendan O'Dwyer
Ruan
Bansha
Co Tipperary
or
48, Perth Road
Finsbury Park
London N4 3HB
England
**Tel:** +353 62 54534 / +44 171 2636686
*See banjo page 197.*

## Jason O'Rourke *Bodhrán*

**Contact:** Mr Jason O'Rourke
13, Rutland Street
Belfast
Northern Ireland
**Tel/Fax:** +44 1232 203782
**Email:** jason.orourke@cableol.co.uk
*See concertina page 203.*

## Richard Alan Sterritt *Lambeg Drum*

**Contact:** Mr Richard Sterritt
Kum-Min
3, Forest View
Markethill
Co Armagh, BT601
Northern Ireland
**Tel:** +44 1861 551465

**KEY IRISH PERFORMANCES** (since January 1994):
7.94 St Patrick's Training Centre, promoted by Armagh District Council.
12/13.4.95 Eurovision Song Contest, Armagh Navan Centre, promoted by Bord Failte.
4-6.8.95 County Council, Waterford.
**SELECTED BROADCASTS AND/OR RECORDED WORK:**
3.94 Magilloway's Way, UTV.
7.94 'Blood and Belongings' for BBC.
6.95 Tommy Sands Programme, Downtown Radio.
**PRIZES/AWARDS/APPOINTMENTS:**
From 1990 to 1992 Ulster's Drummer of the Year, awarded by Armagh/ Down Drumming Association.
**AVAILABILITY:**
Weekends.
**ADDITIONAL INFORMATION:**
Also a manufacturer of Lambeg drums (whole drum).

## Frank Torpey

### *Bodhrán, Snare Drum (Brushes) and Bones*

**Contact:** c/o Mr Pat Conway
Lobby Bar
1, Union Quay
Cork
**Tel:** +353 21 311113

**KEY IRISH PERFORMANCES** (since January 1994):
8.95 Whelan's, Dublin, promoted by Des McCullough.

1.9.95 Olympia Theatre, Dublin, promoted by MCD.
9.9.95 Lobby Bar, Cork Folk Festival.
**KEY PERFORMANCES OUTSIDE IRELAND** (since January 1994):
3.94/95 Tour of Germany, promoted by Peter Pandula.
5.95 Oslo, Norway.
9/10.95 Irish Festival, Finland.
**SELECTED RECORDED WORK:**
2.95 'I Won't be Afraid Any More' for Solid.
2.95 'A River of Sound' TV series and album, for Hummingbird Productions and Virgin.
5.95 Nomos 'All the Ways You Wander' for Solid Records.
**SELECTED REVIEWS** (since January 1994):
24.8.94 Irish Times.
26.1.95 The Examiner.
2.95 Irish Times.
**PRIZES/AWARDS/APPOINTMENTS:**
5.91 Received the Brendan McDonagh Award, from the Music Department, University College, Cork.
**TRAINING AND/OR QUALIFICATIONS:**
From 87 to 91, B Mus, University College, Cork.
**REGULARLY PERFORMS WITH:**
Nomos.
**AVAILABILITY:**
General.

# BOUZOUKI

## Pat Ahern *Bouzouki*

**Contact:** Mr Pat Ahern
Clonmoyle East
Coachford
Co Cork
**Tel/Fax:** +353 21 334271
**Email:** pahern@rtc-cork.ie
*See guitar page 220.*

## Séan Corcoran *Bouzouki*

**Contact:** Séan Corcoran
2 Boyne Terrace
Drogheda, Co Louth
**Tel:** +353 41 35082

**REGULARLY PERFORMS WITH:**
Cran.

## Jimmy Crowley *Bouzouki*

**Contact:** Mr Jimmy Crowley
134, Sunday's Well Road
Cork
**Tel:** +353 21 309727
*See singers page 245.*

## Alec Finn *Bouzouki*

**Contact:** Mr Alec Finn
Oranmore
Co Galway
**Tel/Fax:** +353 91 792156

## Michael Howard *Bouzouki*

**Contact:** Mr Michael Howard
53, Balkill Park
Howth
Co Dublin
**Tel:** +353 1 8323475
**Email:** howmac@indigo.ie
*See guitar classical page 21.*

## Barry Kerr *Bouzouki*

**Contact:** Mr Barry Kerr
25, Island View Lane
Kinnego
Lurgan
Co Armagh BT67 9JF
Northern Ireland
**Tel/Fax:** +44 1762 321730 or +44 1762 324660 / +44 1762 324449
*See flute page 216.*

## Donal Lunny *Bouzouki*

**Contact:** Donal Lunny
c/o John Dunford
Top Floor Management
7-9 Sweetman's Avenue
Blackrock
Co Dublin
**Tel/Fax:** +353 1 2834244 / +353 1 2834886

## Gerry McKee *Bouzouki*

**Contact:** Mr Gerry McKee
1, Redbridge Mews
Cove Street
Cork
**Tel:** +353 21 318986

**KEY IRISH PERFORMANCES** (since January 1994):
30.8.95 Whelans, Wexford Street, Dublin, promoted by Des McCullough, appearing with Nomos.
14.10.95 Lobby Bar, Cork, promoted by Pat Conway, appearing with Nomos.
21.10.95 Harcourt Hotel, Dublin, promoted by Des McCullough, appearing with Nomos.
**KEY PERFORMANCES OUTSIDE** (since Janaury 1994):
From 25.9.95 to 9.10.95, Finland Irish Festival, promoted by Olli Pellikka, appearing with Nomos.
**SELECTED RECORDED WORK:**
1.95 'I Won't Be Afraid Anymore', for Solid Records.
5.95 'All The Ways You Wander', Nomos, for Solid Records.
**SELECTED REVIEWS:**
26.1.95 The Examiner.
2.95 Irish Times.
24.8.94 Irish Times.
**REGULARLY PERFORMS WITH:**
Nomos.
**AVAILABILITY:**
General.

## Niall Ó Callanáin *Bouzouki*

**Contact:** Niall Ó Callanáin
1, Park Place
Islandbridge
Dublin 8
**Mobile:** +353 87 414435
**Other instruments:** Electric bouzouki, guitar, mandolin.

**KEY IRISH PERFORMANCES** (since January 1994):
2/3.97 Galway and Cork, promoted by Celtic Flame Festival, appearing with Máire Breatnach.
6.97 Whelan's, Dublin, appearing with Phil Callery.
6.97 Sibín, Galway, promoted by Teilifis na Gaeilge, appearing with Lá Lugh.
**KEY PERFORMANCES OUTSIDE IRELAND** (since January 1994):
7.96 Whitby, England, promoted by Whitby Folk Festival, appearing with Phil Callery.
10.96 Tour of Germany, promoted by Wünder Tütte, Irish Folk Festival, appearing with Máire Breatnach.
3.97 Malaysia, promoted by Selanger Society, appearing with 'Furry Village'.
6/7.97 Trondhéim and Forde, Norway, promoted by Trondheim City Millenium and Forde Folk Festival, appearing with Eimear Quinn and La Lugh.
**SELECTED BROADCASTS AND/OR RECORDED WORK:**
5.96 Deiseal 'Sunshine Dance', for Starc Records.
5.96 Eurovision song contest, appearing with Eimear Quinn with 'The Voice' for RTÉ.
6.96 Máire Breatnach Album - 'Celtic Lovers' for Starc Records.
**REGULARLY PERFORMS WITH:**
Phil Callery Band, Máire Breatnach Band, Lá Lugh and D'Goya.
**AVAILABILITY:**
General.
**ADDITIONAL INFORMATION:**
Producer of the albums by 'D'Goya' and 'Phil Callery. Co-Author with Tommy Walsh of 'The Irish Bouzouki' published by Waltons.

## Cyril O'Donoghue *Bouzouki*

**Contact:** Mr Cyril O'Donoghue
144, Finian Park
Shannon
Co Clare
**Tel/Mobile/Fax:** +353 61 361545 or +353 87 2344978 /
+353 61 364051
**Other instruments:** Guitar, vocals.

**TRAINING AND/OR QUALIFICATIONS:**
Attends the annual Scoil Samhraidh Willie Clancy (teacher Séamus McMahon).
**REGULARLY PERFORMS WITH:**
Doolin and Michael Queally (fiddle).
**AVAILABILITY:**
General.
**ADDITIONAL INFORMATION:**
Has toured Italy with Michael Quelly several times over the past 3 years, performing with the award-winning Italian group, The Birking Tree.

# CONCERTINA

## Terry Crehan *Concertina*

**Contact:** Terry Crehan
Liffey Bank Promotions
21, Colthurst Close
Huntington Glen
Lucan
Co Dublin
**Tel:** +353 1 621 0090
*See fiddle page 206.*

## Séamas Fogarty *Concertina*

**Contact:** Mr Séamas Fogarty
54, Woodlawn Park
Churchtown
Dublin 14
**Tel/Fax:** +353 1 2983028 / +353 1 6763900
**Other instruments:** Harmonica, bones.

**SELECTED BROADCASTS AND/OR RECORDED WORK:**
6.96 'High Reel', for RTÉ.
3.97 Raidio na Gáeltachta.
**AVAILABILITY:**
General.
**ADDITIONAL INFORMATION:**
Enjoys playing music in informal settings.

## Dave Hennessy *Concertina*

**Contact:** Mr Dave Hennessy
Cros Ard
Crosshaven
Co Cork
**Tel/Fax:** +353 21 831386
**Other instruments:** Melodeon.

**KEY IRISH PERFORMANCES** (since January 1994):
10.11.96 Belfast Folk Festival, appearing with Any Old Time and The Fallen Angels.
9.96/97 Cork Folk Festival.
1997 'Geantraí' and 'Sult' for TnaG, appearing with Any Old Time.
**KEY PERFORMANCES OUTSIDE IRELAND** (since January 1994):
3.96 Vienna, Austria promoted by Manfred Hanus, appearing with 'Any Old Time'.
3.96 Shetland Folk Festival appearing with Any Old Time/Peter Rowan.
8.96 Sidmouth Folk Festival, appearing with Any Old Time/Chris Smithers.
3.97 Botswana, Africa, promoted by St Patrick's Society, Botswana appearing with Jimmy Crowley.
**SELECTED BROADCASTS AND/OR RECORDED WORK:**
1982 'Any Old Time' for Mulligan.
1989 'Phoenix' for Dara Records.
1995 'Crossing' for Dara records.
**REGULARLY PERFORMS WITH:**
Séamus Creagh, Any Old Time.
**AVAILABILITY:**
General.

# P.J. Hernon *Concertina*

**Contact:** Mr P.J. Hernon
Rathmadder
Gurteen
Ballymote
Co Sligo
**Tel:** +353 71 82449
*See accordions page 190.*

# Noel Hill *Concertina*

**Contact:** Mr Noel Hill
'Mill Lodge'
Mill Lane
Shankill
Co Dublin
**Tel/Fax:** +353 1 2823249

*"Noel Hill's fame precedes him in the form of albums and broadcasts that serve as a forum for his talents"* New York Times.

**KEY IRISH PERFORMANCES** (since January 1994):
4.96 Town Hall Theatre Galway, promoted by Michael Diskin, appearing with Brendan O'Reagan.
4.96 Seven Oaks Hotel, Carlow, promoted by Bríd de Róiste, appearing with Tony MacMahon.
**KEY PERFORMANCES OUTSIDE IRELAND** (since January 1994):
11.95 The Elm Tree Folk Club, Oxford, promoted by Joe Ryan.
11.95 Angra Do Herdismo, Tercirera, Azores, Portugal.
3.96 The Last Inn, Hengoed, Wales, promoted by John Neilsen.
3.96 The Fir Cone Club, Maidenhead, England.
**SELECTED BROADCASTS AND/OR RECORDED WORK:**
9.95 'Joanie Madden Session', for Green Linnet, New York.
11.95 Radio/television recordings in Portugal.
3.96 'Lifelines' for RTÉ.
**SELECTED REVIEWS:**
L'arena Di Verona, Irish Times.
**PRIZES/AWARDS/APPOINTMENTS:**
1986 Awarded the BBC Radio Traditional Album of the Year Award.
1990 Awarded the BBC Northern Ireland, Irish Voice Album of the Decade.
1995 Appointed to National Board of International Folk Music Centre of Ireland.
1995 Appointed to Advisory Committee of the Irish Music Rights Organisation (IMRO).
**REGULARLY PERFORMS WITH:**
Frankie Gavin (fiddle), Tony MacMahon (accordian), Arty McGlynn (guitar).
**ADDITIONAL INFORMATION:**
Has performed extensively abroad including the Tivoli Gardens, Copenhagen, Royal Albert Hall, London, Yahanderhalle in Cologne and concert halls throughout North America and Australia. Has established a school in Dublin City and in Co Clare for the teaching and development of the concertina.

# Claire Keville *Concertina*

**Contact:** Ms Claire Keville
Claran
Ower
Co Galway
**Tel:** +353 93 35952
**Other instruments:** Tin whistle, piano.

**KEY IRISH PERFORMANCES** (since January 1994):
3.96 University of Limerick, appearing with Liam Lewis (fiddle).
12.96 Old Ground, Ennis, Co Clare, appearing with Durra.
4.97 Temple Gate, Ennis, appearing with Durra.
4.97 Cobblestones, Dublin, appearing with Durra.
**KEY PERFORMANCES OUTSIDE IRELAND** (since January 1994):
Various performances in Brittany, appearing with Patrick Le Roux (guitar) and Frederic Samsun (fiddle).
4.96 'Paddy Go Easy' Festival Aarhus, Denmark, appearing with Durra.
4.96 Aarhus Art Gallery, Denmark, appearing with Durra.
**SELECTED BROADCASTS AND/OR RECORDED WORK:**
3.97 Demo tape with Liam Lewis.
4.97 For Clare FM.
**TRAINING AND/OR QUALIFICATIONS:**
From 1987 to 1990, BA from Univeristy College, Cork.
From 1990 to 1991, B Mus (Hons) from UCC.
From 1991 to 1992, H Dip Ed from UCC.
**REGULARLY PERFORMS WITH:**
Liam Lewis (fiddle), Eithne Ní Dhonaile (harp), John Weir (fiddle).
**AVAILABILITY:**
Weekends, evenings in June, July, August.
**ADDITIONAL INFORMATION:**
Teaches classical piano in 'Maoin Cheoil an Chláir', Co Clare and plays concertina regularly in sessions around Ennis. Has given workshops i.e 1993 to 1995, Scoil Éigse. All-Ireland prizewinner on many occasions. From 1993 to 1995, played with 'Celtic Contraband' in Brittany.

# Gabriel McArdle *Concertina*

**Contact:** Gabriel McArdle
92, Hillview Road
Enniskillen
Co Fermanagh
Northern Ireland
**Tel:** +44 1365 324165
*See singers page 247.*

# Mary MacNamara *Concertina*

**Contact:** Ms Mary MacNamara
Main Street
Tulla
Co Clare
**Tel:** +353 65 35314
**Other instruments:** Accordion, melodeon, fiddle.

*"Highlight of the year"* 12.94 Irish Times.

**KEY IRISH PERFORMANCES** (since January 1994):
7.95 An Scoil Samhraidh Willie Clancy, Co Clare.
3.96 Danlán an Chláir, Ennis, appearing with Martin Hayes.
12.96 Éigse Dhiarmuid, Colea.
**SELECTED BROADCASTS AND/OR RECORDED WORK:**
1994 'Mary MacNamara' Traditional Music From East Clare' for Claddagh Records.
1994/95 For the Irish Traditional Music Archive, Dublin.
1996 'High Reel' for RTÉ.
**PRIZES/AWARDS/APPOINTMENTS:**
1979 All-Ireland Fleadh Cheoil na hÉireann solo concertina winner awarded by CCÉ.
**TRAINING AND/OR QUALIFICATIONS:**
7.92 TTCT from CCÉ.
**REGULARLY PERFORMS WITH:**
Catherine McEvoy, Brendan Begley, Martin Hayes.
**AVAILABILITY:**
General.

## Josephine Marsh *Concertina*

**Contact:** Ms Josephine Marsh
11a, Abbey Street
Ennis, Co Clare
**Tel/Fax:** +353 65 41782 / +353 65 24783
*See accordions page 192.*

## Breanndán Ó Beaglaoich *Concertina*

**Contact:** Breanndán Ó Beaglaoich
Cuas, Baile na nGall
Trá Lí
Cho Chiarraí
**Tel:** +353 66 55399
*See accordions page 192.*

## Fergal O'Brien *Concertina*

**Contact:** Fergal O'Brien
Tulymacrieve Road
Mullaghbawn
Newry
Co Down
Northern Ireland, BT35 9RE
**Tel:** +44 1693 888066
*See bodhrán page 199.*

## Jason O'Rourke *Concertina*

**Contact:** Mr Jason O'Rourke
13, Rutland Street
Belfast
Northern Ireland
**Tel/Fax:** +44 1232 203782
**Email:** jason.orourke@cableol.co.uk
**Other instruments:** Bodhrán.

**KEY IRISH PERFORMANCES** (since January 1994):
1997 Various including venues in: Kiltyclogher, Glencolmcille, Derrygonnelly.
6.97 Ashleigh Hall, Belfast, promoted by the Belfast and District Set Dancing Society, appearing with Hemi-semi-demi-Quavers.
**KEY PERFORMANCES OUTSIDE IRELAND** (since January 1994):
7.96 and 7.97 St Malo, France appearing with Maggie's Leap.
3.97 and 6.97 Rome appearing with Davy Maguire.
**SELECTED BROADCASTS AND/OR RECORDED WORK:**
1993 'Traditional Irish Music' for Orba Records (Prague).
1995 'Traditional Music from Belfast' for Outlet Records (Belfast).
10.97 'Togaí' with Davy Maguire and Martin Dowling for Outlet Records.
**TRAINING AND/OR QUALIFICATIONS:**
From 1991 to 1994, BA from Queen's University, Belfast.
From 1994 to 1995, MA from Queen's University, Belfast.
Since 1995, PhD at Queen's University, Belfast.
**REGULARLY PERFORMS WITH:**
Davy Maguire (flute), Maggie's Leap, Trasna.
**AVAILABILITY:**
General.
**ADDITIONAL INFORMATION:**
Often plays for set dancing and in informal sessions. Member of Belfast Set Dancing Society committee. Has also worked on a project with Scottish Opera and has performed on French radio.

## Annette Owens *Concertina*

**Contact:** Ms Annette Owens
74, Glenn Road
Tempo
Co Fermanagh, BT94 3JW
Northern Ireland
**Tel:** +44 13655 41498
*See accordions page 194.*

## Michael Rooney *Concertina*

**Contact:** Mr Mackie Rooney
Tyraverty
Scotstown
Co Monaghan
**Tel:** +353 47 89161
*See Irish Harp page 230.*

## Niall Vallely *Concertina*

**Contact:** Niall Vallely
c/o Mr Pat Conway
Lobby Bar
1, Union Quay
Cork
**Tel:** +353 21 311113

*"Niall Vallely's technical mastery and genius for improvisation are matched by apparently inexhaustible creative reserves"* 2.95 Irish Times.

**KEY IRISH PERFORMANCES** (since January 1994):
5.8.95 Drogheda Folk Festival, appearing with Mick Daly, John Spillane, Frank Torpey.
30.8.95 Whelan's, Dublin, promoted by Des McCullough, appearing with Nomos.
1.9.95 Olympia Theatre, Dublin, promoted by MCD, appearing with Nomos.
9.9.95 Lobby Bar, Cork, as part of Cork Folk Festival.
**KEY PERFORMANCES OUTSIDE IRELAND** (since January 1994):
3.95 Tour of Germany, promoted by Peter Pandula.
5.95 The Dubliner, Oslo, Norway, promoted by Serge Grando, appearing with Nomos.
11.8.95 Béal Bocht, New York, appearing with Ciarán Coughlan and Cillian Vallelly.
28.9-9.10.95 Irish Festival, Finland, promoted by Olli Pellikka, appearing with Nomos.
**SELECTED BROADCASTS AND/OR RECORDED WORK:**
2.95 'I Won't be Afraid Any More' for Solid.
2.95 'A River of Sound', TV series and album, for Hummingbird productions and Virgin.
4.95 Nomos 'All the Ways You Wander' for Solid Records.
**SELECTED REVIEWS** (since January 1994):
24.8.94 Irish Times.
26.1.95 The Examiner.
**PRIZES/AWARDS/APPOINTMENTS:**
10.88 University College, Cork, Entrance Scholarship, awarded by CCÉ.
7.92 Seán Ó Riada Memorial prize, awarded by UCC.
**TRAINING AND/OR QUALIFICATIONS:**
From 10.88 to 6.92, B Mus, from University College, Cork.
**REGULARLY PERFORMS WITH:**
Nomos.
**AVAILABILITY:**
General.

# FIDDLE

## Daire Bracken *Fiddle*

**Contact:** Mr Daire Bracken
4, Longford Place
Monkstown, Co Dublin
**Tel:** +353 1 2807283
**Email:** obreacan@ucd.ie

*"Yahoo..."* 6.97 Irish Music Magazine.

**KEY IRISH PERFORMANCES** (since January 1994):
8.95 National Concert Hall, Dublin, appearing with Jimmy McGreavy, Kevin Rowsome.
1996 Quays Pub, Galway, appearing with Danú.
1996 Queens, Ennis, Co Clare, appearing with Danú.
11.96 Cultúrlan, Belfast, appearing with Púca.
**KEY PERFORMANCES OUTSIDE IRELAND** (since January 1994):
2.96 Tour of UK, promoted by CCÉ.
8.96 Festival Interceltique Lorient, Brittany, France, appearing with Danú.
3.97 Tour of San Francisco and surroundings appearing Danú.
4.97 Barcelona, appearing with Steve Larkin.
**SELECTED BROADCASTS AND/OR RECORDED WORK:**
1996 'Preab sa Cheol' for Coláiste Eoin-Íosagáin.
7.96 Púca Compilation for SGO Music Managment.
1.97 'Danú' for Claddagh Records.
**SELECTED REVIEWS** (since January 1994): 13.8.96 Guest (France).
13.8.96 Le Télégramme.
**PRIZES/AWARDS/APPOINTMENTS:**
1993 1st Prize in Fiddle (Under 18) at the CCÉ Leinster Fleadh Ceoil.
10.95 2nd Prize in Senior Fiddle at An tÓireachtas competitions (All-Ireland).
**REGULARLY PERFORMS WITH:**
Danú, Púca, Mick Broderick (bouzouki), Niall Lyons (bodhrán) Peter Molloy (flute).
**AVAILABILITY:**
College holidays.

## Paul Bradley *Fiddle*

**Contact:** Mr Paul Bradley
No 1, Parliament Street
Newark, NG24 4UR
England
**Tel:** +44 1636 700271
**Other instruments:** Tin whistle, flute.

**KEY IRISH PERFORMANCES** (since January 1994):
Stray Leaf Folk Club, Mullaghbawn, promoted by Gerry O'Hanlon, appearing with Kieran and Paddy Burns.
Armagh Folk Club, promoted by John Butler, appearing with Paddy Keenan.
'Live Music Now' performances, promoted by Lorna Hastings, appearing with Trasna.
Belfast Folk Festival, Hatfield House, promoted by Nigel Martin, appearing with Trasna.
**KEY PERFORMANCES OUTSIDE IRELAND** (since January 1994):
1994 'Live Music Now' performances, Nottinghamshire, promoted by Lorna Hastings, appearing with Trasna.
8.94 Folk Festival, Italy, promoted by Andrea del Favero.
1995 Oxo Irish Festival, promoted by Roots Music Agency, appearing with Trasna.
1995/96 Oslo, promoted by Roots Music Agency, appearing with Trasna.
**SELECTED BROADCASTS AND/OR RECORDED WORK:**
Irish music session (from Belfast) for Outlet Records, Gordon Street, Belfast.
8.97 'Fuaim na Farraige', featuring Paul Doyle (guitar), John McSherry (pipes), Martin Quinn (accordion), Alan McCartney (guitar) and produced by Rod McVey for Outlet Records.
**TRAINING AND/OR QUALIFICATIONS:**
Since 5.9.95, Qualification received in repairing and making violins from Newark School of Violin making.
**REGULARLY PERFORMS WITH:**
John McSherry (pipes), Martin Quinn (accordion), 'Trasna' (fiddle, flute, concertina, guitar).
**AVAILABILITY:**
July, August, December, January, Easter.
**ADDITIONAL INFORMATION:**
Has played fiddle for over twenty years. Main influences are the great players of Sligo and Donegal and players in the North. Has performed as a guest with Jackie Daly and Paddy Keenan.

## Máire Breatnach *Fiddle/Viola*

**Contact:** c/o Mr Steve Dunford
6, The Avenue
Boden Park
Rathfarnham
Dublin 16
**Tel/Fax:** +353 1 4947615 or +353 1 49323358 / +353 1 4931707
*See Máire Breatnach Band page 257.*

## Kevin Burke *Fiddle*

**Contact:** Mr Kevin Burke
4949 North East 34th Avenue
Portland
Oregan 97211, USA
**Tel/Fax:** +1 503 2812920

**SELECTED BROADCASTS AND/OR RECORDED WORK:**
'If the Cap Fits'. 'Up Close', recorded by Green Linnet Records.
1982 'Portland', duo LP with Michael O'Domhaill.
'Eavesdropper' with Jackie Daly (accordion).
**PRIZES/AWARDS/APPOINTMENTS:**
Grand Prix Du Disque, at 1980 Montreux Jazz Festival, for 'Promenade', duo LP with Michael O'Domhaill.
Six month contract to play for the Danish National Theatre's production of Brendan Behan's play 'The Hostage'.
**ADDITIONAL INFORMATION:**
Worked with Kate Bush, Arlo Guthrie, Doug Dillard and Christy Moore.
From 1976 to 1979 played with the Bothy Band.

## John Carty *Fiddle*

**Contact:** Mr John Carty
Knockroe
Boyle
Co Roscommon
**Tel/Fax:** +353 79 68063
**Other instruments:** Banjo, flute.

*"When a banjo legend masters the fiddle, are some people just too talented? ..."*
6.96 Irish Voice, New York.

**KEY IRISH PERFORMANCES** (since January 1994):
5.96 Wexford Arts Centre, appearing with Brian McGrath.
7.96 Druid Theatre, Galway Arts festival, appearing with Brian McGrath.

2.97 Ulster Folk and Transport Museum.
3.97 Limerick.
**KEY PERFORMANCE OUTSIDE IRELAND** (since January 1994):
5.96 Cannes Film Festival, France.
7.96 Rencontres Irlandais Festival, France.
8.96 Sidmouth Festival, promoted by Mrs Casey Music.
5.97 Hammersmith Irish Centre, London, appearing with Brian McGrath.
**SELECTED BROADCASTS AND/OR RECORDED WORK:**
1996 'Last Night's Fun' for Shanachie Records, USA.
8.97 'The Cat that ate the Candle' for Cló-Iar Chonnachta, Galway.
**SELECTED REVIEWS** (since January 1994):
8.96 Irish Times.
11.96 Folk Roots (UK).
**PRIZES/AWARDS/APPOINTMENTS:**
8.78 Junior CCÉ All-Ireland Fleadh Ceoil na Éireann, banjo champion.
8.80 Senior CCÉ All-Ireland Banjo Champion.
**REGULARLY PERFORMS WITH:**
At the Racket, Francis Gaffney (guitar), Vera Gaffney (vocals), Brian McGrath (piano).
**AVAILABILITY:**
General.
**ADDITIONAL INFORMATION:**
Greatly influenced by the Sligo, Leitrim and Roscommon styles of fiddle and banjo playing.

## Nollaig Casey *Fiddle*

**Contact:** Nollaig Casey
51, Lios Mór
Cappagh Road
Bearna
Co Galway
**Tel:** +353 91 590908
**Other instruments:** Tin whistle, keyboards, singer.

**KEY PERFORMANCES OUTSIDE IRELAND** (since January 1994):
6.95 Hammersmith Apollo, London in 'Riverdance - the Show'.
3.96 Tour of Australia and New Zealand.
8.96 Tour of Japan.
4.97 Barbican, London, appearing with the Donal Lunny Band.
**SELECTED BROADCASTS AND/OR RECORDED WORK:**
1988 'Lead the Knave', for Round Tower Records.
1995 'Causeway', for Tara Records.
1996 'Sult', series for TnaG and RTÉ (15 programmes).
**PRIZES/AWARDS/APPOINTMENTS:**
Winner of several All-Ireland competitions.
**AVAILABILITY:**
General.

## Michael Clarkson *Fiddle*

**Contact:** Mr Michael Clarkson
5, Carmel Street
Belfast BTY 1QE
Northern Ireland
**Tel:** +44 1232 311830 / +44 1232 734000 (day)
**Other instruments:** Flute.

**KEY PERFORMANCES OUTSIDE IRELAND** (since January 1994):
Various Irish pubs throughout Europe.
**SELECTED BROADCASTS AND/OR RECORDED WORK:**
1996 'The High Reel' for RTÉ.
1996/1997 'Music Matters' for BBC Radio 3.
**AVAILABILITY:**
General.

## Bríd Cranitch *Fiddle* 

**Contact:** Ms Bríd Cranitch
13, Hansboro
Belgrave Avenue
Wellington Road
Cork
**Tel/Fax:** +353 21 502037 / +353 21 393333
*See piano page 232.*

## Matt Cranitch *Fiddle*

**Contact:** Mr Matt Cranitch
Kerry Pike
Co Cork
**Tel/Fax:** +353 21 870235 / +353 21 393333
**Email:** mcranitch@rtc-cork.ie

*"... Recognised as one of the finest fiddle players in the country ..."* 14.9.97 The Examiner.

**KEY IRISH PERFORMANCES** (since January 1994):
5.96 Tour of Ireland, promoted by Music Network, appearing with Dónal Murphy, Tommy O'Sullivan and Johnny McCarthy.
8.9.96 Cork Folk Festival, appearing with Dave Hennessy and Mick Daly.
9.11.96 Belfast Folk Festival, appearing with Dave Hennessy and Mick Daly.
24.5.97 Sligo Arts Festival, promoted by SAF, appearing with Dónal Murphy and Tommy O'Sullivan.
**KEY PERFORMANCES OUTSIDE IRELAND** (since January 1994):
29.6.96 Festival Celtique de Savoie, promoted by Chris Buffet, appearing with Dave Hennessy and Mick Daly.
3.8.96 Turin City Festival, promoted by Franco Luca, appearing with Dave Hennessy and Mick Daly.
6.8.96 Sidmouth Folk Festival, promoted by Alan Bearman, appearing with Dave Hennessy and Mick Daly.
30.10.96 'The Burren', Boston, USA, promoted by Tommy McCarthy, appearing with Dónal Murphy and Tommy O'Sullivan.
**SELECTED BROADCASTS AND/OR RECORDED WORK:**
6.95 'Crossing' (CD), recorded by Dara Records.
10.95 'Sliabh notes' (CD), for Cross Border Media.
9.96 'Geantraí', recorded by Forefront Productions for TnaG.
**SELECTED REVIEWS** (since January 1994):
The Examiner (Pat Ahern).
11.11.95 Belfast Telegraph (Neil Johnston).
9.6.97 Evening Echo (Paul Dromey).
**PRIZES/AWARDS/APPOINTMENTS:**
1990 Appointed Lecturer and Performer at the Irish-American Cultural Institute in USA.
Since 1993, Appointed Director of Cork Arts Festival.
**TRAINING AND OR QUALIFICATIONS:**
From 1973 to 1976, B Mus from University College, Cork.
From 1966 to 1970, B Ed From UCC.
**REGULARLY PERFORMS WITH:**
Mick Daly (guitar), Dave Hennessy (melodeon), Dónal Murphy (accordion) and Tommy O'Sullivan (guitar).
**AVAILABILITY:**
General.
**ADDITIONAL INFORMATION:**
Author of The Irish Fiddle Book. Particularly interested in the music of Sliabh Luachra and is engaged in research on the fiddle style of this region. Lectures and gives master classes in Ireland and abroad. Frequent contributor to radio programmmes.

# Séamus Creagh *Fiddle*

**Contact:** Mr Seamas Creagh
8, Croaghta Park
Glasheen Road
Cork
**Tel:** +353 21 314769
**Email:** desplanq@csvax1.ucc.ie

**KEY IRISH PERFORMANCES** (since January 1994):
1995 Éigse Cois Laoi, Cork, promoted by University College Cork, appearing with Jackie Daly.
1996 Castleisland Folk Festival, appearing with Aidan Coffey.
1997 Róisín Dubh pub, Galway, appearing with Jackie Daly.
**KEY PERFORMANCES OUTSIDE IRELAND** (since January 1994):
1995 Forest of Dean Festival, appearing with Pat Grey Sullivan (box).
1996 London, appearing with Johnny Leary (box).
1997 Bangkok, appearing with B Ring, J Neville and P Sullivan.
**SELECTED BROADCASTS AND/OR RECORDED WORK:**
1994 'Came the Dawn' for Ossian.
1996 'Geantraí' for TnaG.
1997 'Sult', for Hummingbird Productions and TnaG.
**REGULARLY PERFORMS WITH:**
Aidan Coffey (box), Eoghan Ó Riabhaig (pipes), Mick Daly (guitar).
**AVAILABILITY:**
General.

# Niall Crehan *Fiddle*

**Contact:** Mr Niall Crehan
110, Courtown Park
Kilcock
Co Kildare
**Tel/Mobile:** +353 1 6287030 / +353 87 481933

**KEY IRISH PERFORMANCES** (since January 1994):
1995 Dublin, promoted by the World Suzuki Conference.
1995 Brazen Head, Dublin, appearing with Boo to a Goose.
1995 St Coleman's, Mullingar, promoted by Deirdre O'Brien.
4.97 Kilcock, promoted by Raidió na Gaeltachta, appearing with Dark Horse.
**KEY PERFORMANCES OUTSIDE IRELAND** (since January 1994):
From 1994 to 1997 Glyndbourne Opera Festival, appearing with the Royal Philharmonic Orchestra.
1996 New Jersey, USA, promoted by the Jean Butler School of Dancing.
1996/97 Frankfurt, Germany, promoted by An Sibín Pub.
**SELECTED BROADCASTS AND/OR RECORDED WORK:**
1996 Music for Team Theatre Company.
**SELECTED REVIEWS** (since January 1994):
1997 Aims Review (for 'Fiddler on the Roof').
**PRIZES/AWARDS/APPOINTMENTS:**
From 1980 and 1987, Runner up in the Fleadh Cheoil na hÉireann (Slow Airs).
1985 Winner at Feis Máithiú.
**TRAINING AND/OR QUALIFICATIONS:**
From 1972 to 1983, Scholarships and prizes from DIT Conservatory of Music and Drama, Dublin.
**REGULARLY PERFORMS WITH:**
Boo to a Goose, Crehan Family, Dark Horse, Enfield Wren Boys.
**AVAILABILITY:**
General.
**ADDITIONAL INFORMATION:**
Began studying at the age of five in the DIT CMD.

# Terry Crehan *Fiddle*

**Contact:** Terry Crehan
Liffey Bank Promotions
21, Colthurst Close
Huntington Glen
Lucan, Co Dublin
**Tel:** +353 1 621 0090
**Other instruments:** Violin, flute, concertina, pipes, guitar, bouzouki, guitar.

**KEY IRISH PERFORMANCES** (since January 1994):
1995/1996 Belfast, promoted by Ardoyne Fleadh.
Several appearances with Eilis Moore and friends.
**KEY PERFORMANCES OUTSIDE IRELAND** (since January 1994):
1995 Estonia, promoted by the Viljonti Folk Festival, appearing with Callino.
1996 Galalia, Spain, appearing with Callino.
**SELECTED BROADCASTS AND/OR RECORDED WORK:**
1994 'Live at Matt Molloys' for World Music.
1994 'The Corner House' for UTV and BBC production.
1996 'The May Morning Dew' for Michael O'Brien and QCM records.
**SELECTED REVIEWS** (since January 1994):
Cara Magazine.
Irish Music Magazine.
**PRIZES/AWARDS/APPOINTMENTS:**
From 1967 to 1982, Various classical and traditional awards.
**TRAINING AND/OR QUALIFICATIONS:**
From 1967 to 1980, Performers Diploma from Royal College of Music (Sheila O'Loughlin).
From 1995 to 1997 Diploma in Psychotherapy.
1995-97 Reiki Mastership.
**AVAILABILITY:**
General.
**ADDITIONAL INFORMATION:**
Teacher and manager of Liffey Bank Promotions.

# Jillian Delaney *Fiddle*

**Contact:** Jillian Delaney
30, Fremont Drive
Melbourn
Bishopstown
Cork
**Tel:** +353 21 544887
*See Irish Harp page 228.*

# Dermot Diamond *Fiddle*

**Contact:** Dr Dermot Diamond
Coolquoy
The Ward
Co Dublin
**Tel/Fax:** +353 1 8351654
**Email:** diamondd@iol.ie
**Other instruments:** Guitar.

**KEY IRISH PERFORMANCES** (since January 1994):
1994 An Scoil Samhraidh Willie Clancy, Co Clare, appearing with Bernadette McCarthy, Henry Benagh and Paul O'Shaughnessy.
1995 Tour of Ireland, promoted by Music Network appearing with Fintan Vallely, Con O'Druisceoil and Mairéad Ní Dhomhnaill.
1996 Olympia, Dublin, appearing with the Fleadh Cowboys.
**KEY PERFORMANCES OUTSIDE IRELAND** (since January 1994):
1994 Mainz, Germany, appearing with Altan.
1995 North Texas Festival, Dallas and Las Cruces, New Mexico, appearing with Altan.

1996 Copenhagen Irish Music Festival.
1996 Shetland Folk Festival, appearing with Martin McGinley, Siobhán Peoples and Paul O'Shaughnessy.
**SELECTED BROADCASTS AND/OR RECORDED WORK:**
1995 'River of Sound' for Hummingbird.
1997 'Willie Clancy Sessions' for RTÉ.
**PRIZES/AWARDS/APPOINTMENTS:**
1974 2nd Prize in the CCÉ All-Ireland Fleadh Cheoil na hÉireann (Duets).
**REGULARLY PERFORMS WITH:**
Tara Diamond (flute).
**AVAILABILITY:**
General.
**ADDITIONAL INFORMATION:**
Experienced player of traditional music and has performed extensively for many years on stage, radio and television. Has played with Frankie Lane, Paul O'Shaughnessy and the members of Altan. Also taught fiddle for several years at the An Scoil Samhraidh Willie Clancy, Co Clare.

# Liz Doherty *Fiddle*

**Contact:** Ms Liz Doherty
Music Department
University College
Cork
**Tel/Fax:** +353 21 902678 or +353 21 551986 / +353 21 271595

*"Ecstatic two-hands fiddle"* 24.8.94 Irish Times.

**KEY IRISH PERFORMANCES** (since January 1994):
4.2.95 Mother Redcaps, Dublin, promoted by Des McCullough, appearing with Nomos.
18.2.95 Rotterdam, Belfast, appearing with Nomos.
22.2.95 Everyman Palace, Cork, promoted by Pat Conway, appearing with Nomos.
14.7.95 National Concert Hall, appearing with Tim Lyons, Maighread Ní Dhomhnaill and Fintan Vallely.
**KEY PERFORMANCES OUTSIDE IRELAND** (since January 1994):
From 2.3.95 to 27.3.95, Tour of Germany, promoted by Petr Pandula, appearing with Nomos.
20.8.95 Ben Eoin, Cape Breton, Nova Scotia, Canada, promoted by An Tullochgorm Society.
30.8.95 Gaelic College, Cape Breton, Nova Scotia, Canada, promoted by Bruc MacPhee and Ryan MacNeil.
From 30.9.95 to 8.10.95 Helsinki, Finland, promoted by Olli Pellikka, appearing with Derek Hickey, Maighread Ní Dhomhnaill, Fintan Vallely
**SELECTED BROADCASTS AND/OR RECORDED WORK:**
1991 'Fiddlesticks' - Irish traditional music from Donegal, for Nimbus.
1995 'I Won't be Afraid Anymore' for Solid Records.
2.95 'Kenny Live', for RTÉ.
**SELECTED REVIEWS** (since January 1994):
24.8.94 Irish Times.
20.2.95 Irish Times.
5.95 Folk Roots.
**REGULARLY PERFORMS WITH:**
Derek Hickey (accordion).
**AVAILABILITY:**
Weekends (weekdays are restricted from October to May).
**ADDITIONAL INFORMATION:**
Particularly interested in the fiddle tradition of Cape Breton Island, Nova Scotia, Canada and is completing a PhD on the subject. Plays many Cape Breton tunes, and is Director of the Cape Breton Ireland Musical Bridge.

# Martin Dowling *Fiddle*

**Contact:** Mr Martin Dowling
16B, Adelaide Road
Belfast BT9 6FX
Northern Ireland
**Tel:** +44 1232 280108

**KEY IRISH PERFORMANCES** (since January 1994):
10.94 Fiddle Grand Concert, Glenties, Co Donegal, appearing with Vincent Campbell, James Byrne and others.
6.95 Belfast Folk Festival, promoted by Nigel Martyn, appearing with Christine Dowling and Daithi Sproule.
8.96 Belfast Folk Festival, promtoed by Nigel Martyn, appearing with Christine Dowling and Daithi Sproule.
5.97 Downpatrick Folk Club, promoted by Nigel Martyn, appearing with Christine Dowling and Daithi Sproule.
**KEY PERFORMANCES OUTSIDE IRELAND** (since January 1994):
8.94/95/96/97 Irish Festival Milwawkee, USA, appearing with Christine Dowling and Daithi Sproule.
8.97 Irish Festival, Minnesota, USA, appearing with Christine Dowling and Daithi Sproule.
**SELECTED BROADCASTS AND/OR RECORDED WORK:**
5.96 'The High Reel', recorded by RTÉ.
6.97 'A Thousand Farewells', recorded by Cottage Music Records.
11.97 'The O'Ales', recorded by Outlet Records.
**REGULARLY PERFORMS WITH:**
Christine Dowling and Daithi Sproule.
**AVAILABILITY:**
General.

# Frankie Gavin *Fiddle*

**Contact:** Mr Frankie Gavin
Ardnasillagh
Oughterard
Co Galway
**Tel:** +353 91 552545
**Other instruments:** Tin whistle, flute, viola, keyboards.

**SELECTED BROADCASTS AND/OR RECORDED WORK:**
1983 'Croch Suas É' for Shanachie.
1989 'Frankie Goes to Town' for Shanachie.
1996 'Shamrocks and Holly' for Shanachie.
Also the 'The Best of Frankie Gavin' compilation.
**REGULARLY PERFORMS WITH:**
De Dannan.
**AVAILABILITY:**
General.
**ADDITIONAL INFORMATION:**
Founding member of De Dannan. Has made two videos including 'Frankie Gavin Live,' (which includes an appearance with violinist Stephane Grapelli). Has also recorded with Charlie Lennon, Carl Hession and Yehudi Menuhin. Appeared on the Rolling Stones album 'Voodoo Lounge' and Elvis Costello's 'Spike'. Has performed for and appeared in 'The Irish RM' and 'A River of Sound' for RTÉ.

# Paddy Glackin *Fiddle*

**Contact:** Mr Paddy Glackin
40, St Lawrences Road
Clontarf, Dublin 3
**Tel:** +353 1 8336014

**TRAINING AND/OR QUALIFICATIONS:**
Studied classical music at the DIT Conservatory of Music and Drama, Dublin.

**ADDITIONAL INFORMATION:**
Member of the Ceoltoiri Laighean in 1970's and also founder member of the Bothy Band. Recorded first solo album on Gael-Linn label, then recorded 'Hidden Ground' album with the late Jolyon Jackson. Performed and recorded with artists such as Van Morrison, Kate Bush and composer John Cage. Recent recordings include 'Ragharta Cheoil' with Donal Lunny and 'Seidan Si' with piper Robbie Hannan. Editor of features and documentary programmes for RTÉ Radio.

# Martin Hayes *Fiddle*

**Contact:** Mr Martin Hayes
c/o Helen Bommarito Agency
Wallingford Avenue North
Seattle
Washington 98103
USA
**Tel/Fax:** +1 206 5477210 or +353 1 4783925 /
+1 206 5475014
**Email:** hbomm@aol.com
agarvey@indigo.ie

*"... Combines an exceptional gift for personal expression with a prodigious musical ear ... great playing and remarkable creativity ..."*

Irish Times (Nuala O'Connor).

**SELECTED RECORDED WORK:**
6.93 'Martin Hayes' for Green Linnet Records.
6.95 'Under the Moon' for Green Linnet Records.
6.97 'The Lonesome Touch'.
**PRIZES/AWARDS/APPOINTMENTS:**
1995 Best Traditional Act, awarded by Hot Press/Heineken Rock Awards of Ireland.
1996 Traditional Musician of the Year, awarded by National Entertainment Awards.
Winner of All-Ireland Championships six times.
**ADDITIONAL INFORMATION:**
Works with musicians from jazz, classical, folk and rock backgrounds. Has performed worldwide including concert tours and appearances on television and radio programmes in Ireland, USA, Canada, Australia, Britain and France. CD 'Martin Hayes' has been named amongst the Top Ten Best Albums of 1993 in polls by both the Irish Times, and the Irish Echo newspapers. Former member of the Tulla Ceili Band.

# Elizabeth Kane *Fiddle*

**Contact:** Elizabeth Kane
Dawrosmore
Letterfrack
Co Galway
**Tel:** +353 95 41157

**KEY IRISH PERFORMANCES** (since January 1994):
2.94 Lobby, Cork, promoted by Pat Conway, appearing with Donnach Moynihan.
3.95 Tour of Ireland, promoted by CCÉ.
9.95 Bonne Chère, Sligo, promoted by Sligo Arts Festival, appearing with Mirella Murray.
9.96 Community School, Clifden, Co Galway, promoted by Clifden Community Arts Week, appearing with Yvonne and Ita Kane.
**KEY PERFORMANCES OUTSIDE IRELAND** (since January 1994):
3.94 Tour of Germany, promoted by Peter Pandula, appearing with Upstairs in a Tent.
7.96 Tour of Wales, appearing with Maimin Cajun Band.
7.96 The Blarney Star, New York, promoted by Don Meade, appearing with Yvonne Kane and Katherine Corrigan.
11.96 Shetland Folk Festival, appearing with Yvonne Kane and Katherine Corrigan.
**SELECTED BROADCASTS AND/OR RECORDED WORK:**
2.94 'The Long Note' with Jackie Small for RTÉ.
5.96 'High Reel' for RTÉ.
8.96 CCÉ Fleadh Cheoil na hÉireann performance for RTÉ.
**SELECTED REVIEWS** (since January 1994):
5.95 Northern Standard (Monaghan).
**PRIZES/AWARDS/APPOINTMENTS:**
7.92 Travel grant awarded at the Fiddler of Dooney Festival, Sligo.
5.96 Travel grant awarded at the Fiddler of Oriel Festival.
**TRAINING AND/OR QUALIFICATIONS:**
B Mus awarded from University College, Cork.
1997 H Dip in Education.
**REGULARLY PERFORMS WITH:**
Katherine Corrigan (piano), Yvonne Kane (fiddle) and Mirella Murray (piano accordion).
**AVAILABILITY:**
Weekends.

# Laoise Kelly *Fiddle*

**Contact:** Ms Laoise Kelly
10, Mountain View
Ennis
Co Clare
**Tel/Fax:** +353 91 528839
*See Irish harp page 228.*

# Gerard Lappin *Fiddle*

**Contact:** Mr Gerard Lappin
24, Greenisland Road
Derrinran
Portadown
Co Armagh
Northern Ireland
**Tel:** +44 1762 851489
*See accordions page 191.*

# Charlie Lennon *Fiddle*

**Contact:** Dr Charlie Lennon
Ard Mhuire
Baily, Howth
Co Dublin
**Tel/Fax:** +353 1 8322409 / +353 1 6615688
**Email:** cathal@chl.ie
**Other instruments:** Piano.

*"Known internationally as an immensely gifted composer, pianist and fiddler in the Irish tradition"* 22.12.93 Irish Echo (New York).

**KEY IRISH PERFORMANCES** (since January 1994):
1994 National Concert Hall, Dublin, promoted by Gael-Linn, appearing with the Lennon family.
1995 Harcourt Hotel, Dublin, appearing with John Sheehan and Ben Lennon.
1996 University College, Cork.
1997 Galway Arts Festival, appearing with the Lennon Family.
**KEY PERFORMANCES OUTSIDE IRELAND** (since January 1994):
3.94 Chicago, promoted by the Chicago Irish Community, appearing with M Coleman Association.

3.95 Australian tour, promoted by John Nicholls, appearing with local orchestras.
8.96 Milwaukee, Irish Festival appearing with an orchestra.
11.96 New York, promoted by Green Linnet, appearing with Joe Burke and Andy McGann.
**SELECTED BROADCASTS AND/OR RECORDED WORK:**
1993 'Island Wedding' CD for RTÉ.
1994 'Dance of the Honey Bees' for Gael-Linn.
1996 'Flight from the Hungry Land' for World Music.
**SELECTED REVIEWS** (since January 1994):
29.3.96 Irish Times.
6.11.96 Irish World.
**PRIZES/AWARDS/APPOINTMENTS:**
1.94 Winner of Irish Echo (New York) Traditional Musician of the Year.
3.96 Commissioned as composer to commemorate the Famine by the Irish Government.
**REGULARLY PERFORMS WITH:**
Éilís Lennon, Seán Lennon.
**AVAILABILITY:**
Weekends.

## Órna Loughnane *Fiddle*

**Contact:** Órna Loughnane
Brockmanngasse 114/9
A-8010
Graz
Austria
**Tel:** +43 316 842344
*See fiddle page 297.*

## Éamon McGivney *Fiddle*

**Contact:** Mr Éamon McGivney
Mullach
Co Clare
**Tel:** +353 65 87417
**Other instruments:** Accordion.

**SELECTED RECORDED WORK:**
'Set Dances of Ireland' (3 volumes) for Séadhna Records.
'Pure Drop' for RTÉ.
**PRIZES/AWARDS/APPOINTMENTS:**
Director, Maoin Cheoil an Chláir.
Director, Scoil Samhraidh Willie Clancy.
**AVAILABILITY:**
Weekends.

## Brendan McGlinchey *Fiddle*

**Contact:** Mr Brendan McGlinchey
50, Highfield Lane
Oving, Chichester
West Sussex PO20 6DL
England
**Tel:** +44 1243 778845

**KEY IRISH PERFORMANCES** (since January 1994):
1994 Tour of Ireland, promoted by Music Network.
1995 Music Department, University College, Cork.
1996 Miltown Malbay, Co Clare, promoted by An Scoil Samhraidh Willie Clancy.
**KEY PERFORMANCES OUTSIDE IRELAND** (since January 1994):
1996 Tour of America, promoted by CCÉ, appearing with the Echos of Erin group.
1996 Cornwall Folk Festival, promoted by Arts Council, England, appearing with Abel Hill.
1997 Tour of Australia, promoted by CCÉ, appearing with the Echos of Erin group.
1997 London Barbican Centre, promoted by Guinness.
**SELECTED BROADCASTS AND/OR RECORDED WORK:**
1973 'Music of Champions' for Silver Hill Records.
1994 'The Pure Drop' for RTÉ.
1996 'The Gathering' for Real World/Virgin.
**PRIZES/AWARDS/APPOINTMENTS:**
1962 1st Prize in CCÉ Senior All-Ireland Fleadh Cheoil na hÉireann.
1964 Winner of 'Champions of former Champions' (fiddle).
**AVAILABILITY:**
General.

## Anne-Marie McGowan *Fiddle*

**Contact:** Anne-Marie McGowan
The Stables
Waterloo Lane
Dublin 4
**Tel:** +353 1 6689845
*See violin page 63.*

## Mary MacNamara *Fiddle*

**Contact:** Ms Mary MacNamara
Main Street
Tulla
Co Clare
**Tel:** +353 65 35314
*See concertina page 202.*

## Séan Maguire *Fiddle*

**Contact:** c/o Outlet Records
15-21 Gordon Street
Belfast, BT1 2LG
Northern Ireland
**Tel:** +44 1232 322826

## Sandi Miller *Fiddle*

**Contact:** c/o Mr Bill Whelan
39, Fairview Gardens
Dublin 3
**Tel:** +353 1 8331920
*See fiddle page 297.*

## Séan Moloney *Fiddle*

**Contact:** Mr Séan Moloney
'Chez Nous'
Maugheraboy Road
Sligo
**Tel:** +353 71 61239
*See flute page 218.*

## Andrew Morrow *Fiddle*

**Contact:** Mr Andrew Morrow
Errew
Carrigallen
Co Leitrim
**Tel:** +353 49 39618
**Other instruments:** Tin whistle.

**KEY IRISH PERFORMANCES** (since January 1994):
7.96 O'Sheas, Dublin, appearing with Ned O'Shea.
8.96 Dublin City University, appearing with Tom and Eamonn Doorley and friends.
10.5.97 Newtowngore, appearing with John McCartin.
**SELECTED BROADCASTS AND/OR RECORDED WORK:**
6.95 'Fleadh 95' for RTÉ.
9.96 Music programme for Shannonside Radio.
11.4.97 'Scholarships' for Raidió na Gaeltachta.
**PRIZES/AWARDS/APPOINTMENTS:**
9.96 Coleman Junior Fiddler of the Year awarded by the Coleman Society.
4.5.97 Winner of Fiddler of Oriel (under 18) at the Féile Oriel.
**REGULARLY PERFORMS WITH:**
Délos, John Morrow (banjo) and Robert Morrow (accordion) and Thomas Morrrow.
**AVAILABILITY:**
Weekends.
**ADDITIONAL INFORMATION:**
Has also been placed in the All-Ireland Fleadh Cheoil na hÉireann on several occasions.

## James Murphy *Fiddle*

**Contact:** Mr James Murphy
Laughtadurcan
Bohola
Claremorris
Co Mayo
**Tel:** +353 94 84405

**KEY IRISH PERFORMANCES** (since January 1994):
6.96 Strokestown House, Co Roscommon, promoted by RTÉ.
11.96 Tuam, promoted by TnaG.
**SELECTED BROADCASTS AND/OR RECORDED WORK:**
1991 'Corner House' for RTÉ.
1993 'Music in Matt Molloys'.
1996/97 'Céili House', for RTÉ.
**AVAILABILITY:**
Subject to schedule.
**ADDITIONAL INFORMATION:**
Plays in Sligo style. Mentor was the late Fred Finn.

## Frances Nesbitt *Fiddle*

**Contact:** Frances Nesbitt
Victoria Ville
Victoria Road
Cork
**Tel:** +353 21 963086
**Other instruments:** Piano, violin (classical).

**PRIZES/AWARDS/APPOINTMENTS:**
1983/84/85 1st Prize CCÉ All-Ireland, Fleadh Cheoil na hÉireann (Senior Slow Airs).
**KEY IRISH PERFORMANCES** (since January 1994):
1995 Cork Municipal School of Music, promoted by Limerick 800.
1995 National Concert Hall, Dublin, promoted by the Famine Commemoration, appearing with the National Folk Orchestra.
**KEY PERFORMERS OUTSIDE IRELAND** (since January 1994):
From 1994 to 1996 Festival Interceltique, Lorient, Brittany, France, appearing with the Nesbitt family.
1995 Valencia Festival, Spain, appearing with Cork Municipal School of Music Orchestra.
**SELECTED BROADCASTS AND/OR RECORDED WORK:**
GAA Centenary Concert, Thurles, for RTÉ.
Siamsa Cois Laoi for RTÉ.
Famine Commemoration Concert for RTÉ.
**TRAINING AND/OR QUALIFICATIONS:**
1993 ALCM performers Diploma (classical violin).
**AVAILABILITY:**
Weekends, (Wednesdays, Thursdays and Fridays during school holidays).

## Kathleen Nesbitt *Fiddle*

**Contact:** Ms Kathleen Nesbitt
Loughmore
Templemore
Co Tipperary
**Tel:** +353 504 31236

**KEY IRISH PERFORMANCES** (since January 1994):
5.94 Garda Training College, Templemore, appearing with the Nesbitt Family.
7.96 Stackstown Sports Centre, promoted by Department of Justice and EU Presidency, appearing with the Nesbitt Family.
**KEY PERFORMANCES OUTSIDE IRELAND** (since January 1994):
8.95 Festival Interceltique, Lorient, Brittany, France, appearing with the Nesbitt and O'Heidhia Family.
8.96 Festival Interceltique, Lorient, appearing with the Nesbitt Family and Jean Quiste Band.
**SELECTED BROADCASTS AND/OR RECORDED WORK:**
GAA Centenary Concert, Thurles, for RTÉ.
Siamsa Cois Laoi, for RTÉ.
'All the Best', for RTÉ.
**PRIZES/AWARDS/APPOINTMENTS:**
1967 Gold Medal winner at An tOireachtas.
**TRAINIG AND/OR QUALIFICATIONS:**
1980 TTCT (Honours) from CCÉ.
**REGULARLY PERFOMS WITH:**
Nesbitt Family.
**AVAILABILITY:**
Weekends, school holidays.
**ADDITIONAL INFORMATION:**
Regularly gives master classes at Scoil Éigse and in Brittany during the Festival Interceltique. Tutor and an assessor on the TTCT Teaching Diploma course since 1984.

## Niamh Ní Bheoláin *Fiddle*

**Contact:** Ms Niamh Ní Bheoláin
104, Captains Road
Crumlin
Dublin 12
**Tel:** +353 1 4903378

**PRIZES/AWARDS/APPOINTMENTS:**
7.92 1st Prize at the Fleadh Cheoil Laigheann.
**TRAINING AND/OR QUALIFICATIONS:**
From 30.9.95 to 1.10.95, Attended fiddle masterclass with Tommy Peoples.
10.96 Attended weekend masterclass with Matt Cranitch.
1-4.97 Jazz improvisation class at Walton's New School of Music, Dublin.
**REGULARLY PERFORMS WITH:**
Dave Cassidy (mandola), Liam Kennedy (mando), Kevin Ward (guitar), Reel Easy String Band.

**AVAILABILITY:**
General.
**ADDITIONAL INFORMATION:**
August 1993, played at the welcoming reception for President Mary Robinson's visit to Auckland's Irish Club, New Zealand. Interested in bluegrass music.

# Máiread Ní Mhaonaigh *Fiddle*

**Contact:** c/o Mr Ciarán Tourish
26, St John's Park Avenue
Sandymount, Dublin 4
**Mobile/Tel/Fax:** +353 87 542054 / +353 1 2839585
**Email:** tourish@indigo.ie

**REGULARLY PERFORMS WITH:**
Altan.

# Josephine Nugent *Fiddle*

**Contact:** Miss Josephine Nugent
Flat 5
122, Malone Avenue
Belfast, BT9 6ET
Northern Ireland
**Tel:** +44 1232 667250
**Other instruments:** Tin whistle, backing vocals.

**KEY IRISH PERFORMANCES** (since January 1994):
7.7.94 DIT College of Education, Rathmines, Dublin, promoted by Kodaly Society of Ireland, appearing with Gerard Flannagan, Adele O'Dwyer and Mary Nugent.
From 28.4.95 to 1.5.95 Champagne and Oyster Festival, Carrigaholt, Co Clare, promoted by Local Council and Mick Coyne, appearing with Eamonn Coyne, Mick Coyne, Liam Lewis, Séamus McMahon and John Wren.
2.6.95 Crescent Arts Centre, Belfast promoted by Belfast and District Set Dancing and Traditional Music Society, appearing with Mary Nugent.
10.6.95 Asleigh Hall, Belfast, promoted by BDSD TMS, appearing with Davy McGuire, Eoghan O'Brien, Kate O'Brien and Jason O'Rourke.
**KEY PERFORMANCES OUTSIDE IRELAND** (since January 1994):
From 30.7.94 to 6.8.94, Firth Hall, University of Sheffield, promoted by Coma, (ensembles of musicians from the Contemporary Music Making For Amateurs) - London branch.
5-12.8.95 Bretton Hall, West Bretton, Wakefield, West Yorkshire, promoted by Coma, appearing with Coma Orchestra, conducted by Steve Montague.
**SELECTED BROADCASTS AND/OR RECORDED WORK:**
7.84 'Fead An Iolar' with Na Casaidigh, for Gael-Linn Records.
3.95 'The Humours of Daryl Runswick' ('Symphony for Voices'), for Quad, Forties Recording Company, England.
11.9.95 'Kelly' for UTV.
**PRIZES/AWARDS/APPOINTMENTS:**
From 1977 to 1983, All-Ireland Champion in solo, duet, trio playing, and also in group work, awarded by CCÉ and Slogadh.
Since 9.91 - Fiddle tutor at Cresent Arts Centre, Belfast.
**TRAINING AND/OR QUALIFICATIONS:**
7.83 TTCT (1st Hons) from CCÉ.
From 1.1.89 to 3.4.90, Piano (Grade 8), with the Associated Board of The Royal Schools of Music.
**REGULARLY PERFORMS WITH:**
Coma Ensembles, Mary Nugent, Davy McGuire and Jason O'Rourke.
**AVAILABILITY:**
General.
**ADDITIONAL INFORMATION:**
Primarily a traditional fiddle player with experience as a fiddle teacher. Member of COMA and enjoys the opportunity of playing contemporary music and exploring new and contemporary ideas in the field of Irish traditional music.

# Eileen O'Brien *Fiddle*

**Contact:** Ms Eileen O'Brien-Minogue
Moanfin
Nenagh
Co Tipperary
**Tel:** +353 67 31716

**KEY PERFORMANCES OUTSIDE IRELAND** (since January 1994):
10/12.3.94 Moscow, promoted by Aer Rianta.
1994 Oslo/Irish Music Festival, promoted by Peter Lynch, appearing with Aonach.
6-23.10.94 Tour of Australia, promoted by Diarmuid Ó Cathaín, appearing with Na Ridirí.
7-21.6.95 Tour of East Coast USA, promoted by Diarmuid Ó Cathaín, appearing with Na Ridirí.
**SELECTED BROADCASTS AND/OR RECORDED WORK:**
1991 and 1992 for RTÉ.
8.93 'The Compositions of Paddy O'Brien', for Ormond Recordings.
**PRIZES/AWARDS/APPOINTMENTS:**
1979 Awarded Senior Fiddle prize by CCÉ Fleadh Cheoil na hÉireann (Slow Airs).
1980 Awarded Senior Fiddle prize by CCÉ Fleadh Cheoil Na hÉireann.
1980 Prizewinner of CCÉ Fleadh Cheoil Na hÉireann (Senior Duet).
1980 Prizewinner with Fleadh Cheoil Na HÉireann (Senior Ceili Band member).
**TRAINING AND/OR QUALIFICATIONS:**
From 1970 to 1979, Grade 8, with the Municipal School of Music, Limerick.
1981 TTCT from CCÉ.
**REGULARLY PERFORMS WITH:**
Paddy Canny (Fiddle), Larry Gavin (Accordion), Deirdre McSherry (flute, Piano).
**AVAILABILITY:**
Weekdays, (weekends during summer).
**ADDITIONAL INFORMATION:**
Member of the organising committee of 'Aonach Paddy O'Brien' traditional music festival, which takes place on the third weekend in August every year in Nenagh. Has compiled a book of compositions by Paddy O'Brien and has written music for a mass in the Irish language entitled 'Aifreann Baile Nua'. Has made numerous appearances since the age of 15 years on RTÉ, and with the Scottish Fiddle Orchestra on UTV.

# Kate O'Brien *Fiddle*

**Contact:** Ms Kate O'Brien
9, Station Road
Magherafelt
Co Derry BT45 5DN
Northern Ireland
**Tel:** +44 1648 31995

**SELECTED BROADCASTS AND/OR RECORDED WORK:**
1996 'Firefly Summer' for BBC.
**PRIZES/AWARDS/APPOINTMENTS:**
1980 winner All-Ireland Fiddle Solo (under 12) at Slógagh.
**TRAINING AND/OR QUALIFICATIONS:**
1988 TTCT from CCÉ.
1993 LTCL from Trinity College, London.
**REGULARLY PERFORMS WITH:**
Déanta.
**AVAILABILITY:**
Weekends, summer months.
**ADDITIONAL INFORMATION:**
Full-time teacher of both classical and traditional music.

## Pádraig O'Brien *Fiddle*

**Contact:** Mr Pádraig O'Brien
9, Belfield Park
Foyle Springs
Derry City
BT48 ONJ Northern Ireland
**Tel:** +44 1504 264212

**KEY IRISH PERFORMANCES** (since January 1994):
1995 Rialto, Derry, promoted by Spirit of Ireland tour, appearing with the Christian Brothers Choir.
1997 Springhill Folk Festival, appearing with the Seven Towers Dancers.
**KEY PERFORMANCES OUTSIDE IRELAND** (since January 1994):
17.3.95 California, USA, promoted by Spirit of Ireland tour, appearing with the Christian Brothers Choir.
Easter 1997 Palma, Majorca, promoted by Seventh World Folkdance Festival, appearing with the Seven Towers Dancing team (3rd prize awarded).
**SELECTED BROADCASTS AND/OR RECORDED WORK:**
1995 Spirit of Ireland tour for Californian local radio.
1996 'Quare Nerve' cassette for Blue Moon Publications (ISBN 872420-65-6).
1996 'High Reel' for RTÉ.
**PRIZES/AWARDS/APPOINTMENTS:**
1981 All-Ireland Group winners (Clan Luaí) at Slógadh.
**TRAINING AND/OR QUALIFICATIONS:**
From 1970 to 1979, Grade 8 violin (practical) and Grade 6 (theory) from Trinity College of Music, London.
1979 GCE O Levels in Music Appreciation.
Since 1996 TTCT from CCÉ.
Since 1995 various workshops with CCÉ.
**REGULARLY PERFORMS WITH:**
Fergal O'Brien (bodhrán, concertina), Eoghan O'Brien (harp, guitar).
**AVAILABILITY:**
General.
**ADDITIONAL INFORMATION:**
Qualified occupational therapist and teacher of Irish traditional music. Keen to develop the area of music for individuals with special needs.

## Marie O'Byrne *Fiddle*

**Contact:** Marie O'Byrne
Shanaway Road
Ennis, Co Clare
**Tel:** +353 65 41602

*"Lovely sounds, high technical achievement ... classical side comes through, with clear traditional background"* 5.97 Slógadh adjudication.

**KEY IRISH PERFORMANCES** (since January 1994):
7.95 Flagmount, Co Clare, promoted by Golden Vale, appearing with Liam O Flynn, Arty McGlynn, Nollaig Casey, Matt Molloy.
Winter 1995, Dromoland Castle, appearing with Noel Hill, Ailbhe McMahon.
2.96 Royal Dublin Society, Dublin, promoted by Coláiste Muire, Ennis, Co Clare, appearing with Ailbhe McMahon, Marie Quigney, Michelle O'Brien.
5.96 Ennis Cathedral, promoted by Maoin Cheoil and Chláir, appearing with Míchéal Ó Súilleabháin and the Irish Chamber Orchestra.
**KEY PERFORMANCES OUTSIDE IRELAND** (since January 1994):
4.96 Finland, promoted by Coláiste Mhuire, appearing with Marie Quigley recorded for Raidió na Gaeltachta and BBC.
**SELECTED BROADCASTS AND/OR RECORDED WORK:**
Summer 1996 'Over the Moor to Maggie' recorded at Harmony Row Studios, Ennis.
5.97 'Over the Moor to Maggie' for BBC.
**PRIZES/AWARDS/APPOINTMENTS:**
1996 3rd prize (Under 18) at the CCÉ All-Ireland at the Fleadh Cheoil.
1997 1st Prize Leaving Certificate All-Ireland awarded by Slógadh.
**REGULARLY PERFORMS WITH:**
Ailbhe McMahon (harp), Rena Queally (banjo), Marie Quigley (piano).
**AVAILABILITY:**
General.
*See also page 64.*

## Gerry O'Connor *Fiddle*

**Contact:** Gerry O'Connor
Lughnasa Music
Ravensdale, Co Louth
**Tel/Fax:** +353 42 71538

*"Gerry's fiddle playing had an attractive flexibility and precision ... his whole performance was a delight"* 10.87 Irish Times (Tomas Ó Canann).

**KEY IRISH PERFORMANCES** (since January 1994):
19.6.95 Lyric Theatre, Belfast, promoted by Belfast Folk Festival, appearing with La Lúgh.
4.8.95 John Field Room, National Concert Hall, Dublin, appearing with La Lúgh.
14.9.95 The County Museum, Dundalk, promoted by Dundalk Arts Committee, appearing with La Lúgh.
4.11.95 St Michael's Church, Limerick, promoted by University of Limerick, appearing with Eithne Ní Uallacháin.
**KEY PERFORMANCES OUTSIDE IRELAND** (since January 1994):
24.3.95 Ursulinenhof, Linz, promoted by Linzart, Austria, appearing with Skylark.
4.5.95 Teatro Garabaldi, Enna, Italy, promoted by Citta Di Enna, Sicily, appearing with Antonio Breschi and Gerry O'Donnell.
27.2.95 The Malting Theatre, Bervick Arts Festival, appearing with Eíthne Ní Uallacháin.
7.10.95 Kammermusiksalen, Kristianstad, Sweden, promoted by Musik i Skåne, appearing with Lá Lugh.
**SELECTED BROADCASTS AND/OR RECORDED WORK:**
1.11.91 'Lá Lugh', CCF29CD, for Claddagh Records.
1.10.93 'Light and Shade', CC57CD, for Claddagh Records.
1.2.96 'Brighid's Kiss', for Lughnasa Music.
**PRIZES/AWARDS/APPOINTMENTS:**
1969 Runner Up in the CCÉ Fleadh Cheoil na hEireann competition.
1979 winner of Fiddler of Meath.
1975 1979 1980 and 1982 winner of Fiddler of Oriel.
**TRAINING AND/OR QUALIFICATIONS:**
From 9.82 to 6.85, Diploma in Violin Making, from the Cork School of Music.
**REGULARLY PERFORMS WITH:**
Eíthne Ní Uallacháin (fiddle, flute, voice), Lá Lugh and The Irish Session.
**AVAILABILITY:**
General.
**ADDITIONAL INFORMATION:**
Has recorded 7 albums in total. Experienced teacher. Maker and repairer of violins.

## Máire O'Keeffe *Fiddle*

**Contact:** Máire O'Keeffe
Locoal Mendon Street
Kinvara
Co Galway
**Tel/Mobile:** +353 91 637649 / +353 88 600709
**Email:** mokeeffe@iol.ie
**Other instruments:** Piano.

*"Demonstrates a remarkable scale of empathy with and ability to beautifully render the fiddle tradition of her native Kerry"* 1994 Evening Echo.

**KEY IRISH PERFORMANCES** (since January 1994):
11.94 Tour of Ireland, promoted by Music Network, appearing with Jackie Daly, Cathal McConnell, Mick O'Brien.
94.95.96 Cork Folk Festival, appearing with Jackie Daly.
**KEY PERFORMANCES OUTSIDE IRELAND** (since January 1994):
8.95/96 Milwaukee Irish Festival, Milwaukee, USA.
10.95/96 Green Linnet Festival, USA, appearing with Jackie Daly.
1.96 Tour of Australia, promoted by Sydney Irish Music Association, appearing with Jackie Daly.
7.96 Celtic Ceilidh Trail School, Cape Breton Island, Nova Scotia, Canada.
**SELECTED BROADCASTS AND/OR RECORDED WORK:**
3.94 'Cóisir - House Party' for Gael-Linn.
9.96 Boston College 'Gaelic Roots CD', for Irish Studies Programme at Boston College.
**PRIZES/AWARDS/APPOINTMENTS:**
From 1990 to 1992, Board member of the Irish Traditional Music Archive, Dublin.
**REGULARLY PERFORMS WITH:**
Jackie Daly (accordion), Paul de Grae (guitar), Aoife O'Keeffe (fiddle).
**AVAILABILITY:**
Weekends, evenings in July, August.
**ADDITIONAL INFORMATION:**
Researcher, scriptwriter and presenter of 'The Long Note', for RTÉ Radio 1. 1990/1992 researcher, scriptwriter and presenter of traditional music programmes for Clare FM. Currently working on Ph D at Irish World Music Centre, University of Limerick. Has given fiddle workshops and seminars on various aspects of traditional music.

## Siobhán Peoples *Fiddle*

**Contact:** Siobhán Peoples
**Tel/Fax:** +353 65 24201

**ADDITIONAL INFORMATION:**
Studied music in University College, Cork. Toured in Germany, USA, Finland, Holland, France and England. Performed on recordings including 'The Maid of Erin', 'The Sanctuary Sessions' and the 'The Sound of Stone'. Teaches in Ennis and at various summer schools.

## Tommy Peoples *Fiddle*

**Contact:** Tommy Peoples
Toonagh, Ennis
Co Clare

*"No other fiddler sounds quite like Tommy Peoples"* PJ Curtis.

**ADDITIONAL INFORMATION:**
Member of Kilfenora Céilí Band and Bothy Band in 1970's. Has recorded several albums including 'Iron Man' and others with Paul Brady and Matt Molloy etc.

## Sebastien Petiet *Fiddle*

**Contact:** c/o Marie Petiet
23, Park Crescent House
Blackhorse Avenue
Dublin 7
**Tel:** +353 1 8681210
*See violin page 65.*

## John Quinn *Fiddle*

**Contact:** John Quinn
30, Parnell Court
Harolds Cross
Dublin 6W
**Tel/Fax:** +353 1 4535699 / +353 1 4933145
**Other instruments:** Whistle, guitar, mandolin and banjo.

**KEY IRISH PERFORMANCES** (since January 1994):
25.2.96 RTÉ 'The Pure Drop', appearing with Séan Maguire.
2.94 RTÉ 'Live at 3', appearing with Johnnie Carroll.
**KEY PERFORMANCES OUTSIDE IRELAND** (since January 1994):
4.97 Branson, Missouri, USA.
6.97 Various venues in Austria.
**SELECTED BROADCASTS AND/OR RECORDED WORK:**
Glenveagh, Donegal, for Annar Communications Ltd.
'Mayo, It's People and Places' for Annar Communications Ltd.
'Connemara, 'It's People and Places', for Charlie Doherty Productions.
**TRAINING AND/OR QUALIFICATIONS:**
From 1972 to 1977, studied at the DIT Conservatory of Music and Drama, Dublin.
**AVAILABILITY:**
General.

## Michael Rooney *Fiddle*

**Contact:** Mr Mackie Rooney
Tyraverty
Scotstown
Co Monaghan
**Tel:** +353 47 89161
*See Irish harp page 230.*

## John Scott-Trotter *Fiddle*

**Contact:** Mr John Scott-Trotter
1, Browning Drive
Londonderry, BT47 1HN
Northern Ireland
**Tel:** +44 1 504 311119
*See trombone page 284.*

## Breda Smyth *Fiddle*

**Contact:** Dr Breda Smyth
47, Bachelors Walk
Dublin 1
**Tel/Fax:** +353 1 8727774
*See tin whistle page 244.*

## Thomas Smyth *Fiddle*

**Contact:** Thomas Smyth
103, Granemore Road
Tassagh
Co Armagh
Northern Ireland
**Tel:** +44 1861 538260

**KEY IRISH PERFORMANCES** (since Janaury 1994):
1994 Belfast Folk Festival, appearing with Craobh Rua.
1995 Belfast Folk Festival, appearing with Nomos.
1995/96 Various performances around Ireland with Nomos.
**KEY PERFORMANCES OUTSIDE IRELAND** (since January 1994):
7.94 London, promoted by Paul Conlon, appearing with Nomos.
3.95 Florida, USA, promoted by Colin McGee Promotions, appearing with Terry Conlon (accordion).
3.96 Oslo, Norway, appearing with Trasna from Belfast.
8.96 Ponterdawe Folk Festival, appearing with Déanta.
**SELECTED RECORDED WORKS:**
1993/95 'The Corner House' for BBC.
1996 'Kelly' Show for BBC 'Mountain Lark' for RTÉ and CCÉ.
**REGULARLY PERFORMS WITH:**
Tiarnán Ó Duinnchinn (uilleann pipes), Rosie Mulholland (fiddle, keyboards), Mairtín Quinn (box).
**AVAILABILITY:**
General.

## Ciaran Tourish *Fiddle*

**Contact:** Mr Ciaran Tourish
26, St John's Park Avenue
Sandymount
Dublin 4
**Tel/Fax/Mobile:** +353 1 2839585 / +353 87 542054
**Email:** tourish@indigo.ie

**REGULARLY PERFORMS WITH:**
Altan.

## Áine Uí Cheallaigh *Fiddle*

**Contact:** Ms Áine Uí Cheallaigh
Cnocán an Phaoraigh
Rinn Ó gCuanach
Co Waterford
**Tel:** +353 58 46201
*See singers page 254.*

## Caoimhín Vallely *Fiddle*

**Contact:** Mr Caoimhín Vallely
Flat 5
4, Wellesey Terrace
Wellington Road
Cork
**Tel:** +353 21 509230
*See piano page 234.*

## Stephen Wickham *Fiddle*

**Contact:** Stephen Wickham
PO Box 282
Sligo
**Tel:** +353 1 4966341
*See violin page 300.*

# TRADITIONAL FLUTE

## Mary Bergin *Flute*

**Contact:** Ms Mary Bergin
Spiddal
Co Galway
**Tel/Fax:** +353 91 83333
*See whistles page 239.*

## Paul Bradley *Flute*

**Contact:** Mr Paul Bradley
No 1, Parliament Street
Newark, NG24 4UR
England
**Tel:** +44 1636 700271
*See fiddle page 204.*

## Ronan Browne *Flute*

**Contact:** Mr Ronan Browne
Mount Slaney
Stratford-on-Slaney
Co Wicklow
**Tel/Fax:** +353 45 404873
**Email:** roro@tinet.ie
*See uilleann pipes page 235.*

## Joe Burke *Flute*

**Contact:** Mr Joe Burke
Tinageeragh
Kilnadeema
Loughrea
Co Galway
**Tel/Fax:** +353 91 842419
*See accordions page 188.*

## John Carty *Flute*

**Contact:** John Carty
Knockroe
Boyle
Co Roscommon
**Tel/Fax:** +353 79 68063
*See fiddle page 204.*

## Michael Clarkson *Flute*

**Contact:** Mr Michael Clarkson
5, Carmel Street
Belfast BTY 1QE
Northern Ireland
**Tel:** +44 1232 311830 / +44 1232 734000 (d)
*See fiddle page 205.*

# Eamonn Cotter *Flute*

**Contact:** Mr Eamonn Cotter
Balleen
Kilmaley
Co Clare
**Tel/Fax:** +353 65 39141

**KEY IRISH PERFORMANCES** (since January 1994):
10.9.95 Clarinbridge Oyster Festival, Co Galway, appearing with Shaskeen.
28.10.95 Cooley Festival, appearing with Shaskeen.
**KEY PERFORMANCES OUTSIDE IRELAND** (since January 1994):
16.9.95 Haringay Irish Centre, London, appearing with Shaskeen.
21.1095 Aberdeen Folk Festival, appearing with Shaskeen.
**SELECTED BROADCASTS AND/OR RECORDED WORK:**
1989/1991 'The Pure Drop', for RTÉ.
1990 'The Mouse Behind the Dresser', for Shaskeen.
1995 1st Solo album released.
**PRIZES/AWARDS/APPOINTMENTS:**
1977 All-Ireland Champion, awarded by CCÉ Fleadh Cheoil na hÉireann.
**TRAINING AND/OR QUALIFICATIONS:**
From 1981 to 1986, ALCM (classical flute) from Limerick School of Music.
**AVAILABILITY:**
Weekdays, weekends.
**ADDITIONAL INFORMATION:**
Teacher and performer at An Scoil Samhraidh Willie Clancy, Co Clare. Has performed with Mícheál O'Sulleabháin and various other groups including Temple House Ceilí Band, Moving Cloud, and the Tulla Ceilí Band.

# Ellen Cranitch *Flute / alto flute*

**Contact:** Ms Ellen Cranitch
33, Westfield Road
Harold's Cross
Dublin 6w
**Tel/Fax:** +353 1 4923486
*See jazz flute page 271.*

# Terry Crehan *Flute*

**Contact:** Terry Crehan
Liffey Bank Promotions
21, Colthurst Close
Huntington Glen
Lucan
Co Dublin
**Tel:** +353 1 621 0090
*See fiddle page 206.*

# P.J. Crotty *Flute*

**Contact:** Mr P.J. Crotty
Main Street
Lahinch
Co Clare
**Tel:** +353 65 81079
**Other instruments:** Tin whistle.

**KEY IRISH PERFORMANCES** (since January 1994):
11.94/95/96 Ennis Traditional Music Festival, Co Clare.
Various recitals and concerts at An Scoil Samhraidh Willie Clancy, Co Clare.
**SELECTED BROADCASTS AND/OR RECORDED WORK:**
'Cursaí Ealaine' for RTÉ.
'Late Late Show' appearing with Matt Molloy, James Crehan and family, for RTÉ.
5.97 Céilí House' for RTÉ.
Other recordings for Raidió na Gaeltachta and Clare FM.
**REGULARLY PERFORMS WITH:**
Carol Cullinan (piano), James Cullinan (fiddle).
**AVAILABILITY:**
General.
**ADDITIONAL INFORMATION:**
Played in London for many years. Was member of the group Le Checke, with whom has made two LP's.

# Gregory Daly *Flute*

**Contact:** Gregory Daly
Tinnecarra
Boyle
Co Roscommon
**Tel:** +353 79 63441
**Other instruments:** Tin whistle.

**SELECTED BROADCASTS AND/OR RECORDED WORK:**
6.96 Strokestown House, Co Roscommon, appearing with John Carty, for RTÉ.
11.96 Appearing with John Carty for TnaG.
**AVAILABILITY:**
General.
**ADDITIONAL INFORMATION:**
Plays in the distinctive style of musicians from south Sligo, north Leitrim area.

# Tara Diamond *Flute*

**Contact:** Tara Diamond
Coolquoy
The Ward
Co Dublin
**Tel/Fax:** +353 8351654
**Email:** diamondd@iol.ie
**Other instruments:** Tin whistle.

**KEY IRISH PERFORMANCES** (since January 1994):
Since 1994, An Scoil Samhraidh Willie Clancy, Co Clare, appearing with Dermot Diamond.
3-5.97 Strings and Flings Festival, Glencolumcille, Co Donegal, appearing with Dermot Diamond.
1-6.1.97 Frankie Kennedy Winter School, Bunbeg, Co Donegal, appearing with Dermot Diamond.
**KEY PERFORMANCES OUTSIDE IRELAND** (since January 1994):
1995 Las Cruces, New Mexico, appearing with Dermot Diamond.
**SELECTED BROADCASTS AND/OR RECORDED WORK:**
8.95 'River of Sound', for Hummingbird.
7.97 'The Miltown Sessions', recorded for RTÉ.
**PRIZES/AWARDS/APPOINTMENTS:**
1972/73 1st in CCÉ All-Ireland Fleadh Cheoil na hÉireann (Flute, Whistle and Duet).
**REGULARLY PERFORMS WITH:**
Dermot Diamond (fiddle).
**AVAILABILITY:**
General.
**ADDITIONAL INFORMATION:**
Experienced player and teacher of traditional music on the timber flute. Has performed extensively for many years on stage, radio and television.

## Christine Dowling *Flute*

**Contact:** Ms Christine Dowling
16B, Adelaide Road
Belfast BT9 6FX
**Tel:** +44 1232 280108
**Other instruments:** Vocals.

**KEY IRISH PERFORMANCES** (since January 1994):
5.97 Downpatrick Folk Club, promoted by Nigel Martyn, appearing with Martin Dowling and Daithi Sproule.
6.95 Belfast Folk Festival, promoted by Nigel Martyn, appearing with Martin Dowling and Daithi Sproule.
8.97 Belfast Folk Festival, promoted by Nigel Martyn, appearing with Martyn Dowling and Daithi Sproule.
**KEY PERFORMANCES OUTSIDE IRELAND** (since January 1994):
8.94/95/96/97 Milwaukee, USA, promoted by Irish Festival, appearing with Martin Dowling and Daithi Sproule.
8.97 Minnesota, USA, promoted by Irish Festival, appearing with Martin Dowling and Daithi Sproule.
**SELECTED BROADCASTS AND/OR RECORDED WORK:**
5.96 The 'High Reel', recorded by RTÉ.
6.97 'A Thousand Farewells', recorded by Cottage Music.
**REGULARLY APPEARS WITH:**
Martin Dowling and Daithi Sproule.
**AVAILABILITY:**
General.

## Brian Dunning *Flute / alto flute*

**Contact:** Mr Brian Dunning
72, Moyglare Village
Maynooth
Co Kildare
**Tel/Fax:** +353 1 628 5678

*See jazz flute page 271.*

## Joseph Finn *Flute*

**Contact:** Mr Joseph Finn
Kilmucklin
Tullamore
Co Offaly
**Tel:** +353 506 31089

*See uilleann pipes page 236.*

## James Galway *Flute*

**Contact:** Mr James Galway
c/o Kathryn Enticott
IMG Artists
Media House
3 Burlington Lane
Chiswick
London W4 2TH
England
**Tel/Fax:** +44 181 233 5800 / +44 181 233 5801

*See classical flute page 14.*

## Frankie Gavin *Flute*

**Contact:** Mr Frankie Gavin
Ardnasillagh
Oughterard
Co Galway
**Tel:** +353 91 552545
*See fiddle page 207.*

## Colin Hamilton *Flute*

**Contact:** Mr Colin 'Hammy' Hamilton
Cúil-Aodha
Macroom
Co Cork
**Tel:** +353 26 45209

*"Top 10' traditional recordings of 1990"*
12.90 Irish Times (Bill Meek) Ref: 'Moneymusk' CD.

**KEY IRISH PERFORMANCES** (since January 1994):
Weekly at The Auld Triangle, Macroom, Co Cork, appearing with Connie O'Connell and Tom Stephens.
22.10.95 University College, Cork, appearing with Tom Stephens.
**KEY PERFORMANCES ABROAD** (since January 1994):
8.95 France, appearing with Geantraí.
**SELECTED BROADCASTS AND/OR RECORDED WORK:**
1990, 'The Moneymusk', for Breac.
1993 'Fead an tSeabhach', for Dord/RTÉ.
**SELECTED REVIEWS** (since January 1994):
The Examiner.
IT Magazine.
**PRIZES/AWARDS/AVAILABILITY:**
Since 1984, Appointed traditional music teacher, at University College, Cork.
From 1.95 to 4.95, Visiting scholar to Univeristy College Los Angeles, awarded by The Fulbright Commission.
**REGULARLY PERFORMS WITH:**
Tom Stephens (guitar), Geantraí.
**AVAILABILITY:**
General.
**ADDITIONAL INFORMATION:**
Author of the 'Irish Fluteplayers Handbook' (1990). Flute maker, repairer and tutor for performance workshops. Has made over 20 appearances on RTÉ. French speaker.

## Barry Kerr *Flute*

**Contact:** Mr Barry Kerr
25, Island View Lane
Kinnego
Lurgan
Co Armagh, BT67 9JF
Northern Ireland
**Tel/Fax:** +44 1762 321730 or +44 1762 324660 /
+44 1762 324449
**Other instruments:** Uilleann pipes, whistles, bouzouki, bodhrán.

**KEY IRISH PERFORMANCES** (since January 1994):
1994 Ardoyne Fleadh, Belfast, promtoed by Eddie Donnelly, appearing with Stone the Crows.
1995 Killyleagh Castle, appearing with Maurice Crawford, accompanying Van Morrison with Celtic Mystery Orchestra.
1995 Ballyshannon Folk Festival, appearing with Anthony Travers.
1997 Waterfront Hall, Belfast.

**PRIZES/AWARDS/APPOINTMENTS:**
8.96 All-Ireland flute title, awarded by CCÉ Fleadh Cheoil na hÉireann.
7.96 Ulster titles, awarded by CCÉ.
**REGULARLY PERFORMS WITH:**
Belfast Harp Orchestra, David Muldrew (singer, songwriter, guitar), Gerard Thompson (guitar).
**AVAILABILITY:**
General.
**ADDITIONAL INFORMATION:**
Available for session recordings and festivals in Ireland and abroad.

# Catherine McEvoy *Flute*

**Contact:** Mrs Catherine McEvoy
Lagore Little
Rathoath
Co Meath
**Tel:** +353 1 8256016

*"A beautiful showcase of a player coming from within the richness of a big tradition - which left a warm afterglow of admiration"*
2.97 Irish Music (Vol 2 No. 6).

**KEY IRISH PERFORMANCES** (since January 1994):
2.97 Harcourt Hotel, Dublin Connaught flute recital, appearing with Séamus Tansey, Patsy Hanly, Peter Horan and friends.
**SELECTED BROADCASTS AND/OR RECORDED WORK:**
11.96 'Ceilí House' for RTÉ.
12.96 Catherine McEvoy and Felix Dolan CD for Cló-Iar Chonnachta.
4.97 The 'High Reel' for RTÉ.
**SELECTED REVIEWS** (since January 1994):
6.2.97 Irish Times.
**TRAINING AND/OR QUALIFICATIONS:**
1981 TTCT from CCÉ.
**REGULARLY PERFORMS WITH:**
Felix Dolan (piano), John Kelly (fiddle).
**AVAILABILITY:**
General.
**ADDITIONAL INFORMATION:**
Has taken part in many festivals and given masterclasses. Tutor at An Scoil Samhraidh Willie Clancy, Co Clare.

# Paul McGlinchey *Flute*

**Contact:** Dr Paul Mc Glinchey
12, Sperrin View
Omagh
Co Tyrone
Northern Ireland
**Tel:** +44 1662 246066

**KEY IRISH PERFORMANCES** (since January 1994):
9.97 Frank's Bar, Lignaskea, promoted by F Maguire, appearing with B McLaughlin and Gerry McMahon.
16.5.97 McAloon's, Trillick, promoted by P McAloon, appearing with Macdara O'Raghalliagh and Gerry McMahon.
5.97 Dungloe Bar, Derry, appearing with Róisín and Paul Harrigan.
Ulster Museum, Belfast, appearing with Eoghain O'Brien.
**KEY PERFORMANCES OUTSIDE IRELAND** (since January 1994):
6.94 Glasgow, promoted by CCÉ.
10.94 Luton, promoted by CCÉ.
2.97 Lund, Sweden, appearing with Déanta.
2.97 Gotthenburg, Sweden, appearing with Déanta.
**SELECTED BROADCASTS AND/OR RECORDED WORK:**
10.94 '25 Bedford Street' for BBC.
10.95 'Céilí House' for RTÉ.
4.96 'High Reel' for RTÉ.

**PRIZES/AWARDS/APPOINTMENTS:**
8.93/94/95 CCÉ All-Ireland Fleadh Cheoil Senior Concert Flute Champion.
**REGULARLY PERFORMS WITH:**
Barry McLaughlin (fiddle) Gerry McMahon (guitar).
**AVAILABILITY:**
General.

# Davy Maguire *Flute*

**Contact:** Mr Davy Maguire
24, Iveagh Street
Belfast BT12 6AU
Northern Ireland
**Tel:** +44 1232 324189
**Other instruments:** Whistle.

**KEY IRISH PERFORMANCES** (since January 1994):
11.95 Ulster Folk and Transport Museum, Belfast, promoted by Robbie Hannon, appearing with Martin Dowling (fiddle) and as support act to Mícheál Ó Súilleabháin.
11.96 Friars Féile, Ennis.
5.97 Glencolmcille Hotel, promoted by Belfast Set Dance and Traditional Music Society.
6.97 Ulster Folk and Transport Museum, promoted by Robbie Hannon, appearing with Martin Dowling, Jason O'Rourke and Paul O'Shaughnessy.
**KEY PERFORMANCES OUTSIDE IRELAND** (since January 1994):
7.94 Tever Expo, Rome, promoted by Nigel Martyn, appearing with Marco Fabbri (fiddle) and Alan McCartney (guitar).
7.95 Padova and Trieste, promoted by the Robin Hood Folk Club, Trieste, appearing with All Set.
3.97 'Finn MacCumhal', Rome, promoted by the 'Rome Fleadh Cheoil', appearing with Paul McSherry, Kate O'Brien and Jason O'Rourke.
7.97 Festival de Cornouaille, Quimper, France appearing with Jamie McMenem.
**SELECTED BROADCASTS AND/OR RECORDED WORK:**
11.9.93 Title music for 'Kelly' for UTV.
25.12.90 'Turn Down the Lamp' for BBC radio.
7.97 Set Dance CD for Outlet Records.
**REGULARLY PERFORMS WITH:**
All Set (set dance and music group), Commonalty, Martin Dowling (fiddle), Jason O'Rourke (concertina).
**AVAILABILITY:**
General.
**ADDITIONAL INFORMATION:**
Has appeared on BBC Radio, Radio Ulster, BBC Radio 2, Raidió na Gaeltachta, RTÉ Radio 1, German National Radio (Ruddstadt Festival, 1992) and Danish National radio. Teaches regularly at classes in the Crescent Arts Centre, Belfast and has given workshops in Ireland, Scotland, Italy and Brittany, in conjunction with performances and tours in various European countries. Recorded a cassette with Commonalty in 1989.

# Emer Mayock *Flute*

**Contact:** Ms Emer Mayock
Key Records
20, Lower Stephen's Street
Dublin 2
**Tel:** +353 1 478 0191
**Other instruments:** Whistle, uillean pipes, fiddle.

*"She combines prodigious playing skills with an ear for composition and this album marks an auspicious start to her recording career"*
23.8.96 Irish Times (Merry Bits of Timber).

**KEY IRISH PERFORMANCES** (since January 1994):
7.96 National Concert Hall, Dublin.
2.97 Whelan's, Dublin.
3.97 Olympia Theatre, Dublin.
6.97 Castlebar Blues Festival.
1997 Tour of Ireland, promoted by Music Network appearing with Paddy Glackin, Séan óg Potts and Michéal O' Domhnaill.
**KEY PERFORMANCES OUTSIDE IRELAND** (since January 1994):
10.96 Kutchens Country Club, New York.
1.96 Mulligan's, Helsinki.
4.97 The Lemon Tree, Aberdeen.
**SELECTED BROADCASTS AND/OR RECORDED WORK:**
8.96 'Moloney after Midnight' for RTÉ.
1.97 'The Late Late Show' for RTÉ.
2.97 'Sult' for TnaG.
**SELECTED REVIEWS** (since January 1994):
30.6.96 Sunday Times.
Winter 1996/97 Rock 'n' Reel.
**REGULARLY PERFORMS WITH:**
Emer Mayock Band.
**AVAILABILITY:**
General.
**ADDITIONAL INFORMATION:**
Flautist, fiddler and uilleann piper, from Co Mayo. Released debut album 'Merry Bits of Timber' in August 1996, entering the traditional charts at number 4 and the Irish album charts at number 39.

## Séan Moloney *Flute / alto flute*

**Contact:** Mr Séan Moloney
'Chez Nous'
Maugheraboy Road
Sligo
**Tel:** +353 71 61239
**Other instruments:** Fiddle, whistle.

*"A fine collection of mostly local music, a great tribute to consisitency in regional playing"*
4.97 Irish Music Magazine ref: 'Bridging the Gap'.

**KEY IRISH PERFORMANCES** (since January 1994):
2.5.95 Monaghan tour, promoted by Feile Oriel, appearing with Verona Ryan and Irene Moloney.
8.3.97 O'Connor's, Salthill, Galway, promoted by Guinness, appearing with Kevin Moloney, Irene Moloney and support musicians.
4.5.97 The Hill, Ballinakill, promoted by Jerry Moloney, appearing with Kevin Moloney and support musicians.
**SELECTED BROADCASTS AND/OR RECORDED WORK:**
1.6.95 'Fleadh' for RTÉ.
8.3.97 'Geantraí' for TnaG.
14.4.97 'Bridging the Gap' CD and cassette tape, for Gael-Linn.
**REGULARLY PERFORMS WITH:**
Lon Dubh (Moloney Family), Irene Moloney (fiddle, bodhrán, mandolin), Kevin Moloney (fiddle).
**AVAILABILTIY:**
General (during April and June to September), otherwise subject to schedule.
**ADDITIONAL INFORMATION:**
Of the fourth generation of flute players from the Moloney family from Ballinakill, East Galway. An exponent of regional traditional music. Plays many varieties of flute including the simple system, boehm system and alto flute and whistle. Interested in giving workshops as well as performances. Has recorded on cassette and CD as part of a duet.

## Eithne Ní Uallacháin *Flute*

**Contact:** Ms Eithne Ní Uallacháin
Ballymakellet
Ravensdale
Co Louth
Ireland
**Tel/Fax:** +353 42 71538
*See singers page 250.*

## Mary Nugent *Flute*

**Contact:** Ms Mary Nugent
9, Gledswood Park
Clonskeagh
Dublin 14
**Tel:** +353 1 2693956
**Other instruments:** Vocals, classical flute.

**KEY IRISH PERFORMANCES** (since January 1994):
11.94 Ennis Folk Festival, promoted by Mick Coyne and Séamus McMahon, appearing with various artists.
27.3.95 Harty Room, Queen's University Belfast, promoted by QUB Music Department, appearing with Dr Anthony Carver.
2.6.95 Cresent Arts Centre, Belfast, promoted by The Belfast District Set Dancing and Traditional Music Society, appearing with Josephine Nugent.
4.7.95 College of Education Rathmines, promoted by Kodály Society, guesting with Adele O'Dwyer and Danusia Oslizlok.
**SELECTED BROADCASTS AND/OR RECORDED WORK:**
1995 'The Cassidys Live', for Release Records Inc. (New York 10550).
1986 'Exhibit A', (programme on Patrick Kavanagh), for RTÉ.
8.95 Listowel Fleadh Cheoil na hÉireann, for RTÉ.
**PRIZES/AWARDS/APPOINTMENTS:**
From 1974 to 1981, Solo, Duet and Trio awards, from CCÉ.
From 1988 to 1990, awarded study leave to the Kodály Institute, Hungary.
From 1992 to 1993, Conductor, for Chamber Choir 'Ceiliúradh'.
Since 1995 Evening course administrator and lecturer, with the Kodály Society of Ireland.
**TRAINING AND/OR QUALIFICATIONS:**
From 1980 to 1983, B Ed (Music, Education), MIC of Ed, Limerick.
From 1988 to 1990, Advanced Dip in Music Education, awarded by Kodály Institute, Hungary.
From 1992 to 1993, ALCM (piano), from the DIT Conservatory of Music and Drama.
From 1993 to 1995 MA in Renaissance Music, awarded by Queen's University, Belfast.
**REGULARLY PERFORMS WITH:**
Josephine Nugent (Fiddle), Gaudette, Chamber Choir, Dublin.
**AVAILABILITY:**
Weekends.
**ADDITIONAL INFORMATION:**
Both a classical and traditional performer and has worked and toured abroad. Experienced as a choirster with choirs having performed in Christchurch, National Gallery (Dublin), Harty Room (Belfast), Wales, Concert Hall (Kecskemét) and Pesti Vigado in Budapest.
*See conductors page 167.*

## Bríd O'Donohue *Flute*

**Contact:** Ms Bríd O'Donohue
Glendine South
Miltown Malbay
Co Clare
**Tel:** +353 65 84473
*See whistles page 243.*

## Ruth O'Sullivan *Flute*

**Contact:** Ms Ruth O'Sullivan
6, Clarinda Park East
Dún Laoghaire
Co Dublin
**Tel/Fax:** +353 1 280 4501 or +353 1 2807268/
+353 1 2301406
*See classical flute page 18.*

## Aidan Prunty *Flute*

**Contact:** Mr Aidan Prunty
2, Willowbank
Armagh BT61 8AD
Northern Ireland
**Tel/Fax:** +44 1861 511004 / +44 1861 529630
**Other instruments:** Tin whistle, pipe band drumming.

*"Together with jigs, reels and hornpipes, are simple undecorated catchy melodies heard in summertime along the country lanes of his native county"* 1991 Music Under the Mountain Festival.

**KEY IRISH PERFORMANCES** (since January 1994):
1996 Cultra Museum, Co Down, for RTÉ's 'High Reel', appearing with Peter Grew.
11.96 Poulaphouca House, Hollywood, Co Wicklow, promoted by Music Under the Mountain Festival (memorial concert for Laura Greaves).
12.96 Armagh City Folk Club, Armagh, set céilí concert, appearing with Itchy Fingers.
4.97 Armagh Pipers Club annual concert.
**KEY PERFORMANCES OUTSIDE IRELAND** (since January 1994):
1995 Oslo, Norway, promoted by The Dubliner, appearing with Paul Bradley, Martin McAllister and Joe Bradley.
1995 Ledminster, Herts, Hertfordshire Wassailing Festival.
**SELECTED BROADCASTS AND/OR RECORDED WORK:**
1995 For 'Kelly Show', for UTV.
1995 Country Céili for Downtown Radio.
1996 'High Reel' for RTÉ.
**PRIZES/AWARDS/APPOINTMENTS:**
1985 All-Ireland winners at GAA Scór competition, National Concert Hall, Dublin.
**REGULARLY PERFORMS WITH:**
Robert McGleenan (fiddle), Goretti Molloy (keyboard), Itchy Fingers.
**AVAILABILITY:**
General.
**ADDITIONAL INFORMATION:**
At present teaches traditional music in primary schools, Armagh Pipers Club and Keady Comhaltas Branch. Prepares students for both group and solo performances and competitions. Member of 'Itchy Fingers' group. Wide range of experience at home and abroad. Repertoire includes folk and traditional music of Ireland, Scotland, France and England. Influenced by Matt Molloy, Desi Wilkinson, Séamus Tansey and Sligo/Leitrim style of flute playing (e.g. Josie McDermot).

## Kathleen Raymond *Flute*

**Contact:** Ms Kathleen Raymond
72, Stack's Villas
Tralee, Co Kerry
**Tel:** +353 66 26973
*See classical flute page 18.*

## Michael Rooney *Flute*

**Contact:** Mr Mackie Rooney
Tyraverty
Scotstown
Co Monaghan
**Tel:** +353 47 89161
*See Irish harp page 230.*

## Andrew Rowan *Flute*

**Contact:** Mr Andrew Rowan
10, Galbraith Gardens
Waringstown BT 66 7QN
Northern Ireland
**Tel:** +44 1762 881097
*See classical flute page 19.*

## Garry Shannon *Flute*

**Contact:** Mr Garry Shannon
Ragairne
Tullyodea
Ruan
Co Clare
**Tel/Fax:** +353 65 37379
**Email:** garryshannon@tinet

**KEY IRISH PERFORMANCES** (since January 1994):
1995 Dublin, promoted by RTÉ ('Up For The Final'), appearing with Kilfenora Ceilí Band.
1995 Dublin, promoted by RTÉ Famine Remembrance Concert, appearing with the National Folk Orchestra.
1997 University of Limerick Concert Hall, Limerick, appearing with Planxty O'Rourke.
1997 St Stephen's Green, Dublin, promoted by St Patricks Day Committee, appearing with Kilfenora Ceilí Band.
**KEY PERFORMANCES OUTSIDE IRELAND** (since January 1994):
1994 Irish Centre, London, promoted by Claremans Association.
1995 Neuchstadt, Germany, appearing with Dolmen.
1997 Ris Orangis, Paris, France, appearing with Kilfenora Ceilí Band.
1997 Lincolin Centre, New York, appearing with Kilfenora Ceilí Band.
**SELECTED BROADCASTS AND/OR RECORDED WORK:**
1984 'Musical Travel, Ireland', for Silex/Auvdis.
1989 'Lose The Head', for A Brick Missing Music.
1997 'Set On Stone', for Dolphin Records.
**PRIZES/AWARDS/APPOINTMENTS:**
1988 All-Ireland Senior Concert Flute winner, awarded by CCÉ.
1993.1994.1995 All-Ireland senior céilí band winner, awarded by CCÉ.
**REGULARLY PERFORMS WITH:**
Kilfenora Ceilí Band, Mossie Griffin and National Folk Orchestra.
**AVAILABILITY:**
Weekends and evenings during June, July, August and Christmas.

## Tony Steele *Flute*

**Contact:** Tony Steele
89, Willow Park Grove
Glasnevin
Dublin 11
**Mobile:** +353 87 487052
*See jazz guitar page 275.*

## Séamus Tansey *Flute*

**Contact:** Mr Séamus Tansey
425, Drumbeg South
Tullygally East
Craigavon
Co Armagh BT65 5AG
Northern Ireland
**Tel:** +44 1762 346026

## Fintan Vallely *Flute*

**Contact:** Mr Fintan Vallely
15, Castlewood Terrace
Rathmines
Dublin 6
**Tel/Fax:** +353 1 4972979
**Email:** fuall@iol.ie
**Other instruments:** Voice.

**KEY IRISH PERFORMANCES** (since January 1994):
1.95 Tour of Ireland promoted by Music Network, appearing with Dermot Diamond, Mairghread Ní Dhomhnaill, Con O'Drisceoil.
4.95 Portlaoise Arts Festival, appearing with Dermot Healy, promoted by Music Network.
7.95 National Concert Hall, Dublin, appearing with Liz Doherty and Maighread Ní Dhomhnaill.
**KEY PERFORMANCES OUTSIDE IRELAND** (since January 1994):
8.95 Verona, appearing with Maighread Ní Dhomhnaill, Dermot McLaughlin, promoted by Musica Celtica.
9.95 Helsinki Irish Festival.
3.96 Jakarta Irish Ball, Indonesia.
8.97 Milwaukee Irish Festival.
**SELECTED BROADCASTS AND/OR RECORDED WORK:**
1979 'Traditional Irish Flute', for Shanachie.
1988 'Knock, Knock, Knock', for UMFA.
1991 'Starry Lane to Monaghan', for Whinstone.
**REGULARLY PERFORMS WITH:**
Tim Lyons, Dermot Healy (poet).
**AVAILABILITY:**
General.
**ADDITIONAL INFORMATION:**
Freelance commentator on traditional music with Irish Times and music consultant for RTÉ's 'High Reel' series. Joint organiser of 1996 Crossroads Conference. Ethnomusicologist, flute teacher, lecturer and commentator on Irish and International Folk Music. Author of 'Timber', 'The Flute Tutor', 'Balcony of the Nation' (satirical song), 'Rake's Almanaz' (traditional music performance directory), 'Companion to Irish Traditional Music' (Cork University Press), 'Crossroads Jigg' (traditional music and the Protestant community).

## Desie Wilkinson *Flute*

**Contact:** Mr Desie Wilkinson
41, Oaklawns
Castletroy
Limerick
**Tel/Fax:** +353 61 335403 / +353 61 330316
**Other instruments:** Highland bagpipes, singer.

*"... He is an articulate and humourous presenter of the music ... if traditional music is about searching, absorption, retention and change, so is Desi"*
9.90 Outlook Booklet for Arts Council Northern Ireland (Ciarán Carson).

**KEY IRISH PERFORMANCES** (since January 1994):
6.7.95 Community Hall, Miltown Malbay, An Scoil Samhraidh Willie Clancy, appearing with Leon Agnew.
17.9.95 Dublin promoted by Bank of Ireland appearing with Cran.
25-29.9.95 Co Down, promoted by SELB, promoted by the Arts Council Northern Ireland appearing with Gerry O'Connor.
**KEY PERFORMANCES OUTSIDE IRELAND** (since January 1994):
3.95 Quimper, Rennes, France, promoted by Le Carré Magique, appearing with Cran and Mairtin O'Connor.
5.8.95 Tréguier, France, promoted by Art Scene appearing with Paddy O'Neill.
27.8.95 St Brieue, France, promoted by EDF appearing with Paddy O'Neill.
29.8.95 Pluzunet, France, promoted by Le Moulin Musicien appearing with Paddy O'Neill.
**SELECTED BROADCASTS AND/OR RECORDED WORK:**
1986 'Cosa Gan Bhroga' for Gael-Linn.
1987 'The Three Piece Flute' for Spring.
12.92 'The Crooked Stairs' with Cran for CBM records.
1998 Black, Black, Black with Cran. Also working on a solo album.
**SELECTED REVIEWS** (since January 1994):
16.3.95 Ouest France.
16.3.95 Telegramme.
28.8.95 Ouest France.
**PRIZES/AWARDS/APPOINTMENTS:**
1987 Bursary awarded by the Arts Council.
From 1988 to 1991, Awarded 'Musician in the Community', by the Arts Council of Northern Ireland.
**TRAINING AND /OR QUALIFICATIONS:**
From 1975 to 1978, B Ed, St Joseph's College Belfast.
From 1988 to 1990, MA, from Queen's University. Belfast.
Currently studying for a PhD in Breton music.
**REGULARLY PERFORMS WITH:**
Cran.
**AVAILABILITY:**
General.
**ADDITIONAL INFORMATION:**
Tours regularly abroad, and has played with several well known Irish musicians. Wide knowledge of celtic music, and is especially interested in world music. Was involved in a Pan European Music project while living in Brittany, France between 1992 and 1994. Has presented papers at several musicological conferences in Athens, Belfast, and at the National University of Ireland, Maynooth. Annual tutor at An Scoil Samhraidh Willie Clancy. Member of traditional group, Cran

# GUITAR

## Pat Ahern *Guitar*

**Contact:** Mr Pat Ahern
Clonmoyle East
Coachford
Co Cork
**Tel/Fax:** +353 21 334271
**Email:** pahern@rtc-cork.ie
**Other instruments:** Bouzouki.

**KEY IRISH PERFORMANCES** (since January 1994):
11.95 National Concert Hall, Dublin, promoted by Na Píobairí Uileann, appearing with C Ó Drisceoil and J McCarthy.
7.96 Miltown Malbay, promoted by Scoil Samhraidh Willie Clancy.
11.96 School of Music, Cork, promoted by the Cork Arts Festival, appearing with Máire Ní Ghráda.

5.97 Opera House, Cork, promoted by Dara, appearing with J McCarthy, P Crowley, F Thomas.
**KEY PERFORMANCES OUTSIDE IRELAND** (since January 1994):
8.94 Wadebridge, Cornwall, promoted by the Wadebridge Rock Festival, appearing with J McCarthy, C Ó Drisceoil.
3.94/95 Bangkok, promoted by St Patrick's Society of Bangkok, appearing with J McCarthy, C Ó Drisceoil, P O'Sullivan and B Ridge.
2.95 MJC, Paris, promoted by Association Irlandaise, appearing with J McCarthy, C Ó Drisceoil.
**SELECTED BROADCASTS AND/OR RECORDED WORK:**
3.96 Open University.
11.96 'Geantraí' for TnaG.
7.97 'The Square Triangle' for Craft.
**REGULARLY PERFORMS WITH:**
Four Star Trio.
**AVAILABILITY:**
General.

## Máire Breatnach *Guitar*

**Contact:** c/o Mr Steve Dunford
6, The Avenue
Boden Park
Rathfarnham
Dublin 16
**Tel/Fax:** +353 1 4947615 or +353 1 49323358 / +353 1 4931707
*See Máire Breatnach Band page 257.*

## Barry Carroll *Guitar*

**Contact:** Mr Barry Carroll
25, Céide na gCrann Creathach
Cúirt Cheann Sáile
Sord
Cho Áth Cliath
**Tel:** +353 1 840 5684
*See Hammer Dulcimer page 226.*

## Danny Carthy *Guitar*

**Contact:** Mr Danny Carthy
46, Laurence Avenue
Maynooth
Co Kildare
**Tel:** +353 1 6285276
*See singers page 244.*

## Jane Cassidy *Guitar*

**Contact:** Mrs Jane Cassidy
12, Landsdowne Road
Belfast, BT15 4DA
Northern Ireland
**Tel:** +44 1232 773525
*See piano page 232.*

## Aidan Coleman *Guitar*

**Contact:** Mr Aidan Coleman
28, Lisalea
Frascati Park
Blackrock
Co Dublin
**Tel:** +353 1 2835117
*See Bass Baritone page 112.*

## Sonny Condell *Guitar*

**Contact:** Mr Sonny Condell
**Tel:** +353 1 2892635
**Other instruments:** Piano, percussion.

**SELECTED BROADCASTS AND/OR RECORDED WORK:**
1977 'Camouflage', for Mulligan Records.
1994 'Someone to Dance With', for Starc Records.
**SELECTED REVIEWS** (since January 1994):
1995 Hot Press, (S Long).
1995 Irish Times, (Joe Jackson).
**AVAILABILITY:**
General.

## Anne Conroy Burke *Guitar*

**Contact:** Ms Anne Conroy Burke
Tinageeragh
Kilnadeema
Loughrea
Co Galway
**Tel/Fax:** +353 91 842419
*See accordion page 189.*

## Steve Cooney *Guitar*

**Contact:** Mr Steve Cooney
Ceann Tra
Tralee
Co Kerry
**Fax only:** +353 66 59779

**REGULARLY PERFORMS WITH:**
Séamus Begley.

## Ewan Cowley *Guitar*

**Contact:** Mr Ewan Cowley
c/o 18, Belmont Crescent
Derry, BT48 7RR
Northern Ireland
**Tel/Fax:** +44 1504 354455 / +44 1504 350916
**Other instruments:** Piano, bass guitar, voice.

**KEY IRISH PERFORMANCES** (since January 1994):
From 1992 to 1995, Derry.

**SELECTED BROADCASTS AND/OR RECORDED WORK:**
11.94 For Radio Foyle, Northern Ireland.
12.94 Ulster Hall, Belfast, promoted by BBC Northern Ireland
**REGULARLY PERFORMS WITH:**
Noel Cowley (guitar and vocals) and John McDaid (guitar and vocals).
**AVAILABILITY:**
Weekends.
**ADDITIONAL INFORMATION:**
Currently studying music at King's College, London and Royal Academy of Music, London.

# Christopher Cronin *Guitar*

**Contact:** Mr Christopher Cronin
Killyfad
Aughamore
Carrick-on-Shannon
Co Leitrim
**Tel:** +353 78 24685
**Other instruments:** Piano accordion.

**AVAILABILITY:**
Weekends, evenings.
**ADDITIONAL INFORMATION:**
All-England winner (accordion). Also a singer and guitarist with complete sound backing (ie drums, bass, effects).

# Jimmy Crowley *Guitar*

**Contact:** Mr Jimmy Crowley
134, Sunday's Well Road
Cork
**Tel:** +353 21 309727
*See singers page 245.*

# Karmel "Katie" Daly *Guitar*

**Contact:** Ms Karmel Daly
Cummer
Templeludigan
Enniscorthy
Co Wexford
**Tel:** +353 51 421255

**KEY IRISH PERFORMANCES** (since January 1994):
3.94 The Gaiety Theatre, Dublin, promoted by the theatre festival (jazz and blues performance).
6.96 Union of Students of Ireland, Temple Bar, Dublin, performed title song 'Last Man Down Play'.
4.97 St Michael's Theatre, New Ross, 'Tops of the Town' and Chernobyl Concert Night.
**SELECTED BROADCASTS AND/OR RECORDED WORK:**
7.96 Theme for 'Removing The Spikes' for RTÉ.
**AVAILABILITY:**
Weekends, evenings.
**ADDITIONAL INFORMATION:**
Comes from a traditional background. Played in Ceathrú Rua Gaeltacht and has been performing in pubs since 1980.

# Paul de Grae *Guitar*

**Contact:** Mr Paul de Grae
Frogmore House
The Spa
Tralee
Co Kerry
**Tel/Fax:** +353 66 36111
**Email:** sullgrae@iol.ie
**Other instruments:** Piano.

**KEY IRISH PERFORMANCES** (since January 1994):
3/6.9.96 Granary Theatre, Cork, promoted by Forefront Productions, appearing with Smoky Chimney, Jackie Daly and Máire O'Keeffe.
15.2.97 Temple Bar Music Centre promoted by Hummingbird Productions.
17.3.97 National Concert Hall, Dublin, promoted by KCP Productions, appearing with Smoky Chimney.
12.4.97 Kilworth Arts Centre, Co Cork, appearing with Smoky Chimney.
**SELECTED BROADCASTS AND/OR RECORDED WORK:**
1995 'Many's the Wild Night' with Jackie Daly, for Gael-Linn.
1993 'Coumeenoole' with Eoin Duignan for Gael-Linn.
**REGULARLY PERFORMS WITH:**
Smoky Chimney, Máire O'Keeffe and Jackie Daly
**AVAILABILITY:**
Subject to commitments.

# Dermot Diamond *Guitar*

**Contact:** Dr Dermot Diamond
Coolquoy
The Ward
Co Dublin
**Tel/Fax:** +353 1 8351654
**Email:** diamondd@iol.ie
*See fiddle page 206.*

# Declan Forde *Guitar*

**Contact:** Mr Declan Forde
22, Fernagh Road
Omagh
Co Tyrone BT79 OHX
Northern Ireland
**Tel:** +44 1662 771551 (after 5pm)

**KEY IRISH PERFORMANCES** (since January 1994):
9.95 Old Museum Arts Centre, Belfast, promoted by Belfast Yarnspinners.
9.95 Armagh City Folk Club.
11.95 Newcastle Arts Centre, appearing with Tom Sweeney.
8.96 Rostrevor, promoted by Fiddlers Green Festival.
**SELECTED BROADCASTS AND/OR RECORDED WORK:**
12.96 'Anderson', for BBC Radio Ulster.
6.97 'George Jones' show, for BBC Radio Ulster, Belfast.
7.97 'Brendan Maxwell' for Highland Radio, Donegal.
**PRIZES/AWARDS/APPOINTMENTS:**
8.95 2nd place in singing competition at the Letterkenny Folk Festival.
11.96 2nd place in the Bard of Armagh competition.
**AVAILABILITY:**
General.
**ADDITIONAL INFORMATION:**
Performs self-penned 'folk-poetry' and song. Performances are a blend of music, monologues, drama and poetry.

## Jim McCullagh *Guitar*

**Contact:** Mr Jim McCullagh
c/o Ulster College of Music
13, Windsor Avenue
Belfast BT19
Northern Ireland
**Tel:** +44 1232 381314
*See classical guitar page 21.*

## Eddie McGinley *Guitar*

**Contact:** Eddie McGinley
14, Park Drive Green
Castleknock
Dublin 15
**Tel:** +353 1 8203690
**Other instruments:** Button accordion.

**TRAINING AND/OR QUALIFICATIONS:**
From 1984 to 1985 Centre for Performing Arts, Dublin, Workshop with Agnes Bernelle.
**AVAILABILITY:**
General.

## Arty McGlynn *Guitar*

**Contact:** Mr Arty McGlynn
c/o MBE Artist Management and Agency
6, Seafield Crescent
Blackrock
Co Dublin
**Tel/Fax:** +353 1 2693821 / +353 1 2693777

## Joe McHugh *Guitar*

**Contact:** Mr Joe McHugh
Moneystown North
Roundwood
Co Wicklow
or
Gústr 8
Ch - 8700 Kúsnacht
Switzerland
**Tel:** +353 404 45161
**Email:** mchugh@goldnet.ch
*See uilleann pipes page 236.*

## Michael McInerney *Guitar*

**Contact:** Mr Michael McInerney
36, Sefton
Rochestown Avenue
Dún Laoghaire
Co Dublin
**Tel:** +353 1 2850996
*See harmonica page 226.*

## Paul Desmond Moore
### *Electric Bass Guitar*

**Contact:** Mr Paul Desmond Moore
12, Thor Place
North Circular Road
Dublin 7
**Tel:** +353 1 8384806
**Other instruments:** Double bass, 5-string bass, fretless bass guitar.

**KEY IRISH PERFORMANCES** (since January 1994):
19.5.95 National Concert Hall, promoted by Jimmy McCarthy, appearing with Anto Drennan.
23.12.96 Olympia Theatre, Dublin, promoted by MCD promotions, appearing with Café Orchestra.
29.12.96 National Concert Hall, promoted by Entertainment Awards/ RTÉ, appearing with Café Orchestra.
1.6.97 Leixlip Town Centre, promoted by Leixlip Arts Week, appearing with Stockton's Wing.
**KEY PERFORMANCES OUTSIDE IRELAND** (since January 1994):
11-14.5.96 Bergen, Norway, promoted by Bergen Blues and Folk Festival, appearing with Jimmy McCarthy and Café Orchestra.
28.6.96 Gaelic Park, Bronx, New York, promoted by Rock the Bronx 1996, appearing with Davy Spillane.
1.11.96 Carnegie Hall, New York, promoted by Maggie Cadden, appearing with Phil Coulter.
4.3.97 Disneyland, Paris, promoted by Irish Music Week, Disneyland, appearing with Sharon Shannon.
**SELECTED BROADCASTS AND/OR RECORDED WORK:**
27.2.95 'North and South', with U2 and Christy Moore, for Sony Records.
1996 'Golden Hears', with Mark Knopfler for Mercury Records Ltd, London.
1996 'Topaz', Café Orchestra, for Grapevine.
**SELECTED REVIEWS** (since January 1994):
11.2.95 Irish Times.
6.8.96 Irish Times.
**REGULARLY PERFORMS WITH:**
Café Orchestra, Davy Spillane, Phil Coulter, Mary Coughlan and Dolores Keane.
**AVAILABILITY:**
General.
**ADDITIONAL INFORMATION:**
Primarily works as a freelance musician. Performs almost all genres of music and has worked with many international artists and national groups.

## Johnny Murgrew *Guitar*

**Contact:** Mr Johnny Murgrew
112, Shanreagh Park
Limavady
Co Derry
**Tel:** +44 15047 64820
**Other instruments:** Tenor banjo.

**KEY PERFORMANCES OUTSIDE IRELAND** (since January 1994):
Summer 1994 Palm Beach, Orlando, Florida, appearing with Paddy Reilly and Jim McCann.
1996 Key West, Palm Beach, Orlando, Florida, appearing with Dublin City Ramblers.
**SELECTED BROADCASTS AND/OR RECORDED WORK:**
1992 'Rose of Annagrey' (own cassette).
1994 'Farewell to Derry' for Music Box, Castleblaney, Co Monaghan.
'Bibi' for RTÉ.
**SELECTED REVIEWS** (since January 1994):
Daily Journal, Northern Constitution.
**PRIZES/AWARDS/APPOINTMENTS:**
1989 1st Prize for Solo Singing at Ballyshannon Talent Competition.
**REGULARLY PERFORMS WITH:**
Fiddlers Elbow (duo).

**AVAILABILITY:**
General.
**ADDITIONAL INFORMATION:**
Tapes have been broadcast on several radio stations throughout the country. Wide repertoire available

# Eoghan O'Brien *Guitar*

**Contact:** Mr Eoghan O'Brien
77, Main Street
Portglenone
Co Antrim BT44 8HR
Northern Ireland
**Tel/Fax:** +44 1266 821333 / +44 1266 822181
**Other instruments:** Celtic harp, fiddle.

**KEY IRISH PERFORMANCES** (since January 1994):
16.2.96 Queen's University, Belfast promoted by Carolyn Mason.
10.10.96 Ulster Museum, Belfast, appearing with Brendan Hendry, Séamus O'Kane, Paul McGlinchey and Francis McIlduff.
15.11.96 Portaferry, promoted by Rod Patterson and Ards District Council, appearing with Marcus Ó Murchú and Séamus O'Kane.
11.96 Culloden Hotel, Belfast, promoted by the Northern Ireland Tourist Board, appearing with Brendan Hendry, Ivan Gough and Francis McIlduff.
**SELECTED BROADCASTS AND/OR RECORDED WORK:**
1996 'High Reel' for RTÉ.
27.2.97 'Wham Bam Strawberry Jam' for BBC.
3.97 'Traditional Sounds' for BBC.
**PRIZES/AWARDS/APPOINTMENTS:**
1985 2nd Prize in CCÉ All-Ireland Fleadh Cheoil na hÉireann (Celtic Harp) age category 15-18 years.
**TRAINING AND/OR QUALIFICATIONS:**
Late 1980's, TTCT (harp) from CCÉ.
**REGULARLY PERFORMS WITH:**
Déanta.
**AVAILABILITY:**
General.
**ADDITIONAL INFORMATION:**
Experienced accompanist of traditional music and song, on both acoustic guitar (dagdad) and celtic harp. Regularly teaches and gives workshops on traditional guitar.

# Niall Ó Callanáin *Guitar*

**Contact:** Niall Ó Callanáin
1, Park Place
Islandbridge
Dublin 8
**Mobile:** +353 87 414435
*See bouzouki page 201.*

# Seoirse Ó Dochartaigh *Guitar*

**Contact:** Ms Margaret Rhatigan
Errigal Promotions
1, Chapel Street
Sligo
**Tel/Fax:** +353 71 42316 / +353 73 22677
*See singers page 251.*

# Séan O'Driscoll *Guitar*

**Contact:** Mr Séan O'Driscoll
Castle View
Blarney
Co Cork
**Tel:** +353 21 385386
*See banjo page 196.*

# Brendan O'Dwyer *Guitar*

**Contact:** Mr Brendan O'Dwyer
Ruan
Bansha
Co Tipperary
or
48, Perth Road
Finsbury Park
London N4 3HB
England
**Tel:** +353 62 54534 / +44 171 2636686
*See banjo page 197.*

# Tom O'Farrell *Guitar*

**Contact:** Mr Tom O'Farrell
12, Restelouet
22340 Plévin
France
**Tel:** +33 2 962 96792
**Other instruments:** Viola da gamba, guitar, lute.

**KEY IRISH PERFORMANCES** (since January 1994):
11.94 Padraig O'Keeffe Festival, Castleisland, Kerry, promoted by M. Kenny, appearing with B Begley, John Carty, Donal O'Connor.
**KEY PERFORMANCES OUTSIDE IRELAND** (since January 1994):
7/8.97 Tour of Europe Rennes, Montreux, Lisbon, Milan, Brussels, appearing with the Chieftains.
**SELECTED BROADCASTS AND/OR RECORDED WORK:**
1982 'Tom O'Farrell' for KIRT (Paris).
1990 'Súil a Rún' for Restouelen (Brittany).
1994 'Chatterbox' (guest for M O'Connor).
**PRIZES/AWARDS/APPOINTMENTS:**
1992 1st Prize for original setting of traditional text at the An tÓireachtas competition.
**TRAINING AND/OR QUALIFICATIONS:**
From 1996 to 1997, Diplome d'État (DÉ), from Conservatoire Regionale, Lorient.
**REGULARLY PERFORMS WITH:**
Gary O'Briain, Mairtín O'Connor (accordion).
**AVAILABILITY:**
General.
**ADDITIONAL INFORMATION:**
Interested in all art forms which have as their aim the breaking of boundaries in current conceptions of art, especially the role of music and poetry.

# Mark O'Leary *Guitar*

**Contact:** Mr Mark O'Leary
59, Greenhills Court
South Douglas Road, Cork
**Tel:** +353 21 361808
*See jazz guitar page 274.*

## Brendan O'Regan *Guitar*

**Contact:** Brendan O'Regan
**Tel/Fax:** +353 91 592852
**Other instruments:** Mandolin, bouzouki.

*"O'Regan is widely acknowledged as one of the classiest musicians in Irish music today"* Hot Press.

**SELECTED RECORDED WORK:**
'Song for Ireland' album with De Dannan.
1992 'Wind of Change', solo album.
**ADDITIONAL INFORMATION:**
Member of De Danann in 1983. Worked with Druid Theatre, Galway directing, arranging and composing music for Brendan Behan's 'The Hostage', with Jim Sheridan. Other productions include 'Cheapside', 'St Patrick's Day', 'At The Black Pigs Dyke' and 'The Yellow Bittern'. Other recorded work includes 'Collected' with Mary Black, 'Fisherman's Blues' with The Waterboys, 'Music From Galway' with Ceol Tigh Neachtain, 'Nomads' with John Faulkner, 'The Piper's Apron' with Tommy Keane, 'Smaointe' with Deirbhile Ní Bhrolachain, 'Flick of the Wrist' with Brendan Larrissey, 'Lion in a Cage/Dolores Keane', with Dolores Keane, 'Boys From Blue Hill' with Vinnie Kilduff, 'Time to Time' with Gerry O'Connor and 'Blue Fiddle' with Sean Smyth.

## Sebastien Petiet *Guitar*

**Contact:** c/o Marie Petiet
23, Park Crescent House
Blackhorse Avenue
Dublin 7
**Tel/Fax:** +353 1 8681210
*See violin page 65.*

## John Quinn *Guitar*

**Contact:** John Quinn
30, Parnell Court
Harolds Cross
Dublin 6W
**Tel:** +353 1 4535699 / +353 1 4933145
*See fiddle page 213.*

## Frank Simon *Guitar*

**Contact:** Mr Frank Simon
The Plains
Boyle
Co Roscommon
**Tel:** +353 79 62245
**Other instruments:** Keyboards, mandolin, whistles, jazz guitar.

*"... The like never heard on guitar before ... ... breathtaking ... Frank Simon is a name to watch ..."* 8/9 Musikblatt.

**SELECTED BROADCASTS AND/OR RECORDED WORK:**
1991 'Slipstream' own cassette and CD.
1994 'Strings of my Soul', own cassette.
**PRIZES/AWARDS/APPOINTMENTS:**
8.93 1st Prize in the Keadue Song Contest, Keadue, Boyle, Co Roscommon.
1994 Runner-up Prize, Gay Byrne Show, World Cup Song Contest.
**AVAILABILITY:**
General.
**ADDITIONAL INFORMATION:**
Annually, since 1992, has been teaching the art of playing Irish music on the guitar at the South Sligo Summer School, Tubbercurry, Co Sligo. Plays and composes jazz influenced jigs, reels, hornpipes etc. in the flatpicking style.

## John Spillane
### *Guitar and Electric Bass Guitar*

**Contact:** Mr John Spillane
1, Idaville, Sharman
Crawford Street
Cork
**Tel:** +353 21 315091
**Other instruments:** Singer.

**KEY IRISH PERFORMANCES** (since January 1994):
7.8.95 Mitchelstown Deer Festival, appearing with Nomos.
27.8.95 Pinelodge, Cork.
30.8.95 Whelan's Bar, Dublin, promoted by Des McCullough, appearing with Nomos.
14.10.95 Lobby Bar Cork, promoted by Pat Conway, appearing with Nomos.
**KEY PERFORMANCES OUTSIDE IRELAND** (since January 1994):
From 28.9 to 9.10.95 Tour of Finland, Irish Festival of Finland, promoted by Olli Pellikka, appearing with Nomos.
**SELECTED BROADCASTS AND/OR RECORDED WORK:**
1.95 'I Won't Be Afraid Anymore', for Solid Records.
5.95 'All the Ways You Wander', Nomos, Solid Records.
7.95 'Irishtown', two original tracks, for Hummingbird Records.
**SELECTED REVIEWS** (since January 1994):
2.95 Irish Times.
26.1.95 The Examiner.
**REGULARLY PERFORM WITH:**
Nomos, John Spillane, Mick Daly, Áine Whelan and Dave Murphy Band
**AVAILABILITY:**
General.
**ADDITIONAL INFORMATION:**
Member of the group Nomos. Sean-Nós singer. Played with swing-harmony group Stargazers for seven years. Solo album released in 1996 on the Hummingbird label.

## Rosemary Woods *Guitar*

**Contact:** Miss Rosemary Woods
6, Abbacy Road
Ardkeen
Portaferry
Co Down, BT22 1HH
Northern Ireland
**Tel:** +44 12477 28747
*See singers page 255.*

# HAMMER DULCIMER

## Eilín Begley *Hammer Dulcimer*

**Contact:** Ms Eilín Begley
Loughlane
Caulstown
Dunboyne
Co Meath
**Tel/Fax:** +353 1 8256337
*See traditional groups page 256.*

## Barry Carroll *Hammer Dulcimer*

**Contact:** Mr Barry Carroll
25, Céide na gCrann Creathach
Cúirt Cheann Sáile
Sord
Cho Áth Cliath
**Tel:** +353 1 840 5684
**Other instruments:** Guitar.

**KEY PERFORMANCES OUTSIDE IRELAND** (since January 1994):
1994 Copenhagen Irish Festival, appearing with 'Rattlin Strings' group.
1995 Oslo Irish Festival, appearing with 'Rattlin Strings' group.
**SELECTED RECORDED WORK:**
1992 'The Long Finger'/'An Mhéar Fhada', duo with Piper Joe McHugh, distributed by Claddagh.
1995 'Musclaíonn an Mhaidin' for Raidió na Life.
1997 Backing tracks for Sharon Shannon's, CD 'Each Little Thing'.
**REGULARLY PERFORMS WITH:**
Joe McHugh (pipes).
**AVAILABILITY:**
General.
**ADDITIONAL INFORMATION:**
Repertoire is based mainly in the traditional Irish and celtic idiom, with some light classical compositions.

# HARMONICA

## Séamas Fogarty *Harmonica*

**Contact:** Mr Séamas Fogarty
54, Woodlawn Park
Churchtown, Dublin 14
**Tel/Fax:** +353 1 2983028 / +353 1 6763900
*See concertina page 201.*

## Michael McInerney *Harmonica*

**Contact:** Mr Michael McInerney
36, Sefton
Rochestown Avenue
Dún Laoghaire
Co Dublin
**Tel:** +353 1 2850996
**Other instruments:** Guitar (acoustic and electric).

**KEY IRISH PERFORMANCES** (since January 1994):
6.97 Project Arts Centre, Dublin, promoted by the Gaiety School of Acting.
6.97 The Granary Theatre, Cork, promoted by Gaiety School of Acting.
**SELECTED RECORDED WORK:**
10.95 'Three Steps Sideways' for Fourth Wall Productions.
6.96 'Flatley's Reel' and 'Mellow Funk' for McGee Composition Mikes.
10.96 'Memento Mori' (film soundtrack) for Morning Star Productions.
**TRAINING AND/OR QUALIFICATIONS:**
From 9.96 to 6.97, Grade 5 exam in Plectrum Guitar from Walton's School of Music, Dublin, (awarded from the Guildhall School of Music and Drama).
**REGULARLY PERFORMS WITH:**
Colin Marr (guitar).
**AVAILABILITY:**
General.
**ADDITIONAL INFORMATION:**
Harmonica teacher. Can repair and re-tune the instrument. Wide repertoire and playing style encompasses anything that can be played on a harmonica (chromatic or single reed diatonic).

## John Murphy *Harmonica*

**Contact:** Mr John Murphy
Ballygow
Bannow
Co Wexford
**Tel:** +353 51 561375

**KEY IRISH PERFORMANCES** (since January 1994):
8.95 Feakle Traditional Music Festival, Co Clare, appearing with Pip Murphy.
10.96 Cork, promoted by students of University College, Cork.
4.97 Wexford Arts Centre, appearing with Pip Murphy.
**KEY PERFORMANCES OUTSIDE IRELAND** (since January 1994):
4.94 Colombus, Ohio, as part of the Colombus Harmonica Convention.
6.94 Cleveland, Ohio, promoted by the Northern Aid Convention.
7.94 Memphis, Ohio, as part of the Memphis Folk Roots Festival.
**SELECTED RECORDED WORK:**
6.89 'The Trip to Cullenstown' for Claddagh Records.
7.94 'River of Sound' for Hummingbird.
2.95 'The Late Late Show' for RTÉ.
**PRIZES/AWARDS/APPOINTMENTS:**
9.73 1st Prize at the CCÉ All-Ireland Fleadh Cheoil na hÉireann.
**REGULARLY PERFORMS WITH:**
Pip Murphy (harmonica).
**AVAILABILITY:**
General.

# IRISH HARP

## Derek F. Bell *Irish Harp*

**Contact:** Derek F. Bell
74, Bryanburn Road
Bangor, Co Down BT20 3SB
Northern Ireland
**Tel:** +44 1247 457923
**Other instruments:** Piano, cimbalom (psaltery and dulcimer), the oboe family (except the heckelphone), tuned percussion, keyboards.

*"He gave that old 'War Horse' Paderewsky's Minuet a new lease of life and made the delicate passages memorable"* 1997 Brunswick Times.

**KEY IRISH PERFORMANCES** (since January 1994):
Since 1972 (annually with The Chieftains), Ulster Hall, Belfast, appearing with the Northern Ireland Symphony Orchestra.
8.91 Ulster Hall, Belfast and 11.91 the National Concert Hall, Dublin in performances of Symphony No. 2 'The Violet Flame'.
Belfast, Shankill and Anderstown, playing 'Derek Bell Variations'.
1/2.97 appearing with Studio Symphony Orchestra (Openshaw conducting).
**KEY PERFORMANCES OUTSIDE IRELAND** (since January 1994):
6.6.96 Hollywood Steiner School, USA.
6.10.97 Brunswick, Georgia, promoted by Artiss de Volt, appearing with Carolyn Benson (piano).
**SELECTED BROADCASTS AND/OR RECORDED WORK:**
1978 'Derek Bell's Concert Party' video.
1980 'Derek Bell Plays Eight Instruments' for Claddagh.
1990 'One Man Band' video for BBC.
**PRIZES/AWARDS/APPOINTMENTS:**
1980 Gold Disc for 'Carolan's Favourite', awarded by Portugal University.
5 Grammy Awards, awarded by the US Academy of Record and Sound.
Other awards include the Altcarr Fellowship (Royal College of Music) and Manns Prize for Woodwind (Royal College of Music).
**TRAINING AND/OR QUALIFICATIONS:**
1953 Studied piano with D Parke and composition with Helen Rhoden.
From 1954 to 1957, Attended Royal College of Music, London, studying with Howells, Greenwood, Graeme and L. Goossens.
From 1964 to 1965, USA, Studied harp with Artiss de Volt, piano with Rosina Lhévinne and oboe with Harry Schulman.
Awarded B Mus, ARCM (pf) ARCM (t), LRAM (oboe).
**REGULARLY PERFORMS WITH:**
Members of The Chieftains, other orchestras and various rock musicians.
**AVAILABILITY:**
Subject to touring schedule.
**ADDITIONAL INFORMATION:**
Compositions include: 'Pastoral Overture', Overture - 'The Burgomaster' (in style of Suppé) Symphony No. 1, 'The Tragic', Symphony No 2. 'The Violet Flame' - Comte de Germárne, Waltz for piano and orchestra, Wind Sextet. 'Agincourt' Song variations, Légende, Ballade, and Toccata Burlesca for oboe and piano. Songs (adaptions of poetry by Blake and Yeats), Dance Rhapsody and several sonatas for piano solo. Has recorded 9 solo CD's (for Claddagh, Ogham, Crystal Clarity USA, the Grain of Wheat, London and Athene, London). The Chieftains also have recorded 34 CD's.

## Patricia Daly *Irish Harp*

**Contact:** Ms Patricia Daly
19, Magherydogherty Road
Markethill
Co Armagh BT60 1TY
Northern Ireland
**Tel:** +44 1861 551087
**Other instruments:** Piano, vocals.

*"Patricia Daly has single-handedly revived harp playing in Armagh and played abroad extensively with Armagh Pipers Club."* 1996 Armagh Gazette.

**KEY IRISH PERFORMANCES** (since January 1994):
4.97 Burrendale Hotel, Newcastle, Co Down, Palace Stables, Armagh and the Ulster Transport Museum, Armagh.
5.97 Navan Centre, Armagh.
**SELECTED BROADCASTS AND/OR RECORDED WORK:**
'Armagh one Fair County' video for Fast Forward Productions.
'Song of the Chanter' vinyl for Outlet Records.
5.96 'High Reel' for RTÉ.
**SELECTED REVIEWS** (since January 1994):
3.94 Foreward provided for own publication (harp tutor) manual by Derek Bell.
1997 Armagh Observer.
**PRIZES/AWARDS/APPOINTMENTS:**
1977/78 Senior Championship winner with the CCÉ Fleadh Cheoil na hÉireann.
1978 Senior Harp Championship at An tÓireachtas.
**TRAINING AND/OR QUALIFICATIONS:**
Ballycastle, Co Antrim, attended masterclass on harp.
Has attended the Edward Bunting Summer School, Benburb, Co Armagh.
1988 TTCT in Irish Harp and Irish Music from CCÉ.
From 11.1.97 to 8.3.97 Teaching Certificate in Traditional Irish music from Open College and Armagh Pipers Club.
**REGULARLY PERFORMS WITH:**
Brian Vallely, Eithne Vallely, Gold Ring Band.
**AVAILABILITY:**
General.
**ADDITIONAL INFORMATION:**
Has been Senior All-Ireland harp champion and Senior National An tÓireachtas harp champion. Toured extensively with Armagh Pipers Club in Germany, Israel, France and Ireland. Currently compiling a harp tutor accompanying CD.

## Cormac de Barra *Irish Harp*

**Contact:** Mr Cormac de Barra
21, Northbrook Avenue
Ranelagh
Dublin 6
**Tel/Mobile:** +353 1 4963324 / +353 87 445562
**Email:** cormac.d@usa.net

**KEY IRISH PERFORMACES** (since January 1994):
10.95 An t-Óireachtas, Dún Garbhán, promoted by An t-Óireachtas and RTÉ, appearing with Begley and Cooney (accordion and guitar).
3.96 John Field Room, National Concert Hall, Dublin, promoted by Cló Chaisil, appearing with Anne-Marie O'Farrell.
16.3.97 Royal Hibernian Art Gallery, Dublin, promoted by Michael Scott and The Machine, appearing with Anne-Marie O'Farrell.
16.5.97 National Concert Hall, Dublin, promoted by An t-Óireachtas, appearing with Délos.
**KEY PERFORMANCES OUTSIDE IRELAND** (since January 1994):
9.94 Turas na bhFilí, Edinburgh, promoted by Scottish Arts Council, appearing with Cathal Póirtéir.
9.95 De Rode Hoed, Amsterdam, promoted by European Harp Symposium, appearing with Anne-Marie O'Farrell.
7.96 Celtic Congress, Bangor, Wales, promoted by An Chomhdháil Cheilteach.
**SELECTED BROADCASTS AND/OR RECORDED WORK:**
4-9.90 Expo '90, Osaka, for NHK and RTÉ.
1991 'In Search of Carolan', for RTÉ.
1991 'Live at 3', for RTÉ.
**PRIZES/AWARDS/APPOINTMENTS:**
3.89 Awarded 1st prize, An Chruit, Harp competition (under 18) Feis Ceoil, Dublin.
3.90 1st Prize, Corn Uí Chearbhalláin, Feis Ceoil, Dublin.
**REGULARLY PERFORMS WITH:**
Anne-Marie O'Farrell (harp).
**AVAILABILITY:**
General.
**ADDITIONAL INFORMATION:**
Third generation of harpers in de Barra family. Has represented Ireland at festivals and events in Europe, USA and Japan (where he gave a recital of Irish music for the Emperor and Empress of Japan). As well as performing traditional and baroque music, has worked extensively in Irish theatre, adapting music for harp. Currently performs in a harp duo with Anne-Marie O'Farrell.

# Jillian Delaney *Irish Harp*

**Contact:** Jillian Delaney
30, Fremont Drive
Melbourn
Bishopstown
Cork
**Tel:** +353 21 544887
**Other instruments:** Piano, fiddle.

**KEY IRISH PERFORMANCES** (since January 1994):
9.96 Granary Theatre, Cork, live music for production of 'King Lear', appearing with Boomerang Theatre Company.
18.6.97 Blarney Park Hotel, Co Cork.
19/22.6.97 Blackrock Castle, Cork.
**SELECTED BROADCASTS AND/OR RECORDED WORK:**
22.11.96 music for 'Alice in Wonderland' with Boomerang Young Peoples Theatre Company for own cassette.
**TRAINING AND/OR QUALIFICATIONS:**
Grade 8 (harp) from the Cork School of Music (teacher Máire Ní Chathasaigh).
Grade 8 (piano) from the Cork School of Music (teachers Mary O'Herlihy and Maud Hanlon).
**REGULARLY PERFORMS WITH:**
Claire Lalor (flute).
**AVAILABILITY:**
General.
**ADDITIONAL INFORMATION:**
Repertoire includes Irish airs, dance tunes and O'Carolan pieces. Has worked on several productions with the Boomerang Theatre Company, composing, performing and the creating sound effects.

# Fionnuala Gill *Irish Harp*

**Contact:** Ms Fionnuala Gill
151, Ard na Mara
Malahide, Co Dublin
**Tel:** +353 1 8450698
*See soprano page 88.*

# Gráinne Hambly *Irish Harp*

**Contact:** Ms Gráinne Hambly
Knockrickard
Claremorris
Co Mayo
**Tel/Fax:** +353 94 60209 / +353 94 60273
**Email:** grainne@mayo-ireland.ie
**Other instruments:** Concertina.

**KEY IRISH PERFORMANCES** (since January 1994):
8.11.95 National Concert Hall, Dublin promoted by 'Ceolchoirm an Óireachtas', appearing with the CCÉ National Folk Orchestra.
8.12.95 Harty Room, Queen's University, Belfast, promoted by Queen's Music Society.
4.96 Tour of Ireland, promoted by CCÉ, appearing with CCÉ Irish Tour group.
22.1.97 Waterfront Hall, Belfast, promoted by Belfast City Council, appearing with the Belfast Harp Orchestra.
**KEY PERFORMANCES OUTSIDE IRELAND** (since January 1994):
8.96 and 8.97 Lorient, Brittany, France.
9/10.96 Britain 'Spirit of the Dance', promoted by Celebrity Entertainments, appearing with the Irish National Harp Ensemble.
11/12.96 Germany, Austria, Switzerland, promoted by Rüdiger Oppermann.
**SELECTED BROADCASTS AND/OR RECORDED WORK:**
1995 'Feasting with Carolan' with the Belfast Harp Orchestra.
1996 'Come With Me Over the Mountain' for CCÉ.
1996 'The Art of the Harp' for Shamrock Records.
**PRIZES/AWARDS/APPOINTMENTS:**
8.94 1st Prize in Senior Harp and Concertina competitions at CCÉ Fleadh Cheoil na hÉireann.
8.95 1st Prize in Senior Harp at the CCÉ Bun-Fleadh Harp Competition, Granard, Co Longford.
**TRAINING AND/OR QUALIFICATIONS:**
From 1990 to 1995, Studied with Janet Harbison.
From 17.7.94 to 23.7.94, TTCT from CCÉ.
From 1.9.94 to 6.9.94, Studied with Uschi Laar at 'Süddeutchen Harfentreffen' (German harp masterclass).
From 1993 to 1996, B Mus (Hons) from Queens University, Belfast.
**REGULARLY PERFORMS WITH:**
Belfast Harp Orchestra, Clarsheree (J Harbison, Michael Rooney, P Davey, S McAlindan).
**AVAILABILITY:**
General.
**ADDITIONAL INFORMATION:**
Has taught regularly in Belfast since 1994. Has also taught at various summer schools, (Glencolmcille, Scoil Éigse, Dinan). Currently studying part-time for an MA in Music from Queen's University, Belfast. Performs regularly for Live Music Now! Has appeared on a number of television programmes for RTÉ, BBC and UTV.

# Denise Kelly *Irish Harp*

**Contact:** Denise Kelly
66, Dartmouth Square
Ranelagh
Dublin 6
**Tel:** +353 1 6689366
*See concert harp page 7.*

# Laoise Kelly *Irish Harp*

**Contact:** Ms Laoise Kelly
10, Mountain View
Ennis
Co Clare
**Tel/Fax:** +353 91 528839
**Other instruments:** Fiddle, piano.

*"... Laoise has broken all boundaries of harp playing with her fresh approach, attack and unique style"* 6.95 Cara Magazine (Nuala O'Connor).

**KEY IRISH PERFORMANCES** (since January 1994):
5.95 Point, Dublin, Eurovision '95, appearing in 'Lumen'.
5.95 University of Limerick Concert Hall, 'River of Sound" concerts, appearing with Donal Lunny.
9.95 National Concert Hall, Dublin, in a performance for President Mary Robinson, of Charlie Lennon's 'Famine Suite'.
10.96 University of Limerick, lunchtime concert appearing with Mel Mercier and Donal Lunny.
**KEY PERFORMANCES OUTSIDE IRELAND** (since January 1994):
11.95 Boston, USA, appearing in 'Famine Suite'.
3.96 Tour of Australia, promoted by Jon Nicholas, appearing in 'Famine Suite' with Australian orchestras.
7.96 Milan, Verona, Venice, and Northern Italy, promoted by Gigi Breschi.
4.97 Barbican Centre, London, promoted by the 'From the Heart' Festival, appearing with Bumblebees.
**SELECTED BROADCASTS AND/OR RECORDED WORK:**
3.95 'River of Sound' CD and television recording for Hummingbird and Virgin.

1.96 'Common Ground' CD for EMI.
4.96 'Sult' for Hummingbird and TnaG.
**SELECTED REVIEWS** (since January 1994):
31.12.94 Irish Times.
10.96 Éamonn de Buitléar.
**PRIZES/AWARDS/APPOINTMENTS:**
7.92 1st Prize in the Belfast Bi-Centennial Harp Festival (Waterford Crystal Brian Boru Harp).
7/8.92 winner of Senior Harp Competition at the CCÉ All-Ireland Fleadh Cheoil na hÉireann, Clonmel.
**REGULARLY PERFORMS WITH:**
Bumblebees.
**AVAILABILITY:**
General (prepared to travel any distance).

## Emer Kenny *Irish Harp*

**Contact:** Ms Emer Kenny
c/o Mr John Murphy
48, Balreask Village
Navan, Co Meath
**Tel:** +353 46 71459
**Other instruments:** Concert harp, voice.

*"Her brand of music and the way she performs ... is something special"* BBC (Gerry Anderson).

**KEY IRISH PERFORMANCES** (since January 1994):
1994 Whelans Pub, Dublin.
1994 Mother Redcap's, Dublin.
1995 Tinakilly House, Wicklow.
1995 Jury's Hotel, Dublin.
**KEY PERFORMANCES OUTSIDE IRELAND** (since January 1994):
1995 Hilton, Trinidad.
1995 Mount Irvine, Tobago.
**SELECTED BROADCASTS AND/OR RECORDED WORK:**
1994 'Late Late Show', for RTÉ.
1994 'Anderson on the Box', for BBC.
1994 'The Folk Club', for BBC radio.
**SELECTED REVIEWS:**
1994 Hot Press.
1994 Evening Herald.
1994 World Music Magazine.
**PRIZES/AWARDS/APPOINTMENTS:**
1984 Awarded Jameson String Rosebowl, by Feis Ceoil, Dublin.
1986 Scholarship awarded by Alfred Beit Foundation.
1987 Scholarship to Trinity College of Music, London.
**TRAINING AND/OR QUALIFICATIONS:**
From 1978 to 1986, DIT Conservatory of Music and Drama, Dublin.
From 1986 to 1989, LTCL Trinity College of Music, London.
**AVAILABILITY:**
General.

## Aibhlín McCrann *Irish Harp*

**Contact:** Ms Aibhlín McCrann
50, Wyvern
Killiney
Co Dublin
**Tel/Fax:** +353 1 2856345 / +353 1 676 8007
**Other instruments:** Concert harp.

**SELECTED BROADCASTS AND/OR RECORDED WORK:**
Recordings for RTÉ.
Incidental music for film with Éamonn De Buitléar.
Two recordings for Gael-Linn.
**TRAINING AND/OR QUALIFICATIONS:**
BA and B Mus from University College, Dublin.
Diploma (Perf) and Diploma (Teaching) from Royal Irish Academy of Music.
**AVAILABILITY:**
General.
**ADDITIONAL INFORMATION:**
Founder of the Meath Harp School and Secretary of Cáirde Na Cruite. 1971 to 1987, harper with Ceoltóirí Laighean. From 1992 to 1997, Director of the International Summer School for Harp 'An Chúirt Chruitireachta'. Has developed a worldwide network of harp contacts.

## Antoinette McKenna *Irish Harp*

**Contact:** Antoinette McKenna
Moneystown North
Roundwood
Co Wicklow
**Tel/Fax:** +353 404 45139 / +353 404 45146

**REGULARLY PERFORMS WITH:**
Joe McKenna (uilleann pipes), Mary Bergin (whistle), Slua Nua.
**AVAILABILITY:**
General.

## Ailbhe McMahon *Irish Harp*

**Contact:** Ms Ailbhe McMahon
1, Knocknamana Heights
Clarecastle, Co Clare
**Tel:** +353 65 24400

*"A natural musician ... has achieved a remarkably high standard of performamce on the ancient instrument"* 12.7.96 Kerryman.

**KEY IRISH PERFORMANCES** (since January 1994):
8.95/96 'Gig Rig', Listowel, promoted by CCÉ, appearing with the O'Brien-Vaughan group.
19.3.96 Siamsa Tíre, Tralee, promoted by Micheál Carr, appearing with Ceol Chiarraí.
3.96 Royal Dublin Society, promoted by Association of String Teachers of Ireland, Coláiste Mhuire.
10-12.5.96 Bantry Mussel Festival, appearing with Ceol Chiarraí.
**KEY PERFORMANCES OUTSIDE IRELAND** (since January 1994):
9.4.96 Irish American Heritage Centre, appearing with Ceol Chiarraí.
27.4.96 Sydney Town Hall, Australia, promoted by Margaret Winnett, appearing with Ceol Chiarraí.
6.96 Rheims International Festival, France, appearing with Ceol Chiarraí.
8.96 International Folklore Festival, Hassalt, Belgium, appearing with Rinceoirí an Chláir.
**SELECTED BROADCASTS AND/OR RECORDED WORK:**
2.96 'High Note' (own cassette) 'The Spirit of Ireland' (own video).
3.96 'Live at 3', for RTÉ.
8.96 Fleadh Cheoil na hÉireann programme, for RTÉ.
**PRIZES/AWARDS/APPOINTMENTS:**
1994 1st Prize in Amhráin Le Cruit at Taibhdhearc na Gaillimhe for the Féile Idirnáisiúnta Phan Cheilteach.
1996 1st Prize in Imbusch Cup, Féile Luimní.
**TRAINING AND/OR QUALIFICATIONS:**
Since 11.92, Taught by Deirdre O'Brien-Vaughan.
8.93 Scoil Éigse.
**REGULARLY PERFORMS WITH:**
Marie O'Byrne, Rena Quealy, Marie Quigney.
**AVAILABILITY:**
General.
**ADDITIONAL INFORMATION:**
Has performed on both local and national radio in Ireland, France,

USA, Australia, Singapore and on television in Ireland and Germany. Has played at venues including Dromoland Castle, Old Ground Hotel, West County Inn and Limerick Inn. Holds several All-Ireland titles from Fleadhanna, Slógadh and An tÓireachtas events.

## Máire Ní Chathasaigh *Irish Harp*

**Contact:** Ms Ellen Thorpe
Garsdale
Easby Drive
Ilkley
West Yorkshire LS29 9BE
UK
**Tel/Fax:** +44 1 943 607030
**Email:** thorpe_garsdale@compuserve.com

*"Music of fire and brilliance from the high wire act in traditional music"*

8.12.95 Irish Times (album review).

**FORMED:** 1987.
**KEY IRISH PERFORMANCES** (since January 1994):
11.95 Belfast Festival at Queen's University, Belfast, appearing with Chris Newman.
8.95/96 Keadue, Co Roscommon, promoted by the O' Carolan Festival, appearing with Chris Newman.
9/10.96 Tour of Ireland promoted by Clifden, Ballymena and Coleraine Arts Festivals and arts centres in Belfast, Cork and Clones, appearing with Chris Newman.
4.97 Tour promoted by arts centres in Downpatrick, Cavan, Dundalk, Sligo and Castlebar, appearing with Chris Newman.
**KEY PERFORMANCES OUTSIDE IRELAND** (since January 1994):
1994 Irish Folk Festival tour of Germany and Switzerland, appearing with Chris Newman, Liam O'Flynn, Seán Keane and friends.
1995 Tour of Australia and New Zealand, promoted by Guinness Celebration of Irish Music appearing with Mary Black, Altan, Sharon Shannon, Dónal Lunny etc.
1995 Tønder, Denmark, promoted by Tønder Folk Festival, appearing with Chris Newman.
1995 Royal Concert Hall, Glasgow, promoted by Celtic Connections Festival.
**SELECTED BROADCASTS AND/OR RECORDED WORK:**
1988 Four duo albums with Chris Newman; 'The Living Wood', 'Out of Court', 'The Carolan Albums', 'Live in the Highlands' for Old Bridge Music.
'Late Late Show', 'Live at Three' for RTÉ.
'Sult' for TnaG.
'Woman's Hour' for Radio 4.
**SELECTED REVIEWS** (since January 1994):
3.96 Folk Roots (album review).
7.8.96 Irish Times (live review).
**PRIZES/AWARDS/APPOINTMENTS:**
1974/75/76 1st place in Fleadh Cheoil na hÉireann Senior All-Ireland Harp Championship.
1974 Pan-Celtic Festival, Killarney, 1st place Senior Harp Competition.
**REGULARLY PERFORMS WITH:**
Chris Newman (guitar, mandolin).
**AVAILABILITY:**
General.
**ADDITIONAL INFORMATION:**
Since the 1987 Cambridge Folk Festival debut has given over 1,000 performances in 21 countries, sold 25,000 albums and made TV/radio broadcasts on 5 continents (all with Chris Newman).

## Méav Ní Mhaolchatha *Irish Harp*

**Contact:** Méav Ní Mhaolchatha
Flat 2
130 Sandford Road
Ranelagh
Dublin 6
**Tel:** +353 1 4973873
*See soprano page 94.*

## Anne-Marie O'Farrell *Irish Harp*

**Contact:** Ms Anne-Marie O'Farrell
28, Grange Manor Drive
Rathfarnham
Dublin 16
**Tel:** +353 1 4931873
*See concert harp page 8.*

## Claire Roche *Irish Harp*

**Contact:** Ms Claire Roche
34, Hampton Crescent
St Helen's Wood
Booterstown
Co Dublin
**Tel:** +353 1 2835135
*See concert harp page 8.*

## Michael Rooney *Irish Harp*

**Contact:** Mr Mackie Rooney
Tyraverty
Scotstown
Co Monaghan
**Tel:** +353 47 89161
**Other instruments:** Concertina, piano, flute, tin whistle, fiddle.

*"Now recognised as one of the outstanding harpists of this generation ... Mícheál is also a noted concertina player"*

Summer 1995 Treoir (CCÉ Quarterly).

**KEY IRISH PERFORMANCES** (since January 1994):
9.95 Derry, official opening of new Foyle Shopping Centre.
9.95 Mansion House, Dublin, 'Today with Pat Kenny' for RTÉ (pre South Africa Tour promotion).
**KEY PERFORMANCES OUTSIDE IRELAND** (since January 1994):
6.95 Padova, Italy, promoted by Margaret Rhatigan appearing with Harpers Bizarre Group.
6.95 Zurich Switzerland, promoted by Margaret Rhatigan appearing with HB.
6.95 Bonn appearing with the Belfast Harp Orchestra, promoted by EU Cultural Committee.
9/10.95 Tour of Johannesburg, South Africa, performing with Harpers Bizarre.
10.95 Twenty three day tour of America, promoted by CCÉ appearing with Harpers Bizarre.
**SELECTED BROADCASTS AND/OR RECORDED WORK:**
Various with The Chieftains and the Belfast Harp Orchestra.
Accompanist and has played with various musicians at Scoil Éigse for CCÉ recordings.

**PRIZES/AWARDS/APPOINTMENTS:**
All-Ireland Fleadh Cheoil na hÉireann champion on harp, concertina and tin whistle (age category U12, U15, U18).
1993 All-Ireland Senior Harp Champion.
1995 All-Ireland Senior Accompaniment Champion. Achieved Grade 7 (piano).
**TRAINING AND/OR QUALIFICATIONS:**
From 1.85 to 6.95, Studied with Janet Harbison.
From 1992 to 1995, BA Hons (Ethnomusicology), from Queen's University, Belfast. TTCT from CCÉ.
**REGULARLY PERFORM WITH:**
National Folk Orchestra of Ireland. Belfast Harps.
**AVAILABILITY:**
General.
**ADDITIONAL INFORMATION:**
Has written a number of the arrangements for National Folk Orchestra and for the group Harpers Bizarre. Senior teacher at the Glencolmcille Harp Summer School, and on 8/9.92 taught harp at the University of Wisconsin, Milwaukee.

## Lynn Saoirse *Irish Harp*

**Contact:** Ms Lynn Saoirse
The Round House
Lower Sky Road
Clifden
Co Galway
**Tel:** +353 95 21800
**Other instruments:** Keyboard, piano.

*"Saoirse's harping is always engaging, rhythmically precise and clear in tone"*
10/11.95 Dirty Linen (US folk music magazine).

**KEY IRISH PERFORMANCES** (since January 1994):
9.94/95/96 Clifden Community Arts Week, appearing with Cluain.
8.95/96 Ballina Salmon Festival, appearing with O'Carolan Consort.
**KEY PERFORMANCES OUTSIDE IRELAND** (since January 1994):
3.94/95 Cologne, Germany.
3.94 Lens and Lille (France).
4.94 Washington DC, harp workshop and solo concert.
**SELECTED BROADCASTS AND/OR RECORDED WORK:**
1993 'Enchantment' with Cluain.
1994 'Champions of Ireland' for RSE records.
**PRIZES/AWARDS/APPOINTMENTS:**
1992/97 1st Prize in Galway and Connacht CCÉ Fleadh Cheoil na hÉireann (both solo and trio).
8.94 2nd Prize in the O'Carolan Harp Festival Competition Keadue, Co Roscommon, awarded by CCÉ.
**REGULARLY PERFORMS WITH:**
Cluain, Cath Taylor (flute), The Carolan Consort.
**AVAILABILITY:**
General.

## Caitríona Yeats *Irish Harp*

**Contact:** Ms Caitríona Yeats
Sophus Baudizvej 8
DK 2800 Lyngby
Denmark
**Tel:** +45 45 871161
*See concert harp page 8.*

# MANDOLIN

## Ronan Browne *Mandolin*

**Contact:** Mr Ronan Browne
Mount Slaney
Stratford-on-Slaney
Co Wicklow
**Tel/Fax:** +353 45 404873
*See uilleann pipes page 235.*

## Kieran Hanrahan *Mandolin*

**Contact:** Mr Kieran Hanrahan
4, The Rise
Woodpark
Ballinteer
Dublin 16
**Tel:** +353 1 2988650
*See tenor banjo page 196.*

## Michael Howard *Mandolin*

**Contact:** Mr Michael Howard
53, Balkill Park
Howth
Co Dublin
**Tel:** +353 1 8323475
**Email:** howmac@indigo.ie
*See classical guitar page 21.*

## Vinnie Kilduff *Mandolin*

**Contact:** Vinnie Kilduff
**Mobile:** +353 87 588683
**Email:** Kilduff@dojo.ie
*See whistles page 241.*

## Órna Loughnane *Mandolin*

**Contact:** Órna Loughnane
Brockmanngasse 114/9
A-8010
Graz
Austria
**Tel:** +43 316 842344
*See violin page 297.*

## Sandi Miller *Mandolin*

**Contact:** Mr Bill Whelan
39, Fairview Gardens
Dublin 3
**Tel:** +353 1 8331920

*See fiddle page 297.*

## Niall Ó Callanáin *Mandolin*

**Contact:** Niall Ó Callanáin
1, Park Place
Islandbridge
Dublin 8
**Mobile:** +353 87 414435
*See bouzouki page 201.*

## Frank Simon *Mandolin*

**Contact:** Mr Frank Simon
The Plains
Boyle
Co Roscommon
**Tel:** +353 79 62245
*See guitar page 225.*

## Stephen Wickham *Mandolin*

**Contact:** Stephen Wickham
P.O. Box 282
Sligo
**Tel:** +353 1 4966341
*See violin page 300.*

# PIANO

## Derek F. Bell *Piano*

**Contact:** Derek F. Bell
74, Bryanburn Road
Bangor
Co Down BT20 3SB
Northern Ireland
**Tel:** +44 1247 457923
*See Irish harp page 226.*

## Máire Breatnach *Piano*

**Contact:** c/o Mr Steve Dunford
6 The Avenue
Boden Park
Rathfarnham
Dublin 16
**Tel/Fax:** +353 1 4947615 or +353 1 49323358 / +353 1 4931707
*See Máire Breatnach Band page 257.*

## Nollaig Casey *Piano*

**Contact:** Nollaig Casey
51, Lios Mór
Cappagh Road
Bearna, Co Galway
**Tel:** +353 91 590908
*See fiddle page 205.*

## Jane Cassidy *Piano*

**Contact:** Mrs Jane Cassidy
12, Landsdowne Road
Belfast, BT15 4DA
Northern Ireland
**Tel:** +44 1232 773525
**Other instruments:** Guitar.

**KEY PERFORMANCES OUTSIDE IRELAND** (since January 1994):
4.97 Lugano, Switzerland, appearing with Antonio Breschi and Ronnie Drew.
**SELECTED BROADCASTS AND/OR RECORDED WORK:**
1982 'Waves of Time' album for Claddagh Records.
1985 'The Empty Road' album for Claddagh Records.
1995 Mary Ann McCracken album for Ashgrove Music, distributed by Claddagh Records.
1995/96 Composed and performed theme song for television series 'Places Apart' for BBC Northern Ireland.
10.97 Composed and performed music for the radio play 'Blood of the Ring Finger' for BBC.
**AVAILABILITY:**
Weekends.
**ADDITIONAL INFORMATION:**
Singer, songwriter, composer. Interprets local Ulster folk songs. Has recorded three albums and a single. Composes music and songs for television and radio.

## Sonny Condell *Piano*

**Contact:** Mr Sonny Condell
**Tel:** +353 1 2892635
*See guitar page 221.*

## Bríd Cranitch *Piano*

**Contact:** Ms Bríd Cranitch
13, Hansboro
Belgrave Avenue
Wellington Road
Cork
**Tel/Fax:** +353 21 502037 / +353 21 393333
**Other instruments:** Fiddle.

**KEY IRISH PERFORMANCES** (since January 1994):
1995 McCarthy's, Baltimore, Co Cork, promoted by D McCarthy, appearing with Frankie Gavin.
1996 'Geantraí' (TnaG), appearing with Matt Cranitch and Seán Ó Sé.
9.96 Metropole Hotel, Cork promoted by Cork Folk Festival, appearing with Island Céilí Band.
**KEY PERFORMANCES OUTSIDE IRELAND** (since January 1994):
National Concert Hall, Dublin, promoted by Gael-Linn, appearing with Seán Maguire.
Aula Maxima University College Cork, promoted by UCC Irish Music Society, appearing with Kowloon Bridge.
West County Hotel, appearing with Moving Cloud.
Clifden Arts Festival, appearing with Jimmy Crowley Band.
**SELECTED BROADCASTS AND/OR RECORDED WORK:**
Éistigh Seal, recorded by Gael-Linn.
'Small Island' recorded by Ossian.
1997 'We won't go home till Morning', with Brendan Begley.
**TRAINING AND/OR QUALIFICATIONS:**
From 1971 to 1974 B Mus from UCC.
**REGULARLY PERFORMS WITH:**
Brendan Begley (box), Matt Cranitch (fiddle), Island Céilí Band.

**AVAILABILITY:**
General.
**ADDITIONAL INFORMATION:**
Piano driver backer vamper and accompanist. Capable of playing with musicians and singers in concert or E flat pitch.

## Patricia Daly *Piano*

**Contact:** Ms Patricia Daly
19, Magherydogherty Road
Markethill
Co Armagh BT60 1TY
Northern Ireland
**Tel:** +44 1861 551087
*See Irish harp page 227.*

## Paul de Grae *Piano*

**Contact:** Mr Paul de Grae
Frogmore House
The Spa
Tralee
Co Kerry
**Tel/Fax:** +353 66 36111
*See guitar page 222.*

## Jillian Delaney *Piano*

**Contact:** Jillian Delaney
30, Fremont Drive
Melbourn
Bishopstown
Cork
**Tel:** +353 21 544887
*See Irish Harp page 228.*

## Laoise Kelly *Piano*

**Contact:** Ms Laoise Kelly
10, Mountain View
Ennis
Co Clare
**Tel/Fax:** +353 91 528839
*See Irish harp page 228.*

## Claire Keville *Piano*

**Contact:** Ms Claire Keville
Claran
Ower
Co Galway
**Tel:** +353 93 35952
*See concertina page 202.*

## Charlie Lennon *Piano*

**Contact:** Dr Charlie Lennon
Ard Mhuire
Baily, Howth
Co Dublin
**Tel/Fax:** +353 1 8322409 / +353 1 6615688
**Email:** cathal@chl.ie
*See fiddle page 208.*

## Tríona Ní Dhomhnaill *Piano*

**Contact:** Agent: Al Evers
A Train Management
PO Box 29242
Oakland
California 94604
USA
or
c/o Mrs Bríd O'Donnell
7, Ashgrove Court
Dundrum
Dublin 14
**Tel/Fax:** +1 510 893 4705 or +353 1 2982413 /
+1 510 893 4807

**KEY PERFORMANCES OUTSIDE IRELAND** (since January 1994):
3-18.10.95 Tour of Spain, Valencia, Barcelona, Sevilla, Madrid, promoted by Julio Marti Y Mauolo Serra appearing with Nightnoise.
**SELECTED RECORDED WORK:**
From 1975 to 1995, 4 recordings with The Bothy Band, for Mulligan Records.
One recording with Skara Brae for Gael-Linn.
2 recordings with Relativity for Green Linnet Records.
Solo recording with Green Linnet Records.
Six recordings with Nightnoise for Windham Hill Studios.
**TRAINING AND/OR QUALIFICATIONS:**
Approximately eight years of piano studies.
**REGULARLY PERFORMS WITH:**
Máighread Ní Dhomhnaill, Nightnoise.
**AVAILABILITY:**
General.
**ADDITIONAL INFORMATION:**
Twenty-five years recording experience and has performed worldwide.

## Charles O'Connor *Piano*

**Contact:** Mr Charles O'Connor
'St Gabriel's'
Magheraboy Road
Sligo
**Tel:** +353 71 45722
**Other instruments:** Piano accordion.

**KEY IRISH PERFORMANCES** (since January 1994):
1.97 Ballyshannon, appearing with Famine Remembrance Group.
4.97 Hawk's Well Theatre, Sligo, appearing with Famine Remembrance Group.
**KEY PERFORMANCES OUTSIDE IRELAND** (since January 1994):
8.95 Crozon-Morgat, France, appearing with Fred Finn Branch CCÉ (Sligo).
**SELECTED BROADCASTS AND/OR RECORDED WORK:**
3.97 With the Famine Remembrance Group, recorded at LG studios, Longford.
**PRIZES/AWARDS/APPOINTMENTS:**
8.91 1st Prize at the CCÉ All-Ireland Fleadh Cheoil na hÉireann (Piano

Accordion) (age category 12-15 years).
8.94 1st Prize at the CCÉ All-Ireland Fleadh Cheoil na hÉireann Piano (15-18).
**TRAINING AND /OR QUALIFICATIONS:**
7.95 TTCT from CCÉ.
**REGULARLY PERFORMS WITH:**
Famine Remembrance Group, Innisfree Céilí Band.
**AVAILABILITY:**
General.
**ADDITIONAL INFORMATION:**
Has competed at the CCÉ Fleadhanna for over seven years and, in addition to All-Ireland successes, has been Connacht champion on the piano for the last five years. Teaches music in Sligo.

## Con Ó Drisceoil *Piano*

**Contact:** Mr Con Ó Drisceoil
61, Maryborough Avenue
Douglas
Co Cork
**Tel:** +353 21 362878
*See accordion page 194.*

## Máire O'Keeffe *Piano*

**Contact:** Máire O'Keeffe
Locoal Mendon St
Kinvara
Co Galway
**Tel/Mobile:** +353 91 637649 / +353 88 600709
**Email:** mokeeffe@iol.ie
*See fiddle page 212.*

## Mícheál Ó Súilleabháin *Piano*

**Contact:** Prof Mícheál Ó Súilleabháin
Irish World Music Centre
University of Limerick
Co Limerick
**Tel:** +353 61 202065

*"... Has infuriated folk purists in Ireland by his use of orchestra ...[his music] is all the better for embracing innovations"* 5.1.96 London Times.

**KEY IRISH PERFORMANCES** (since January 1994):
1.94 National Concert Hall, Dublin, appearing with RTÉ Concert Orchestra.
5.96 University Concert Hall, Limerick, appearing with Hiberno Jazz.
5.96 Royal Hospital Kilmainham, Dublin, promoted by RTÉ Proms, appearing with Hiberno Jazz.
3.97 Killaloe Cathedral, Co Clare appearing with the Irish Chamber Orchestra.
**KEY PERFORMANCES OUTSIDE IRELAND** (since January 1994):
6.96 Radio France Concert Hall, Paris, appearing with the ICO.
2.97 Gothenburg, Sweden appearing with the ICO.
3.97 Barbican Arts Centre, London, appearing with the ICO.
**SELECTED BROADCASTS AND/OR RECORDED WORK:**
1987 'The Dolphin's Way' for Virgin Records.
1989 'Oileán/Island' for Virgin Records.
1995 'Between Worlds' for Virgin Records.
**TRAINING AND/OR QUALIFICATIONS:**
From 1973 to 1987, B Mus and MA from University College, Cork.
LTCL from Trinity College, London.
PhD from Queen's University, Belfast.
**PRIZES/AWARDS/APPOINTMENTS:**
From 1987 to 1993, Senior Lecturer in Music at UCC.
Since 1994 Professor of Music at University of Limerick.
**REGULARLY PERFORMS WITH:**
Irish Chamber Orchestra, Hiberno Jazz.
**AVAILABILITY:**
General.
**ADDITIONAL INFORMATION:**
Directs orchestra from the keyboard in a programme of his own compositions and arrangements.

## Annette Owens *Piano*

**Contact:** Ms Annette Owens
74, Glenn Road
Tempo
Co Fermanagh
BT94 3JW
Northern Ireland
**Tel:** +44 13655 41498
*See accordion page 194.*

## Michael Rooney *Piano*

**Contact:** Mr Mackie Rooney
Tyraverty
Scotstown
Co Monaghan
**Tel:** +353 47 89161
*See Irish harp page 230.*

## Lynn Saoirse *Piano*

**Contact:** Ms Lynn Saoirse
The Round House
Lower Sky Road
Clifden
Co Galway
**Tel:** +353 95 21800
*See Irish harp page 231.*

## Caoimhín Vallely *Piano*

**Contact:** Mr Caoimhín Vallely
Flat 5
4, Wellesey Terrace
Wellington Road
Cork
**Tel:** +353 21 509230
**Other instruments:** Fiddle.

*"The variety of tastes and influences can only be described as eclectic"* 1.3.95 Armagh Together Magazine.

**KEY IRISH PERFORMANCES** (since January 1994):
4.7.95 Armagh Folk Club accompanied by Upstairs in a Tent.
6.8.95 Drogheda Folk Festival appearing with with Armagh Rhymers.
4-10.8.95 Newlodge Community Festival, promoted by Martin Campbell appearing with Truflais.
11.8.95 Ardoyne Fleadh, Belfast, promoted by Eddie Donnelly.

**KEY PERFORMANCES OUTSIDE IRELAND** (since January 1994):
2-19.3.94 Tour of Northern Italy, promoted by FolkItalia, appearing with Armagh Pipers Club.
14.1.95 Glasgow Concert Hall, promoted by Celtic Connections appearing with Brian Finnegan Band.
2-19.3.95 Tour of Germany, promoted by Magnetic Music, appearing with Upstairs in a Tent.
5-21.7.95 Tour of Norway, promoted by Roots Music Agency appearing with Upstairs in a Tent.
**SELECTED BROADCASTS AND/OR RECORDED WORK:**
17.2.95 Truflais 'Uncovered' for Spring Records.
6.95 Eurovision singers visit to Armagh for BBC, ITV and RTÉ.
**SELECTED REVIEWS** (since January 1994):
2.4.95 Ulster Gazzette.
**PRIZES/AWARDS/APPOINTMENTS:**
21.12.94 Musician of the Year, St Patrick's Grammer School, Armagh, Northern Ireland.
23.4.95 Winner with Slógadh Naisiúnta, Gael-Linn.
**TRAINING AND/OR QUALIFICATIONS:**
2.10.94 B Mus, University College, Cork.
**REGULARLY PERFORMS WITH:**
The Moving Pint, Truflais.
**AVAILABILITY:**
General.
**ADDITIONAL INFORMATION:**
Taught fiddle and tin whistle at the Armagh Pipers Club for 5 years. Performs classical, jazz and world music.

# UILLEANN PIPES

## Ronan Browne *Uilleann Pipes*

**Contact:** Mr Ronan Browne
Mount Slaney
Stratford-on-Slaney
Co Wicklow
**Tel/Fax:** +353 45 404873
**Email:** roro@tinet.ie
**Other instruments:** Flute, whistles, mandolin.

*"One of the finest pipers of his generation ... an innovator who has developed his own unique style"* 2.7.96 Irish Times (Robbie Hannan).

**KEY IRISH PERFORMANCES** (since January 1994):
2.95 'Late Late Show' for RTÉ, Dublin, appearing with River of Sound group.
7.95 St Patrick's Cathedral, Dublin, promoted by Michael McGlynn, appearing with Anúna.
11.95 Tour of Ireland, promoted by 57th Street, appearing with Finbar Wright.
1997 Millstreet Famine Commemoration Concert, Co Cork.
**KEY PERFORMANCES OUTSIDE IRELAND** (since January 1994):
6.95 Royal Festival Hall, London, promoted by South Bank Centre, appearing with Elvis Costello and Anúna.
8.95 Mull of Kintyre Festival, Scotland, promoted by Tennants Lager, appearing with Cran.
7.96 Womad World Music Festival, promoted by Womad, appearing with Afro Celt Sound System.
7.97 Montreal Jazz Festival appearing with Afro Celt Sound System.
**SELECTED BROADCASTS AND/OR RECORDED WORK:**
994 'Riverdance', recorded by Celtic Heartbeat.
1995 'A River of Sound', recorded by Hummingbird Productions. Contributed to 'Sound Magic' with the Afro Celt Sound System (CD Vol. 1).
Album 'Black, Black, Black' with Cran.
**SELECTED REVIEWS** (since January 1994):
8.96 Irish Music Magazine.
14.7.97 Irish Times.
**REGULARLY PERFORMS WITH:**
Cran and Guests inc. Kevin Glackin and Triona Ní Dhomhnaill. Clavinet (uilleann pipes, flute, fiddle, bouzouki and voice whistles). Duo with Kevin Glackin. Finbar Wright.
**AVAILABILITY:**
General.
**ADDITIONAL INFORMATION:**
Has collaborated on the film soundtracks: 'The Dolphin's Gift', 'Circle of Friends', 'The Secret of Roan Inish', 'Rob Roy', 'Robin of loxley' and 'Fierce Creatures'. Although is known for his playing of purely traditional music, regularly takes part in contemporary musical ventures with the Afro Celt Sound System, Deep Forest and Jam Nation. Member of Cran.

## Noel Carberry *Uilleann Pipes*

**Contact:** Mr Noel Carberry
1, Derryhawn
Kenagh, Co Longford
**Tel:** +353 43 25194
**Other instruments:** Tin whistle, bodhrán.

**KEY IRISH PERFORMANCES** (since January 1994):
Derrygonnelly, Co Fermanagh, promoted by Eddie Duffy Memorial Festival, appearing with Peter Carberry and Karena Dowling.
May (annually), Na Píobáirí Uilleann seminar.
July (annually), Scoil Samhraidh Willie Clancy, appearing with Peter Carberry.
7.96 Longford, promoted by Feis Longfoirt.
**KEY PERFORMANCES OUTSIDE IRELAND** (since January 1994):
3.96/97 Uganda, promoted by Irish Community Festival, appearing with the Dowling Family and F McDonald.
**REGULARLY PERFORMS WITH:**
Peter Carberry, Karena Dowling.
**AVAILABILITY:**
General.
**ADDITIONAL INFORMATION:**
Has performed for many years in various seisiúns. Toured several countries with CCÉ and performed for 2 years at 'Brú Ború' Cashel, Co Tipperary. Has made numerous television appearances: 'Late Late Show', 'Bibi', 'Sunday Night at the Gaiety' and St Patrick's day shows, all for RTÉ.

## Jim Carrigan *Uilleann Pipes*

**Contact:** Mr Jim Carrigan
Clarabricken
Clifden, Co Kilkenny
**Tel:** +353 56 59817 (h) / +353 61 471655 ext 2404 (w)

**KEY IRISH PERFORMANCES** (since January 1994):
30.9.95 Clifden Community Arts Festival.
4.97 Carrigaholt Festival.
**KEY PERFORMANCES OUTSIDE IRELAND** (since January 1994):
6-14.7.95 Tour of Italy, appearing with Dermot Cernahan (accordion), James Duddy (bodhrán), Séamus McMahon (fiddle), Cyril O'Donoghue (guitar, bouzouki, vocals).
1996 Baltimore (USA), Louisbourg (Canada), appearing with Pat Olwel (flute).
**SELECTED BROADCASTS AND/OR RECORDED WORK:**
12.94 'The Sanctuary Sessions' (live) for Kerbstone. Plus various live local radio performances
**REGULARLY PERFORMS WITH:**
Liam Lewis (fiddle), Maurice McHugh (guitar), Séamus McMahon (fiddle).
**AVAILABILITY:**
General.

# Joseph Finn *Uilleann Pipes*

**Contact:** Mr Joseph Finn
Kilmucklin
Tullamore
Co Offaly
**Tel:** +353 506 31089
**Other instruments:** Concert flute, whistles.

**KEY IRISH PERFORMANCES** (since January 1994):
Numerous venues throughout the country.
**KEY PERFORMANCES OUTSIDE IRELAND** (since January 1994):
Venues in Washington DC and London.
**SELECTED BROADCASTS AND/OR RECORDED WORK:**
Has recorded for national radio.
Has recorded in Roseland Studios, Moate, Co Westmeath.
**PRIZES/AWARDS/APPOINTMENTS:**
First prize (solo and group), awarded by CCÉ All-Ireland Fleadh Cheoil na hÉireann.
**AVAILABILITY:**
General.
**ADDITIONAL INFORMATION:**
Available to play solo or with groups.

# Tommy Keane *Uilleann Pipes*

**Contact:** Mr Tommy Keane
Treanlaur
Maree, Co Galway
**Tel/Fax:** +353 91 794344
**Other instruments:** Concert flute, tin whistle.

*"Keane's compass points towards the master pipers"* 25.8.95 Irish Times.

**KEY IRISH PERFORMANCES** (since January 1994):
11.96 The Point, Dublin, promoted by Enigma, appearing with Iarla Ó Lionaird and the Irish Philharmonic Orchestra.
**KEY PERFORMANCES OUTSIDE IRELAND** (since January 1994):
11.95 Denmark, promoted by Eskil Romme, appearing with Jacqueline McCarthy.
10.96 Tour of Europe, promoted by Florian Furst, Bremen, appearing with Tony McMahon and Séamus Tansey.
**SELECTED BROADCASTS AND/OR RECORDED WORK:**
1991 'The Piper's Apron' for Mulligan Records.
1995 'The Wind Among the Reeds' for Maree Music Company.
11.96 'Faith of our Fathers', live at The Point for RTÉ and Enigma.
**SELECTED REVIEWS** (since January 1994):
Galway Advertiser.
Irish Echo (New York).
**PRIZES/AWARDS/APPOINTMENTS:**
6.95 Traditional Album of the Year from the Irish Voice Newspaper, New York (for 'The Wind Among the Reeds').
**REGULARLY PERFORMS WITH:**
Alec Finn (bouzouki), Jacqueline McCarthy (concertina).
**AVAILABILITY:**
General.
**ADDITIONAL INFORMATION:**
Has played on over 20 albums with various artists and groups including Clannad, Ralph McTell and The Pogues. Has played in the UK, USA, Europe, Russia, Zambia and New Zealand. Involved in television and radio broadcasts and is a teacher at piping schools worldwide.

# Barry Kerr *Uilleann Pipes*

**Contact:** Mr Barry Kerr
25, Island View Lane
Kinnego, Lurgan
Co Armagh, BT67 9JF
Northern Ireland
**Tel/Fax:** +44 1762 321730 or +44 1762 324660 / +44 1762 324449
*See flute page 216.*

# Vinnie Kilduff *Uilleann Pipes*

**Contact:** Vinnie Kilduff
**Mobile:** +353 87 588683
**Email:** Kilduff@dojo.ie
*See whistles page 241.*

# Joe McHugh *Uilleann Pipes*

**Contact:** Mr Joe McHugh
Moneystown North
Roundwood, Co Wicklow
or
Gústr 8, Ch - 8700 Kúsnacht
Switzerland
**Tel:** +353 404 45161
**Email:** mchugh@goldnet.ch
**Other instruments:** Whistles, bouzouki, keyboard, mandolin, guitar.

*"One of the best recordings of Irish instrumental music I've heard all year"* 1.94 Folk Roots.

**KEY PERFORMANCES OUTSIDE IRELAND** (since January 1994):
8.94 Tour of Poland, appearing with Bob Bales.
11.94 Copenhagen Festival, appearing with Barry Carroll.
7.96 Varese Festival, Italy, appearing with Antonio Breschi.
**SELECTED BROADCASTS AND/OR RECORDED WORK:**
6.90 Soviet Session, recorded by BBC/Channel 4/BBC Northern Ireland.
12.94 'Late Late Show' Christmas show, for RTÉ.
1.95 'Late Late Show' for RTÉ.
**SELECTED REVIEWS** (since January 1994):
1.94 Folk Roots Magazine.
Dirty Linen.
Rock 'n' Roll.
**PRIZES/AWARDS/APPOINTMENTS:**
1977 1st Prize All-Ireland Senior Pipes, awarded by Fleadh Cheoil na hÉireann.
**REGULARLY PERFORMS WITH:**
Antonio Breschi, Barry Carroll, Shirley Grimes.
**AVAILABILITY:**
General.

# Joe McKenna *Uilleann Pipes*

**Contact:** Joe McKenna
Moneystown North
Roundwood, Co Wicklow
**Tel/Fax:** +353 404 45139 / +353 404 45146

**REGULARLY PERFORMS WITH:**
Antoinette McKenna (harp), Mary Bergin (whistle), Slua Nua.
**AVAILABILITY:** General.

## Gay McKeon *Uilleann Pipes*

**Contact:** Mr Gay McKeon
77, Hermitage Drive
Lucan
Co Dublin
**Tel:** +353 1 6240542

**SELECTED BROADCASTS AND/OR RECORDED WORK:**
1975 'Silly Sisters' for Chrysalis.
1979 'Iron Behind the Velvet' for Tara Records.
1994 'Drones' Volume Two for Claddagh Records.
**PRIZES/AWARDS/APPOINTMENTS:**
All-Ireland Champion holder.
**AVAILABILITY:**
General.
**ADDITIONAL INFORMATION:**
Teaches and performs at a number festivals and summer schools. Co-presenter on the ninty minute video, 'The Art of Uilleann Piping' Volume One.

## Paddy Moloney *Uilleann Pipes*

**Contact:** Paddy Moloney
The Stores
Milltown Bridge
Dundrum Road
Dublin 14
**Tel/Fax:** +353 1 2697430

**REGULARLY PERFORMS WITH:** The Chieftains.

## Diarmuid Moynihan *Uilleann Pipes*

**Contact:** Diarmuid Moynihan
65, The Rise
Bishopstown
Cork
**Tel:** +353 21 542958
**Other instruments:** Whistles.

*"The musical alchemy on display tonight suggests a major new force in Irish music ..."*
1.95 Living Tradition Magazine, Scotland.

**KEY IRISH PERFORMANCES** (since January 1994):
15.5.95 Harcourt Hotel, Dublin, promoted by Mary Cashin, appearing with Calico.
25.5.95 Belfast Folk Club, promoted by Pat Connolly, appearing with Calico.
27.5.95 Downpatrick Folk Club, promoted by Pat Connolly, appearing with Calico.
10.9.95 Lobby Bar, Cork, promoted by Cork Folk Festival, appearing with Calico.
**KEY PERFORMANCES OUTSIDE IRELAND** (since January 1994):
19.6.95 Guildhall Concert Hall, London, appearing with Patricia Moynihan (flute).
From 25.6.95 to 2.7.95, Haapovesi Folk Festival, Finland, promoted by Timo Hanula, appearing with Calico.
From 2.8.95 to 15.8.95, Tour of Brittany, France, promoted by Hammy Hamilton, appearing with Geanntraí.
From 1.12.95 to 16.12.95, Scandinavia tour, promoted by Svend Kieldson, appearing with Calico.
**SELECTED BROADCASTS AND/OR RECORDED WORK:**
5.95 'The Mountain Road', recorded by Ossian Records.
**SELECTED REVIEWS** (since January 1994):
10.94 Evening Echo.
5.95 Living Tradition, Scotland.
**PRIZES/AWARDS/APPOINTMENTS:**
8.87 1st Prize All-Ireland under 18 tin whistle competition, awarded by the CCÉ.
9.87 Scholarship to study traditional music at Cork School of Music.
28.10.89 1st Prize for senior uilleann pipe competition at Lorient Festival, awarded by An tÓireachtas Festival.
**AVAILABILITY:**
General.
**ADDITIONAL INFORMATION:**
Has appeared with the Cork Symphony Orchestra, Alan Stivell's Celtique Symphonie and others.

## Néillidh Mulligan *Uilleann Pipes*

**Contact:** Mr Néillidh Mulligan
2, Eachlann Ashington
Bóthar na hUaimhe
Baile Átha Cliath 7
**Tel/Fax:** +353 1 8682078 or + 353 1 8044600 / +353 1 8726182
**Other instruments:** Tin whistle.

**KEY IRISH PERFORMANCES** (since January 1994):
5.94 Tour of Ireland, promoted by Music Network appearing with Noel Hill, B McGlinchey, J Stewart.
7.96 Drumshanbo, Co Leitrim, promoted by Joe Mooney Summer School, appearing with fellow teachers and artists.
11.96 Dunsill Hotel, Armagh, promoted by the William Kennedy Piping Festival, appearing with pipers from Ireland and abroad.
4.97 Arús Chrónáin, Dublin, appearing with Noel Hill.
**KEY PERFORMANCES OUTSIDE IRELAND** (since January 1994):
6.95 Irish Centre, Camden Town, London, promoted by London Piper's Club.
8.95 Kremsmunster, Austria, promoted by Ambros Schiffermuller.
9.96 Mulligan's, Amsterdam.
**SELECTED BROADCASTS AND/OR RECORDED WORK:**
1991 'Barr na Cúille' for Spring Records, Rostrevor, Co Down.
1996 'High Reel' for RTÉ.
1997 'The Leitrim Thrush' for Spring Records, Rostrevor, Co Down.
**SELECTED REVIEWS** (since January 1994):
7.97 Irish Music.
**PRIZES/AWARDS/APPOINTMENTS:**
1968/70 Winner of the CCÉ All-Ireland Fleadh Cheoil na hÉireann (Under 14 and Under 18).
1986 Appointed Cathaoirleach by Na Píobairí Uilleann.
**TRAINING AND/OR QUALIFICATIONS:**
From 1968 to 1970, Studied at the DIT Conservatory of Music and Drama.
From 1968 to 1970, Studied with Leo Rowsome (Cumann na bPíobairí Uilleann).
**REGULARLY PERFORMS WITH:**
Vincent Harrison, Larry Kinsella, Séan Ó Broin.
**AVAILABILITY:**
General.

## Martin Nolan *Uilleann Pipes*

**Contact:** Mr Martin Nolan
34, St Mary's Drive
Drimnagh
Dublin 12
**Tel/Fax:** +353 1 4563144
**Other instruments:** Tin whistle, low whistle.

*"Both Martin's tape and his live performance are energetic affairs full of great playing, good tunes and cheerful Irish humour"*

Canberra Times, Australia (Michael Jackson).

**KEY IRISH PERFORMANCES** (since January 1994):
5.95 Omagh, Portstewart, Belfast promoted by Improvised Music Company and Arts Council of Northern Ireland, appearing with Khanda.
5.96 King House, Boyle, Co Roscommon, promoted by Music Network, appearing with Khanda.
9.96 Triskel Arts Centre, Cork, promoted by Music Network, appearing with Khanda.
11.96 St Mary's Church of Ireland, Nenagh, promoted by Music Network, appearing with Khanda.
**KEY PERFORMANCES OUTSIDE IRELAND** (since January 1994):
1-2.95 Cross-Canada tour with Celtic Craft.
2.96 East West Festival in Bangalore, India.
2.97 Tour of Germany.
**SELECTED BROADCASTS AND/OR RECORDED WORK:**
1990 'Travel in Style', own cassette and CD release.
1997 'Khanda' for IMC.
**REGULARLY PERFORMS WITH:**
Khanda.
**AVAILABILITY:**
General.
**ADDITIONAL INFORMATION:**
Has extensive touring experience in Northern Europe, France, Canada, Australia and New Zealand. Debut solo album received critical acclaim both in Ireland and abroad. Gives workshops and masterclasses and has been a teacher at An Scoil Samhraidh Willie Clancy for over 8 years.

# Tomás Ó Canainn *Uilleann Pipes*

**Contact:** Tomás Ó Canainn
Ard Barra
Glanmire
Co Cork
**Tel:** +353 21 821003
**Email:** stee8006@ucc.ie
**Other instruments:** Traditional singer.

**KEY IRISH PERFORMANCES** (since January 1994):
1996 Derry, promoted by the Derry Central Library.
1996 Dublin, promoted by CCÉ.
1997 Derry, promoted by the Central Library.
1997 Dublin, promoted by CCÉ.
**KEY PERFORMANCES OUTSIDE IRELAND** (since January 1994):
8.95 Milwaukee Irish Festival.
10.95 Tour of America and Canada, promoted by CCÉ.
1996 Tour of Galicia, Spain.
**SELECTED BROADCASTS AND/OR RECORDED WORK:**
'Tomás Ó Canainn (with pipe and song)', for Outlet CD (PT1CD/1035).
Traditional slow airs of Ireland (Ossian) book and cassettes.
4.97 Four 'Sounds Traditional' programmes for RTÉ.
**PRIZES/AWARDS/APPOINTMENTS:**
1987 Winner of Séan O'Boyle Award for services to Irish Traditional Music.
**AVAILABILITY:**
General.
**ADDITIONAL INFORMATION:**
Author of the following books: 'Traditional Music in Ireland' (Ossian). 'A Lifetime of Notes' (Collins Press). 'New Tunes for Old' (Ossian). Co-author of 'Sean Ó Riada' (Gartan). Composer and arranger of Irish choral works.

# Tiarnán Ó Duinnchinn *Uilleann Pipes*

**Contact:** Tiarnán Ó Duinnchinn
3, Glen Road
Monaghan
Co Monaghan
**Tel/Mobile:** +353 47 82065 / +353 88 2781917
**Other instruments:** Low whistles.

**KEY IRISH PERFORMANCES** (since January 1994):
11.96 Monaghan Folk Club, appearing with Paddy Keenan.
11.96 Armagh International Piping Festival.
4.97 Harcourt Hotel, Dublin, appearing with Aoife Ní Fhearraigh.
5.97 Mullaghbane Folk Club, Armagh, appearing with Martin Quinn and Paul Meehan.
**KEY PERFORMANCES OUTSIDE IRELAND** (since January 1994):
1995 San Francisco, Boston, Chicago and St Louis, appearing with Martin Quinn.
1996 Amsterdam, Italy and USA.
1997 Romania.
**SELECTED BROADCASTS AND/OR RECORDED WORK:**
1993/97 'The Pure Drop' and 'High Reel' for RTÉ.
1995 recording with 'Spiral Bound', (American folk band), San Francisco.
1996 'Uilleann Pipe Tutor', recorded in Sands Studio.
**PRIZES/AWARDS/APPOINTMENTS:**
1990 Winner of CCÉ All-Ireland Fleadh Cheoil na hÉireann.
**REGULARLY PERFORMS WITH:**
Aoife Ní Fhearraigh Band, Paul Meehan, Martin Quinn.
**AVAILABILITY:**
General.

# Liam O'Flynn *Uilleann Pipes*

**Contact:** Mr Liam O'Flynn
c/o MBE Artist Management and Agency
6, Seafield Crescent
Blackrock
Co Dublin
**Tel/Fax:** +353 1 2693821 / +353 1 2693777
**Email:** mbe@indigo.ie

*"Cynics might argue ... all traditional music sounds the same. Experience a [Liam O'Flynn] concert and you will have to think otherwise"*

27.10.95, Irish Times.

**SELECTED BROADCASTS AND/OR RECORDED WORK:**
1995 'The Given Note', recorded with Tara records (3034).
1995 Recorded with Mark Knopfler on the 'Golden Heart' album, for Vertigo records 514 7324.
1996 Recorded with Mike Oldfield on the 'Voyager' album, for WEA 0630 15896.
1997 Recorded with Brendan Begley on the 'We Won't go Home Till Morning', for Kells Music.
**ADDITIONAL INFORMATION:**
Has toured extensively in Ireland, Europe and America.

# Séan Óg Potts *Uilleann Pipes*

**Contact:** Mr Séan Óg Potts
7, St Aidans Park Road
Marino, Dublin 3
**Tel:** +353 1 8338613 (h) / +353 1 7055650 (w)

## Séan Potts *Uilleann Pipes*

**Contact:** Mr Séan Potts
25, Kinvara Drive
Navan Road
Dubin 7

## Kevin Rowsome *Uilleann Pipes*

**Contact:** Mr Kevin Rowsome
**Mobile/Tel:** +353 87 2358533 / +353 1 8474201

**KEY IRISH PERFORMANCES** (since January 1994):
10.94 National Concert Hall, Dublin promoted by Pipers Club.
**KEY PERFORMANCES OUTSIDE IRELAND** (since January 1994):
7.94 Scoil Samhraidh Willie Clancy, Milltown Malbay, Co Clare appearing solo.
**PRIZES/AWARDS/APPOINTMENTS:**
10.96 Awarded Brendan Breathnach Cup for Solo Piping at An tÓireachtas.
**AVAILABILITY:**
General.
**ADDITIONAL INFORMATION:**
Fifth generation of pipers and pipe-makers. Grandson of Leo Rowsome, renowned concert-pitch pipemaker who dedicated his life to promoting, performing and making the instrument.

## Davy Spillane *Uilleann Pipes*

**Contact:** Mr Davy Spillane
Liscannor
Co Clare
**Other instruments:** Low whistle

## Trevor Stewart *Uilleann Pipes*

**Contact:** Mr Trevor Stewart
14, Wandsworth Place
Belfast BT4 3GB
Northern Ireland
**Tel:** +44 1232 656162

**KEY IRISH PERFORMANCES** (since January 1994):
1995 Dublin, 'The Pure Drop' for RTÉ.
**KEY PERFORMANCES OUTSIDE IRELAND** (since January 1994):
1997 O'Donnell's Bar, Amsterdam, appearing with Andy Dickson.
**SELECTED BROADCASTS AND/OR RECORDED WORK:**
1970 'Irish Country Four' LP for Topic.
'P stands for Paddy', a track on a compilation CD 'Irish Voices' for Topic.
**PRIZES/AWARDS/APPOINTMENTS:**
1976 Winner in the CCÉ All-Ireland Fleadh Cheoil na hÉireann.
**REGULARLY PERFORMS WITH:**
Andy Dickson.
**AVAILABILITY:**
General.

# WHISTLES

## Mary Bergin *Tin Whistles*

**Contact:** Ms Mary Bergin
Spiddal
Co Galway
**Tel/Fax:** +353 91 83333
**Other instruments:** Flute.

*"Just about the best tin whistle player this century"* Irish Times.

**KEY IRISH PERFORMANCES** (since January 1994):
Several appearances throughout the Country including Nenagh, Galway and Longford, appearing with Dordán.
**KEY PERFORMANCES OUTSIDE IRELAND** (since January 1994):
7.95 Tour of Italy, appearing with Martina Goggin.
8.95 Tour of England, appearing with Dordán.
7.96 and 7.97 Tour of USA appearing with Joe and Antoinette McKenna.
**SELECTED RECORDED WORK:**
1976 Mary Bergin - 'Geadoza Stain' for Gael-Linn.
1992 'Mary Bergin Part 2' for Gael-Linn.
1994 'Jigs To The Moon' with Dordán, for Gael-Linn.
**PRIZES/AWARDS/APPOINTMENTS:**
'Prix de Musique Folklorique' awarded from Radio Bratislava in association with a competition between European radio stations (RTÉ facilator, Ciarán Mac Mathuna).
**TRAINING AND/OR QUALIFICATIONS:**
Lecturer on teacher training courses for CCÉ.
Lecturer on music education course in University College, Galway.
**REGULARLY PERFORMS WITH:**
Dordán, Alec Finn, Johnny Ring McDonagh and Joe and Antoinette McKenna.
**AVAILABILITY:**
General.
**ADDITIONAL INFORMATION:**
Performer and teacher.

## Paul Bradley *Tin Whistles*

**Contact:** Mr Paul Bradley
No 1, Parliament Street
Newark, NG24 4UR
England
**Tel:** +44 1636 700271
*See fiddle page 204.*

## Cormac Juan Breatnach
### *Low Whistles and Tin Whistle*

**Contact:** Mr Cormac Juan Breatnach
6, Cearnóg Heuston
Bóthar Inse Chór, Baile Átha Cliath 8
**Tel/Fax:** +353 1 4530334 / +353 1 4530408

*"Breatnach is not the first musician to add modern rhythms and jazz style improvisation to Irish traditional music, but he has taken the concept further than anybody else"*
5-11.10.94 Irish Voice (Don Meade).

**KEY IRISH PERFORMANCES** (since January 1994):
9.9.95 Mother Redcap's Tavern, Dublin, promoted by Éilis Moore and Máire Davitt, appearing with Deiseal.
19.9.95 Trinity College, Dublin promoted by Top Floor Management and APSO, appearing with Nollaig Casey, Donal Lunny and The Dunni Quartet.
**KEY PERFORMANCES OUTSIDE IRELAND** (since January 1994):
7/8.95 Aberdeen (Scotland), Dranoutter (Belgium), London, promoted by Brass Tacks, appearing with Deiseal.
1.96 Celtic Connections Festival, Glasgow, appearing with Deiseal.
5.96 England, appearing with Deiseal.
**SELECTED BROADCASTS AND/OR RECORDED WORK:**
3.94 'River of Sound' for Virgin.
1996 'Celtic Heartbeat Christmas' for Celtic Heartbeat.
1996 'Sunshine Dance' (Deiseal) for Stark Records.
**SELECTED REVIEWS** (since January 1994):
26.2.95 Irish Times.
23.7.95 Scotland on Sunday.
**PRIZES/AWARDS/APPOINTMENTS:**
1988 3rd Prize (as part of Donal Lunny band with Elvis Costello) from the Celtic Film Festival.
1994 The Golden Fiddle Award (as part of the Donal Lunny Band with Elvis Costello).
**REGULARLY PERFORMS WITH:**
Máire Breatnach, Steve Cooney, Donal Lunny, Deiseal (trad/jazz fusion).
**AVAILABILITY:**
Weekends.
**ADDITIONAL INFORMATION:**
Has also performed on the soundtrack of number of films: 'Mannions of America', 'Moondance', 'The War of the Buttons' and 'The Secret of Roan Inish'. Frequently appears on television and radio. Interpretation of Irish music and jazz, features on two Deiseal albums 'The Long Long Note' and 'Sunshine Dance'.

## Máire Breatnach *Whistles*

**Contact:** c/o Mr Steve Dunford
6 The Avenue
Boden Park
Rathfarnham
Dublin 16
**Tel/Fax:** +353 1 4947615 or +353 1 49323358 / +353 1 4931707

*See Máire Breatnach Band page 257.*

## Ronan Browne *Whistles*

**Contact:** Mr Ronan Browne
Mount Slaney
Stratford-on-Slaney
Co Wicklow
**Tel/Fax:** +353 45 404873
**Email:** roro@tinet.ie

*See uilleann pipes page 235.*

## Conor Byrne *Whistles*

**Contact:** Mr Conor Byrne
3, Ardenza Terrace
Monkstown
Co Dublin
**Tel/Fax:** +353 1 2804547
**Other instruments:** Flute.

## Noel Carberry *Whistles*

**Contact:** Mr Noel Carberry
1, Derryhawn
Kenagh
Co Longford
**Tel:** +353 43 25194

*See uilleann pipes page 235.*

## Nollaig Casey *Tin Whistle*

**Contact:** Nollaig Casey
51, Lios Mór
Cappagh Road
Bearna
Co Galway
**Tel:** +353 91 590908

*See fiddle page 205.*

## Adèle Commins *Whistles*

**Contact:** Ms Adèle Commins
Rathbrist
Tallanstown
Dundalk
Co Louth
**Tel:** +353 42 74272

*See accordion page 189.*

## Gregory Daly *Whistles*

**Contact:** Gregory Daly
Tinnecarra
Boyle
Co Roscommon
**Tel:** +353 79 63441

*See flute page 215.*

## Brian Dunning *Whistles*

**Contact:** Mr Brian Dunning
72, Moyglare Village
Maynooth
Co Kildare
**Tel/Fax:** +353 1 628 5678

*See jazz flute page 271.*

## Joseph Finn *Whistles*

**Contact:** Mr Joseph Finn
Kilmucklin
Tullamore
Co Offaly
**Tel:** +353 506 31089

*See uilleann pipes page 236.*

## James Galway *Penny Whistle*

**Contact:** Mr James Galway
c/o Kathryn Enticott
IMG Artists
Media House
3, Burlington Lane
Chiswick
London W4 2TH
England
**Tel/Fax:** +44 181 2335800 / +44 181 2335801
*See flute page 14.*

## Frankie Gavin *Whistles*

**Contact:** Mr Frankie Gavin
Ardnasillagh
Oughterard
Co Galway
**Tel:** +353 91 552545
*See fiddle page 207.*

## Shayron Hobbs *Tin Whistle*

**Contact:** Ms Shayron Hobbs
110, Earlwood Estate
The Lough, Cork
**Tel:** +353 21 962 370
*See soprano page 89.*

## Barry Kerr *Whistles*

**Contact:** Mr Barry Kerr
25, Island View Lane
Kinnego
Lurgan
Co Armagh, BT67 9JF
Northern Ireland
**Tel/Fax:** +44 1762 321730 or +44 1762 324660 / +44 1762 324449
*See flute page 216.*

## Claire Keville *Whistles*

**Contact:** Ms Claire Keville
Claran
Ower, Co Galway
**Tel:** +353 93 35952
*See concertina page 202.*

## Vinnie Kilduff *Whistles*

**Contact:** Vinnie Kilduff
**Mobile:** +353 87 588683
**Email:** kilduff@dojo.ie
**Other instruments:** Uilleann pipes, mandolin, guitar, piano, harmonica, vocals, bodhrán.

*"U2, The Waterboys, Clannad, Mary Black, In Tua Nua - successful, influential bands with one common thread: Vinnie Kilduff"*

**KEY IRISH PERFORMANCES** (since January 1994):
5.96 Mean Fiddler, Dublin, appearing with Clannad.
5.97 'The Gathering', Millstreet, Co Cork, promoted by MCD, appearing with 'The Rocking Chairs' and Patrick Bergin.
**KEY PERFORMANCES OUTSIDE IRELAND** (since January 1994):
1995 Tour of Europe, appearing with Secret Garden.
1996 Tour of Europe and Asia, appearing with Clannad.
1997 St Patricks Cathedral, New York and Chicago, appearing with Patrick Cassidy and the RTÉ Concert Orchestra.
**SELECTED BROADCASTS AND/OR RECORDED WORK:**
1982 'October' with U2, for Island.
1990 'Boys from the Blue Hill', for Mulligan records.
1992/1996 'Fishermans Blues' with The Waterboys and Clannad, for Chrysalis BMG.
**PRIZES/AWARDS/APPOINTMENTS:**
All-Ireland Champion in whistle, singing and bodhrán, awarded by CCÉ.
**TRAINING AND/OR QUALIFICATIONS:**
1979 Diploma in Music Theory from DIT Conservatory of Music and Drama, Dublin.
**REGULARLY PERFORMS WITH:**
Clannad.
**AVAILABILITY:**
Weekdays.
**ADDITIONAL INFORMATION:**
A multi-instrumentalist, composer, producer, singer and songwriter. Practises a wide range of musical styles.

## Gerard Lappin *Tin Whistle*

**Contact:** Mr Gerard Lappin
24, Greenisland Road
Derrinran
Portadown
Co Armagh
Northern Ireland
**Tel:** +44 1762 851489
*See button accordion page 191.*

## Gabriel McArdle *Whistles*

**Contact:** Gabriel McArdle
92, Hillview Road
Enniskillen
Co Fermanagh
Northern Ireland
**Tel:** +44 1365 324165
*See singers page 247.*

## Margo McGeeney *Tin Whistle*

**Contact:** Ms Margo McGeeney
Geeha South
Kinvara
Co Galway
**Tel:** +353 91 637505
*See harpsichord page 125.*

## Joe McHugh *Whistles*

**Contact:** Mr Joe McHugh
Moneystown North
Roundwood
Co Wicklow
or
Gústr 8
Ch - 8700 Kúsnacht
Switzerland
**Tel:** +353 404 45161
**Email:** mchugh@goldnet.ch
*See uilleann pipes page 236.*

## Davy Maguire *Whistles*

**Contact:** Mr Davy Maguire
24, Iveagh Street
Belfast BT12 6AU
Northern Ireland
**Tel:** +44 1232 324 189
*See flute page 217.*

## Josephine Marsh *Tin Whistle*

**Contact:** Ms Josephine Marsh
11a, Abbey Street
Ennis
Co Clare
**Tel/Fax:** +353 65 41782 / +353 65 24783
*See accordions page 192.*

## Séan Moloney *Tin Whistle*

**Contact:** Mr Séan Moloney
'Chez Nous'
Maugheraboy Road
Sligo
**Tel:** +353 71 61239
*See flute page 218.*

## Andrew Morrow *Tin Whistle*

**Contact:** Mr Andrew Morrow
Errew
Carrigallen
Co Leitrim
**Tel:** +353 49 39618
*See fiddle page 210.*

## Diarmuid Moynihan *Whistles*

**Contact:** Mr Diarmuid Moynihan
65, The Rise
Bishopstown
Cork City, Co Cork
**Tel:** +353 21 542958
*See uilleann pipes page 237.*

## Néillidh Mulligan *Tin Whistle*

**Contact:** Mr Néillidh Mulligan
2, Eachlann Ashington
Bóthar na hUaimhe
Baile Átha Cliath 7
**Tel/Fax:** +353 1 8682078 or +353 1 8044600 /
+353 1 8726182
*See uilleann pipes page 237.*

## Tríona Ní Dhomhnaill *Whistle*

**Contact:** Agent: Al Evers
A Train Management
PO Box 29242
Oakland
California 94604, USA
or
Mrs Bríd O'Donnell
7, Ashgrove Court
Dundrum
Dublin 14
**Tel/Fax:** +1 510 893 4705 or +353 1 2982413 /
+1 510 893 4807
*See piano page 233.*

## Eithne Ní Uallacháin *Whistles*

**Contact:** Ms Eithne Ní Uallacháin
Ballymakellet
Ravensdale
Co Louth
Ireland
**Tel/Fax:** +353 42 71538
*See singers page 250.*

## Martin Nolan

***Tin Whistle and Low Whistle***

**Contact:** Martin Nolan
34, St Mary's Drive
Drimnagh
Dublin 12
**Tel/Fax:** +353 1 4563144
*See uilleann pipes page 237.*

## Josephine Nugent *Tin Whistle*

**Contact:** Miss Josephine Nugent
Flat 5
122, Malone Avenue
Belfast, BT9 6ET
Northern Ireland
**Tel:** +44 1232 667250
*See fiddle page 211.*

## Seoirse Ó Dochartaigh *Whistles*

**Contact:** c/o Ms Margaret Rhatigan
Errigal Promotions
1, Chapel Street
Sligo
**Tel/Fax:** +353 71 42316 / +353 73 22677
*See singers page 251.*

## Bríd O'Donohue *Tin Whistle*

**Contact:** Ms Bríd O'Donohue
Glendine South
Miltown Malbay
Co Clare
**Tel:** +353 65 84473
**Other instruments:** Concert flute

**KEY IRISH PERFORMANCES** (since January 1994):
1994 Shannon, promoted by the Arts Council, appearing with Peadar O'Lochlainn.
6.95 Feakle Traditional weekend concert, appearing with Junior Crehan (fiddle).
7.96 Miltown Malbay, An Scoil Samhraidh Willie Clancy.
4.97 Scoil Leacht Uí Chonchúir.
**SELECTED BROADCASTS AND/OR RECORDED WORK:**
1989/90 'The Pure Drop' for RTÉ.
7.96 'Heartlands' for RTÉ.
4.97 'High Reel' for RTÉ.
**PRIZES/AWARDS/APPOINTMENTS:**
1977 Ist Prize in the CCÉ All-Ireland Fleadh Cheoil (slow airs).
1978 1st Prize in the All-Ireland Slógadh and Gradam awards.
**TRAINING AND/OR QUALIFICATIONS:**
Studied with Tessie Walsh, JC Talty (Tulla Céilí band), Mary Ann Sexton, Willie Clancy.
**AVAILABILITY:**
General.
**ADDITIONAL INFORMATION:**
Teaches tin whistle at An Scoil Samhraidh Willie Clancy in Miltown Malbay every year for the last 20 years. Holds workshops at Collins Memorial Weekend Gort, Co Galway and Lahinch Folklore school. Has performed for their Royal Highnessess, King Juan Carlos and Queen Sophia of Spain during their visit to Miltown Malbay.

## Tiarnán Ó Duinnchinn *Whistles*

**Contact:** Tiarnán Ó Duinnchinn
3, Glen Road
Monaghan
Co Monaghan
**Tel/Mobile:** +353 47 82065 / +353 88 2781917
*See uilleann pipes page 238.*

## Colette O'Leary *Whistles*

**Contact:** Ms Colette O'Leary
7, Rathgar Avenue
Rathgar
Dublin 6
**Tel:** +353 1 490 5480
*See piano accordion page 194.*

## Charlie Piggott *Tin Whistle*

**Contact:** Charlie Piggott
Mountscribe
Kinvara
Co Galway
**Tel:** +353 91 637 499
*See accordion page 195.*

## Aidan Prunty *Whistles*

**Contact:** Mr Aidan Prunty
2, Willowbank
Armagh BT61 8AD
Northern Ireland
**Tel/Fax:** +44 1861 511004 / +44 1861 529630
*See flute page 219.*

## John Quinn *Tin Whistle*

**Contact:** John Quinn
30, Parnell Court
Harolds Cross
Dublin 6W
**Tel/Fax:** +353 1 4535699 / +353 1 4933145
*See fiddle page 213.*

## Kathleen Raymond *Tin Whistle*

**Contact:** Ms Kathleen Raymond
72, Stack's Villas
Tralee
Co Kerry
**Tel:** +353 66 26973
*See flute page 18.*

## Michael Rooney *Tin Whistle*

**Contact:** Mr Mackie Rooney
Tyraverty
Scotstown
Co Monaghan
**Tel:** +353 47 89161
*See Irish Harp page 230.*

## Andrew Rowan *Tin Whistle*

**Contact:** Mr Andrew Rowan
10, Galbraith Gardens
Waringstown BT66 7QN
Northern Ireland
**Tel:** +44 1762 881097
*See flute page 19.*

## Frank Simon *Whistles*

**Contact:** Mr Frank Simon
The Plains
Boyle
Co Roscommon
**Tel:** +353 79 62245
*See guitar page 225.*

## Breda Smyth *Tin Whistle*

**Contact:** Dr Breda Smyth
47, Bachelors Walk
Dublin 1
**Tel/Fax:** +353 1 8727774
**Other instruments:** Fiddle.

*"She plays the tin whistle like you'd imagine birds singing in heaven."* 3.97 San Francisco Globe.

**KEY IRISH PERFORMANCES** (since January 1994):
12.96 Kinvara, promoted by Winkles.
5.97 Harcourt Hotel, Dublin.
**KEY PERFORMANCES OUTSIDE IRELAND** (since January 1994):
3.97 San Francisco, promoted by Eddie Stack.
**SELECTED BROADCASTS AND/OR RECORDED WORK:**
5.96 'Basil and Thyme' for RTÉ.
9.96 'Geantraí' for TnaG.
3.97 'Basil and Thyme' (video) for TnaG.
**REGULARLY PERFORMS WITH:**
The Lahawns, Andrew McNamara, Seosifín Ní Begley.
**AVAILABILITY:**
General.

## Davy Spillane *Low Whistle*

**Contact:** Mr Davy Spillane
Liscannor
Co Clare
**Other instrument:** Uilleann pipes.

# TRADITIONAL SINGERS

## Eilín Begley *Singer*

**Contact:** Ms Eilín Begley
Loughlane
Caulstown
Dunboyne
Co Meath
**Tel/Fax:** +353 1 8256337
*See traditional groups page 256.*

## Máire Breatnach *Singer*

**Contact:** c/o Mr Steve Dunford
6, The Avenue
Boden Park, Rathfarnham
Dublin 16
**Tel/Fax:** +353 1 4947615 or +353 1 49323358 / +353 1 4931707
*See Máire Breatnach Band page 257.*

## Danny Carthy *Singer*

**Contact:** Mr Danny Carthy
46, Laurence Avenue
Maynooth, Co Kildare
**Tel:** +353 1 6285276
**Other instruments:** Guitar.

*"Blessed with a tuneful and distinctive voice"*
'Live at 3' (Derek Davis, TV presenter).

**KEY PERFORMANCES OUTSIDE IRELAND** (since January 1994):
10.97 Jameson's Distillery, Koln, Germany
**SELECTED REVIEWS** (since January 1994):
1997 The Leinster Leader.
**AVAILABILITY:**
General.
**ADDITIONAL INFORMATION:**
Played with the folk band Fiddlers Green. Received the Rehab Showbiz Award in 1965. Also a songwriter.

## Nollaig Casey *Singer*

**Contact:** Nollaig Casey
51, Lios Mór
Cappagh Road
Bearna, Co Galway
**Tel:** +353 91 590908
*See fiddle page 205.*

## Aidan Coleman *Singer*

**Contact:** Mr Aidan Coleman
28, Lisalea
Frascati Park
Blackrock, Co Dublin
**Tel:** +353 1 2835117
*See Bass Baritone page 112.*

## Ursula Connolly *Singer*

**Contact:** Ms Ursula Connolly
9, Temple Court
Palatine Square
Arbour Hill, Dublin 7
**Tel:** +353 1 6717589

*"... One of the most hauntingly beautiful voices I have ever heard"* 1994 Irish Heritage Links.

**KEY IRISH PERFORMANCES** (since January 1994):
1.94 Tivoli Theatre, Dublin, promoted by Tara Music Company, appearing with The Rita Connolly Band.
8.96 Kilkenny Arts Festival, appearing with The Fallen Angels.
22.10.96 Whelans, Dublin, appearing with the Fallen Angels.
11.96 Queen's University Festival, at Queens, Belfast, appearing with The Fallen Angels.
**KEY PERFORMANCES OUTSIDE IRELAND** (since January 1994):
7.96 Stuttgart Irish Folk Music Festival, appearing with The Fallen Angels.
8.96 Broadstairs Folk Festival, England, appearing with The Fallen Angels.
11.96 Copenhagen Irish Music Festival, appearing with The Fallen Angels.
7.96 Celtic Connections, Glasgow, appearing with The Fallen Angels.
**SELECTED BROADCASTS AND/OR RECORDED WORK:**
1991 'Glenveagh, Heart of Donegal' for Anner Productions.
1992 'Mayo, It's People and Places' for Anner Productions.
1994 'Connemara, It's People and Places' for Charlie Doherty Productions.
**SELECTED REVIEWS** (since January 1994):
1994 Irish Heritage Links.
10.96 Irish Times
**REGULARLY PERFORMS WITH:**
Peter Connolly (guitar), Rita Connolly Band, Liam O'Flynn, Peter Moore.
**AVAILABILITY:**
General.
**ADDITIONAL INFORMATION:**
Has done extensive session work with composer/producer Shaun Davey. Sang lead vocal on the title track of The Fallen Angels album 'Happy Ever After' and co-wrote one of the tracks on the album with Peter Connolly. Launched solo career officially in February 1997. Currently recording 1st complete original demo.

## Ewan Cowley *Singer*

**Contact:** Mr Ewan Cowley
C/o 18, Belmont Crescent
Derry
BT48 7RR
Northern Ireland
**Tel/Fax:** +44 1504 354455 /+44 1504 350916
*See guitar page 221.*

## Jimmy Crowley *Singer*

**Contact:** Mr Jimmy Crowley
134, Sunday's Well Road
Cork
**Tel:** +353 21 309727
**Other instruments:** Guitar, mandola, bouzouki.

*"Jimmy Crowley is a living legend in Irish folk music. He is the consumate stage performer and song-writer of note"* University of Pennsylvania, USA, Folklore Department, Professor Mick Moloney.

**KEY IRISH PERFORMANCES** (since January 1994):
18.5.96 Downpatrick Folk Club, appearing solo.
4.6.96 'High Reel' for RTÉ.
7.9.96 Cork Folk Festival, appearing with 'Stokers Lodge'.
27.11.96 'Spraoi Cois Laoí' with University College Cork Festival.
**KEY PERFORMANCES OUTSIDE IRELAND** (since January 1994):
8.94 Perth and Freemantle, Australia.
5.96 Scottish Folk Festivals.
2.97 Boston, USA.
3.97 Botswana, Africa.

**SELECTED BROADCASTS AND/OR RECORDED WORK:**
1977 'Boys of Fairhill' for Mulligan Records.
1979 'Camp-House Ballads' for Mulligan Records.
1995 'My Love is a Tall Ship' for Dino Records.
**SELECTED REVIEWS** (since January 1994):
Folk Roots, Hot Press, Irish Times.
**PRIZES/AWARDS/APPOINTMENTS:**
1997 BA Léann Dúchais (Irish Cultural Studies and Irish language) from University College, Cork.
**AVAILABILITY:**
General.

## Adèle Commins *Singer*

**Contact:** Ms Adèle Commins
Rathbrist
Tallanstown
Dundalk
Co Louth
**Tel:** +353 42 74272
*See accordion page 189.*

## Karmel "Katie" Daly *Singer*

**Contact:** Ms Karmel Daly
Cummer
Templeludigan
Enniscorthy
Co Wexford
**Tel:** +353 51 421255
*See guitar page 222.*

## Patricia Daly *Singer*

**Contact:** Ms Patricia Daly
19, Magherydogherty Road
Markethill
Co Armagh BT60 1TY
Northern Ireland
**Tel:** +44 1861 551087
*See Irish harp page 227.*

## Tim Dennehy *Singer*

**Contact:** Mr Tim Dennehy
Markham's Cross
Mullach
Co Clare
**Tel:** +353 65 87219

*" 'A Winter's Tear' - A perky, enjoyable album, full of lovely verses, wit and words and of well crafted songs"* 11.96 Folk Roots.

**KEY IRISH PERFORMANCES** (since January 1994):
8.95 Ballyvaughan, promoted by Cumann Merriman, appearing with Liam Lewis and Eamon Ó Bróithe.
11.96 University of Limerick, promoted by Mícheál Ó Súilleabháin, appearing Charlie Harris and Des Mulkere.
1.97 Góilín Club, Dublin, promoted by Luke Cheevers appearing solo.
1.97 Grand Hotel, Dublin, promoted by Connie Ryan appearing solo.

**KEY PERFORMANCES OUTSIDE IRELAND** (since January 1994):
8.94 Wadebridge, Cornwall, promoted by John Webb, appearing with the Voice Squad, Any Old Time etc.
11.95 The Hague, Netherlands, promoted by Willem Verhulst, appearing with musicians from The Netherlands.
**SELECTED BROADCASTS AND/OR RECORDED WORK:**
6.93 'A Winter's Tear' for Cló Iar-Chonnachta CIC CD 087.
12.96 'A Thimbleful of Song' (re-issue) for Sceilig Records SRCD 001.
7.97 'Farewell to Miltown Malbay' for Sceilig Records SRCD 002.
**SELECTED REVIEWS** (since January 1994):
1994 The Living Tradition.
2.97 Irish Times.
**REGULARLY PERFORMS WITH:**
Garry O'Briain.
**AVAILABILITY:**
Weekends, months of July and August.
**ADDITIONAL INFORMATION:**
Co-founder of the Góilín Singers Club (Dublin) and the Clare Singing Festival. Presenter of 'Keep In Touch', a 2 hour radio programme on traditional music, song and poetry on Clare FM.

## Christine Dowling *Singer*

**Contact:** Christine Dowling
16B, Adelaide Road
Belfast BT9 6FX
**Tel:** +44 1232 280108
*See traditional flute page 216.*

## Fionnuala Gill *Singer*

**Contact:** Ms Fionnuala Gill
151, Ard na Mara
Malahide, Co Dublin
**Tel:** +353 1 8450698
*See soprano page 88.*

## Deirdre Gilsenan *Singer*

**Contact:** Ms Deirdre Gilsenan
Loughan
Kells, Co Meath
**Mobile:** +353 88 2756326
*See soprano page 88.*

## Len Graham *Singer*

**Contact:** Mr Len Graham
Teach a'Ghleanna
Mullaghbawn
Newry BT35 9N
Northern Ireland
**Tel:** +44 1693 888135

*"Len Graham is one of the most majestic singers on God's earth"* 11.97 Folk Roots.

**KEY IRISH PEROFRMANCES** (since January 1994):
27.5.95 Northern Lights Festival, Ballycastle, Co Antrim, promoted by Moyle District Council, appearing with John Campbell.
21.6.95 Belfast Folk Festival, promoted by N Martyn, appearing with John Campbell.
29.7.95 P Murray Festival, Bannow, Co Wexford, promoted by J Murphy, appearing with John Campbell.
**KEY PERFORMANCES OUTSIDE IRELAND** (since January 1994):
From 20.3.95 to 9.4.95 Tour of Germany, promoted by S Macker, appearing with Skylark.
9.95 Tour of USA, promoted by Music Tree, appearing with Cathal McConnell.
4.11.95 Irish Festival, Estonia, promoted by Estonian Government, appearing with John Campbell.
**SELECTED BROADCASTS AND/OR RECORDED WORK:**
1983 'Do Me Justice', for Claddagh records.
1993 'For the Sake of Old Decency', for Sage Arts.
1995 'Raining Bicycles' (Skylark), for Claddagh Records.
**PRIZES/AWARDS/APPOINTMENTS:**
1953 1st Prize, awarded by Ballymena Feis.
1964 2nd Prize, awarded at the CCÉ All-Ireland Fleadh Cheoil na hÉireann.
1966 1st Prize at the Ulster Fleadh.
1971 1st Prize awarded at the CCÉ All-Ireland Fleadh Ceoil na hÉireann.
**REGULARLY PERFORMS WITH:**
Skylark, Cathal McConnell, John Campbell.
**AVAILABILITY:**
General.

## Sarah Grealish *Singer*

**Contact:** Ms Sarah Grealish
Muicineach Camus
Co na Gaillimhe
**Tel:** +353 91 572225

**SELECTED BROADCASTS AND/OR RECORDED WORK:**
1985 Own tape for Gael-Linn.
1989 Cló-Íar Chonnachta recordings for Raidió na Gaeltachta.
1990 Cló-Íar Chonnachta for RTÉ.
**PRIZES/AWARDS/APPOINTMENTS:**
1985 Winner in the Celtic Traditional Singing category at the Pan Celtic Festival, Killarney.
Ó'Riada Cup winner at an tÓireachtais, Dublin.
**AVAILABILITY:**
General.
**ADDITIONAL INFORMATION:**
From a family with a rich musical tradition. Has travelled throughout Europe and USA.

## Frank Harte *Singer*

**Contact:** Frank Harte
93, Martin's Row
Chapelizod
Dublin 20
**Tel:** +353 1 6231455
**Email:** hartef@indigo.ie

*"Frank gives the song the voice: his love is for songs that tell a story, and it is in their songs that a people keep their history and tell their emotions unclouded by interpretation"*
1997 Irish Music.

**KEY IRISH PERFORMANCES** (since January 1994):
1997 Ennistymon, promoted by The Ballad Singing Festival, appearing solo.
1997 Ballyliffen, Songs of the Sea Festival.
1997 Wexford, Singing Festival.
**KEY PERFORMANCES OUTSIDE IRELAND** (since January 1994):
1994 Ville Nova University, guest singing lecturer to music faculty, appearing with Mick Moloney.

1995 East Durham, New York, promoted by the Irish/American University.
1996 Davis Eckins University, West Virginia, USA appearing with Mick Moloney.
1997 English National Folk Festival, Sutton, Bonnington, appearing with Máighread Ní Dhomhnaill.
**SELECTED BROADCASTS AND/OR RECORDED WORK:**
1997 5 programmes on 'Sounds Traditional' for RTÉ.
1997 two records, for (Claddagh) Records.
1997 one recording for the Smithsonian Institute.
**SELECTED REVIEWS** (since January 1994):
1996 Irish Music.
**PRIZES/AWARDS/APPOINTMENTS:**
All-Ireland Ballad Singing Champion, awarded by CCÉ.
**REGULARLY PERFORMS WITH:**
Donal Lunny, Maighréad Ní Dhomhnaill.
**AVAILABILITY:**
General.
**ADDITIONAL INFORMATION:**
Has given several masterclasses including a week at Pinewoods Mass, USA and at the Davis Elkins College, West Virginia, USA. Published 'Dublin Street Songs', Ossian (1997).

## Séan Keane *Singer*

**Contact:** Mr Séan Keane
"Hollygrove"
Castlegar
Kilcolgan
Co Galway
**Tel/Fax:** +353 91 796357

## Emer Kenny *Singer*

**Contact:** Ms Emer Kenny
C/o Mr John Murphy
48, Balreask Village
Navan
Co Meath
**Tel:** +353 46 71459
*See Irish harp page 229.*

## Órna Loughnane *Singer*

**Contact:** Órna Loughnane
Brockmanngasse 114/9
A-8010
Graz
Austria
**Tel:** +43 316 842344
*See violin page 297.*

## John Lyons *Singer*

**Contact:** Mr John Lyons
Ryans Cross
Ralahine South
Newmarket-on-Fergus
Co Clare
**Tel:** +353 61 368720
*See accordion page 191.*

## Tim Lyons *Singer*

**Contact:** Mr Tim Lyons
Roshill Road
Roscam
Co Galway
**Tel:** +353 91 752180
**Other instruments:** Accordion, bodhrán.

*"... Had his audience shaking in mirth at some of his fine songs"* 10.91 The Examiner.

**KEY IRISH PERFORMANCES** (since January 1994):
5.95 Ennis, Co Clare, promoted by Mick Coyne for CCÉ, appearing with Tim Donnelly and The Voice Squad.
14.7.95 National Concert Hall, Dublin, appearing with Mairéad Ní Dhomhnaill, Liz Doherty and Fintan Vallely.
9.95 Tallaght, promoted by Alternative Entertainments, appearing with Jackie Daly, Gary Ó Bróin and Fintan Vallely.
16.9.95 Oslo Hotel, Galway, promoted by Peter Galligan, appearing with John Faulkener, Dolores Keane and Mick Lally.
**KEY PERFORMANCES OUTSIDE IRELAND** (since January 1994):
5-6.5.95 Sea Shantie Weekend, Swansea, South Wales, appearing with Crazy Crow, Stormalong and The Keelers.
16.8.95 Llantrissant Folk Club, Llantrissant, South Wales, appearing with Fintan Vallely.
18.8.95 Irish Centre, Sheffield, appearing with Fintan Vallely.
8.95 Whitby Folk Festival, Whitby, England promoted by Malcolm Storey, appearing with Patricia Flynn, Archie Fisher and Fintan Vallely.
**SELECTED BROADCASTS AND/OR RECORDED WORK:**
1970 'The Green Linnet', for Leader Sound, London.
1977 'Easter Show', for Green Linnet.
1989 'Knock, Knock, Knock', for UFMA Tapes.
**SELECTED REVIEWS** (since January 1994):
8.95 Irish Music.
**PRIZES/AWARDS/APPOINTMENTS:**
9.69 1st Prize, awarded by All-England Fleadh, CCÉ.
8.89 1st Prize, awarded by Rought Valley, New Song Festival.
**AVAILABILITY:**
General.
**ADDITIONAL INFORMATION:**
Uses lilting when performing. One of his songs is currently used in the Northern Ireland Education Curriculum in a 'Traditional Song Education Pack', produced by St Mary's College, Belfast and prepared by John Moulden.

## Gabriel McArdle *Singer*

**Contact:** Mr Gabriel McArdle
92, Hillview Road
Enniskillen
Co Fermanagh
Northern Ireland
**Tel:** +44 1365 324165
**Other instruments:** Concertina, tin whistle.

*"An LP being worn out on the turntables of traditional music across Ireland now, and of the four songs, two are sung séan nos, by Gabriel McArdle, whose understated vocal style is quietly effective"* 3.2.90 Irish Voice, New York.

**KEY IRISH PERFORMANCES** (since January 1994):
24.7.94 Carrick-on-Bannow Festival, Wexford, promoted by John Murphy, appearing with Séamus Quinn, Ben Lennon and Ciáran Curran.
8.5.95 Louisburgh, Co Mayo, appearing with M. O'Grady.
28.5.95 Feil Oriel, Monaghan Town, promoted by Eamon Curran.
18.9.95 Harcourt Hotel, Dublin, promoted by Ben Lennon, appearing with Ben Lennon, Séan Quinn, Ciáran Curran and John Carty.
**KEY PERFORMANCES OUTSIDE IRELAND** (since January 1994):
5.91 Girvan Folk Festival, Scotland, promoted by Pete Heywood.
9.94 Bremen Folk Club, Germany, promoted by V Laing.
**SELECTED BROADCASTS AND/OR RECORDED WORK:**
1975 'Fleadh Ceoil, Buncrana', for Dolphin records.
1978 'Na Draiddóire', for French Label.
1990 'Dog Big, Dog Little', for Claddagh Records.
**PRIZES/AWARDS/APPOINTMENTS:**
6.79 and 6.85 1st prize for solo singing, awarded by Fermanagh Fleadh Ceoil.
**REGULARLY PERFORMS WITH:**
Ciaran Curran (bouzouki), Séamus Quinn (fiddle) and Ben Lennon (fiddle).
**AVAILABILITY:**
General.
**ADDITIONAL INFORMATION:**
Has performed in Britain, Germany and France and travels regularly throughout Ireland. Has appeared on various television and radio programmes for RTÉ, UTV, BBC.

# Jim MacFarland *Singer*

**Contact:** Mr Jim MacFarland
37, Crestwood Road
Ashbourne
Co Meath
**Tel:** +353 1 8351717

**KEY IRISH PERFORMANCES** (since January 1994):
Regular appearances at all major Irish traditional singing festivals.
**SELECTED BROADCASTS AND/OR RECORDED WORK:**
1984/87 Traditional programme for BBC (Radio Foyle).
1995 Traditional programme for RTÉ.
1997 Programme for RTÉ.
**PRIZES/AWARDS/APPOINTMENTS:**
8.94 CCÉ All-Ireland Fleadh Cheoil na hÉireann Senior Singer award (English).
**AVAILABILITY:**
General.

# Catherine McLaughlin *Singer*

**Contact:** Mrs Catherine McLaughlin
Dooish Crossoads
Drumquin
Co Tyrone BT78 4KE
Northern Ireland
**Tel:** +44 1662 831713
**Other instruments:** Banjo.

**KEY IRISH PERFORMANCES** (since January 1994):
7.95 Ulster Fleadh Ceoil, Coothill, Co Cavan.
8.95 All-Ireland Fleadh Cheoil na hÉireann, Listowel, Co Kerry. Also at the opening of the Dún Uládh Centre, Co Tyrone.
**KEY PERFORMANCES OUTSIDE IRELAND** (since January 1994):
3.95 Chicago, Singing at CD launch with Laurence Nugent.
6.96 Chicago/Indiana/New York, concert performance.
**SELECTED BROADCASTS AND/OR RECORDED WORK:**
1995 'Ceilí House' recording with 'Pride of Erin Band' for RTÉ.
1995 Opening of Dún Uládh, Co Tyrone, videotape.
1995/96 CCÉ Champions concert, (videotape).
**PRIZES/AWARDS/APPOINTMENTS:**
1979 1st Prize for singing in English at Fleadh Cheoil na hÉireann.
1995 1st Prize Senior Ballad Champion at Fleadh Cheoil na hÉireann.
**TRAINING AND/OR QUALIFICATIONS:**
Scoil Eigse class (up to senior level singing). Has attended various other classes and workshops.
**REGULARLY PERFORMS WITH:** Laurence Nugent.
**AVAILABILITY:**
General.
**ADDITIONAL INFORMATION:**
Comes from a family background in traditional music and song. Singing at Fleadhanna since 12 years of age. Late father, Séan Nugent was All-Ireland fiddle champion and the leader of the 'Pride of Erin Band' (3 times All-Ireland champions). Uncle was the well-known Ulster poet and songwriter, the late Felix Kearney of Omagh.

# Sandi Miller *Singer*

**Contact:** c/o Mr Bill Whelan
39, Fairview Gardens
Dublin 3
**Tel:** +353 1 8331920
*See fiddle page 297.*

# Kevin Mitchell *Singer*

**Contact:** Mr Kevin Mitchell
36, Lawrence Street
Partick
Glasgow G11 5HD
Scotland
**Tel:** +44 141 3346614

**KEY IRISH PERFORMANCES** (since January 1994):
1995 'The Pure Drop' for RTÉ.
1996 Belfast Folk Festival, appearing with La Lúgh.
1996 Forkhill, Armagh.
1997 Ennistymon Festival of Traditional Singing.
**KEY PERFORMANCES OUTSIDE IRELAND** (since January 1994):
4.95 English National Folk Festival, Sutton Bonnington, promoted by John Haydon.
8.95 Whitby Folk Festival, promoted by Malcolm Storey.
10.95 Folk Clubs, London.
7.96 Pinewood Camp, Massachussetts, USA, promoted by the Traditional Music and Song Association, USA.
**SELECTED BROADCASTS AND/OR RECORDED WORK:**
1977 'Free and Easy' for Topic.
1996 'I sang that sweet refrain' for Green Trax.
**REGULARLY PERFORMS WITH:**
Ellen Mitchell (traditional Scottish singer), Stramash (group).
**AVAILABILITY:**
General.
**ADDITIONAL INFORMATION:**
From Derry City, but now living in Glasgow. Noted for his lyrical style, mainly in the Ulster tradition. He has performed at festivals and folk clubs all over England, Scotland, Canada and the USA. Performs regularly with his wife Ellen Mitchell.

# Eilish Moore *Singer*

**Contact:** Ms Eilish Moore
30, South Square
Inchicore
Dublin 8
**Tel:** +353 1 4543936

**KEY IRISH PERFORMANCES** (since January 1994):
1992 Liberty Hall, Dublin, appearing with the Fallen Angels.
1994, Gaiety Theatre, Dublin, Arthur Lappin, appearing as a street singer in 'The Risen People'.
1995 Sligo Arts Festival.
1997 Bealtaine Festival, Newbridge (open air concert).
**KEY PERFORMANCES OUTSIDE IRELAND** (since January 1994):
3.95 Edinburgh Céilí House, Aberdeen Folk Club and Glasgow Folk Club, appearing with Jimmy Hutchinson.
**SELECTED BROADCASTS AND/OR RECORDED WORK:**
1989 and 1991 'Late Late Show' for RTÉ.
1993 'Folk Wave' for BBC Wales radio.
**AVAILABILITY:**
General.

## John Moulden *Singer*

**Contact:** Mr John Moulden
10, Apollo Walk
Portrush
Co Antrim, BT56 8HQ
Northern Ireland
**Tel:** +44 1265 825080
**Email:** jmoul81075@aol.com
**Other instruments:** Spoons, bódhran.

**KEY IRISH PERFORMANCES** (since January 1994):
11.96 University of Limerick, promoted by the Irish World Music Centre, appearing with P.J Crotty and Geraldine Cotter.
5.97 Ballycastle, promoted by the Cultural Coalition.
**KEY PERFORMANCES OUTSIDE IRELAND** (since January 1994):
8.94 Staunton, Virginia, USA promoted by Ulster American Heritage, lecture and solo recital.
**SELECTED BROADCASTS AND/OR RECORDED WORK:**
1995 'Thousands are Sailing', for Ulster Songs, Portrush.
**PRIZES/AWARDS/APPOINTMENTS:**
1996 Bass Ireland Arts Award, awarded by the Arts Council of Northern Ireland.
**AVAILABILITY:**
General.

## Ann Mulqueen *Singer*

**Contact:** Ann Mulqueen
An Rinn
Co Phortlairge
**Tel:** +353 58 46115

*"One of the greatest of all traditional singers who remains on top after quite a few years"*
10.95 Cló-Iar Chonnachta, Galway.

**KEY IRISH PERFORMANCES** (since January 1994):
1996 Various concert and workshops throughout Ireland.
**KEY PERFORMANCES OUTSIDE IRELAND** (since January 1994):
10.96 Tour of USA and Canada promoted by CCÉ.
**SELECTED BROADCASTS AND/OR RECORDED WORK:**
1995 Recordings for RTÉ and Cló-Iar Chonnachta.
**PRIZES/AWARDS/APPOINTMENTS:**
1959, 1960, 1961 All-Ireland CCÉ Fleadh Ceoil na hÉireann singing champion.
**AVAILABILITY:**
General.
**ADDITIONAL INFORMATION:**
International recognised exponent of traditional singing.

## Sorcha Ní Chéilleachair *Singer*

**Contact:** Sorcha Ní Chéilleachair
84, Taney Road
Goatstown
Dublin 14
**Tel:** +353 1 2980251

**KEY IRISH PERFORMANCES** (since January 1994):
10.95 Corn Uí Riada, Dublin, promoted by An tÓireachtas.
10.96 Corn Uí Riada, Donegal, promoted by An tÓireachtas.
3.97 Féile na nDéise, Co Waterford, appearing with Ann Mulqueen and Odharnait Ní Chéilleachair.
4.97 Séan-nós Cois Life, Dublin, guest singer.
**KEY PERFORMANCES OUTSIDE IRELAND** (since January 1994):
8.96 Lorient, promoted by the Festival Interceltique Lorient, appearing with Odharnait Ní Chéilleachair.
**SELECTED BROADCASTS AND/OR RECORDED WORK:**
3.95 'Lifelines' for RTÉ.
8.96 'Fleadh '96' for RTÉ.
8.96 Programmes recorded as part of Festival Interceltique Lorient for French television.
**PRIZES/AWARDS/APPOINTMENTS:**
1991 CCÉ All-Ireland Fleadh Cheoil na hÉireann champion.
1994 2nd Prize in Comhartas na mBan with An tOireachtas.
**REGULARLY PERFORMS WITH:**
Odharnait Ní Chéilleachair, Ann Mulqueen, Ciarán Ó Gealbháin.
**AVAILABILITY:**
General.
**ADDITIONAL INFORMATION:**
Séan-nós and traditional English singer.

## Maighread Ní Dhomhnaill *Singer*

**Contact:** Maighread Ní Dhomhnaill
42, Marley Court
Rathfarnham
Dublin 14
**Tel:** +353 1 2982413

*"Assured performances sung in a medium sweet voice of head-turning expressiveness and immense charm"* 1992 Folkroots, review of Gan Dhá Phingin Spré - (No Dowry), Gael-Linn CEFCD 152.

**KEY IRISH PERFORMANCES** (since January 1994):
1.95 Tour of Ireland promoted by Music Network, appearing with Fintan Vallely, Con O'Drisceoil and Dermot Diamond.
5.95 Limerick, promoted by Hummingbird Productions, appearing with Mícheál Ó Súilleabháin and 'River of Sound' group members.
7.95 Ionad Cois Locha, Dunlewey, Donegal, promoted by Ionad Cois Locha appearing with Tríona Ní Dhomhnaill,
7.95 National Concert Hall, Dublin.
**KEY PERFORMANCES OUTSIDE IRELAND** (since January 1994):
8.95 Tour of Northern Italy, appearing with Dermot McLaughlin, Fintan Vallely.
9.95 Cornwall, promoted by Folk Festival, appearing with Frank Harte.
9/10.95 Tour of Finland, promoted by Sibelius Institute Helsinki, appearing with Fintan Vallely, Liz Doherty.
**SELECTED BROADCASTS AND/OR RECORDED WORK:**
10.91 Gan Dhá Phingin Spré, Gael-Linn.
8.94 A Woman's Heart 2 for Dara.
7.95 A Celtic Christmas for Windham Hill.
**REGULARLY PERFORMS WITH:**
Tríona Ní Dhomhnaill, Dónal Lunny.
**AVAILABILITY:**
General.

## Tríona Ní Dhomhnaill *Singer*

**Contact:** Agent: Al Evers
A Train Management
PO Box 29242
Oakland
California 94604
USA
or
Mrs Bríd O'Donnell
7, Ashgrove Court
Dundrum
Dublin 14
**Tel/Fax:** +1 510 893 4705 or +353 1 2982413 / +1 510 893 4807
*See piano page 233.*

## Máiread Ní Mhaonaigh *Singer*

**Contact:** c/o Mr Ciarán Tourish
26, St John's Park Avenue
Sandymount
Dublin 4
**Mobile/Tel/Fax:** +353 87 542054 / +353 1 2839585
**Email:** tourish@indigo.ie

**REGULARLY PERFORMS WITH:**
Altan.

## Treasa Ní Mhiolláin *Singer*

**Contact:** Treasa Ní Mhiolláin
Sruthán
Inis Mór
Árainn
Co na Gaillimhe
**Tel:** +353 99 61262

**KEY IRISH PERFORMANCES** (since January 1994):
1994 Heritage Centre, Dúnchaoin, promoted by Michéal de Mórdha, appearing with other singers and musicians.
1995 Ennis, promoted by Fleadh Nua.
1996 Miltown Malbay, promoted by An Scoil Samhraidh Willie Clancy.
1996 Town Hall Theatre, Galway, concert for EU Ministers.
**KEY PERFORMANCES OUTSIDE IRELAND** (since January 1994):
1996 Tour of England, promoted by Peta Webb and Ken Hall, appearing with Róisín White (singer).
1996/1997 Latvia, appearing with other singers and musicians.
**SELECTED BROADCASTS AND/OR RECORDED WORK:**
1972 Amhráin as Árainn, Conamara, recorded by Gael-Linn.
1989 An Clochar Bán, recorded by Cló Iar-Chonnachta.
1993 Concert for radio DRS, Switzerland.
**PRIZES/AWARDS/APPOINTMENTS:**
1972/1979 Over-all prize from An tÓireachtas.
1996 Award from Sean-Nós Cois Life.
**AVAILABILITY:**
General.
**ADDITIONAL INFORMATION:**
Gives workshops all over Ireland and abroad.

## Nóirín Ní Riain *Singer*

**Contact:** Ms Nóirín Ní Riain
Dromore House
Newport
Co Tipperary
**Tel/Fax:** +353 61 378293 / +353 61 378793

*"An artist who belongs at the top of every world music fan's list"* 9.3.96 Billboard USA.

**KEY PERFORMANCES OUTSIDE IRELAND** (since January 1994):
7.95 Maastricht, Holland, promoted by Musica Sacra, appearing solo.
4.96 Indiana, USA, lead role of Anima in 'Ordo Virtutum', appearing with the Schola Gregoriana of Notre Dame University.
6.96 Royal Festival Hall, London, promoted by Lynn Franks, appearing with Sinéad O'Connor.
4.97 Aberystwyth, Wales, promoted by Living Voice, appearing solo.
**SELECTED BROADCASTS AND/OR RECORDED WORK:**
1980 'Caoineadh na Maighdine' for Gael-Linn.
1987 'Soundings' for Ossian.
1997 'Celtic Soul' for Living Music USA.
**SELECTED REVIEWS** (since January 1994):
The Boston Globe, Charleston Daily Mail Irish Times.
**TRAINING AND/OR QUALIFICATIONS:**
From 1968 to 1971, B Mus from University College Cork.
From 1978 to 1980, MA Music from UCC.
From 1970 to 1971, Voice Diploma from Cork School of Music.
**AVAILABILITY:**
General.
**ADDITIONAL INFORMATION:**
For the past seven years has been a guest singer in the Winter and Summer Solstice concerts at the Cathedral of St John The Devine, New York. Has represented Ireland at many international festivals including four UN Summits.

## Eithne Ní Uallacháin *Singer*

**Contact:** Ms Eithne Ní Uallacháin
Ballymakellett
Ravensdale, Co Louth
**Tel/Fax:** +353 42 71538
**Other instruments:** Flute, whistles.

*"Eithne's voice is as clear as hand blown crystal"*

1992 Time Out, London.

**KEY IRISH PERFORMANCES** (since January 1994):
Various venues nationwide including Belfast Folk Festival, Boyle Arts Festival, National Concert Hall - Dublin, Clifden Community Arts Week, appearing with Lá Lugh.
**KEY PERFORMANCES OUTSIDE IRELAND** (since January 1994):
8.94 Dranquter, Belguim, appearing with Lá Lugh.
1-8.10.95 Sweden, promoted by Swedish Music Authority, appearing with Gerry O'Connor, Ronan Browne and Martin O'Hare.
**SELECTED BROADCASTS AND/OR RECORDED WORK:**
1988 'Cosa Gan Bhróga', recorded by Gael-Linn Records.
1991 'Lá Lugh', recorded by Claddagh Records.
1995 'Brighid's Kiss', recorded by Lughnasa Music.
**PRIZES/AWARDS/APPOINTMENTS:**
1992 'Fiddler in Gold' CD, awarded by Irland Journal, Germany.
1992 Shortlisted as part of Lá Lugh for the IRMA Milk Music Awards.
**TRAINING AND/OR QUALIFICATIONS:**
From 1974 to 1977, BA (Hons) Irish Studies, awarded by National University of Ulster, Coleraine, Northern Ireland.
From 1977 to 1978, Diploma in Education (Hons), awarded by St Patricks Teacher Training College, Drumcondra, Dublin.

**REGULARLY PERFORMS WITH:**
Gerry O'Connor (fiddle), Lá Lugh.
**AVAILABILITY:**
General.
**ADDITIONAL INFORMATION:**
Researches and records Irish songs from the South Ulster/Oriel tradition.

## Pádraigín Ní Uallacháin *Singer*

**Contact:** Ms Pádraigín Ní Uallacháin
4, Glendesha Road
Mullaghbawn
Newry, BT35 9XN
Northern Ireland
**Tel:** +44 1693 888135

*"She and Garry Ó Briain create airs and arrangements ranging from the etherial to the earthy with absolute surefootedness"*
Irish Times (Nuala O'Faolain).

**KEY IRISH PERFORMANCES** (since January 1994):
25.7.95, Glencolmkille, Co Donegal, promoted by Oideas Gael.
28.7.95, Hewitt Summer School, Glens of Antrim, promoted by the Arts Council of Northern Ireland.
21.10.95, Rath Chairn, Co Meath, promoted by Eigse Dharach Uí Chathaín.
25.11.95 Belfast Festival at Queen's appearing with Mark Kelly.
**KEY PERFORMANCES OUTSIDE IRELAND** (since January 1994):
1994 Tolcane, France.
1995 Stornoway, Isle of Lewis, Scotland, promoted by Mary Smith.
**SELECTED BROADCASTS AND/OR RECORDED WORK:**
94 'A Stór a Stóirín - 36 Songs for all ages', Gael-Linn CEFCD 166.
95 'An Dara Craiceann - Beneath the Surface', Gael-Linn CEFCD 174.
**SELECTED REVIEWS** (since January 1994):
Irish Times (Fintan Valleły).
Hot Press (Colm O'Hare).
RTÉ Guide (Paddy Kehoe).
**PRIZES/AWARDS/APPOINTMENTS:**
From 1993 to 1994, 1995 Ist Prize winner 'New Music Composition' awarded by An tÓireachtas, Dublin.
1994 Joint Album of the Year, 'A Stór a Stóirín' awarded by Irish Times, Dublin.
1995 Ist Prize winner for research on Sean-Nós singing, awarded by An tÓireachtas.
**TRAINING AND/OR QUALIFICATIONS:**
From 1973 to 1976 BA Hons, University of Ulster, Northern Ireland.
From 1980 to 1981 Broadcaster, RTÉ, Dublin.
From 1982 to 1983 Dip Ed (Hons), St Patrick's College of Education, Dublin.
**REGULARLY PERFORMS WITH:**
Garry Ó Briain, Len Graham, Mark Kelly.
**AVAILABILITY:**
Subject to schedule.
**ADDITIONAL INFORMATION:**
Seán Nos singer - accompanied/unacompanied. Special interest in keening/religious/love songs from the Irish tradition, with or without accompaniment. Five songs from 'A Stór a Stóirín' album used for television series Rí-Rá on Channel 4, (scripted and presented by Pádraigín Ní Uallacháin). Has also composed other music for film.

## Mary Nugent *Singer*

**Contact:** Ms Mary Nugent
9, Gledswood Park
Clonskeagh
Dublin 14
**Tel:** +353 1 2693956
*See flute page 218.*

## Breanndán Ó Beaglaoich *Singer*

**Contact:** Breanndán Ó Beaglaoich
Cuas
Baile na nGall
Trálí
Cho. Chiarraí
**Tel:** +353 66 55399
*See button accordion page 192.*

## Tomás Ó Canainn *Singer*

**Contact:** Tomás Ó Canainn
Ard Barra
Glanmire
Co Cork
**Tel:** +353 21 821003
*See uilleann pipes page 238.*

## Seoirse Ó Dochartaigh *Singer*

**Contact:** Ms Heather Innes
Alive Music
8, Williamsburgh Cottages
Forneth
Blairgowrie
Perthshire
Scotland PH10 6SP
**Tel/Fax:** +44 1350 724275 / +353 73 22677
**Other instruments:** Guitar, Whistles.

*"A strong, supple and distinctive vocalist ... the premier Gaelic song exponent of this generation ..."* 9.94 Issue 19, Rock 'n' Reel (John O'Regan).

**KEY IRISH PERFORMANCES** (since January 1994):
5.95 Ard na Móna, Donegal, promoted by Amabell Clarke.
6.95 Harvey's Point, Pushkin Prizes Trust, promoted by Ann McKay.
7.95 Oideas Gael Gleann Cholm Cille, promoted by Liam Ó Cuinneagáin appearing with Chris Cassidy.
9.95 Cultúrlann McAdam Ó Fiaich, Belfast, promoted by Janet Muller appearing with Heather Innes and Steafán Hannigan.
**KEY PERFORMANCES OUTSIDE IRELAND** (since January 1994):
8.94 O'Casey's Folk Club, The Hague, Holland, promoted by Liesbeth Nieuwenhuijse.
11.94 Duisburg, Germany, promoted by Harald Jüngst appearing with Andreas Völlmeike, Kultur Zentrum.
8.95 Ashington Folk Club, England appearing with Heather Innes.
8.95 Tuirean Arts Centre, Skye, Scotland, appearing with Heather Innes, promoted by Susan Richardson.

**SELECTED BROADCASTS AND/OR RECORDED WORK:**
88 "Slán agus Beannacht" CD, Errigal Records.
92 "Bláth Buí" CD, Errigal Records.
94 "Oíche go Maídin" CD, Errigal Records.
**SELECTED REVIEWS** (since January 1994):
4.5.94 Irish Echo, New York.
22.8.94 Irish Times.
16.9.95 Andersonstown News.
**PRIZES/AWARDS/APPOINTMENTS:**
1992 and 1994 Ist Prize in Dréacht Ceoil Dúchais, awarded by An tÓireachtas.
**TRAINING AND/OR QUALIFICATIONS:**
From 1966 to 1970 BA Hons, Belfast College of Art.
From 1970 to 1971 ATC, Cardiff University.
From 1979 to 1981 MA Music (Research), University College, Cork.
**REGULARLY PERFORMS WITH:**
Dúlamán.
**AVAILABILITY:**
General.
**ADDITIONAL INFORMATION:**
Speciality is Gaelic song. Programmes include songs in English as well as solos on guitars and whistle.

# Con Ó Drisceoil *Singer*

**Contact:** Mr Con Ó Drisceoil
61, Maryborough Avenue
Douglas
Co Cork
**Tel:** +353 21 362878
*See accordion page 194.*

# Risteard Ó hÉidhin *Singer*

**Contact:** Mr Risteard Ó hÉidhin
Cill Chiarain
Connmara
Co na nGaillimhe
**Tel:** +353 95 33401

**REGULARLY PERFORMS WITH:**
Carna Comhaltas Ceotóirí Éireann.
**AVAILABILITY:**
General.
**ADDITIONAL INFORMATION:**
1988 and 1990 winner of two All-Ireland Sean-nós singing titles. Winner of two An tÓireachtas Ist Prizes (Senior). From 1988 to 1996, winner of Ennis Fleadh, Co Clare and of many smaller competitions over a number of years.

# Antaine Ó Farach※áin *Singer*

**Contact:** Mr Antaine Ó Faracháin
13, Bóthar Emmet
Cill Mhaighneann
Baile Átha Cliath 8
**Tel:** +353 1 4538192

*"Manages unique double loyalty to the songs of his native Dublin and ... of the Connemara Gaeltacht"*

1995 Feakle Traditional Singing Festival Programme.

**KEY IRISH PERFORMANCES** (since January 1994):
An Scoil Samhraidh Willie Clancy (various) in Co Clare and other music festivals in Derrygonnelly, Co Fermanagh.
1996 Inishowen, Co Donegal, promoted by the Inishowen Singers Festival.
6.97 Ennistymon, Co Clare, promoted by Tom Munnelly and the Ennistymon Traditional Singing Festival.
**KEY PERFORMANCES OUTSIDE IRELAND** (since January 1994):
1996 Le Quartz, Brest, Brittany, promoted by L'Imaginaire Irlandais, appearing solo and with other singers.
1997 Sidmouth Folk Festival, promoted by John Howson, appearing with other singers.
1997 Milwaukee Musicfest, promoted by Mary June Hanrahan.
**SELECTED BROADCASTS AND/OR RECORDED WORK:**
1995 'Fleadh' for RTÉ.
1995 'Lumen' (interval piece in Eurovision) for RTÉ/Virgin.
1997 'Síbín' for TnaG.
**SELECTED REVIEWS** (since January 1994):
1995 Feakle Traditional Singing Festival Programme.
1996 Le Télégramme (L'Imaginaire Irlandais).
1997 Ennistymon Traditional Singing Festival Programme.
**PRIZES/AWARDS/APPOINTMENTS:**
Various prizes for Séan-nós singing from An tÓireachtas and drama awards from Comhaltás Náisiúnta Drámaíochta.
**TRAINING AND/OR QUALIFICATIONS:**
From 1984 to 1987 B Ed from Coláiste Phádraig.
**REGULARLY PERFORMS WITH:**
Ceolfhoireann Tíre na hÉireann and Vox Gadelica.
**AVAILABILITY:**
General.
**ADDITIONAL INFORMATION:**
Researchs, records, produces and presents a radio programme on traditional music, singing and folklore. Organises the festival 'Sean-nós Cois Life' which promotes traditional singing. Has presented various singing workshops and classes, and has appeared on stage, film and television.

# Anne-Marie O'Farrell *Singer*

**Contact:** Ms Anne Marie O'Farrell
28 Grange Manor Drive
Rathfarnham
Dublin 16
**Tel:** +353 1 4931873
*See concert harp page 8.*

# Lillis Ó Laoire *Singer*

**Contact:** Mr Lillis Ó Laoire
Department of Languages
University of Limerick
Ireland
**Tel/Fax:** +353 61 202159 / +353 61 202556
**Email:** lillis.olaoire@ul.ie

**KEY IRISH PERFORMANCES** (since January 1994):
8.94 Christian Brothers, Westland Row Church, Dublin, promoted by Missa Gadelica/Michéal Ó Súilleabháin, appearing with Irish Concert Orchestra, Evelyn Glennie and Michéal Ó Suilleabháin.
**KEY PERFORMANCES OUTSIDE IRELAND** (since January 1994):
1995 Stornoway, promoted by the Gaelic Arts Project, appearing with other Irish singers.
**SELECTED BROADCASTS AND/OR RECORDED WORK:**
1996 'Bláthgach Géag Dá dTig' for Cló Iar-Chonnachta.
1997 'Datgan' for Fflach Records, Wales.
1997 'Echoings' for Cló Iar-Chonnachta.
**PRIZES/AWARDS/APPOINTMENTS:**
From 1991 to 1994, Prize winner, Corn Uí Riada at An tÓireachtas.
1994 Winner, Corn Uí Riada at An tÓireachtas.
**AVAILABILITY:**
General.

**ADDITIONAL INFORMATION:**
A singer in the tradition of the Donegal Gaeltacht - (the northern séan-nós tradition).

# Iarla Ó Lionáird *Singer*

**Contact:** Iarla Ó Lionáird
28, Belgrave Square East
Monkstown
Co Dublin
**Mobiles:** +353 86 471075 / +353 87 2225671
(David Caren, agent)

*"Count yourself lucky to hear a celtic artist like this, once in your lifetime"*
12.97, Time Out, New York (Susan Anday)

**KEY PERFORMANCES OUTSIDE IRELAND** (since January 1994):
1996 Womad, UK.
1997 Carnegie Hall, New York, Glastonbury Rock Festival, Central Park, New York, Adelaide, Australia, Yokohama, Japan.
**SELECTED BROADCASTS AND/OR RECORDED WORK:**
1996 Sound Magic Vol I with Afro Celt Sound System.
1997 The Seven Steps to Mercy on Virgin Real World.
'Later with Jools Holland' for BBC.
**REGULARLY PERFORMS WITH:**
Afro Celt Sound System.

# Sylvia O'Regan *Singer*

**Contact:** Sylvia O'Regan
169, Glenageary Park
Dún Laoghaire
Co. Dublin
**Tel:** +353 1 2854108
*See mezzo-soprano page 105.*

# Brian O'Rourke *Singer*

**Contact:** Dr Brian O'Rourke
36, Lakeshore Drive
Renmore
Co Galway
**Tel:** +353 91 757251

**KEY IRISH PERFORMANCES** (since January 1994):
12.96 Belfast, BBC Orchestra.
2.97 University of Limerick, promoted by the Irish World Music Centre, appearing with Niall Vallely.
**SELECTED BROADCASTS AND/OR RECORDED WORK:**
1992 'When I grew up' for Camus Productions.
3.97 'Late Late Show' for RTÉ.
**AVAILABILITY:**
Weekends.
**ADDITIONAL INFORMATION:**
Singer in the traditional mode. A specialist in 'jocoserious' songs, and his piece - 'Chantal de Champignon' - has achieved cult status with a 'Club Chantal' existing for its devotees. Holds a summer school and winter school each year.

# Niamh Parsons *Singer*

**Contact:** Niamh Parsons
117, Grange Abbey Crescent
Donaghmede
Dublin 13
or
Artistic Upstarts
65A Dundas Street
Edinburgh GR3 6RS
Scotland
**Tel/Fax:** +353 1 8473673
**Email:** upstarts@evolve. ftech. co.uk
*See Niamh Parsons and the Loose Connections page 264.*

# Eimear Quinn *Singer*

**Contact:** Ms Eimear Quinn
c/o Pat Egan
24, Merchants Court
Merchants Quay
Dublin 8
**Tel/Fax:** +353 1 6797701 or +353 1 6798572 / +353 1 6797495
*See soprano page 96.*

# John Spillane *Singer*

**Contact:** Mr John Spillane
1, Idaville
Sharman
Crawford Street
Cork
**Tel:** +353 21 315091
*See guitar page 225.*

# Grace Toland *Singer*

**Contact:** Ms Grace Toland
24, Garden Village Drive
Kilpedder, Co Wicklow
**Tel/Fax:** +353 1 2819091 / +353 1 2811608
**Email:** doyleb@iol.ie

**KEY IRISH PERFORMANCES** (since January 1994):
From 1995 to 1996 Cushendall, promoted by the Heart of the Glens Festival, appearing with other traditional singers.
1996 Trinity Inn, Dublin, promoted by Goilín Singers Club.
1996 Ionad Cois Locha, promoted by Tionscoil Lugh, appearing with Dermot Toland (guitar).
1997 Inishowen, Co Donegal, promoted by Inishowen Traditional Singers Circle, appearing with national and international traditional singers.
**KEY PERFORMANCES OUTSIDE IRELAND** (since January 1994):
1995 Dorset, promoted by John Waltham, appearing with British and Irish traditional singers.
1997 Sidmouth, promoted Sidmouth International Festival of Folk Arts, appearing with Goilín Singers Club.
**SELECTED BROADCASTS AND/OR RECORDED WORK:**
1993 ITMA Archive Recordings for Irish Traditional Music Archive.
1994 'Path Across the Ocean' for Wave Length.
1997 'High Reel' for RTÉ.
**PRIZES/AWARDS/APPOINTMENTS:**
From 1981 to 1982 Ulster Winner (unaccompanied Irish singing) from CCÉ.

From 1991 to 1993, Tutor (seminars) in traditional singing at the Department of Music, Trinity College, Dublin.
**AVAILABILITY:**
General.
**ADDITIONAL INFORMATION:**
Since 1980 has been a regular performer at professional sessions, concerts, workshops and recordings, both formal and informal. Wide repertoire of traditional songs but concentrates mainly on English songs of the Inishowen Peninsula.

# Áine Uí Cheallaigh *Singer*

**Contact:** Ms Áine Uí Cheallaigh
Cnocán an Phaoraigh
Rinn Ó gCuanach
Co Waterford
**Tel:** +353 58 46201
**Other instruments:** Fiddle.

*"The sheer beauty, resplendence and clarity of her voice causes the listener to sit up and take notice"* 1.97 Irish Music Magazine.

**KEY IRISH PERFORMANCES** (since January 1994):
1995 The Point, Dublin, solo singer in 'Riverdance' by Bill Whelan.
1996 National Concert Hall, Dublin, soloist with the RTÉ Concert Orchestra.
1996 Cork Folk Festival.
1997 Tour of Ireland promoted by Music Network, appearing with Kevin Burke and Máirtín Ó Connor.
**KEY PERFORMANCES OUTSIDE IRELAND** (since January 1994):
8.94 and 8.96 Sidmouth Folk Festival, England, appearing with 'Any Old Time', with the Voice Squad.
1996 Lyons, France, promoted by L'Imaginaire Irlandais, with the Voice Squad.
**SELECTED BROADCASTS AND/OR RECORDED WORK:**
1992 'Idir Dhá Chomhairle' ('In Two Minds') for Gael-Linn.
1995 'Riverdance' for Celtic Heartbeat.
1997 'Who Fears to Speak' for Enigma Productions Limited.
**SELECTED REVIEWS** (since January 1994):
1.97 Irish Music Magazine.
**PRIZES/AWARDS/APPOINTMENTS:**
1990 and 1992 Awarded Corn Uí Riada Prize by An tOireachtas.
**TRAINING AND/OR QUALIFICATIONS:**
1978 to 1981, BA Music and Irish from University College, Dublin.
**REGULARLY PERFORMS WITH:**
Frankie Lane (guitar/dobro).
**AVAILABILITY:**
General.

# Fintan Vallely *Singer*

**Contact:** Mr Fintan Vallely
15, Castlewood Terrace
Rathmines
Dublin 6
**Tel/Fax:** +353 1 4972979
**Email:**

*"Witty lyrics consummately sung - this devastating divilment is the last word in 'diddlydee'!"* 12.88 Belfast Telegraph

*See flute page 220.*

# Róisin White *Singer*

**Contact:** Ms Róisin White
5, Messancy Place
Cavanacaw
Co Antrim BT60 2HN
Northern Ireland
**Tel:** +44 1861 526541

*"A meaty repertoire of strong songs, secure, firm intonation - punchy delivery"*
10/11.92 Folk Roots Magazine.

**KEY IRISH PERFORMANCES** (since January 1994):
9.94 Carraig-on-Bannon, promoted by J Murphy Committee.
4.95 University of Limerick, promoted by Míchéal Ó Súilleabháin.
6.96 Cushendall, Co Antrim, promoted by local folk/singers club.
11.96 Dublin, promoted by Sean-nós Cois Life, appearing with Vincent Campbell.
**KEY PERFORMANCES OUTSIDE IRELAND** (since January 1994):
6.94 Zurich, promoted by Eliz.
Zollinger, appearing with Treasa Ní Mhiolláin.
8.95 Sidmouth, Devon, promoted by the Sidmouth Festival.
7.96 London, promoted by the Musical Traditions Club.
**SELECTED BROADCASTS AND/OR RECORDED WORK:**
1992 'First of my Rambles' on UT126 cassette.
1996 'Pure Drop' for RTÉ.
**SELECTED REVIEWS** (since January 1994):
11.92 Irish Times.
11.92 Belfast Telegraph.
**PRIZES/AWARDS/APPOINTMENTS:**
Past member of the Irish Traditional Music Archive and a member of the Ennistymon Singing Committee.
**AVAILABILITY:**
Weekends, school holidays.
**ADDITIONAL INFORMATION:**
Choice of songs are of Ulster origin in the English language but also sings in Irish. Presents/hosts workshops at many gatherings and also undertakes adjudicating at Fleadhanna and Feiseanna.

# Stephen Wickham *Singer*

**Contact:** Stephen Wickham
P.O. Box 282
Sligo
**Tel:** +353 1 4966341

*See violin page 300.*

# Desie Wilkinson *Singer*

**Contact:** Mr Desie Wilkinson
41, Oaklawns
Castletroy
Limerick
**Tel/Fax:** +353 61 335403 / +353 61 330316

*See flute page 220.*

## Rosemary Woods *Singer*

**Contact:** Miss Rosemary Woods
6, Abbacy Road
Ardkeen, Portaferry
Co Down, BT22 1HH
Northern Ireland
**Tel:** +44 12477 28747
**Other instruments:** Guitar.

**KEY IRISH PERFORMANCES** (since January 1994):
14.10.95 Omagh Town Hall, Co Tyrone, promoted by D Hull appearing with Brian Keenan.
**KEY PERFORMANCES OUTSIDE IRELAND** (since January 1994):
10.95 Tour of Scotland, promoted by Doris Ronguie.
**SELECTED RECORDED WORK:**
From 1991 to 1992 'Walking Together', Album CD, Tape, for Spring Records, Rostrevor, Co Down.
1995 'Go it Alone Together', CD, Tape, Spring Records, Rostrevor, Co Down.
**PRIZES/AWARDS/APPOINTMENTS:**
8.92 Ist Prize, Letterkenny Song Competition.
**REGULARLY PERFORMS WITH:**
Siobhan S Kates, Guitar.
**AVAILABILITY:**
General.
**ADDITIONAL INFORMATION:**
Singer and song writer of contemporary folk music.

# TRADITIONAL GROUPS

**Most traditional group playing is informally organised at sessions amongst traditional musicians. In recent years with the increasing popularity of Irish traditional music, there has been an increase in the number of regularly performing groups with an established membership.**

## Altan

**Contact:** c/o Mr Ciarán Tourish
26, St John's Park Avenue
Sandymount, Dublin 4
**Mobile/Tel/Fax:** +353 87 542054 / +353 1 2839585
**Email:** tourish@indigo.ie

*"Thought by many to be the finest trad combo working today, seemlessly blend dazzling instrumental prowess and the gorgeously delicate vocals of [Mairéad Ní Mhaonaigh]"*

1995 Chicago Weekly.

**FORMED:** 1985.
**GROUP MEMBERS:**
Dermot Byrne (accordion), Ciarán Curran (bouzouki), Mark Kelly (guitar), Mairéad Ní Mhaonaigh (fiddle, vocals), Daithí Sproule (guitar, vocals), Ciaran Tourish (fiddle, whistles).
**KEY IRISH PERFORMANCES** (since January 1994):
1995 Big Top, Galway.
1996 Millstreet Festival, Co Cork.
1996 Olympia, Dublin.
12.96 Belfast Waterfront Hall.
**KEY PERFORMANCES OUTSIDE IRELAND** (since January 1994):
1995 Great American Music Hall, San Francisco; UCLA, Los Angeles and Berkeley Performance Theatre, Boston, USA.
1996 Town Hall, New York.
1997 Royal Festival Hall and Barbican Centre, London.
**SELECTED BROADCASTS AND/OR RECORDED WORK:**
1995 'Island Angel' for Green Linnet.
1996 'Blackwater' for Virgin International.
1997 'Runaway Sunday' for Virgin International.
**PRIZES/AWARDS/APPOINTMENTS:**
1995 One of 'Best 100 albums ever' with 'Island Angel' (Q Magazine).
1996 Hot Press Music Award.
Recipient of the Best 'Celtic Group' category award from the National Association of Independent Record Distributors, USA.
**REGULARLY PERFORMS WITH:**
Mary Black, Paul Brady, Donal Lunny, Sharon Shannon.
**AVAILABILITY:**
General.

## Anam

**Contact:** Mr Brian Ó hÉadhra
'An Glas' Tibradden
Dublin 16
**Tel/Fax:** +353 1 4937087

*"Exemplary musicianship provides tight multi-layered arrangements as the group explores a balanced repertoire of both traditional and original tunes and songs"* 8.95/9.95 Dirty Linen.

**FORMED:** 1993.
**GROUP MEMBERS:**
Myles Farrell (bouzouki), Aimée Leonard (vocals, bodhrán), Treasa Ní Earcáin (button accordion, flute and whistle), and Brian Ó headhra (vocals, guitar, harmonica).
**KEY IRISH PERFORMANCES** (since January 1994):
16.9.95 John Field Room, National Concert Hall, Dublin, appearing with De Jembe and others.
20.9.95 The Lobby, Cork.
9.10.95 Harcourt Hotel, Dublin.
16.11.95 Charlemont Hotel, Armagh.
**KEY PERFORMANCES OUTSIDE IRELAND** (since January 1994):
4.95 Shetland Folk Festival, Scotland.
8.11.95 Edinburgh Folk Club, Scotland.
From 20.11.95 to 23.11.95 Celts in Kent Festival, England.
27.11.95 'The Swan', Stockwell, London, England.
**SELECTED BROADCASTS AND/OR RECORDED WORK:**
8.94 'Anam' for Ceirníní Anam.
1.95 'Saoirse' for Ceirníní Anam (two tracks from 'Saoirse' also feature on the compilation album of Women singers - 'Sisters 1 - Folksong'.
**SELECTED REVIEWS** (since January 1994):
7.95 Hot Press.
9.95/10.95 The Living Tradition.
**PRIZES/AWARDS/APPOINTMENTS:**
8.93 Best Band, awarded by Lorient Interceltic Festival, Brittany, France.
**AVAILABILITY:**
General.
**ADDITIONAL INFORMATION:**
Primarily play at folk arts festivals, arts centres and in theatres. Also offer workshops in traditional instrumentation, folklore, ethnomusicology and storytelling.

## Anúna

**Contact:** Michael McGlynn
PO Box 4468, Churchtown
Dublin 14
**Tel/Fax:** +353 1 2835533
**Email:** info@anuna.ie
**WWW:** http://www.anuna.ie
*See choirs and choral groups page 153.*

# Any Old Time

**Contact:** Mr Dave Hennessy
Cros Ard
Crosshaven
Co Cork
**Tel/Fax:** +353 21 831386

**FORMED:** 1980.
**GROUP MEMBERS:**
Matt Cranitch (fiddle), Mick Daly (guitar, vocals, banjo), Dave Hennessy (melodeon).
**KEY IRISH PERFORMANCES** (since January 1994):
10.11.96 Belfast Folk Festival, appearing with the Fallen Angels.
1997 'Geantraí' and 'Sult' for TnaG.
**KEY PERFORMANCES OUTSIDE IRELAND** (since January 1994):
3.96 Vienna, Austria, promoted by Manfred Hanus, Vienna.
3.96 Shetland Folk Festival, appearing with Peter Rowan (singer).
8.96 Sidmouth Folk Festival, appearing with Chris Smithers.
**SSELECTED BROADCASTS AND/OR RECORDED WORK:**
1982 'Any Old Time' for Mulligan.
1989 'Phoenix' for Dara.
1995 'Crossing' for Dara.
**REGULARLY PERFORMS WITH:** Séamus Creagh.
**AVAILABILITY:**
General.
*See Dave Hennessy page 201, Matt Cranitch page 205.*

# At the Racket

**Contact:** John Carty
Knockroe
Boyle
Co Roscommon
**Tel/Fax:** +353 79 68063

**FORMED:** 1997.
**GROUP MEMBERS:**
John Carty (fiddle, banjo, flute), Brian McGrath (piano, banjo, mandolin), Garry O'Briain (mandocello, guitar, vocals), Séamus O'Donnell (saxophone, flute, vocals).
**KEY IRISH PERFORMANCES** (since January 1994):
20.5.97 Corn Mill Theatre, Carrigallen.
21.5.97 The Victoria, Tramore.
25.5.97 Matt Molloy's, Westport.
26.5.97 Harcourt Hotel, Dublin.
**AVAILABILITY:**
Unlimited (prepared to travel any distance).
**ADDITIONAL INFORMATION:**
The band takes its name from a 1920's recording by the Flanagan Brothers. The overall theme of the band is based on music recorded during that era.
*See John Carty page 204.*

# Barrowside

**Contact:** Ms Yvonne Stacey
Shanbogh
New Ross
Co Wexford
**Tel/Fax:** +353 51 22006 / +353 51 25240

*"They sang what people want to hear ... intelligent lyrics, interesting songs, fabulous harmonies and they're exciting live",*
10.93 New Ross Standard (People Newspapers).

**GROUP MEMBERS:**
Ollie Grace (vocals, guitar and whistle), Sean Reidy (accordion, vocals), Yvonne Stacey (vocals), Jack Stacey (vocals, guitar, percussion), Bob Van-Son (vocals, guitar), Maria Van-Son (clarinet).
**KEY IRISH PERFORMANCES** (since January 1994):
7.94 Cleeere's Theatre, Kilkenny, promoted by John Cleere.
9.94 Whelan's, Dublin, promoted by Round Tower music, appearing with Katie Moffatt.
12.94 The Viking, New Ross, promoted by Barrowside, appearing with Ronnie Drew.
4.95 Bewley's Cafe Theatre, Dublin.
**KEY PERFORMANCES OUTSIDE IRELAND** (since January 1994):
2.94 Cruise Cafe, Oslo.
2.94 Winter Olympics, Lillehammor, promoted by the Irish Trade Board.
4.94 La Renaissance, Hartford, USA, promoted by the JFK Trust, appearing with John McNally.
**SELECTED BROADCASTS AND/OR RECORDED WORK:**
1993 'The Wash and The Way', for Round Tower Music.
1995 'The Hidden Corner', for Round Tower Music.
**SELECTED REVIEWS:**
6.94 People Newspapers.
6.94 Evening Herald.
29.7.94 Irish World, UK.
**PRIZES/AWARDS/APPOINTMENTS:**
5.92 1st Prize for the regional folk competition sponsored by Smithwicks, Mac Ivers Inn, New Ross.
**AVAILABILITY:**
General.
**ADDITIONAL INFORMATION:**
Performs predominatly its own original contemporary material. Have appeared on 'The Gay Byrne Radio Show, and 'Ireland Tonight' for RTÉ and Boston Public Radio.

# Begley and Cooney

**Contact:** Séamus Begley
Baile na bPúc
Baile na nGall,
Trá Lí, Co Kerry
**Tel:** +353 66 55155
**Tel/Fax:** +353 66 55155 / +353 66 59779

# Begley Sisters

**Contact:** Eilín Begley
Loughnane, Caulstown
Dunboyne, Co Meath
**Tel/Fax:** +353 1 8256337

*"Versatile"* Cló Iar-Chonnachta Booklet.

**FORMED:** 1960's.
**GROUP MEMBERS:**
Cian Begley (fiddle, electric guitar), Órna Begley, (violin, fiddle), Siona Begley, (violin, fiddle).
**KEY IRISH PERFORMANCES** (since January 1994):
9.94/95/96 Clifden Community Arts Festival, Cork Folk Festival and Belfast Anderstown Festival.
**KEY PERFORMANCES OUTSIDE IRELAND** (since January 1994):
5.96 Madrid, Irish tour with other artists.
7.96 Amsterdam, multi-cultural folk festival.
8.96 USA tour.
**SELECTED BROADCASTS AND/OR RECORDED WORK:**
1992 CD's for Gael-Linn.
Music for 'Secret of Roan Inis' and 'Draiocht'.
**PRIZES/AWARDS/APPOINTMENTS:**
1995 Siona Begley appointed violinist in Residence at the Toronto Music Academy.

**TRAINING AND/OR QUALIFICATIONS:**
From 1985 to 1990 Siona Begley attended the Liszt Academy in Budapest, Hungary.
From 1992 to 1995, Cian Begley attended Ballyfermot Rock School.
Since 1990, Órna has studied in Austria.
**AVAILABILITY:**
General.
**ADDITIONAL INFORMATION:**
Extensive repertoire.

# Belfast Harp Orchestra

**Contact:** Janet Harbison
Brookfield Mill
333, Crumlin Road
Belfast BT14 7EA
Northern Ireland
**Tel/Fax:** +44 1232 352555 / +44 1232 740288
**Email:** jharbison@harps.dnet.co.uk
*See large performing groups page 143.*

# Bonfire

**Contact:** Ms Ruth O'Sullivan
6, Clarinda Park East
Dún Laoghaire
Co Dublin
**Tel/Fax:** +353 1 2804501 or +353 1 2807268 / +353 1 2301406

**FORMED:** 1993.
**GROUP MEMBERS:**
Harry Long (whistles, guitar, voice), Ruth O'Sullivan (flute, whistle), John Sweeney (guitar, bodhrán).
**AVAILABILITY:**
General.
*See Ruth O'Sullivan page 18.*

# Boys of the Lough

**Contact:** Mr Dave Richardson
31, Fountainhall Road
Edinburgh EH9 2LN
Scotland
**Tel/Fax:** +44 131 6624992 / +44 131 6620956
**Email:** botl@compuserve.com

*"A benchmark of authenticity .... brimming with ferocious artistry .... one of the most powerful tonics going"* 1989 Boston Phoenix.

**FOUNDED:** 1967.
**GROUP MEMBERS:**
Aly Bain (fiddle), Cathal McConnell (vocals, flute, whistle), Chris Newman (guitar), Christy O'Leary (vocals, uilleann pipes, whistle, harmonica), Dave Richardson (mandolin, cittern, concertina, button accordion).
**KEY IRISH PERFORMANCES** (since January 1994):
11.95 Belfast Festival at Queen's.
1996 Ballymena Arts Festival, Co Antrim.
1996 Ardhowen Theatre, Enniskillen, Co Fermanagh.
**KEY PERFORMANCES OUTSIDE IRELAND** (since January 1994):
10.96 Beijing, People's Republic of China, promoted by the China International Cultural Exchange Centre.
12.96 Fairbanks, Alaska, promoted by the Arts Council of Alaska.
7.97 Falun Folk Festival, Sweden.
7.97 Kaustinen Festival, Finland.
**SELECTED BROADCASTS AND/OR RECORDED WORK:**
1990 'Live at Carnegie Hall' for Lough Records.
1992 'The Fairhills of Ireland' for Lough Records.
11.94 'The Day Dawn' for Lough Records.
**SELECTED REVIEWS** (since January 1994):
21.8.95 The Scotsman.
**PRIZES/AWARDS/APPOINTMENTS:**
1983 Freedom of the cities of El Paso, Texas and Reading, Pennsylvania.
1994 Aly Bain received an MBE from the British Government for Service to Folk Music.
**AVAILABILITY:**
General.
**ADDITIONAL INFORMATION:**
Group comprises of players between the two strands of celtic tradition (Scottish/Irish). Uses acoustic instruments (traditionally played).

# Máire Breatnach Band

**Contact:** c/o Mr Steve Dunford
6, The Avenue
Boden Park
Rathfarnham
Dublin 16
**Tel/Fax:** +353 1 4947615 or 4932358 / +353 1 4931707

*"A unique and atmospheric collection of original pieces ... her ability to compose original music is truly remarkable"*
Bill Whelan, composer of Riverdance.

**FORMED:** 1993.
**MUSICAL/ARTISTIC DIRECTOR:**
Máire Breatnach.
**GROUP MEMBERS:**
Máire Breatnach (fiddle, viola, keyboards, synthesizer, vocals), Conor Byrne (flute, whistles), Steve Dunford (bodhrán, percussion, vocals), Niall Ó Callanáin (bouzouki, vocals), Gavin Rolsten (guitar and vocals).
**KEY PERFORMANCES OUTSIDE IRELAND** (since January 1994):
9.95 Gdansk, Poland.
9.96 The Hague, The Netherlands, promoted by the Crossing Border Festival.
10.96 Circus Krone, Munich, Germany, promoted by the Irish Folk Festival.
4.97 The Barbican, London.
**SELECTED BROADCASTS AND/OR RECORDED WORK:**
'Late Late Show' for RTÉ.
'Bringing it all Back Home' for BBC/Hummingbird.
'Riverdance' for Tyrone Productions.
**ADDITIONAL INFORMATION:**
Has performed in the Point Depot and Belfast Waterfront Hall with Donal Lunny and friends.

# Bumblebees

**Contact:** Bumblebees
10, Mountain View
Ennis, Co Clare
**Tel/Fax:** +353 91 528839

*"In essence, bumblebees encapsulate the current spirit of fun, adventure and diversity within Irish traditional music."* 6.97 Irish Music.

**FORMED:** 1996.
**GROUP MEMBERS:**
Dr Liz Doherty (fiddle), Laoise Kelly (harp, fiddle), Colette O'Leary (accordion), Mary Shannon (banjo, mandolin, mandola, fiddle)
**KEY IRISH PERFORMANCES** (since January 1994):
From 20.2.97 to 3.3.97, Galway, Cork, Limerick, 'Celtic Flame Festival'.
3.5.97 The Fiddler of Oriel, Monaghan.
14.5.97 The Lobby, Cork.
28.5.97 Róisín Dubh, Galway.
**KEY PERFORMANCES OUTSIDE IRELAND** (since January 1994):
4-13.4.97 Barbican Centre, London, promoted by 'From the Heart' Festival.
**SELECTED BROADCASTS AND/OR RECORDED WORK:**
11.96 'The Kelly Family Special' for Sky and satellite television.
9.1.97 'Síbín' for TnaG.
26.2.97 'Sult' for Hummingbird/TnaG.
**AVAILABILITY:**
General.
**ADDITIONAL INFORMATION:** Are all tutors of their various instruments.
*See Liz Doherty page 207, Laoise Kelly page 228, Colette O'Leary page 194.*

# Calico

**Contact:** Mr Diarmaid Moynihan
65, The Rise
Bishopstown
Cork
**Tel:** +353 21 542958

**FORMED:** 1994.
**GROUP MEMBERS:**
Ed Boyd (bouzouki), Donal Clancy (bouzouki), Tola Custy (fiddle), Pat Marsh (bouzouki), Deirdre Moynihan (fiddle), Diarmaid Moynihan (uilleann pipes, whistle), Donncha Moynihan (guitar).
**KEY IRISH PERFORMANCES** (since January 1994):
9.95 Cork Folk Festival, appearing with Niamh Parsons and Máire Breatnach.
9.95 Mullaghbawn Folk Club, promoted by Gerry O'Hanlon.
11.95 Lobby Cork, promoted by Pat Conway, appearing with Niamh Parsons and Máire Breatnach.
1.96 Harcourt Hotel, Dublin, promoted by Mary Cashin.
**KEY PERFORMANCES OUTSIDE IRELAND** (since January 1994):
6.95 Haapauasi Folk Festival, Finland, promoted by Timo Hanula, appearing with Laurie Lee and friends.
12.95 Tour of Norway, promoted by Roots Music Agency, Norway.
**SELECTED REVIEWS** (since January 1994):
10.94 Living Tradition Folk Magazine.
1.96 Irish Times.
**AVAILABILITY:**
General, summer and Easter preferable.
*See Diarmuid Moynihan page 237.*

# Céide

**Contact:** Mr John McGlynn
69, Kingscourt
Parnell Street
Dublin 1
**Tel/Fax:** +353 1 8786468

**MEMBERS OF GROUP:**
Miriam Blennerhassett (vocal), Frances Cranny (vocal, flute), Deirdre Gilsenan (vocal), John McGlynn (vocal, guitar, lute), Maev Ní Mhaolchatha (vocal, harp), Garrath Patterson (vocal, flute), and others.
**ADDITIONAL INFORMATION:**
Pool of fourteen members, which combine singers, instrumentalists and dancers, in one integrated show.
*See Deirdre Gilsenan page 88, Méav Ní Mhaolchatha page 94.*

# Céoltóiri Bunraite *(Bunratty Singers)*

**Contact:** Joan Sheehy
Ballycalla
Newmarket-on-Fergus
Co Clare
**Tel:** +353 61 362730

**FORMED:** 1987.
**GROUP MEMBERS:**
Tim Schinnick (accordian and piano), Joan Sheehy (fiddle), Ger Stack (bódhran), Deirdre Stephenson (harp).
**KEY IRISH PERFORMANCES** (since January 1994):
1994 Festival of the Rose of Tralee, Tralee, Kerry, promoted by ABTA.
1994 Dromoland Castle, Co Clare, promoted by ABTA.
1994 Bunratty Castle, Co Clare, promoted by ABTA.
**KEY PERFORMANCES OUTSIDE IRELAND** (since January 1994):
Have toured throughout Germany, Holland and France.
**SELECTED BROADCASTS AND/OR RECORDED WORK:**
Numerous recordings for television and radio.
**PRIZES/AWARDS/APPOINTMENTS:**
Appointed to perform at St Patricks Day state banquets in Seattle, Washington and Dubai.
**TRAINING AND/OR QUALIFICATIONS:**
Members are all professional entertainers and teachers of music, song and dance.
**AVAILABILITY:**
Evenings, from November to March.

# Chulrua

**Contact:** Mr Paddy O'Brien
3441, 23rd Avenue South
Minneapolis
MN 55407
USA
**Tel/Fax:** +1 612 721 7452
**Email:** paddyob@mci2000.com

*"... They played with an elegance, grace and spaciousness that really showed this kind of music off..."* 25.4.97 Caroline Foty, Baltimore, Maryland for Conradh na Gaeilge, IRTRAD listserv/Internet.

**FORMED:** 1996.
**GROUP MEMBERS:**
Michael Cooney (uilleann pipes, whistle), Pat Egan (guitar, vocals), Michael Cooney (uilleann pipes and whistle), Paddy O'Brien (2 row button accordion).
**KEY PERFORMANCES OUTSIDE IRELAND** (since January 1994):
10.96 Center for Popular Music, promoted by Middle Tennessee State University, Murfreesboro.
10.96 Kentuck Festival of the Arts Tuscalooosa, Alabama, USA.
3.97 Irish Music Academy of Cleveland, Ohio, USA.
4.97 Irish Arts Center, New York, USA.
**SELECTED BROADCASTS AND/OR RECORDED WORK:**
6.96 'Chulrua at the Skylight Exchange', live promotional recording at Chapel Hill, North Carolina.
10.96 Live promotion at the Station Inn, Nashville, Tennessee.
4.97 Studio recording.
**SELECTED REVIEWS** (since January 1994):
9.4.97 IRTRAD listserv/internet (Mike Dugger).
**AVAILABILITY:**
General.
*See Paddy O'Brien page 193.*

# Cran

**Contact:** Mr Ronan Browne
Mount Slaney
Stratford-on-Slaney
Co Wicklow
**Tel/Fax:** +353 45 404873
**Email:** roro@tinet.ie

*"They combine multi instrumental virtuosity with great reservoires of talent and ingenuity ... one of the most exciting bands in Europe at the moment"* Irish Times.

**FORMED:** 1984.
**GROUP MEMBERS:**
Ronan Browne (uilleann pipes, whistles) Séan Corcoran, (vocals, bouzouki, guitar) Desi Wilkinson (flute, whistles, vocals).
**SELECTED BROADCASTS AND/OR RECORDED WORK:**
1993 'Crooked Stair', for CBM.
Second album Black Black Black for Claddagh Records.
**REGULARLY PERFORMS WITH:**
Kevin Glackin, Triona Ní Dhomhnaill.
**AVAILABILITY:**
General.
*See Ronan Browne page 235, Desi Wilkinson page 220, Séan Corcoran page 200.*

# Ellen Cranitch and Anne-Marie O'Farrell

**Contact:** Ms Ellen Cranitch
33, Westfield Road
Harolds Cross
Dublin 6
**Tel/Fax:** +353 1 4923486

**GROUP MEMBERS:**
Ellen Cranitch (flutes) and Anne-Marie O'Farrell (harp).
**ADDITIONAL INFORMATION:**
A newly established flute and harp duo, presenting music from the traditional and jazz repertoire. Emphasis on developing the harp in a jazz context.
*See Ellen Cranitch page 271 and Anne-Marie O'Farrell page 8.*

# Dark Horse

**Contact:** Mr Niall Crehan
110, Courtown Park
Kilcock, Co Kildare
**Tel/Mobile:** +353 1 6287030 / +353 87 481933

**FORMED:** 1996.
**GROUP MEMBERS:**
Niall Crehan (fiddle), Mick Dempsey (bodhrán, vocals), John Dooley (guitar, vocals), Roger Mularkey (flute), Daragh O'Rourke (fiddle), Lisa O'Rourke (concertina).
**KEY IRISH PERFORMANCES** (since January 1994):
4.97 Kilcock, Co Kildare for Raidió na Gaeltachta.
**SELECTED BROADCASTS AND/OR RECORDED WORK:**
7.97 Willie Clancy 'Sessions' for RTÉ.
**AVAILABILITY:**
General.
*See Niall Crehan page 206.*

# De Dannan

**Contact:** Mr Frankie Gavin
Ardnasillagh
Oughterard
Co Galway
**Tel:** +353 91 552545

*"Any discussion of the evolution of Irish traditional music must include the enormous contribution of De Dannan"* Wall Street Journal.

**FORMED:** 1972.
**GROUP MEMBERS:**
Alec Finn (bouzouki, guitar), Tommie Flemming (voice), Frankie Gavin (fiddle, flute, tin whistle), Derek Hickey (button accordion), Colm Murphy (bodhrán).
**KEY PERFORMANCES OUTSIDE IRELAND** (since January 1994):
1996 International Boot Fair, Frankfurt, Germany.
**SELECTED BROADCASTS AND/OR RECORDED WORK:**
1987 'The Best of De Dannan' for Shanachie.
1991 'Set in Harlem' for Bees Knees and Green Linnet.
1996 'Hibernian Rhapsody' for Bees Knees and Green Linnet.
**AVAILABILITY:**
General.
**ADDITIONAL INFORMATION:**
Have won three best album awards. Encourage links between other musical genres and cultures.
*See Frankie Gavin page 207, Alec Finn page 200.*

# Déanta

**Contact:** Eoghan O'Brien
77, Main Street
Portglenone
Co Antrim BT44 8HR
**Tel/Fax:** +44 1 266 821333 / +44 1 266 822181

*"A part time band with a full time attitude and an international reputation to match"*
22.11.94 Irish Times.

**FORMED:** 1980.
**GROUP MEMBERS:**
Mary Dillon (vocals), Deirdre Havlin (flute, whistles), Rosie Mulholland (keyboards, fiddle), Eoghan O'Brien (guitar (acoustic), celtic harp), Kate O'Brien (fiddle, viola), Clodagh Warnock (bouzouki, fiddle, bodhrán).
**KEY IRISH PERFORMANCES** (since January 1994):
30.7.94 Ballyshannon Folk Festival, promoted by Anthony Travers, appearing with the Sands Family and Sharon Shannon.
17.11.94 Belfast Festival at Queen's, promoted by Jim Sheridan.
31.3.95 'Anderson on the Box' for BBC.
30.8.96 Belfast Folk Festival, Elmwood Hall, Belfast, promoted by Nigel Martin, appearing with Eileen Ivers.
**KEY PERFORMANCES OUTSIDE IRELAND** (since January 1994):
12.7.95 Falun Folk Festival, Sweden, promoted by Magnus Backstrom.
26.8.95 Tander Festival, Denmark, promoted by Carsten Pandoro.
5.1.96 Celtic Connections Festival, Glasgow, promoted by Glasgow Royal Concert Hall and Colin Heinz.
25.7.96 Viljandi Folk Festival, Estonia, promoted by Ando Kiviberg.
**SELECTED BROADCASTS AND/OR RECORDED WORK:**
1990 'Déanta' for Spring Records (licensed to Green Linnet 1993).
1994 'Ready for the Storm' for Green Linnet.
1997 'Whisper of a Secret' for Green Linnet.
**SELECTED REVIEWS** (since January 1994):
12.94 Folk Roots (album review of 'Ready for the Storm').
23.12.94 Irish News.

**PRIZES/AWARDS/APPOINTMENTS:**
1980's 1st Prize 'Opportunity Knocks' at Ballyshannon Folk Festival.
4.85 Winners of Slógadh, (Under 21) Traditional Group.
**AVAILABILITY:**
Weekends.
*See Eoghan O'Brien page 224, Kate O'Brien page 211.*

# Dervish

**Contact:** Brian McDonagh / Felip Carbonell
Cairns Hill
Aughamore Near
Co Sligo
**Tel/Fax:** +353 71 60334
**Email:** whirling@iol.ie

*"Live in Palma"... simply a brilliant and uncluttered testimonial to music imagination and talent"* 17.10.97 Irish Times

**MEMBERS IN GROUP:**
Michael Holmes (bouzouki, guitar), Cathy Jordan (vocals, bodhrán and bones), Liam Kelly (flute, whistle, vocals), Shane McAleer (fiddle), Brian McDonagh (mandola, mandolin) Shane Mitchell (accordion).
**ADDITIONAL INFORMATION:**
Have toured Denmark, Finland, Spain, Germany, Austria and Switzerland, Asia and North America. Have won a number of awards with Hot Press and Irish Music magazine.

# Doolin

**Contact:** Mr Cyril O'Donoghue
144, Finian Park
Shannon
Co Clare
**Tel/Fax:** +353 61 361545 or +353 87 2344978 / +353 66 364051

*"One of the most exciting and energetic new sounds to come out of Clare (Setting Free)"*
13.7.94 Hot Press. (Ref: Album 'Setting Free')

**FORMED:** 1995.
**GROUP MEMBERS:**
Jim Carrigan (pipes), Dermot Linehan (accordion), Séamus McMahon (flute, fiddle), Cyril O'Donoghue (bouzouki, guitar, vocals), Michéal Queally (fiddle).
**KEY IRISH PERFORMANCES** (since January 1994):
8.94/95/96 Ennis, promoted by the Guinness Traditional Irish Music Festival.
**KEY PERFORMANCES OUTSIDE IRELAND** (since January 1994):
7.95 Savona and Milano, promoted by Fabio Rinaud and Connemara Irish Festival, Italy.
11.95 Triesta and Milano, promoted by Fabio Rinauda.
2.96 Milano and Parma, promoted by Fabio Rinauda.
10.96 Tour of Italy, promoted by Fabio Rinauda.
**SELECTED BROADCASTS AND/OR RECORDED WORK:**
1993 'Out in the Night' (Fisherstreet) for Mulligan.
1994 'Setting Free' for Cló Iar Chonnachta Galway.
1997 'The Trip Over the Mountain' for QOD.
**SELECTED REVIEWS** (since January 1994):
1993 Hot Press.
1994 Hot Press.
1994 il Cazzetino (Milano).
**AVAILABILITY:**
General.
**ADDITIONAL INFORMATION:**
Group members Cyril O'Donoghue and Michael Queally tour Italy annually with the award-winning Italian Band, The Birking Tree. Have played in Finland (Haapavasi Folk Festival) and in Belgium at the Dranouter Folk Festival and at the Belfast Folk Festival with Fisherstreet. Séamus McMahon is a teacher at An Scoil Samhraidh Willie Clancy, Co Clare.
*See Cyril O'Donoghue page 201.*

# Dordán

**Contact:** Martina Goggin
Bothúna
An Spideál
Co Galway
**Tel/Fax:** +353 91 553255

*"Bringing together Irish traditional and classical baroque music in a most harmonious marriage without compromising either of these two traditions"* 8.94 RTÉ (Ciarán MacMathúna).

**FORMED:** 1990.
**GROUP MEMBERS:**
Mary Bergin (whistles, flutes), Martina Goggin (percussion, vocals), Kathleen Loughnane (viola, harp), Dearbhaill Standún (fiddle).
**KEY IRISH PERFORMANCES** (Since January 1994):
16.3.94 National Concert Hall, Dublin, promtoed by Gael-Linn.
20.10.95 Armagh Arts Festival, Armagh.
9.96 Town Hall Theatre, Galway.
16.5.97 NCH, An tÓireachtas concert.
**KEY PERFORMANCES OUTSIDE IRELAND** (Since January 1994):
19/21.8.94 Irish Festival, Milwaukee.
7.95 Northern Italian Tour.
24.8.95 Purcell Room, London.
4.97 Harp/Folk Festival Edinburgh.
**SELECTED BROADCASTS AND/OR RECORDED WORK:**
9.91 'Dordán-Traditional and Baroque' for Gael-Linn.
9.94 'Jigs to the Moon' for Gael-Linn.
12.96 'Christmas Capers' own label.
**SELECTED REVIEWS** (since January 1994):
Irish Times.
Hot Press.
Sunday Tribune.
**AVAILABILITY:**
General.
**ADDITIONAL INFORMATION:**
Music is arranged and adapted by the group members but remains rooted in the Irish tradition. Aims to reflect the musical links between Europe and Ireland over the last number of centuries.
*See Mary Bergin page 239.*

# Duchás Siamsa Group

**Contact:** Sr Angela Lawless
Dominican Convent
Taylors Hill
Galway
**Tel:** +353 91 522124 / +353 91 523975
**Group instruments:** Violin, banjo, mandolin, tin whistle, keyboards and flute.

**MUSICAL/ARTISTIC DIRECTOR:**
Sr A Lawless.
**FORMED:** 1996.

**AVAILABILITY:**
General.
**ADDITIONAL INFORMATION:**
Received an EU grant under the New Opportunities Scheme for Women. In 1997 staged a production entitled 'O Galvia go Galvi' in Galway during Arts Festival week and in the John Lennon Hall, Liverpool.

# Dúlamán

**Contact:** Ms Heather Innes
Alive Music
8, Williamsburgh Cottages
Farneth
Blairgowrie
Perthshire PH10 6SP
Scotland
**Tel/Fax:** +44 1350 724275 / +353 73 22677

**GROUP MEMBERS:**
Steafán Hannigan (bouzouki, pipes, flutes, African/Asian percussion), Heather Innes (vocals, percussion), Aodh MacRuairí (guitar, harmony vocals, percussion), Seoirse Ó Dochartaigh (vocals, guitar, whistles), Bob Paylor (percussion).
*See Seoirse Ó Dochartaigh page 251.*

# Durra

**Contact:** Christy MacNamara
Drumbaniff
Crusheen
Co Clare
**Tel/Fax:** +353 65 74615 / +353 65 27366

**FORMED:** 1996.
**GROUP MEMBERS:**
Eamonn Cotter (flute), Liam Lewis (fiddle), Christy MacNamara (accordion), Paul Stafford (guitar, vocals), Peter Woods (poet, writer).
**AVAILABILITY:**
General.
**ADDITIONAL INFORMATION:**
Performances based on the images in the publication 'The Living Note'. Performances can incorporate music and readings.
*See Eamonn Cotter page 215.*

# For Folk Sake

**Contact:** Ms Una Hannon
21, Brankinstown Road
Aghalee
Northern Ireland
**Tel/Fax:** +44 410 604348 or +44 1846 651441 / +44 1846 651995
**Email:** cmcconville@qubacuk

**KEY IRISH PERFORMANCES** (since January 1994):
Dunloy, Co Antrim.
8.97 Shinrone, Co Offaly.
**SELECTED BROADCASTS AND/OR RECORDED WORK:**
9.97 For RTÉ.
**PRIZES/AWARDS/APPOINTMENTS:**
1997 County Champions and Ulster Champions, awarded by Scór Sinsear.
**ADDITIONAL INFORMATION:**
Winners of the Killcormac Busking Festival in June 1997.

# Four Men and a Dog

**Contact:** Myriad Media Manangement
23, Monastery Gate Green
Clondalkin, Dublin 22
**Tel/Fax:** +353 1 4640094

**KEY IRISH PERFORMANCES** (since January 1994):
1995 Performed for President Clinton's visit to Belfast.
**KEY PERFORMANCES OUTSIDE IRELAND** (since January 1994):
1996 Olympic Games, Atlanta, USA.
**SELECTED BROADCASTS AND/OR RECORDED WORK:**
1991 'Barking Mad', for CBM Topic Records.
**PRIZES/AWARDS/APPOINTMENTS:**
1992 Ist Prize for musical skill and interpretation at Grand Prix de Musique de Radio Bratislava.
**ADDITIONAL INFORMATION:**
Have toured Canada, USA, Australia, China, Europe, Scandinavia. Have appeared on 'Kenny Live', 'Late Late Show', 'Bibi Baskin Show', 'Cursai', 'Pure Drop', 'Live at 3', 'Sult' for RTÉ, UTV and BBC.
*See Gerry O'Connor page 196.*

# Kieran Hanrahan Trio

**Contact:** Mr Kieran Hanrahan
4 The Rise
Woodpark
Ballinteer
Dubin 16
**Tel:** +353 1 2988650

**GROUP MEMBERS:**
Derek Blair (guitar), John Canny (accordion), Kieran Hanrahan (tenor banjo/mandoline).
*See Kieran Hanrahan page 196.*

# Gerry Harrington and Eoghan Ó Sullivan

**Contact:** Eoghan Ó Sullivan
8, King Street
Mitchelstown
Co Cork
**Tel:** +353 25 24715 / +353 58 53144

*"The listener will readily appreciate this captivating sound and great affinity between two mighty musicians"* 31.5.93 Evening Echo (Paul Dromey).

**FORMED:** 1991.
**MEMBERS IN GROUP:**
Gerry Harrington (fiddle), Eoghan Ó Sullivan (accordion and flute).
**KEY IRISH PERFORMANCES** (since January 1994):
6.95 Kilworth Arts Centre, Kilworth, Co Cork.
8.95 Feakle Traditional Music Festival, appearing with Martin Hayes, Begley and Cooney, Séan Tyrell.
8.95 Kilkenny Arts Fringe Festival.
**KEY PERFORMANCES OUTSIDE IRELAND** (since January 1994):
12-23.7.95 Tour of England: Playhouse Theatre Cheltenham, Hibernian in Bermingham, The Swan in London, Cheltenham Folk Club.
**SELECTED BROADCASTS AND/OR RECORDED WORK:**
6-7.92 'Scéal Eile' for Mulligan Records.
9.93 'The Pure Drop', Ballinteer, Dublin, RTÉ.
4.95 'Both Sides Now', for RTÉ.

**SELECTED REVIEWS:**
16.8.93 Evening Echo (Jimmy McCarthy).
4.9.93 The Examiner.
**REGULARLY PERFORMS WITH:** The Smoky Chimney.
**AVAILABILITY:**
Weekends, during July and August.
**ADDITIONAL INFORMATION:**
Supported Altan at Cork Folk Festival 1993. Have a particular interest in the music of Sliabh Luachra.

# Itchy Fingers

**Contact:** Mr Aidan Prunty
2, Willowbank
Armagh BT61 8AD
Northern Ireland
**Tel/Fax:** +44 1861 511004 / +44 1861 529630

**ADDITIONAL INFORMATION:**
Flute, fiddle and piano/keyboard group, specialising in Irish dance music with rhythm and melody in traditional style.
*See Aidan Prunty page 219.*

# Kilfenora Céilí Band

**Contact:** Mr John Lynch
c/o John Lynch
Ballybeg
Ennis
Co Clare
**Tel:** +353 65 23177
**Email:** garryshannon@tinet.ie

*"Some hotshot musicians playing serious traditional music make the Kilfenora Céilí Band still among the all-time greats"*
1996 Irish Music Magazine.

**FORMED:** 1907.
**NUMBER IN GROUP:** 10.
**KEY IRISH PERFORMANCES** (since January 1994):
1995 Kilkenny Arts Festival.
1995/1996 Galway, promoted by World Set Dancing Championships.
1996 The Dome, Dungloe, Donegal, promoted by Mary of Dungloe Festival.
1997 Stephens Green, Dublin, promoted by St Patrick's Festival committee.
**KEY PERFORMANCES OUTSIDE IRELAND** (since January 1994):
1995/1996 Manchester, promoted by the Clare Association.
1996/1997 La Grande Halle, Paris, promoted by the Festival de St Patrique.
1997 Lincoln Centre, New York, promoted by Midsummer Night Swing.
1997 Cleveland, USA, promoted by Irish Cultural Festival.
**SELECTED BROADCASTS AND/OR RECORDED WORK:**
1974 'The Kilfenora Céilí Band', recorded by Transatlantic Records.
1995 'Kilfenora Céilí Band', recorded by GTD Records.
1997 'Set on Stone', recorded by Dolphin/Dara Records.
**SELECTED REVIEWS** (since January 1994):
1997 Folk Roots Magazine.
**PRIZES/AWARDS/APPOINTMENTS:**
1954/1955/1956/1961/1993/1994/1995 All-Ireland Céilí Band Champions, awarded by CCÉ.
**AVAILABILITY:**
Weekends.

# King's River Band

**Contact:** Mr Noel Kennedy
Carrig
Blessington
Co Wicklow
**Tel:** +353 45 865425

**FORMED:** 1994.
**GROUP MEMBERS:**
Tony Burke (bouzouki, guitar, vocals), Eric Greaves (banjo, mandolin), Noel Kennedy (accordion, flute, whistle), Tadhg O'Sullivan (fiddle).
**KEY IRISH PERFORMANCES** (since January 1994):
1995 Armagh Folk Club.
5.96 Carrick-on-Bannow, Co Wexford, promoted by 'Folk, Blues and Beyond' Festival, Co Wexford.
5.97 Bealtaine Festival, Newbridge, Co Kildare.
**SELECTED BROADCASTS AND/OR RECORDED WORK:**
1995 'Midnight on the Water' for Beaumex Music.
1995 for Raidió Na Life.
**AVAILABILITY:**
General.

# Lá Lugh

**Contact:** Mr Gerry O'Connor
Lughnasa Music
Ravensdale
Co Louth
**Tel/Fax:** +353 42 71538

*"As fine and strong an Irish heartbeat as you're likely to hear"* 1992 Hot Press.

**FORMED:** 1992.
**GROUP MEMBERS:**
Séanie McPhail (vocals and guitar), Eithne Ní Uallacháin (voice and flute), Gerry O'Connor (fiddle and viola), Clare O'Donoghue (cello), Martin O'Hare (bodhrán and bones).
**KEY IRISH PERFORMANCES** (since January 1994):
19.6.95 Lyric Theatre, Belfast, promoted by Belfast Folk Festival, appearing with The Voice Squad.
18.6.95 Eigst Cartharlaoch, promoted by Carlow Arts Week.
2.8.95 Boyle Arts Festival, promoted by Fergus Ahern.
4.8.95 John Field Room, National Concert Hall, Dublin.
**KEY PERFORMANCES OUTSIDE IRELAND** (since January 1994):
5.8.94 Dranoutra Folk Festival, Belgium, appearing with Christy Moore, Luca Bloom and others.
17.3.95 Hotel De France, promoted by Federation of British Fruit Importers.
3.6.95 Ayrshire Arts Festival, England.
7.10.95 Kammermusik Salon, Kristianstad, Sweden.
**SELECTED BROADCASTS AND/OR RECORDED WORK:**
1.11.91 'Lá Lugh', for Claddagh Records.
22.10.93 'Cursai' for RTÉ.
1.2.96 'Brighid's Kiss' for Lughnasa Music.
**PRIZES/AWARDS/APPOINTMENTS:**
2.2.92 'Fiddler in Gold' prize, awarded by Ireland Journal.
**AVAILABILITY:**
General.
**ADDITIONAL INFORMATION:**
Particularly interested in the music and culture of North Louth and South East Ulster.
*See Gerry O'Connor page 212, Eithne Ní Uallacháin page 250.*

# Josephine Marsh Band

**Contact:** Ms Josephine Marsh
11a, Abbey Street
Ennis
Co Clare
**Tel/Fax:** +353 65 41782 / +353 65 24783

*"Her version of Raitlin Island sends sparks through your hair"* 11.96 Folk Roots (Gearóid de Mhall).

**FORMED:**
1995.
**GROUP MEMBERS:**
Declan Carey (mandolin, bouzouki), Josephine Marsh (button accordion), Pat Marsh (bouzouki), Pat O'Driscoll (double bass).
**KEY IRISH PERFORMANCES** (since January 1994):
1995 Harcourt Hotel, Dublin, promoted by the Harcourt Hotel.
7.96 Salthill Festival, Galway, appearing with Tommy Peoples and friends.
7.97 Carrick-on-Bannow, Wexford, promoted by John Murphy, appearing with Kevin Burke and friends.
1995/96/97 Harcourt Hotel, Dublin, promoted by the Harcourt Hotel.
10.96 Old Ground Hotel, Ennis, promoted by the 'ITMEX' Showcase, appearing with Siobhan Peoples and friends.
**KEY PERFORMANCES OUTSIDE IRELAND** (since January 1994):
8.97 Tour of France, promoted by San Nazarea Festival, appearing with Cran.
**SELECTED BROADCASTS AND/OR RECORDED WORK:**
1995 'Josephine Marsh' for own label.
**SELECTED REVIEWS** (since January 1994):
Summer 1996 Folk Roots.
3.97 Evening Herald.
**AVAILABILITY:**
General.
**ADDITIONAL INFORMATION:**
Featured at many festivals in Ireland during summer of 1997.
*See Josephine Marsh page 192.*

# Emer Mayock Band

**Contact:** Ms Emer Mayock
c/o Key Records
20, Lower Stephen's Street
Dublin 2
**Tel:** +353 1 4780191
*See Emer Mayock page 217.*

# Moloney Family

**Contact:** Seán or Irene Moloney
'Chez Nous'
Maugheraboy Road
Sligo
**Tel:** +353 71 61239

*"This is a reclaiming of the 'Golden Age'"*
4.97 Irish Music.

**FORMED:** 1995.
**GROUP MEMBERS:**
Pat Eade (bouzouki, singer), Walter Marren (guitar, banjo, singer), Irene Moloney (bodhrán, mandolin, fiddle), Kevin Moloney (fiddle), Seán Moloney (flutes, fiddle),.
**KEY IRISH PERFORMANCES** (since January 1994):
8.3.97 O'Connor's, Salthill, Galway.
3.5.97 Dooly's Hotel, Birr, Co Offaly.
4.5.97 The Hill, Ballinakill, Co Galway.
31.5.97 Kilcoran's, Tubbercurry, Co Sligo.
**SELECTED BROADCASTS AND/OR RECORDED WORK:**
8.3.97 'Bridging the Gap' for Gael-Linn.
**AVAILABILITY:**
April, June to September.
**ADDITIONAL INFORMATION:**
Play in the traditional East Galway style of the 1920's. Also fifth generation of Moloneys (young teens) available for extended group where appropriate. Experienced in public performance and broadcasting.
*See Séan Moloney page 218.*

# Máire Ní Chathasaigh and Chris Newman

**Contact:** Ms Ellen Thorpe
Garsdale
Easby Drive, Ilkley
West Yorkshire LS29 9BE, UK
**Tel/Fax:** +44 1943 607030
**Email:** thorpe_garsdale@compuserve.com

**FORMED:** 1987.
**GROUP MEMBERS:**
Chris Newman (guitar and mandolin), Máire Ní Chathasaigh (harp).
**AVAILABILITY:**
General.
*See Máire Ní Chathasiagh page 230.*

# Nomos

**Contact:** Mr Pat Conway
The Lobby Bar
1, Union Quay
Cork
**Tel/Fax:** +353 21 311113 / +353 21 318202

*"Inventive, imaginative music with new and interesting ideas around every corner"*
26.1.95 The Examiner.

**FORMED:** 1990.
**GROUP MEMBERS:**
Gerry McKee (bouzouki and mando-cello), Vince Milne (fiddle), John Spillane (vocals, guitar, electric bass), Frank Torpey (bodhrán), Niall Vallely (concertina).
**KEY IRISH PERFORMANCES** (since January 1994):
30.8.95 Whelan's, Dublin, promoted by Des McCullough.
8.9.95 Olympia Theatre, Dublin, promoted by MCD.
9.9.95 Lobby Bar, Cork, promoted by Cork Folk Festival.
21.10.95 Harcourt Hotel, Dublin, promoted by Des McCullough.
**KEY PERFORMANCES OUTSIDE IRELAND** (since January 1994):
3.95 Tour of Germany, promoted by Peter Pandula.
5.95 The Dubliner, Oslo, Norway, promoted by Serge Grando.
From 25.9 to 9.10.95, Irish Festival in Finland, promoted by Olli Pellikka.
**SELECTED BROADCASTS AND/OR RECORDED WORK:**
2.95 'I Won't be Afraid Any More', for Solid Records.
5.95 'All the Ways You Wander', for Solid Records.
**SELECTED REVIEWS** (since January 1994):
24.8.94 Irish Times.
12.95 Irish Times.
**AVAILABILITY:**
General.

**ADDITIONAL INFORMATION:**
Have also toured in Italy, England and Brittany and have performed at the North Texas Irish Festival in Dallas and London's Fleadh Cheoil in Finsbury Park.
*See Gerry McKee page 200, John Spillane page 225, Frank Torpey page 199, Niall Vallely page 203.*

# Ogygia

**Contact:** Órna Loughlane
Brockmanngasse 114/9
A-8010 Graz
Austria
**Tel/Fax:** +43 316 842344

*"Beautiful Irish traditional music from 'Ogygia' - come and hear that voice"*
14.5.97 University of Graz, Bulletin

**FORMED:** 1996.
**GROUP MEMBERS:**
Órna Loughnane (violin, voice, mandolin), Lakis Tzimkas (guitar, bass, vocals).
**KEY PERFORMANCES OUTSIDE IRELAND** (since January 1994):
1996 Graz, Austria, promoted by 'Gilma' Grazbachgasse, Graz.
1997 Graz, Austria, 'Gilma', promoted by Grazbachgasse, Graz.
1997 University of Gráz, promoted by Dr P Bierbaumer.
1997 Arts Centre, Kozani, Greece, promoted by M Koutsounanos.
**SELECTED REVIEWS** (since January 1994):
1997 University of Graz Bulletin.
**TRAINING AND/OR QUALIFICATIONS:**
Since 1995 Jazz Music Degree at Music Academy Graz.
Since 1995 Classical Music Degree at Music Academy, Graz.
**AVAILABILITY:**
July to October.
**ADDITIONAL INFORMATION:**
Musicians both come from traditional music backgrounds, Greek and Irish respectively.
*See Órna Loughnane page 297.*

# Niamh Parsons and the Loose Connections

**Contact:** Niamh Parsons
117, Grange Abbey Crescent
Donaghmede, Dublin 13
or
Artistic Upstarts
65a, Dundas Street
Edinburgh EH3 6RS
Scotland
**Tel/Fax:** +353 1 8473673
**Email:** upstarts@evolve.ftech.co.uk

**FORMED:** 1990.
**GROUP MEMBERS:**
Colm Fitzpatrick (percussion, drums) Dee Moore (bass, voice), Dave Munnelly (accordion, piano), Niamh Parsons (voice), Colin Reid (guitar).
**KEY PERFORMANCES OUTSIDE IRELAND** (since January 1994):
2/3.97 to 7/8.97 Tour of USA.
3.97 North Texas Irish Festival, Dallas promoted by the Nancy Carlin Association, California, USA, appearing with Solas, Brother and the Black Family.
6.97 Wolfenbuttel Festival, Hanover promoted by Artistic Upstarts, Edinburgh, appearing with Alias Ron Kavana.
7.97 Mendiceno, California, promoted by Artistic Upstarts.
**SELECTED BROADCASTS AND/OR RECORDED WORK:**
1992 'Loosely Connected' for Green Track Records.
1996 'Many Happy Returns' for Dara Records.
**AVAILABILITY:**
General.

# Riffs and Reels

**Contact:** Pat O'Brien
Castle Road
Butlerstown
Co Waterford
**Tel:** +353 51 384565

*"Riffs and Reels have earned a reputation as a band who play traditional music with great flair and energy"* 15.9.95 Munster Express.

**FORMED:** 1995.
**GROUP MEMBERS:**
Padraic O'Brien (button accordion), Pat O'Brien (tenor banjo, mandola), Gerry Power (guitar).
**KEY IRISH PERFORMANCES** (since January 1994):
4.96 Quay's Bar, Galway.
7.96 Carrick-on-Bannow, promoted by Philip Murphy Memorial Concert.
8.96 City Hall, Waterford, promoted by Waterford Corporation.
5.97 Dungarvan as part of Féile na nDéise.
**KEY PERFORMANCES OUTSIDE IRELAND** (since January 1994):
Tour of Germany.
**SELECTED BROADCASTS AND/OR RECORDED WORK:**
1.96 'Paddy's Trip to Scotland' for own cassette.
**SELECTED REVIEWS** (since January 1994):
14.5.96 Waterford News and Star.
7.96 Irish Music Magazine.
**AVAILABILITY:**
General.
**ADDITIONAL INFORMATION:**
Repertoire includes traditional Irish music and song and some American ragtime tunes.

# Samhain

**Contact:** Mr Breanndán Ó Beaglaoich
Cuas
Baile na nGall
Trá Lí, Cho Chiarraí
**Tel:** +353 66 55399

**FORMED:** 1996.
**GROUP MEMBERS:**
Paul McGrattan (flute, tin whistle), Breanndán Ó Beaglaoich (accordion, melodeon, vocals), Noel O'Grady (bouzouki), Paul O'Shaughnessy (fiddle).
**KEY IRISH PERFORMANCES** (since January 1994):
6.96 Whelan's, Dublin, appearing with Máiréad and Tríona Ní Dhomhnaill.
6.96 Róisín Dubh, Galway, appearing with Máiréad and Triona Ní Dhomhnaill.
10.96 Matt Molloy's, Westport, Co Mayo, appearing with Máiréad and Tríona Ní Dhomhnaill.
4.97 Siamsa Tíre, Tralee, Co Kerry, appearing with Máiréad Ní Mhaonaigh.
**KEY PERFORMANCES OUTSIDE IRELAND** (since January 1994):
3.2.97 Paris, promoted by Pipers Club.
**SELECTED BROADCASTS AND/OR RECORDED WORK:**
18.2.97 'Beo le Brid Óg' for RTÉ.
17.3.97 '12 to 1' for RTÉ.

**AVAILABILITY:**
General.
**ADDITIONAL INFORMATION:**
A newly formed group.
*See Breanndán Ó Beaglaoich page 192.*

## Shantalla

**Contact:** Mr Gerard Murray
12, Rue Denis Deceuster
1330 Rixensart
Belgium
**Tel/Fax:** +32 2 6536987 / +32 2 6536987
**Email:** Shantalla@hotmail.com
**WWW:** http://users.skynet.be/johennon/shantalla

*"Completely brilliant, leading you to think of the intrumental bravura of the top Irish groups such as Dervish"* 11.96 t'Bourdonske.

**FORMED:** 1992
**GROUP MEMBERS:**
Kieran Fahy (fiddle, vocals), Helen Flaherty (vocals, bodhrán), Joe Hennon (guitar, vocals, bodhrán), Michael Horgan (uilleann pipes, flutes, whistles), Gerard Murray (accordion, bouzouki, keyboards).
**SELECTED BROADCASTS AND/OR RECORDED WORK:**
1993 'Sean Talamh' for ARC Musik GMSH.
**AVAILABILITY:**
General.

## Slua Nua

**Contact:** Mr Joe McKenna
Moneystown North
Roundwood
Co Wicklow
**Tel/Fax:** +353 404 45139 / +353 404 45146

**FORMED:**
1992.
**AVAILABILITY:**
General.

## Temple House Céilí Band

**Contact:** Mr Kieran Hanrahan
4 The Rise
Woodpark
Ballinteer
Dubin 16
**Tel:** +353 1 2988650
*See Kieran Hanrahan page 196.*

## The Chieftains

**Contact:** Paddy Moloney
The Stores
Miltown Bridge
Dundrum Road
Dublin 14
**Tel/Fax:** +353 1 2697430

## The Conways

**Contact:** Zöe Conway
Newtownbalregan
Dundalk
Co Louth
**Tel:** +353 42 36827

**FORMED:** 1990.
**GROUP MEMBERS:**
Lisa Conway (fiddle, tin whistle), Patrick Conway (flute, guitar, tin whistle and bodhrán) Suzanne Conway (concertina, tin whistle, piano, fiddle) and Zöe Conway (fiddle, banjo, tin whistle, piano and mandolin).
**KEY PERFORMANCES OUTSIDE IRELAND** (since January 1994):
8.96 Auditorium, la Coruna, Spain.
9.96 Jörgis, Mitterdorf, Austria. 9.96 Kapfenberg, Austria, promoted by Professsor Kovacic.
**SELECTED BROADCASTS AND/OR RECORDED WORK:**
1.92 at 'The Corner House', Forkhill, for BBC.
6.96 ' High Reel' (Bellurgan, Co Louth), for BBC and RTÉ.
2.97 Stray Leaf Folk Club, Mullaghbawn, Co Armagh.
**SELECTED REVIEWS** (since Janauary 1994):
1997 Stray Leaf review.
**TRAINING AND/OR QUALIFICATIONS:**
All members have attended An Scoil Samhraidh Willie Clancy and Scoil Eigse Summer Schools.
**AVAILABILITY:**
General.

## The Deirdre Cunningham Band

**Contact:** Deirdre Cunningham
Lake Recording Studio
Cootehall
Boyle
Co Roscommon
**Tel:** +353 79 67055
*See page 303.*

## The Fallen Angels

**Contact:** The Fallen Angels
c/o MBE
6, Seafield Crescent
Blackrock
Co Dublin
**Tel/Fax:** +353 1 2693821 / +353 1 2693777
**Email:** mbe@indigo.ie

**FORMED:** 1986.
**GROUP MEMBERS:** 4.
**AVAILABILITY:**
General.
**ADDITIONAL INFORMATION:**
All female acapella group.

## The Four Star Trio

**Contact:** Mr Pat Ahern
Clonmoyle East
Coachford
Co Cork
**Tel:** +353 21 334271
**Email:** pahern@rtccork.ie

**FORMED:**
1989.
**GROUP MEMBERS:**
Pat Ahern (guitar, bouzouki), Johnny McCarthy (fiddle, flute, whistle), Con Ó Drisceoil (accordion).
**KEY IRISH PERFORMANCES** (since January 1994):
7.11.95 National Concert Hall, Dublin, promoted by Na Píobairí Uilleann.
7.96 Miltown Malbay, promoted by An Scoil Samhraidh Willie Clancy.
**KEY PERFORMANCES OUTSIDE IRELAND** (since January 1994):
8.94 Wadenbridge, Cornwall, promoted by Wadenbridge Folk Festival.
2.95 MJC, Paris, promoted by Association Irlandaise.
7.96 Tocane St Apre, France, promoted by Tocane Committee.
**SELECTED BROADCASTS AND/OR RECORDED WORK:**
11.96 'Geantraí' for TnaG.
9.96 'High Reel' for RTÉ.
7.97 'The Square Triangle' for Craft Records (CRD02).
**SELECTED REVIEWS** (since January 1994):
11.95 Irish Times.
**AVAILABILITY:**
General.
**ADDITIONAL INFORMATION:**
Have a particular interest in the music of Sliabh Luachra. Repertoire includes tunes and songs from Ireland and abroad.
*See Con Ó Drisceoil page 194, Pat Ahern page 220.*

# The Tommy Hayes Group

**Contact:** Mr Tommy Hayes
Capparoe
Scariff
Co Clare
**Tel/Fax:** +353 61 921716

**FORMED:** 1996.
**GROUP MEMBERS:**
Ronan Browne (uilleann Pipes), Meta Costelloe (vocals), Kenneth Edge (saxophones), Máire Ní Grada (pipes, flutes), Julia Haines (harp), Tommy Hayes (percussion), Brendan Hearty (guitar).
**AVAILABILITY:**
General.
*See Ronan Browne page 235, Kenneth Edge page 52.*

# The Lahawns

**Contact:** Dr Breda Smyth
47, Bachelors Walk
Dublin 1
**Tel/Fax:** +353 1 8727774

**FORMED:**
1994.
**GROUP MEMBERS:**
Jim Higgins (drums, bodhrán, piano), Kevin Hough (guitar), Andrew McNamara (accordion), Breda Smyth (tin whistle, fiddle).
**KEY IRISH PERFORMANCES** (since January 1994):
12.96 Kinvara, Co Clare, promoted by Winkles tour.
5.97 Harcourt Hotel, Dublin.
**KEY PERFORMANCES OUTSIDE IRELAND** (since January 1994):
3.97 Tour of San Francisco, promoted by Eddie Stack .
**SELECTED BROADCASTS AND/OR RECORDED WORK:**
5.96 'Kenny Live' for RTÉ.
9.96 'Geantraí' for TnaG.
3.97 'Basil and thyme' (video) for TnaG.
**AVAILABILITY:**
General.
*See Breda Smyth page 244.*

# The Mandies

**Contact:** Ms Niamh Ní Bheoláin
The Music Lab
Tymon Bawn Community Centre
Aylesbury
Tallaght
Dublin 24
**Tel/Fax:** +353 1 4520611 or +353 1 462 1029 / +353 1 4520611

*"This grandly-clad ensemble of eight string players, under the pastoral baton of Liam Kennedy, played to a full house of warm kin and camaraderie"* 8.3.96 Irish Times.

**FORMED:** 1994.
**GROUP MEMBERS:**
Jimmy Cahill (guitar), Dave Cassidy (mandola), Liam Kennedy (mandolin), Mickey McKenna (mandolin), Tom Moran (mandolin), John Quearney (double bass), Kevin Ward (guitar/mandolin).
**KEY IRISH PERFORMANCES** (since January 1994):
3/4.8.96 Waterford, promoted by Spraoi.
8.96 Dundalk, promoted by the Global Radio Festival.
11.96 Gaiety, Dublin, promoted by Midnight at the Gaiety.
**SELECTED BROADCASTS AND/OR RECORDED WORK:**
18.11.96 'Gerry Ryan Tonight' for RTÉ.
18.11.96 'Joe Duffy Morning Show' for RTÉ.
8.5.97 'Live at 3' for RTÉ.
**SELECTED REVIEWS** (since January 1994):
2.6.96 Sunday Business Post.
1.5.97 Echo (Tallaght).
**TRAINING AND/OR QUALIFICATIONS:**
From 25.10-96 to 27.10.97, jazz masterclass with Dave O'Rourke.
**AVAILABILITY:**
General.
**ADDITIONAL INFORMATION:**
Originated from the Music Lab in Tallaght. Although most of the band have roots in traditional music, interests have expanded over the years and they now combine diverse genres.

# The Mulloy Brothers

**Contact:** Mr Thomas Mulloy
Mulraney
Westport
Co Mayo
**Tel/Mobile:** +353 98 36103 / +353 87 2357722

**FORMED:** 1966.
**GROUP MEMBERS:**
Thomas Mulloy (accordion and bodhran), Patrick Mulloy (accordion, vocals and mandolin), Martin Mulloy (banjo) and Enda Mulloy (guitar and vocals).
**KEY IRISH PERFORMANCES** (since January 1994):
12.7.96 Gerrightys Tavern, Westport, Co Mayo.
8.8.96 Welcome Inn Hotel, Castlebar, Co Mayo.
18.8.96 The Anglers Rest, Westport, Co Mayo.
7.9.96 Ray Walshe's, Cross, Ballinrobe, Co Mayo.
**KEY PERFORMANCES OUTSIDE IRELAND** (since January 1994):
17.3.96 Florida, U.S.A.
25.4.96 Angies, Willsdon, London.
28.4.96 White Swan, Crystal Palace, London.
**SELECTED BROADCASTS AND/OR RECORDED WORK:**
1976 'I'm A Rover', for Pollydor records.
1977 'Coastline Of Mayo', for Heritage records.
1979 'Coastline Of Mayo', for Celtic records.
**SELECTED REVIEWS** (since January 1994):
Featured on 'My Own Native Land' video, produced in 1996.

# The Sands Family

**Contact:** Colum Sands
50, Shore Road
Rostrevor
Co Down BT34 3EW
Northern Ireland
**Tel/Fax:** +44 16937 38015

**FORMED:** 1969.
**GROUP MEMBERS:**
Colum Sands (guitar, fiddle, concertina), Tommy Sands (vocals, guitar), Ben Sands (vocals, mandoline), Anne Sands (vocals).
**AVAILABILITY:**
General.
*See Tommy Sands page 299.*

# The Smoky Chimney

**Contact:** Gerry Harrington
Monatarriv
Lismore
Co Waterford
**Tel:** +353 58 53144

*"This album is about music - sweet, unhurried, depth and passion, darkness and lightness"*
2.97 Irish Music.

**FORMED:** 1996.
**GROUP MEMBERS:**
Paul de Grae (guitar) Gerry Harrington (fiddle), Eoghan O'Sullivan (accordion).
**KEY IRISH PERFORMANCES** (since January 1994):
12.4.97 Kilworth, Village Arts Centre promoted by Liam Howard.
17.3.97 National Concert Hall, Dublin, promoted by KCP Productions.
15.2.97 Temple Bar Music Centre, Dublin, promoted by Hummingbird Productions.
9.96 Granary Theatre, Cork, promoted by Forefront Productions, appearing with Jackie Daly and Máire O'Keefe.
**SELECTED BROADCASTS AND/OR RECORDED WORK:**
12.96 'The Smoky Chimney' for Claddagh Records.
**SELECTED REVIEWS** (since January 1994):
10.1.97 Irish Times.
**AVAILABILITY:**
General.
*See Paul de Grae page 222, Gerry Harrington and Eoghan O'Sullivan Duo page 261.*

# Trasna

**Contact:** Mr Bréandán O'Hare
35, Hatfield Street
Belfast, BT7 2FB
Northern Ireland
**Tel:** +44 1232 238557

**FORMED:** 1991.
**MEMBERS IN GROUP:**
Paul Bradley (fiddle), Alan McCartney (guitar, fiddle), Bréandán O'Hare (concert flute), Jason O'Rourke (concertina).
**KEY IRISH PERFORMANCES** (since January 1994):
25.10.95 Lanther House Belfast, promoted by Live Music Now.
26.10.95 Cuba Walk Day Centre, promoted by LMN.
30.10.95 Holywell Hospital, Antrim, promoted by LMN.
7.11.95 Downshire Hospital, Downpatrick, promoted by LMN.
**KEY PERFORMANCES OUTSIDE IRELAND** (since January 1994):
30.11.94 and 10.8.95 Dubliner, Oslo, Norway, promoted by Roots Music.
15.4.95 Irish Pub, Bergen, promoted by Roots Music.
24.5.95 Thrumpton Village Hall, Leicestershire, England, promoted by LMN.
**SELECTED BROADCASTS AND/OR RECORDED WORK:**
20.10.95 'Traditional Irish Music from Belfast', for Outlet Records.
**AVAILABILITY:**
General.
**ADDITIONAL INFORMATION:**
Work as part of 'Live Music Now' scheme performing concerts in hospitals and schools for children with special needs, etc. Also play in bars, halls and folk clubs.
*See Paul Bradley page 204, Jason O'Rourke page 203.*

# Section ten

## Jazz Instrumentalists Singers and Groups

# JAZZ CLARINET

## Neil Buckley *Clarinet*

**Contact:** Mr Neil Buckley
Bridgetown
Glen
Carrigart
Letterkenny
Co Donegal
**Tel/Fax:** +353 74 55560
*See tenor and soprano saxophones page 282.*

## Keith Donald *Clarinet (inc bass)*

**Contact:** Keith Donald
Boathouse
Rockbrook
Dublin 16
**Tel:** +353 1 4934499
*See soprano saxophone page 282.*

## Brendan Doyle *Clarinet*

**Contact:** Mr Brendan Doyle
**Tel:** +353 1 4517742
*See saxophones page 283.*

## Len McCarthy *Clarinet*

**Contact:** Mr Len McCarthy
'Hillgrove'
Tramore Road
Cork
**Tel:** +353 21 965108
**Other instruments:** Alto saxophone, flute.

**KEY IRISH PERFORMANCES** (since January 1994):
25.4.95 'Live At 3', for RTÉ.
Regular appearances in the Conrad Hotel, Dublin, appearing with Louis Stewart.
1996 Guinness Cork International Jazz Festival.
**KEY PERFORMANCES OUTSIDE IRELAND** (since January 1994):
21-28.8.95 Eindhoven Jazz Festival, Netherlands.
**SELECTED BROADCASTS AND/OR RECORDED WORK:**
'Len McCarthy, Guinness Allstars and Louis Stewart'.
1993 CD with Selena Jones (singer).
1993 Recording with Arnie Laurence (saxophone).
**SELECTED REVIEWS** (since January 1994):
17.95 Irish Independent.
28.4.95 Irish Times.
**REGULARLY PERFORMS WITH:**
Jim Doherty Trio, Louis Stewart Duo and Len McCarthy.
**AVAILABILITY:**
General.
**ADDITIONAL INFORMATION:**
Feature soloist in Louis Stewart's 'James Joyce Suite'. Guest soloist for Sandika Big Band in Oslo. Co-leader with Louis Stewart Quartet in Mont Martre, Copenhagen.

## Neil McMahon *Clarinet*

**Contact:** Mr Neil McMahon
"Hazel Hatch"
Thormanby Road
Howth, Co Dublin
**Tel:** +353 1 839 1174
**Other instruments:** Flute
*See saxophones page 284.*

## Charles Meredith *Clarinet*

**Contact:** Mr Charles Meredith
6 Cross Avenue
Blackrock
Co Dublin
**Tel:** +353 1 2885183
*See trumpet page 285.*

## Patrick O'Keeffe *Clarinet*

**Contact:** Mr Patrick O'Keeffe
126 North Main Street
Youghal
Co Cork
**Tel:** +353 24 92820
*See classical clarinet page 5.*

# JAZZ DOUBLE BASS

## Michael Coady *Double Bass*

**Contact:** Michael Coady
**Mobile:** +353 88 2754862
**Other instruments:** Bass guitar.

**TRAINING AND/OR QUALIFICATIONS:**
Studied bass guitar with Ronan Guilfoyle and has participated in workshops with Kenny Werner and Dave Holland, Newpark Music Centre, Dublin.
Has attended the International Jazz Summer School at the University of Ulster, Jordanstown and the Banff Centre, Canada.
**REGULARLY PERFORMS WITH:**
Brendan Doyle Jazz Quartet, Louis Stewart, Hugh Buckley Quartet.
**ADDITIONAL INFORMATION:**
Toured Northern Ireland with Khanda and has performed with Conor Guilfoyle's Latin Jazz Quartet. Currently plays with a nine piece band performing the music of Charles Mingus.

## Dave Fleming *Double Bass*

**Contact:** Mr Dave Fleming
Apartment 6
11, Clonskeagh Road, Dublin 6
**Tel/Mobile/Fax:** +353 1 2837175 / +353 88 2745725 / +353 1 2837175
**Email:** dfleming@iol.ie

**KEY IRISH PERFORMANCES** (since January 1994):
10.94 Guinness Cork International Jazz Festival, appearing with Art Farmer (trumpet).
10.96 Guinness Cork International Jazz Festival, appearing with Lynne Arriale Trio.
3.97 Tour of Ireland, promoted by Music Network, appearing with Rory McGuinness.
4.97 Dublin, promoted by Dublin Jazz Society, appearing with Scott Hamilton (tenor saxophone).
**SELECTED BROADCASTS AND/OR RECORDED WORK:**
8.95 'Anda' with Tommy Halferty Quartet for the Improvised Music Company.
3.95 'Gravity Still Works' with Irish Jazz Orchestra for Coyote Records (Northern Ireland).
1997 'Live at 3' with Scott Hamilton for RTÉ.
**REGULARLY PERFORMS WITH:**
Jim Doherty Trio, Drazen Derek (guitar), Richie Buckley Quartet.
**AVAILABILITY:**
General.
**ADDITIONAL INFORMATION:**
Has performed in sacramento, USA, Finland and France. Has extensively toured Ireland and the UK with Louis Stewart, Jim Doherty and US tenor sax Spike Robinson.

## Barry Guy *Double Bass*

**Contact:** Mr Barry Guy
Carrickmourne
Thomastown
Co Kilkenny
**Tel/Fax:** +353 56 58708 / +353 56 58709
**Email:** maya@tinet.ie
*See double bass page 295.*

## Michael McGinty *Double Bass*

**Contact:** Mr Michael McGinty
Calhame
Letterkenny
Co Donegal
**Tel:** +353 74 23007
**Other instruments:** Electric bass guitar.

**SELECTED BROADCASTS AND/OR RECORDED WORK:**
1994 and 1995 played in the 'house band' for the 'Gerry Kelly Show', UTV.
**TRAINING AND/OR QUALIFICATIONS:**
Associated Board Royal School of Music, Grade 5 practical and theory
**REGULARLY PERFORMS WITH:**
The Gay McIntyre Quartet, Neil Buckley Quartet.
**AVAILABILITY:**
General.
**ADDITIONAL INFORMATION:**
Repertoire of about 60 standard jazz tunes.

## Paul Desmond Moore *Double Bass*

**Contact:** Mr Paul Desmond Moore
12, Thor Place
North Circular Road
Dublin 7
**Tel:** +353 1 8384806
*See guitar traditional page 223.*

## Alan Niblock *Double Bass*

**Contact:** Mr Alan Niblock
2, Irwin Crescent
Upper Newtownards Road
Belfast BT4 BAQ
Northern Ireland
**Tel:** +44 1232 673752
**Other instruments:** 5-string fretted electric guitar.

**KEY IRISH PERFORMANCES** (since January 1994):
1.6.95 Boat Club, Stramillis, Belfast, promoted by Riverside Jazz Foundaton, appearing with Louis Stewart and Kenny Davern.
25.10.95 Boat Club, Stramillis, Belfast, promoted by the Riverside Jazz Festival, appearing with Harry Allen and George Masso.
7.6.96 Boat Club, Stranmillis, Belfast, promoted by The RJF, appearing with Scott Hamilton and Dave McKenna.
26-27.10.96 Opera House, Cork, promoted by Guinness Cork International Jazz Festival, appearing with Hugh Frazer and the Irish Jazz Orchestra.
**SELECTED BROADCASTS AND/OR RECORDED WORK:**
14.6.95 'Anthony Kerr Quartet', recorded by Holywood Jazz Festival for Radio Ulster.
12.3.97 Tribute to Dermod Harland, recorded by Radio Ulster.
21.3.97 Irish Jazz Orchestra, recorded by RTÉ at the Guinness Cork International Jazz Festival.
**SELECTED REVIEWS** (since January 1994):
1.6.95 Belfast Telegraph.
27.11.95 Belfast Telegraph.
**TRAINING AND/OR QUALIFICATIONS:**
From 1992 to 1993, Foundation Studies Course in music, awarded by University of Ulster, Jordanstown.
1994 Workshop with Belfast Music Collective.
1995 Workshop with North Down College of Further Education.
From 1995 to 1997, workshops at various centres.
**REGULARLY PERFORMS WITH:**
Café Society Quartet, Irish Jazz Orchestra, The Electric Band.
**AVAILABILITY:**
General.

## Rod Patterson *Double Bass*

**Contact:** Mr Rod Patterson
47, Pommern Parade
Belfast BT6 9FY
Northern Ireland
**Tel/Fax/Mobile:** +44 1232 705098 / +44 1232 705098 / +44 831 197600
*See bass guitar page 275.*

## Mike Quellin *Double Bass*

**Contact:** Mike Quellin
11, Primate's Manor
Armagh, BT60 2LP, Northern Ireland
**Tel/Mobile:** +44 1861 526304 / +44 850 247582

**TRAINING AND OR QUALIFICATIONS:**
1960's Classical training with Hallé orchestra member.
1987 and 1988 Wavendon Music Course in Jazz.
1989 Studies with Jeff Cleyne (double bass).
**AVAILABILITY:**
General.
**ADDITIONAL INFORMATION:**
Has a wide range of experience in jazz and has worked with most of the names in London such as Humphrey Littleton, Dick Morrisey, Don Wella, Don Rendell, Pete King, Bill Le Sage, Roy Williams, Eddie Thompson etc. Has appeared at many festivals and can cover all styles from dixiland to free form.

# JAZZ FLUTE

## Michael Buckley *Flute*

**Contact:** Mr Michael Buckley
17 St Peter's Drive
Walkinstown
Dublin 12
**Mobile:** +353 87 415580
*See saxophones page 282.*

## Ellen Cranitch *Flute*

**Contact:** Ms Ellen Cranitch
33, Westfield Road
Harold's Cross
Dublin 6w
**Tel/Fax:** +353 1 4923486
**Other instruments:** Jazz keyboards, classical/alto flute.

**KEY IRISH PERFORMANCES** (since January 1994):
1.7.94 John Field Room, National Concert Hall, Dublin, promoted by the Improvised Music Company, appearing with Khanda.
1.95 Old Museum Arts Centre, Belfast appearing with the Two Chairs Co.
11.95 Irish Museum of Modern Art, Dublin promoted by the Museum, appearing with the Two Chairs Co.
11.95 Triskel Arts Centre, Cork, promoted by the Cork Guinness International Jazz Festival appearing with Khanda.
**KEY PERFORMANCES OUTSIDE IRELAND** (since January 1994):
5.95 Heritage Centre, Isle of Skye, Scotland, promoted by the Netherbo Arts Centre, Edinburgh, appearing with the Two Chairs Co.
6.96 Lejre, Copenhagen, Foreningen International storytelling festival appearing with the Two Chairs Co.
10.96 Birmingham Repertory Company, promoted by Dr Vayu Naidu, appearing with Sarwar Sabri and Peter Badejo.
4.97 Purcell Room, London promoted by Dr Vayu Naidu appearing with Sarwar Sabri and Peter Badejo.
**SELECTED BROADCASTS AND/OR RECORDED WORK:**
8.96 Karst (solo CD) for Bush Telegraph.
11.96 'Ros na Rún' theme music for TnaG.
3.97 'Cursaí Ealaíne' for RTÉ.
**TRAINING AND OR QUALIFICATIONS:**
From 1973 to 1980, ARIAM from the Royal Irish Academy of Music, Dublin.
From 1980 to 1984, BA from Trinity College, Dublin.
**REGULARLY PERFORMS WITH:**
Khanda, The Two Chairs Company, Anne-Marie O'Farrell (harp).
**AVAILABILITY:**
General.
**ADDITIONAL INFORMATION:**
Has been working as a freelance flautist with the National Symphony Orchestra of Ireland, the RTÉ Concert Orchestra and various ballet, opera and theatre orchestras in Ireland. Particularly interested in music and theatre, and works closely with actor Nuala Hayes. Has written music for several television documentaries and dance presentations. Was composer in residence with the Amadé Theatre Company of Montpelier. Currently working on a feature length film score, directed by BAFTA award winner Kfir Yefet.

## Thomas Dunne *Flute*

**Contact:** Mr Thomas Dunne
50, Dodder Park Road, Dublin 14
**Tel:** +353 1 4906027
*See guitar page 272.*

## Brian Dunning *Flute*

**Contact:** Mr Brian Dunning
72, Moyglare Village
Maynooth, Co Kildare
**Tel/Fax:** +353 1 6285678
**Other instruments:** Alto flute, whistles, bodhrán, bones.

*"A thorough mastery of his instrument and a style characterised by artistry, imagination and feeling"* 25.8.96 Sunday Independent.

**KEY IRISH PERFORMANCES** (since January 1994):
9.96 Cork School of Music, appearing with Tommy Halferty.
10.96 Limerick Jazz Society, appearing with Anthony Kerr.
1.97 Whelan's, Dublin, appearing with Brendan Doyle and Tommy Halferty.
4.97 Temple Bar Music Centre, appearing with Nightnoise.
**KEY PERFORMANCES OUTSIDE IRELAND** (since January 1994):
3.96 Toyko Concert Hall, promoted by Mimori Vusa appearing with Nightnoise.
5.96 Madrid, Barcelona and Valencia, promoted by Julio Marti, appearing with Nightnoise.
**SELECTED BROADCASTS AND/OR RECORDED WORK:**
1.96 'A Distance Shore' for Windham Hill BMG.
1.97 'Celtic Legends' on Windham Hill BMG.
1.97 'The White Horse Sessions' on Windham Hill BMG.
**SELECTED REVIEWS** (since January 1994):
25.8.96 Sunday Independent
**PRIZES/AWARDS/APPOINTMENTS:**
1977 Awarded a study grant (USA) from the Arts Council.
**TRAINING AND/OR QUALIFICATIONS:**
From 1977 to 1979, LRSM from Berklee College of Music, Boston.
**REGULARLY PERFORMS WITH:**
Myles Drennan, Tommy Halferty and Nightnoise.
**AVAILABILITY:** General.

## Tom Harte *Flute*

**Contact:** Tom Harte
2, Saint Mary's Terrace
Arbour Place, Stoneybatter
Dublin 7
**Tel:** +353 1 6711361
*See guitar page 273.*

## Len McCarthy *Flute*

**Contact:** Mr Len McCarthy
'Hillgrove'
Tramore Road, Cork
**Tel:** +353 21 965108
*See clarinet page 269.*

## Neil McMahon *Flute*

**Contact:** Mr Neil McMahon
"Hazel Hatch", Thormanby Road
Howth, Co Dublin
**Tel:** +353 1 839 1174
**Other Instruments:** Clarinet
*See saxophones page 284.*

## Colm O'Sullivan *Flute*

**Contact:** Mr Colm O'Sullivan
40, Terenure Road West
Dublin 6w.
**Tel:** +353 1 4904297
**Other instruments:** Alto flute.

**KEY IRISH PERFORMANCES** (since January 1994):
2.97 Brogan's, Dublin, promoted by the Improvised Music Company, appearing with Brian Dunning.
Since 1996, regular duo with Hugh Buckley at the Hibernian Hotel, Dublin.
**KEY PERFORMANCES OUTSIDE IRELAND** (since January 1994):
Performed informally at 'jam sessions', Blue Note, New York and at Small's.
**REGULARLY PERFORMS WITH:**
Hugh Buckley, Myles Drennan, Louis Stewart.
**AVAILABILITY:**
General.

# JAZZ GUITAR

## Hugh Buckley *Guitar*

**Contact:** Mr Hugh Buckley
21, Bayside Walk
Dublin 13
**Tel:** +353 1 8390004

**KEY IRISH PERFORMANCES** (since January 1994):
10.96 Guinness Cork Jazz International Festival, appearing with James Williams and Bobby Wats.
6.97 Dublin, promoted by MCD, appearing with Van Morrison.
6.97 Dublin, promoted by Dublin Jazz Society, appearing with Mike Carr.
7.97 Dublin and Galway, promoted by IMC, appearing with James Williams.
5.9.97 Dublin, promoted by IMC, appearing with Bobby Williams and Hugh Buckley Trio.
**KEY PERFORMANCES OUTSIDE IRELAND** (since January 1994):
3.95 New York, USA, appearing with Peter Bernstein Duo.
3.96 New York, USA, appearing with Selino Clarke Group.
3.97 New York, USA, appearing with Dave O'Rourke Duo.
**SELECTED BROADCASTS AND/OR RECORDED WORK:**
11.96 'In Arrears' (Richie Buckley), for IMC.
9.97 'Yes Indeed', recorded in New York with James Williams and Peter Washington.
**SELECTED REVIEWS** (since January 1994):
7.97 Evening Herald.
7.97 Sunday Independent.
**REGULARLY PERFORMS WITH:**
Dave Fleming Trio, Louis Stewart Duo, Richie Buckley Duo.
**AVAILABILITY:**
General.

## Aidan Coleman *Guitar*

**Contact:** Aidan Coleman
28, Lisalea
Frascati Park
Blackrock
Co Dublin
**Tel:** +353 1 2835117
*See singers page 112.*

## Jerry Creedon *Guitar*

**Contact:** Mr Jerry Creedon
25, Melbourn Court
Model Farm Road, Cork
**Tel:** +353 21 341826
*See classical guitar page 19.*

## Thomas Dunne *Guitar*

**Contact:** Mr Thomas Dunne
50, Dodder Park Road
Dublin 14
**Tel:** +353 1 4906027
**Other instruments:** Piano, flute, voice.

**AVAILABILITY:**
General.

## Trevor England *Electric Bass Guitar*

**Contact:** Mr Trevor England
38, Edenderry Cottages
Shaw's Bridge
Belfast BT8 8RY
Northern Ireland
**Tel:** +44 1232 641148

**TRAINING AND/OR QUALIFICATIONS:**
From 1980 to 1984, B Mus from Berklee College of Music.
From 1993 to 1997, MA Music from the University of Ulster.
**ADDITIONAL INFORMATION:**
Composer and arranger.

## Richard Farrelly *Guitar*

**Contact:** Richard Farrelly
132, Braemor Road
Churchtown
Dublin 14
**Mobile:** +353 87 529680
**Other instruments:** Piano, electric bass.

**REGULARLY PERFORMS WITH:**
Café Orchestra.
**AVAILABILITY:**
General.
**ADDITIONAL INFORMATION:**
Has worked in UK with jazz notaries including Don Weller, Stan Tracey and saxophonist Dudu Pukwana and in Ireland with Honor Heffernan (as arranger/guitarist) and Mary Coughlan.

## Damien Gallagher *Guitar*

**Contact:** Mr Damien Gallagher
c/o Mr Bill Whelan
Home for the "Bewildered" Music Co
39, Fairview Green
Dublin 3
**Tel:** +353 1 8331920

**KEY IRISH PERFORMANCES** (since January 1994):
From 28.4.95 to 30.4.95, Galway Rythmn and Roots Festival, promoted by MCD, appearing with 'Slightly Bewildered String Band'.
From 5.5.95 to 7.5.95, Paddy Expo, Limerick, promoted by Irish Distillers Ltd, appearing with Slightly Bewildered String Band.
From 2.6.95 to 4.6.95, Castlebar Blues Festival, promoted by Gerry Roddy, appearing with Slightly Bewildered String Band.
From 10.8.95 to 13.8.95, Feakle Festival of Traditional Music, Co Clare, promoted by Gary Pepper, appearing with Slightly Bewildered String Band.
**KEY PERFORMANCES OUTSIDE IRELAND** (since January 1994):
From 3.3.95 to 5.3.95, Hobart, Tasmania, promoted by Tim Whelan, appearing with Slightly Bewildered String Band.
From 10.3.95 to 12.3.95, Portfairy, South Australia, promoted by Tim Whelan, appearing with SBSB.
17.3.95 Adelaide, South Australia, promoted by Tim Whelan, appearing with SBSB.
18.3.95 Port Elliot, South Australia, promoted by Tim Whelan, appearing with SBSB.
**SELECTED BROADCASTS AND/OR RECORDED WORK:**
20.5.95 'Kenny Live' for RTÉ.
9.9.95 'The Slightly Bewildered String Band', recorded by Starc Records.
7.10.95 'Kenny Live', for RTÉ.
**REGULARLY PERFORMS WITH:**
Don Baker (acoustic, slide guitar, harmonica and vocals),
Nancy Beaven (acoustic, fingerstyle and slide guitar and vocals) and Tommy Feeney (acoustic, fingerstyle and slide guitar and vocals).
**AVAILABILITY:**
General.
**ADDITIONAL INFORMATION:**
Special interest areas are the performance of the works of Albéniz on resophonic and twelve-string guitar and compositions derived and influenced by poetry.

## Ronan Guilfoyle *Acoustic Bass Guitar*

**Contact:** Mr Ronan Guilfoyle
10, O'Rourke Park
Sallynoggin
Co Dublin
**Tel:** +353 1 2853497

**PRIZES/AWARDS/APPOINTMENTS:**
Current Director of the Jazz Department, Newpark Music Centre, Dublin.
**REGULARLY PERFORMS WITH:**
Khanda, Dev Sirme, TIME.
**ADDITIONAL INFORMATION:**
Began his career in Ireland in the early 1980's. Has played with many of the great figures in contemporary jazz including Dave Liebman, John Abercrombie, Larry Coryell, Richie Beirach and Enrico Pieranunzi. Has led his own bands and performed with them throughout Europe, the US, India, China and Turkey. Has been guest teacher at many schools and colleges throughout the world including Berklee College of Music in Boston. Active composer and has written several pieces for symphony orchestra and chamber groups as well as for theatre productions and jazz ensembles.

## Tommy Halferty *Guitar*

**Contact:** Tommy Halferty
**Tel:** +353 1 2856883

*"Marks an overdue recognition on disc of the soloistic skills of Tommy Halferty ... supple, rhythmically alert solo work"* Sunday Times.

**KEY IRISH PERFORMANCES** (since January 1994):
1994 Tour of Ireland, promoted by Music Network, appearing with Martin Nolan (pipes) and Ellen Cranitch (flute).
1996 Coach House, Dublin Castle for visit by President Clinton, appearing with Ronan Guilfoyle.
**KEY PERFORMANCES OUTSIDE IRELAND** (since January 1994):
1986 Cais Cais Festival, Portugal, appearing with Art Themen (saxophone).
1991 German television appearance with 'Ethnology', appearing with Tommy Hayes and Ronan Browne.
1992 Parthenay Jazz Festival, France, appearing with organ trio.
1994 Israel International Guitar Festival, Tel Aviv, appearing with guitar duo.
**TRAINING AND/OR QUALIFICATIONS:**
BA, H Dip M ED.
**SELECTED BROADCASTS AND/OR RECORDED WORK:**
1995 'Anda' for the Improvised Music Company.
1996 'Irish Connection' for Steeplechase Records, Denmark.
**PRIZES/AWARDS/APPOINTMENTS:**
1991 Tutorship appointment at University of Ulster, at Jordanstown.
1994 Critic's Choice, Israel International Guitar Festival, Tel Aviv.
**REGULARLY PERFORMS WITH:**
Tommy Halferty Trio.
**AVAILABILITY:**
General.
**ADDITIONAL INFORMATION:**
Regularly tours France, Spain and Portugal. Since the beginning of the 1980's has led many groups of his own. In 1988 formed the France Irish Trio and the Irish French Connection. Jazz teacher at Newpark Music Centre, Dublin and gives many seminars throughout Ireland.

## Tom Harte *Guitar*

**Contact:** Tom Harte
2, Saint Mary's Terrace
Arbour Place
Stoneybatter
Dublin 7
**Tel:** +353 1 6711361
**Other instruments:** Flute.

**KEY IRISH PERFORMANCES** (since January 1994):
2.94 National Concert Hall, Dublin, promoted by RTÉ and the Arts Council, appearing with Dublin Jazz Collective.
5.94 'Paddy Expo', The Savoy, Limerick, appearing with Dublin Jazz Collective.
**SELECTED BROADCASTS AND/OR RECORDED WORK:**
3.91 'Nighthawks' for RTÉ.
2.94 'Inside Cut' for RTÉ.
3.96 'Forty Shades of Blue' for IBC Records.
**PRIZES/AWARDS/APPOINTMENTS:**
7.92 Awarded a scholarship to attend the International Association of Jazz Schools, Italy from the Newpark Music Centre, Dublin.
**TRAINING AND/OR QUALIFICATIONS:**
8.93/94/95 Attended the International Jazz Summer school at the University of Ulster at Jordanstown.
5.94 Masterclass with Dave Holland.
1.96 Masterclass with Kenoy Usknsr.
**REGULARLY PERFORMS WITH:**
Fintan Jones, Haji Aohkso, Hugh Buckley.
**AVAILABILITY:**
General.

## Eugene Macari *Guitar*

**Contact:** Mr Eugene Macari
33, River Forest
Leixlip, Co Kildare
**Tel:** +353 1 6242128

**KEY IRISH PERFORMANCES** (since January 1994):
3.5.97 Eurovision, The Point Depot, Dublin, appearing with the RTÉ Concert Orchestra.
21/23.5.97 RDS proms, appearing with the RTÉCO.
8.97 National Concert Hall, Dublin appearing with the RTÉCO.
**REGULARLY APPEARS WITH:**
RTÉCO, Joan Talbot (vocals) and Jim Farrelly (saxophone).
**AVAILABILITY:**
General.

# Jim McCullagh *Guitar*

**Contact:** Mr Jim McCullagh
c/o Ulster College of Music
13, Windsor Avenue
Belfast BT19
Northern Ireland
**Tel:** +44 1232 381314
*See guitar page 21.*

# Michael McGinty

## *Electric Bass Guitar*

**Contact:** Mr Michael McGinty
Calhame
Letterkenny
Co Donegal
**Tel:** +353 74 23007
*See double bass page 270.*

# Michael McInerney *Guitar*

**Contact:** Mr Michael McInerney
36, Sefton
Rochestown Avenue
Dún Laoghaire
Co Dublin
**Tel:** +353 1 2850996
*See harmonica page 226.*

# Paul Desmond Moore

## *Electric Bass Guitar*

**Contact:** Mr Paul Desmond Moore
12, Thor Place
North Circular Road
Dublin 7
**Tel:** +353 1 8384806
*See traditional guitar page 223.*

# Mike Nielsen *Guitar*

**Contact:** Mr Mike Nielsen
1, Whitechurch Abbey
Grange Park
Rathfarnham
Dublin 14
**Tel:** +353 1 4938744

*"... Definitely one of Europe's most 'worth hearing' on his instrument today' "*
1993 Arbetet (Swedish Newspaper).

**KEY IRISH PERFORMANCES** (since January 1994):
Has toured nationwide - Cork, Roscommon, Sligo and Belfast, with Albert Bover (piano), Stephen Keogh (drums) and Arne Somoghyi (bass).
Has also performed at the Guinness Cork Jazz Festival.
**KEY PERFORMANCES OUTSIDE IRELAND** (since January 1994):
17.10.95 Istanbul Concert Hall, appearing with Okay Tamiz from the Karnatik College of Percussion, India.
1995 Manhattan, USA.
1995 Jamboree Jazz Club, Barcelona, appearing with Julian Arquelles (saxophone).
**SELECTED BROADCASTS AND/OR RECORDED WORK:**
Various for the Improvised Music Company.
**PRIZES/AWARDS/APPOINTMENTS:**
1982 Scholarship to attend Berklee College of Music, Boston.
**TRAINING AND/OR QUALIFICATIONS:**
Studied classical guitar, at the Royal Academy of Irish Music and the DIT Conservatory of Music and Drama.
Studied for two years at Berklee College of Music, Boston.
**REGULARLY PERFORMS WITH:**
Brendan Doyle Jazz Quartet.
**ADDITIONAL INFORMATION:**
While studying in Boston, had the opportunity of playing at local jazz clubs. Has performed with Kenny Wheeler, Dave Liebman, Sonny Fortune, Pat La Barbera. Teaches at DIT Conservatory of Music and Drama, Newpark Music School and, Queen's University, Belfast. Has been guest teacher at schools in Copenhagen, Sweden, New York, Canada, Boston, London. Also does some composing.

# Bill O'Haire *Guitar*

**Contact:** Mr Bill O'Haire
2, Youghals
Clonakilty
Co Cork
**Tel:** +353 23 34546

**KEY IRISH PERFORMANCES** (since January 1994):
5.97 Metropole Hotel, Cork, appearing with Harry Connelly.
4.97 Jury's Hotel, Cork, appearing with the Len McCarthy Band.
3.97 Firkin Krane, Cork, appearing with the Len McCarthy Band.
**KEY PERFORMANCES OUTSIDE IRELAND** (since January 1994):
1994 Amsterdam Blues Festival, appearing with Bill O'Haire Trio.
1995 Ankara Jazz Festival, Turkey appearing with Bill O'Haire Trio.
**SELECTED BROADCASTS AND/OR RECORDED WORK:**
1986 'Hip Chops' for Tramp Records, Amsterdam.
1990 'London 1990' for Konk Studios, London.
1995 'Guitar Movies' for O'Haire Songs, Amsterdam.
**SELECTED REVIEWS** (since January 1994):
3.97 The Examiner (Pearce Harvey).
**TRAINING AND/OR QUALIFICATIONS:**
From 1972 to 1973, Attended Kent State University, Kent, Ohio, USA.
**AVAILABILITY:**
General.
**ADDITIONAL INFORMATION:**
American guitarist who studies with Charlie Banacos. Plays modern jazz with a blues feeling.

# Mark O'Leary *Guitar*

**Contact:** Mr Mark O'Leary
59, Greenhills Court
South Douglas Road, Cork
**Tel:** +353 21 361808

**TRAINING AND/OR QUALIFICATIONS:**
From 1987 to 1989, studied at Guitar Institute of Technology, Los Angeles.
**REGULARLY PERFORMS WITH:**
Larry Coryell, David Murray, John Hicks, Kenny Wheeler, Hein van de Geyn Trio, Ed Schuller Trio, Kenny Werner.
**ADDITIONAL INFORMATION:**
Member of Irish Music Teacher's Association and International Association of Jazz Educators.

# David O'Rourke *Guitar*

**Contact:** Mr David O'Rourke
c/o Mr Terry Dunne
'Tramps' 45, West 21st Street
New York 10010, USA
**Tel/Fax:** +1 212 727 3088 / +1 212 475 8700

*"The gifted Irish jazz guitarist has a warm silvery sound and a rare ability to penetrate familiar material"* 1992 Village Voice, Gary Giddins.

**KEY IRISH PERFORMANCES** (since January 1994):
10.91 and 10.94 Guinness Cork International Jazz Festival.
10.95 Guinness CJF appearing with Cedar Walton Trio.
**KEY PERFORMANCES OUTSIDE IRELAND** (since January 1994):
7.95 Palace Stamford Theatre, Conneticut, USA.
9.95 Jazz and Blues cruise, Bermuda, promoted by Naaten.
10.95 966 Jazz Club, Brooklyn, New York, appearing with Seleno Clarke Quintet.
10.95 New York City, USA.
**SELECTED BROADCASTS AND/OR RECORDED WORK:**
2.95 'Stateside', for WNYC and RTÉ.
3.95 'Jazz in Harlem', for Black Entertainment Television.
2.96 Live recording for cd at 'Tramps', New York, City, for Chiara Scuro.
**SELECTED REVIEWS** (since January 1994):
8.95 Jazz Times.
8.95 Village Voice.
**PRIZES/AWARDS/APPOINTMENTS:**
1981/1982 Winner of the RTÉ Young Musician of the Future, (jazz section).
1983 Awarded 'Best Club Band', by Guinness CJF.
**REGULARLY PERFORMS WITH:**
David O'Rourke Trio, David O'Rourke Quartet, David O'Rourke and David Lee Jones Duo.
**AVAILABILITY:**
General.
**ADDITIONAL INFORMATION:**
Has performed with George Benson, Larry Willis, Seleno Clarke, Kirk Lightsey, Cedar Walton, Russell Malone. Guest faculty speaker of the Jazz Department of The New School, New York and has acted as subsitute lecturer for Mr Don Sickler, Columbia University. Own compositions have been published by 'Second Floor Music'.

# Rod Patterson *Bass Guitar*

**Contact:** Mr Rod Patterson
47 Pommern Parade
Belfast BT6 9FY
Northern Ireland
**Tel/Fax/Mobile:** +44 1232 705098 / +44 1232 705098 / +44 831 197600
**Other instruments:** Double bass, singer.

**KEY IRISH PERFORMANCES** (since January 1994):
A variety of large function engagements within Northern Ireland with 'Nightswing'.
**KEY PERFORMANCES OUTSIDE IRELAND** (since January 1994):
9.96 Scarborough, UK, promoted by Summer Season (Haven), appearing with various musicians.
12.96, 1.97 Worthing, UK, promoted by Hammond Productions.
**SELECTED BROADCASTS AND/OR RECORDED WORK:**
14.2.97 'Kelly' for UTV.
**TRAINING AND/OR QUALIFICATIONS:**
From 1987 to 1990 Graduate Diploma (1st Hons) in Light Music Studies from the School of Music and Performing Arts, Newcastle College, Newcastle-upon-Tyne.
**REGULARLY PERFORMS WITH:**
Nightswing, Siobhán Pettit and Her Band.
**AVAILABILITY:**
General.
**ADDITIONAL INFORMATION:**
Performer, musical director, bandleader, arranger, composer. Also involved in fixing, arranging, writing and working as a freelance player. Reading situations include: theatre, television, studio big band, and function work. Non-reading gigs include jazz, pub gigs etc. Doubling on vocals has also enabled fronting of bands.

# Frank Simon *Guitar*

**Contact:** Mr Frank Simon
The Plains
Boyle
Co Roscommon
**Tel:** +353 79 62245
*See guitar page 225.*

# Tony Steele *Electric Bass Guitar*

**Contact:** Tony Steele
89, Willow Park Grove
Glasnevin
Dublin 11
**Mobile:** +353 87 487052
**Other instruments:** Keyboards, Irish flute.

**KEY IRISH PERFORMANCES** (since January 1994):
12.95 Crescent Arts Centre, Belfast, promoted by Moving on Music, appearing with Saoco.
**SELECTED RECORDED WORK:**
1997 'Descargo Saoco' for IMC.
1997 'Change', with Garret Wall for K-Tel.
**REGULARLY PERFORMS WITH:**
Saoco (Latin Jazz).
**AVAILABILITY:**
General.

# Louis Stewart *Guitar*

**Contact:** Mr Louis Stewart
1, St Anthony's Crescent
Greenhills, Dublin
**Tel:** +353 1 4506052

*"... Extraordinary high levels of focused, deep, creative playing ..."* Downbeat magazine, USA.

**PRIZES/AWARDS/APPOINTMENTS:**
1980 1st Prize as male soloist, awarded at the Nordring Radio Festival.
Grand Prix Prize awarded, at the Montreux Jazz Festival.
Received a Bank of Ireland Arts Show Award for contribution to music.

**SELECTED BROADCASTS AND/OR RECORDED WORK:**
8.93 'Here's to Life', with Joe Williams and the Robert Farnon Orchestra, for Telarc Records.
2.94 'That Shearing Sound', with The New George Shearing Quartet, for Telarc Records.
7.94 'Tangence', with J.J Johnson (with guest Wynton Marsalis) and the Robert Farnon Orchestra, for Gitanes Records.
**ADDITIONAL INFORMATION:**
Has toured with Eddy Louis, Pepper Adams, Dizzy Gillespie, the Benny Goodman Orchestra and the Ronnie Scott Quartet. Played in the Turin Jazz Festival, the Estoril Jazz Festival in Cascais in Portugal, the Royal Festival Hall in London and the North Sea Jazz Festival. Performed in the Blue Note, New York with the George Shearing Trio. 1982 composed a jazz suite named 'Joycenotes' for an eight piece band.

# HARMONICA

## Michael Kinsella *Harmonica*

**Contact:** Mr Michael Kinsella
c/o 'Home For the Bewildered Music Company'
39, Fairview Green
Dublin
**Tel:** +353 1 8331920

**KEY IRISH PERFORMANCES** (since January 1994):
From 28.4.95 to 30.8.95, Galway Rhythm and Roots Festival, promoted by MCD, appearing with Slightly Bewildered String Band.
From 5.7.95 to 7.5.95, Paddy Expo Limerick, promoted by Irish Distributors Limited, appearing with SBSB.
From 2.4.95 to 4.6.95, Castlebar Blues Festival, promoted by Larry Roddy, appearing with SBSB.
Feakle Festival, promoted by Gary Pepper, appearing with SBSB.
**KEY PERFORMANCES OUTSIDE IRELAND** (since January 1994):
From 3.5.95 to 5.3.95, Hobart Oyster Festival, Australia, promoted by T.Whelan, appearing with SBSB.
From 10.3.95 to 12.3.95, Portfairy Festival and Snakewake, Adelaide, Australia, promoted by T.Whelan, appearing with SBSB.
**SELECTED BROADCASTS AND/OR RECORDED WORK:**
10.3.95 'Musicdeli' for Australian TV.
20.5.95 'Kenny Live', for RTÉ.
9.9.95 'The Slightly Bewildered Stringband', CD recording for Starc Records.
**PRIZES/AWARDS/APPOINTMENTS:**
3.95 1st Prize, Portfairy Championship, awarded by Australian Harmonica Association.
1995 1st Prize Winner in traditional and folk section at Paddy Expo, Limerick.
**REGULARLY PERFORMS WITH:**
Bloomin leaders, Liam Merriman (congas and harmonica).
**AVAILABILITY:**
General.
**ADDITIONAL INFORMATION:**
Has worked and recorded with Thom Moore, Brendan Power, Noel Bridgeman, Liam Merriman, Bloomin Headers, The Moss House Project, and 'River of Sound' for RTÉ. Has written an introductory book to the blues harp.

## Michael McInerney *Harmonica*

**Contact:** Mr Michael McInerney
36, Sefton, Rochestown Ave
Dún Laoghaire, Co Dublin
**Tel:** +353 1 2850996
*See harmonica page 226.*

## Eamon Murray *Harmonica*

**Contact:** Eamon Murray
**Tel/Fax:** +353 404 46096
**Other instruments:** Saxophone, vocals.

**KEY IRISH PERFORMANCES** (since January 1994):
From 1994 to 1997, Regular appearances in Bad Bobs and Whelan's, Dublin.
1996 and 1997 Guinness Cork International Jazz Festival.
7.95/96/97 Temple Bar, promoted by the Guinness Blues Festival.
**SELECTED BROADCASTS AND/OR RECORDED WORK:**
1980 Barry Moore and Eamon Murray 'In Grönigen' (KLOET 001).
Rhythm Kings for Scoff Records and Dark Fox (DT 008).
1988 'No Comment' (film music) for RTÉ and The Picture House Company.
**TRAINING AND/OR QUALIFICATIONS:**
8-9.95 and 8-9.96 Studied saxophone at University of Ulster, Jordanstown (Jazz summer school).
9.96 to 6.97 Studied voice with Veronica Dunne at the Leinster School of Music.
**REGULARLY PERFORMS WITH:**
Fattenin' Frogs for Snakes, Cajun Kings.
**AVAILABILITY:**
General.
**ADDITIONAL INFORMATION:**
Plays saxophone, harmonica and vocals both on tour and for studio recordings.

## Ray Preston *Harmonica*

**Contact:** Mr Ray Preston
6, Willbrook Lawn
Dublin 14
**Tel:** +353 1 4931916
**Other instruments:** Voice.

*"Not only did he achieve an incredible sound, but exhibited a real bluesy jazz feeling"*
1988 Jazz Journal.

**KEY IRISH PERFORMANCES** (since January 1994):
10.94 Metropole Hotel Cork, promoted by Guinness Cork International Jazz Festival, appearing with Dick Keating and Dave Mason.
10.95 Metropole Hotel Cork, promoted by Guinness Jazz Festival, appearing with John Donegan and the Blue Notes.
8.96 Brogan's Jazz Club, Dublin, appearing with Ray Preston Quartet.
10.96 Metropole Hotel Cork, promoted by Guinness Jazz Festival, appearing with the Blue Notes.
**SSELECTED BROADCASTS AND/OR RECORDED WORK:**
1993 'Off The Record' for RTÉ.
Freddie White album 'Long Distance Runner'
**REGULARLY PERFORMS WITH:**
John Donegan (piano), Justin Carroll (hammond organ and piano), Ray Preston Quartet, Blue Notes.
**AVAILABILITY:**
General.
**ADDITIONAL INFORMATION:**
Has guested with Spike Robinson, Michael Garrick Trio, Digby Fairweather as well as most of Ireland's top jazz musicians, in addition to recording and television work. Gives regular performances at the Guinness Cork International Jazz Festival.

# JAZZ PERCUSSION

## Peter Ainslough *Drums*

**Contact:** Mr Peter Ainslough
52, Michael Collins Park
Dublin 22
**Tel:** +353 1 4574246

## Darren Beckett *Drums*

**Contact:** Mr Darren Beckett
92, Rickamore Road
Upper Templepatrick
Co Antrim BT39 OJE
Northern Ireland
**Tel:** +44 18494 32378
**Other instruments:** Piano.

**KEY IRISH PERFORMANCES** (since January 1994):
1995 Jazz by the River, promoted by Gerry Godley appearing with Kenny Davern.
10.96 Guinness Cork International Jazz Festival, promoted by Jack McGouran appearing with Grant Stewart Anthony.
11.96 Belfast Jazz Festival, promoted by Brian Carson appearing with Louis Stewart.
11.96 Brogan's, Dublin promoted by Gerry Godley appearing with the Michael Buckley Trio.
**KEY PERFORMANCES OUTSIDE IRELAND** (since January 1994):
1.96 Slovinia Jazz Festival appearing with Christoph Singer.
5.96 Bradleys, New York appearing with Phil Markivitz.
6.96 London appearing with Tina May.
12.96 Smuck Kitchen, Cologne, Germany appearing with Kenny Wheeler.
**SELECTED RECORDED WORK:**
5.95 'Miles Away' for Acoustic Music.
7.97 Jurgen Freidrich with Kenny Wheeler for CTI.
11.97 'The Pendulum' for IMC.
**SELECTED REVIEWS** (since January 1994):
1996 Paris, Jerome Sabbagh.
6.97 Evening Herald.
**PRIZES/AWARDS/APPOINTMENTS:**
11.94 Bass Ireland Award from the Arts Council.
9.95 Scholarships received to study in New York and Germany.
**TRAINING AND OR QUALIFICATIONS:**
From 9.93 to 7.94, Studied with Keith Copeland at the Cologne Conservatory of Music.
From 1.7.94 to 1.8.94, Banff Centre of Arts, Canada.
9.95 Degree in Fine Arts from the Carl Allen New School, New York.
**REGULARLY PERFORMS WITH:**
Michael Buckley Trio, Kenny Wheeler, Jean Toussaint.
**AVAILABILITY:**
General.
**ADDITIONAL INFORMATION:**
Has played and toured throughout Europe, America and Canada. Now living in New York and performing in various clubs. Has recorded up to 7 CD's with various musicians.

## Charlie Burton *Drums*

**Contact:** Mr Charlie Burton
3, Knockdene, Bangor
Co Down, BT20 4UZ, Northern Ireland
**Tel:** +44 1247 458141
**Other instruments:** Voice.

*".... In a class parallel to the quality of front line jazz stars ...."* 5.96 Belfast Telegraph.

**KEY IRISH PERFORMANCES** (since January 1994):
Various dates, Belfast, promoted by Jazz by the river, appearing with Scott Hamilton, Warren Vache, George Masso, Harry Allen, Ken Deplouski and Al Cohn.
1996 Promoted by ACNI, appearing with Dermod Harland and Louis Stewart.
**KEY PERFORMANCES OUTSIDE IRELAND** (since January 1994):
6.97 Sacramento, California, USA, promoted by Sacramento Jazz Festival, appearing with Apex Jazz Band.
7.97 Whitley Bay, appearing with Apex Jazz Band.
Various jazz festivals around Great Britain.
**RECORDED WORK:**
6.94 Scott Hamilton and Warren Vache concert for UTV.
**REGULARLY PERFORMS WITH:**
The Apex Jazz Band.
**AVAILABILITY:**
General.
**ADDITIONAL INFORMATION:**
Drummer/singer with experience of performing in a wide range of musical styles including folk, dance, pop, blues, jazz and big band. Speciality is jazz and has performed with many visiting American artists.

## Myles Drennan *Drums*

**Contact:** Myles Drennan
22 Beechdale
Kilcoole
Co Wicklow
**Tel/Mobile:** +353 1 2873726 / +353 86 8116421
**Other instruments:** Piano.

**REGULARLY PERFORMS WITH:**
Brendan Doyle Jazz Quartet, Louis Stewart, Richie Buckley.
**ADDITIONAL INFORMATION:**
Has worked as both drummer and pianist with foremost Irish jazz musicians, as well as US visitors George Coleman, Rickey Woodard, Harry Allen, Guy Parker, Jean Toussaint and Canadian trumpet player Ingrid Jensen.

## Nigel Flegg *Drumset*

**Contact:** Mr Nigel Flegg
Saint Nicholas House
Rostrevor Road
Rathgar
Dublin 6
**Tel/Mobile:** +353 1 4961369 / +353 87 2365112

**KEY IRISH PERFORMANCES** (since January 1994):
6.96 Olympia Theatre, Dublin, promoted by MCD, appearing with Dead Can Dance.
11.96 Metropole Hotel, Cork, promoted by the Guinness Cork International Jazz Festival, appearing with the Irish Jazz Orchestra.
12.96 Whelan's, Dublin, promoted by Improvised Music Company, appearing with the Night in Havana Orchestra.
6.97 Crescent Arts Centre, Belfast, promoted by Moving on Music, appearing with the Mike Nielsen Project.
**KEY PERFORMANCES OUTSIDE IRELAND** (since January 1994):
15.6.96 Sale Pleyel, Paris, appearing with Dead Can Dance.
11.8.96 Universal Amphitheatre, Los Angeles, appearing with Dead Can Dance.
21.8.96 Olympia, Sao Paulo, appearing with Dead Can Dance.
28.8.96 Met, Mexico City, appearing with Dead Can Dance.

**SELECTED BROADCASTS AND/OR RECORDED WORK:**
11.96 'Descarga Saoco' for IMC Records.
5.97 Appearing with the 'La Luna' group for RTÉ.
6.97 'Latin Soul' for RTÉ.
**TRAINING AND/OR QUALIFICATIONS:**
From 15.9.90 to 30.9.92, Studied with Keith Copeland at the University of Ulster, Jordanstown.
From 1.94 to 2.94, Diploma de Musica Popular from the National School of Art, Havana, Cuba.
**REGULARLY PERFORMS WITH:**
Dead Can Dance, Mike Nielsen Project, Saoco.
**AVAILABILITY:**
General.
**ADDITIONAL INFORMATION:**
Has also performed with Mike Nielsen, Ronan Guilfoyle, Tommy Halferty, Richie Buckley etc. Teaches drums and percussion at Newpark Music Centre, Dublin.

## Conor Guilfoyle *Drum set*

**Contact:** Conor Guilfoyle
23, Cherrywood
Killiney
Co Dublin
**Tel:** +353 1 2720461
**Other instruments:** Tablas, Dumbeck, latin percussion.

**PRIZES/AWARDS/APPOINTMENTS:**
Scholarship for the Banff Centre for the Arts, Canada.
1995 Scholarship to attend the National School of Music, Havana, Cuba awarded by the Arts Council.
**TRAINING AND/OR QUALIFICATIONS:**
Studied at the Drummers Collective, New York.
**REGULARLY PERFORMS WITH:**
Khanda, Saoco, Guilfoyle Nielson Trio, Dev Sirme.
**AVAILABILITY:**
General.
**ADDITIONAL INFORMATION:**
Freelance artist. Has performed throughout Europe, the USA, China and India. Teacher at the Newpark Music Centre. Has worked with David Leibman, John Abercromby, Sonny Fortune, Pucho and others. Has lectured at the Hague Conservatory and has written tutors on the drum set.

## Stephen Keogh *Drums*

**Contact:** Mr Stephen Keogh
31, Attico
La Primera
8012 Barcelona
Spain
**Tel:** +34 3 2372582

## Anthony Kerr *Vibraphone and Marimba*

**Contact:** Mr Anthony Kerr
3, Priory Walk
Street
Albans AL1 2JA
England
**Tel:** +44 1727 859400

*"Brilliant young vibes player"* 1995 Belfast Telegraph.

**KEY IRISH PERFORMANCES** (since January 1994):
1993 Belfast Festival at Queen's, appearing with Louis Stewart.
1996 Cork International Jazz Festival, appearing with Grant Stewart.
10.97 Tour of Ireland, promoted by Music Network and Moving on Music, appearing with Albert Bover, Matt Miles and Steve Brown.
**KEY PERFORMANCES OUTSIDE IRELAND** (since January 1994):
1992 BBC Proms, Royal Albert Hall, London, appearing with the Mike Westbrook Orchestra.
**SELECTED BROADCASTS AND/OR RECORDED WORK:**
1994 'First Cry' for EFZ.
**SELECTED REVIEWS** (since January 1994):
1993 Jazz Mag.
1994 The Guardian.
**TRAINING AND/OR QUALIFICATIONS:**
From 1986 to 1988, Studied with David Friedman.
**PRIZES/AWARDS/APPOINTMENTS:**
1994 Award from EMA.
1994 British Jazz Award, for Best Instrumentalist.
**AVAILABLE:**
General.

## Andrew Lavery *Drums*

**Contact:** Mr Andrew Lavery
37, Glengoland Gardens
Dunmurry
Belfast BT17 OJE
Northern Ireland
**Tel:** +44 1232 621505
*See page 296.*

## David Mason *Drums*

**Contact:** Mr David Mason
**Tel:** +353 1 8333987

**KEY IRISH PERFORMANCES** (since January 1994):
1.95 Tullyhally Castle, Castlepollard, Co Roscommon, promoted by Derravaragh Music Association, appearing with Louis Stewart and Martin Curry.
10.95 Guinness Cork International Jazz Festival, appearing with Young Lions and Ingrid Jensen.
10.95 Trinity College, Dublin, appearing with Art Farmer, Alan Sheilds, Louis Stewart and Noel Kelehan.
9.96 Mother Redcaps, Dublin, appearing with Dublin Jazz Society, appearing with Louis Stewart, Arnie Somdogi and Charles McPherson.
**SELECTED BROADCASTS AND/OR RECORDED WORK:**
1995 'Niggle Squiggle' CD, recorded by Improvised Music Company.
**SELECTED REVIEWS** (since January 1994):
1994 Sunday Independent.
14.1.96 Sunday Tribune.
**PRIZES/AWARDS/APPOINTMENTS:**
1995 Awarded scholarship to Cologne Music Academy, Germany.
**TRAINING AND/OR QUALIFICATIONS:**
From 1988 to 1992, Walton's School of Music, Dublin.
From 1992 to 1995, classes with John Wadham.
1994 International Jazz Summer School at University of Ulster.
Since 1995, Hochschule für Musik, Köln, Germany.
Since 1995 Classes with Keith Copeland.
**REGULARLY PERFORMS WITH:**
Myles Drennan (piano), Alan Shields (bass), Louis Stewart (guitar).
**AVAILABILITY:**
General.

# Kieran Phillips *Drums*

**Contact:** Mr Kieran Phillips
25, Mount Merrion Avenue
Blackrock
Co Dublin
**Tel:** +353 1 2886049

**KEY IRISH PERFORMANCES** (since January 1994):
7.96 Brogans, Dublin, appearing with Michael Buckley.
10.96 Brogans, Dublin, appearing with Wednesday Night Prayer Meeting (tribute to Charles Mingus).
2.97 Brogans, Dublin, appearing with Ronan Guilfoyle and Tommy Halferty.
4.97 Brogans, Dublin, appearing with Dorothy Murphy and Mike Nielsen.
**TRAINING AND/OR QUALIFICATIONS:**
From 8.94 to 9.94, Attended the International Jazz Summer School, University of Ulster, Jordanstown.
From 10.94 to 5.96, Attended improvisation workshops at the Newpark Music Centre, Dublin.
7.95 Attended IASJ workshop, Israel.
**REGULARLY PERFORMS WITH:**
Wednesday Night Prayer Meeting.
**AVAILABILITY:**
General.

# Bernard Reilly *Drums / Vibraphone*

**Contact:** Mr Bernard Reilly
26, Sandyford Downs
Dublin 13
**Tel:** +353 1 2958742
**Email:** breilly@tinet.ie
*See percussion classical page 31.*

# John Simons

## *Percussion, conga's, timabale, chimes*

**Contact:** Mr John Simons
'Old School House'
Bodyke
Co Clare
**Tel/Fax:** +353 61 921483 or +353 65 35559 /
+353 65 35559

*"Awsum Adudu transport their audience from Sowetto to South America via Detroit and Galway"* 4.95 Howth Jazz Programme.

**KEY IRISH PERFORMANCES** (since January 1994):
2.10.95 Roisin Dubh Pub, Galway, appearing with Awsum Adudu.
15.10.95 Dublin, promoted by Warchild Charity, appearing with Awsum Adudu.
10.95 Guinness Cork International Jazz Festival, promoted by Front Line promotions.
**SELECTED BROADCASTS AND/OR RECORDED WORK:**
9.94 Awsum Adudu debut record.
2.95 Recording with Dennis Alan.
5.95 Recording with Dennis Carey.
**SELECTED REVIEWS** (since January 1994):
10.94 Cork Jazz programme.
1995 Westport Arts Programme.
**PRIZES/AWARDS/APPOINTMENTS:**
5.94 1st Prize in jazz category, awarded by European Musical Showcase.
**REGULARLY PERFORMS WITH:**
Adriana Von Runich, The Awsum Adudu Group and The Mary Custy Band.
**AVAILABILITY:**
General.
**ADDITIONAL INFORMATION:**
Percussionist using contemporary and ethnic instruments. Produced a percussion score for a Dermot Healy play 'Last Nights Fun' produced and performed by the Theatre Omnibus Group in Ennis. Will consider all projects offered.

# John Wadham *Drums*

**Contact:** Mr John Wadham
7, Coliemore Road
Dalkey
Co Dublin
**Tel:** +353 1 2859629 / +353 1 2858505

**KEY IRISH PERFORMANCES** (since January 1994):
Annual performances at festivals in Cork, Dublin and Belfast.
**KEY PERFORMANCES OUTSIDE IRELAND** (since January 1994):
Has performed at events in Toronto, Sacramento, Montreux, Prague, Cascais, Helsinki and Berlin.
**SELECTED BROADCASTS AND/OR RECORDED WORK:**
Own programme on RTÉ for 9 years.
**AVAILABILITY:**
General.
**ADDITIONAL INFORMATION:**
Works on many local jazz gigs and teaches drums. Past pupils have been, Larry Mullen of U2, Paul McAteer, Fran Breen, Robbie Brennan, Paul Moran, Noel Bridgeman, Conor Guilfoyle, Stephen Keogh, Darren Beckett and David Mason.

# Thomas Wiegandt

## *Djembe-Drums (West-African)*

**Contact:** Mr Thomas Wiegandt
Nature Art Centre
Ballybane
Ballydehob, Co Cork
**Tel:** +353 28 37323
**Other instruments:** Percussions, plucked string instruments, Tibetan singing bowls.

**KEY IRISH PERFORMANCES** (since January 1994):
1995 Bantry House, Cork.
19.5.95 Triskel Arts Centre, Cork.
5.12.95 Triskel Arts Centre, Cork, appearing with Bas van Eynatten.
13.11.96 Triskel Arts Centre, Cork, appearing with Bas van Eynatten.
**SELECTED BROADCASTS AND/OR RECORDED WORK:**
1988 'Mad Mix: Improvisations' (Jazz Duo with Jeremy Baines) for own label.
1989 'Timetemple: Reflections' (Crossover traditional Japanese/Jazz).
These and other unreleased music can be ordered.
**SELECTED REVIEWS** (since January 1994):
11.94 Art Beat (Skibbereen).
3.11.94 Southern Star (Skibbereen).
**TRAINING AND/OR QUALIFICATIONS:**
From 12.90 to 1.91, Studied Djembe playing and making with Master Drummer Famadou Konate, Guinea, West-Africa.
From 1.91 to 2.92, Studied the Gangsa, main metallophon of the Gamelan instruments, with Gamelan Master Anak Agong Raka in Ubud, Bali, Indonesia.
**REGULARLY PERFORMS WITH:**
Bas van Eynatten (didgeridoo).
**AVAILABILITY:**
General.

**ADDITIONAL INFORMATION:**
Uses 'ethnic' rhythms and scales from different traditions improvising around the theme in jazz style. Also performs meditative concerts on Tibetan singing bowls. Teaches and builder of Djembe-drums. Runs the Nature Arts Centre, a Centre for African drumming in Ballydehob.

# JAZZ PIANO AND KEYBOARDS

## Darren Beckett *Piano*

**Contact:** Mr Darren Beckett
92, Rickamore Road
Upper Templepatrick
Co Antrim BT39 OJE
Northern Ireland
**Tel:** +44 18494 32378
*See percussion page 277.*

## Aidan Coleman *Piano*

**Contact:** Aidan Coleman
28, Lisalea
Frascati Park
Blackrock, Co Dublin
**Tel:** +353 1 2835117
*See Singer page 112.*

## Ellen Cranitch *Keyboards*

**Contact:** Ms Ellen Cranitch
33, Westfield Road
Harold's Cross
Dublin 6w
**Tel/Fax:** +353 1 4923486
*See jazz flute page 271.*

## Jim Doherty *Piano*

**Contact:** Mr Jim Doherty
125, Tritonville Road
Sandymount
Dublin 4
**Tel:** +353 1 6684532
**Other instruments:** Electric keyboards, hammond organ.

**KEY IRISH PERFORMANCES** (since January 1994):
1994 Music Network tour.
**KEY PERFORMANCES OUTSIDE IRELAND** (since January 1994):
1995 Tour of USA, Finland, Denmark.
1996 Tour of Sweden.
**SELECTED BROADCASTS AND/OR RECORDED WORK:**
1987 'Spondance', recorded by Livia Records.
1992 'One Man in his Time', recorded by Trend/Cargo Records.
**REGULARLY PERFORMS WITH:**
Jim Doherty Trio, Jim Doherty Big Band, SPON.
**AVAILABILITY:**
General.
**ADDITIONAL INFORMATION:**
Has worked with Bobby Shew, Scott Hamilton, Ken Peplowski, Art Farner, Roy Williams, Masso, Red Holloway, Harry Dison and Teddy Edwards. Plays all jazz styles except avant garde.

## Myles Drennan *Piano*

**Contact:** Myles Drennan
22 Beechdale
Kilcoole
Co Wicklow
**Tel/Mobile:** +353 1 2873726 / +353 86 8116421
*See percussion page 277.*

## Neil Everett *Piano*

**Contact:** Mr Neil Everett
14, Brambleway
Newtownabbey
Co Antrim BT36 8FW
Northern Ireland
**Tel:** +44 1232 842701

*"... With brilliant ornamentation and often dazzling passage work that bore the stamp of virtuosity"* 22.11.94 Belfast Telegraph.

**KEY IRISH PERFORMANCES** (since January 1994):
10.93 Cork City Hall, appearing with City of Belfast Orchestra.
11.94 Whitla Hall, Belfast, appearing with Queen's University Orchestra.
11.94 Harty Room, Queen's University, Belfast.
**KEY PERFORMANCES OUTSIDE IRELAND** (since January 1994):
7.93 Newport Jazz Festival.
9.95 Glasgow, promoted by BBC.
**SELECTED BROADCASTS AND/OR RECORDED WORK:**
11.93 'Hungry Eye', for BBC.
12.94 Radio 2 recording.
From 1.3.94 to 3.3.94 'Go For It' for RTÉ and BBC.
9.95 'Claude Bolling Jazz Concerto' for Telarc.
**SELECTED REVIEWS** (since January 1994):
12.94 Belfast Telegraph.
**PRIZES/AWARDS/APPOINTMENTS:**
1993 Scholarship to study jazz in New York, awarded by The Arts Council of Northern Ireland.
**TRAINING AND/OR QUALIFICATIONS:**
From 1992 to 1994, Attended Queen's University, Belfast.
From 1994 to 1995, BA from the Open University.
MA from the Royal Academy of Music, London.
**AVAILABILITY:**
General.
**ADDITIONAL INFORMATION:**
Began his music studies at the City of Belfast School of Music and continued with Maria Curcio - the Artur Schnabel prodigé. Draws upon influences such as Oscar Peterson and Art Tatum. As a jazz soloist has recorded and broadcast for BBC Radio 3, on Radio 2 as well as broadcasts on the world service.

## Richard Farrelly *Piano*

**Contact:** Richard Farrelly
132 Braemor Road
Churchtown
Dublin 14
**Mobile:** +353 87 529680
*See jazz guitar page 272.*

## Patrick Fitzpatrick *Piano*

**Contact:** Patrick Fitzpatrick
96, Custom House Harbour
IFSC
Dublin 1
**Tel:** +353 1 6701949 or +353 1 8326172 (a)
*See piano page 295.*

## Noel Kelehan *Piano*

**Contact:** Mr Noel Kelehan
40, Anne Devlin Road
Dublin 14
**Tel/Fax:** +353 1 4945396 / +353 1 2082511

**AVAILABILITY:**
General.
*See conductor page 171.*

## Colm 'Stride' O'Brien *Piano*

**Contact:** Mr Colm 'Stride' O'Brien
2, Cleveragh Park
Listowel, Co Kerry
**Tel/Fax:** +353 68 21407 / +353 68 21434

**KEY IRISH PERFORMANCES** (since January 1994):
22.3.96 and 18.4.97 National Concert Hall, Dublin.
4.7.96 National Concert Hall, Dublin, appearing with 'Prof' Peter O'Brien (piano).
25.10.96 University College, Cork, promoted by the Guinness Cork International Jazz Festival.
**KEY PERFORMANCES OUTSIDE IRELAND** (since January 1994):
7.95 Boulder County, USA, promoted by the Rocky Mountain Ragtime Fest.
3.96 Gravenhurst Opera House, Canada.
6.96 Sedalia, Missouri, USA, promoted by the Scott Joplin Festival.
3.97 Lancaster Opera House, Buffalo, USA, promoted by the Queen City Jazz Festival, Buffalo.
**SELECTED BROADCASTS AND/OR RECORDED WORK:**
1988 'Colm O'Brien plays Joplin' (own recording).
1.97 'Late Late Show' for RTÉ.
1997 'Joplin, Gershwin, Fats Waller & All That' (own CD recording).
**AVAILABILITY:**
General.
**ADDITIONAL INFORMATION:**
Specialises in ragtime and vintage jazz music from the era 1900 to 1940. Has performed in many Ragtime/Jazz festivals in the USA and Canada. The only Irish person to be invited to the prestigious Scott Joplin Festival in Missouri, USA.

## Peter O'Brien *Piano*

**Contact:** Professor Peter O'Brien
6 Airfield Court
Dublin 4
**Tel/Mobile/Fax:** +353 1 2695115 / +353 87 2206953 / +353 1 2601573

*"... Diverse musical style woven together by the magical thread of Peter O'Brien's creativity"*
3.3.96 Sunday Independent

**KEY IRISH PERFORMANCES** (since January 1994):
10.94 Guinness Cork International Jazz Festival, appearing with Eiji Kitamura.
9.95 National Concert Hall, Dublin, appearing with Mary Coughlan.
11.95 'Feast of Fiddles', National Concert Hall, Dublin, with Geraldine O'Grady, Oonagh Keogh, Paddy Glackin, Pat Collins and Loyko.
Has given ten concerts in the NCH.
**KEY PERFORMANCES OUTSIDE IRELAND** (since Januar 1994):
1994 Birmingham Jazz Festival.
1994 Ronnie Scotts Club, London appearing with Agnes Bernelle.
1995/1997 Jersey Jazz Festival.
1996 100 Club, London.
**SELECTED BROADCASTS AND/OR RECORDED WORK:**
1994 'Handful of Keys'.
'One for my friends', for POB with Mary Coughlan, Richie Buckley, John Wadham, Dave Fleming, Ken Peplowski, Warren Vache, Ralph Sutton.
'Michael Collins' film sound-track (arranged and played 'Mascushla' with Frank Patterson.
**SELECTED REVIEWS** (since January 1994):
21.4.96 Sunday Independent.
**PRIZES/AWARDS/APPOINTMENTS:**
Royal Irish Academy of Music Gold Medal for composition.
**TRAINING AND/OR QUALIFICATIONS:**
Licenciate of Royal Irish Academy of Music.
**AVAILABILITY:**
General.

## Fintan O'Neill *Piano*

**Contact:** Mr Fintan O'Neill
4902, 69th Street
Woodside
Queens
New York, 11377
USA
**Tel:** +1 718 672 5566

**KEY IRISH PERFORMANCES** (since January 1994):
10.95 Guinness Cork International Jazz Festival, appearing with former members of the Jazz Messengers in a tribute to Art Blake and others.
**KEY PERFORMANCES OUTSIDE IRELAND** (since January 1994):
From 1990 to 1995, New York City, promoted by various jazz clubs, appearing with Bob Cranshaw, Essiet Essiet, Denis Irwin, Jed Levy, Brian Lynch, Cecil McBee, Don Pate and others.
**SELECTED BROADCASTS AND/OR RECORDED WORK:**
1994, Live duo for WNYC.
**PRIZES/AWARDS/APPOINTMENTS:**
1987 Silver medalist, winner in the Feis Ceoil, Dublin.
1987 Medal winner in the Feis Ceoil, Dublin for Bach/Haydn competition.
**TRAINING AND/OR QUALIFICATIONS:**
1989 LTCL, from DIT Conservatory of Music and Drama, Dublin.
**REGULARLY PERFORMS WITH:**
Hugh Buckley, Richie Buckley, Fintan O'Neill Trio, Fintan O'Neill Quartet/Quintet, Ronan Guilfoyle, John Wadham.
**AVAILABILITY:**
General.
**ADDITIONAL INFORMATION:**
Teacher, composer and arranger for bands and large ensembles.

## Charles Stephen Lawrence Parker *Piano*

**Contact:** Mr Stephen Parker
19, Raglan House
Ballsbridge, Dublin 4
**Tel:** +353 1 6603557
*See piano page 49.*

# Fergus Sheil *Piano*

**Contact:** Fergus Sheil (senior)
15, Blackheath Park
Clontarf
Dublin 3
**Tel:** +353 1 8336496

*"Hoagy Carmichael would be extremely proud of this interpretation"* (Georgia On My Mind).
1987 Adjudicator (Feis Ceoil solo jazz competition).

**PRIZES/AWARDS/APPOINTMENTS:**
1980 Winner, Milne Cup at the Feis Ceoil.
1987 1st Prize, Solo Jazz Piano.
Winner of the Jim Doherty Cup at the Feis Ceoil, Dublin.
**TRAINING AND/OR QUALIFICATIONS:**
From 1972 to 1978, DIT Conservatory of Music and Drama Gold Medal Award for Sonata playing.
From 1994 to 1997, FTCL from the Leinster School of Music, Dublin.
**AVAILABILITY:**
General.
**ADDITIONAL INFORMATION:**
Plays a wide selection from the general classical repertoire. Has arranged a large number of the standard American song repertoire in a jazz style.

# Tony Steele *Piano*

**Contact:** Tony Steele
89, Willow Park Grove
Glasnevin
Dublin 11
**Mobile:** +353 87 487052
*See guitar page 275.*

## SAXOPHONES

# Michael Buckley

## *Soprano, Alto and Tenor Saxophones*

**Contact:** Mr Michael Buckley
17, St Peter's Drive
Walkinstown
Dublin 12
**Mobile:** +353 87 415580
**Other instruments:** Flutes.

*"The 25-year-old Dubliner is among the most richly imaginative of the Irish Jazzees"*
1996 Irish Times.

**KEY IRISH PERFORMANCES** (since January 1994):
10.95 Cork, promoted by Guinness Cork International Jazz Festival, appearing with Ingrid Jenson.
1996 Promoted by Guinness CIJF appearing with Grant Stewart.
1996 Limerick, promoted by Limerick Jazz Society, appearing with the Michael Buckley Trio.
1997 Brogans, Dublin, promoted by Brogans, appearing with the Michael Buckley Trio.
**KEY PERFORMANCES OUTSIDE IRELAND** (since January 1994):
6.95 Scotland, appearing with Rita Connolly.
6.96 New York, appearing with college big band.
5.97 Paris, appearing with Mary Coughlan.
**SELECTED BROADCASTS AND/OR RECORDED WORK:**
6.96 Radio France appearing with Ronan Guilfoyle.
11.11.96 Michael Buckley Trio for IMC records.
1996 The Cranberries track 'Salvation' for Sony records.
Rita Connolly album 'Valpariso' for Tara Records.
**PRIZES/AWARDS/APPOINTMENTS:**
1988 Irish Mellenium Jazz Musician.
1996 Tuition at the Skidmore Jazz College, New York as part of the Skidmore Jazz Award.
**REGULARLY PERFORMS WITH:**
Michael Buckley Trio, The Young Lions.
**AVAILABILITY:**
General.
**ADDITIONAL INFORMATION:**
Has played in session work with Cranberries, Mary Coughlan, Harry Rabinowitz (film score).

# Neil Buckley

## *Tenor and Soprano Saxophones*

**Contact:** Mr Neil Buckley
Bridgetown
Glen Carrigart
Letterkenny
Co Donegal
**Tel/Fax:** +353 74 55560
**Other instruments:** Clarinet, soprano saxophone.

**KEY IRISH PERFORMANCES** (since January 1994):
1995 The Beach Hotel, Greystones, Co Wicklow, appearing with Jazz Oddessy.
1996 City Hall, Belfast appearing with the Gerry Rice Quartet.
1996 Queen's University Belfast, promoted by the Belfast Festival at Queen's appearing with the Guinness Jazz Band.
1997 Café Society, Belfast, appearing with the Norman Watson Quartet.
**SELECTED BROADCASTS AND/OR RECORDED WORK:**
1983 'Fuam' by the group Clannad.
1988 'Watermark' by Enya.
1991 Guildford International Music Festival, CD for Bmp Vos, produced by Ken Blair.
**AVAILABILITY:**
General.
**ADDITIONAL INFORMATION:**
Specialises in jazz-folk fusion.

# Keith Donald *Soprano Saxophone*

**Contact:** Keith Donald
Boathouse
Rockbrook
Dublin 16
**Tel:** +353 1 4934499
**Other instruments:** Alto saxophone, tenor saxophone, baritone saxophone, clarinet, bass clarinet, recorder.

**KEY IRISH PERFORMANCES** (since January 1994):
1995 Guinness Cork International Jazz Festival, appearing with Ozone.
1995 Mayday Festival, Dublin, appearing with Moving Hearts.
**KEY PERFORMANCES OUTSIDE IRELAND** (since January 1994):
1995 Glasgow Festival, appearing with Moving Hearts.
1996 Glasgow Festival, appearing with Ronnie Drew.
**SELECTED BROADCASTS AND/OR RECORDED WORK:**
4.3.97 'Study Ireland Music' for BBC Northern Ireland.
**PRIZES/AWARDS/APPOINTMENTS:**
1984 Awarded Platinum Disc by WEA Records.

**TRAINING AND/OR QUALIFICATIONS:**
From 1957 to 1963, Clarinet tuition with John Johnston.
**REGULARLY PERFORMS WITH:**
Noel Kelehan Quintet, Davy Spillane, The Dubliners.
**AVAILABILITY:**
General.
**ADDITIONAL INFORMATION:**
Experiments with traditional Irish music and dance music.

## Brendan Doyle *Saxophone*

**Contact:** Mr Brendan Doyle
**Tel:** +353 1 4517742
**Other instruments:** Clarinet.

**KEY PERFORMANCES OUTSIDE IRELAND** (since January 1994):
5.96 Brest, France promoted by Brest Town Council Arts Office, appearing with the Ronan Guilfoyle Trio.
5.96 La Salle Olivier Messaien, Paris, promoted by Radio France appearing with Septet Music.
2.97 Vancouver, Canada, appearing with the Vancouver International Jazz Orchestra.
**SELECTED BROADCASTS AND/OR RECORDED WORK:**
8.95 'Wiggle Squiggle' for the Improvised Music Company.
8.95 'Septet Music' for the Improvised Music Company.
11.96 'Devsirme' for IMC.
**PRIZES/AWARDS/APPOINTMENTS:**
1993 Received a scholarship to attend the Banff Centre in Canada studying under Pat La Barbera, Kenny Wheeler and Chucho Valdes.
**TRAINING AND OR QUALIFICATIONS:**
From 1984 to 1988, BA Mus and LTCL from Waterford Institute of Technology.
**REGULARLY PERFORMS WITH:**
Brendan Doyle Quartet.
**AVAILABILITY:**
General.
**ADDITIONAL INFORMATION:**
Has worked with many leading jazz artists and played with Kenny Wheeler, Hugh Fraser and John Taylor.

## Kenneth Edge *Saxophone*

**Contact:** Mr Kenneth Edge
41, Kilmore Drive
Artane
Dublin 5
**Mobile:** +353 87 504568
*See saxophone page 52.*

## 'Big' Jim Farrelly

### *Alto, Soprano and Tenor Saxophones*

**Contact:** Mr Jim Farrelly
70, Palmerstown Road
Rathmines
Dublin 6
**Tel/Fax:** +353 1 4960090 / +353 1 8333969

**REGULARLY PERFORMS WITH:**
'Big' Jim Farrelly Group.

## Gerry Godley

### *Tenor and Baritone Saxophone*

**Contact:** Mr Gerry Godley
20, Crostwaithe Park South
Dún Laoghaire, Co Dublin
**Tel/Fax:** +353 1 2805245 / +353 1 2805245

**REGULARLY PERFORMS WITH:**
Blow by Blow and Wednesday Night Prayer Meeting.

## John Hogan *Saxophone*

**Contact:** Mr John Hogan
47, Hermitage Drive
Rathfarnham, Dublin 16
**Tel:** +353 1 4947412
*See saxophone page 296.*

## Nicholas Kiely *Saxophone*

**Contact:** Mr Nicholas Kiely
Flat 1
1 Kenilworth Park
Harold's Cross, Dublin 6
**Tel:** +353 1 4922205 or +353 61 419281

*"Sax Improviso"* Limerick Post.

**KEY IRISH PERFORMANCES** (since January 1994):
7.94 Royal Cinema, Limerick, promoted by Limerick Paddy Expo, appearing with Slackjaw.
31.7.95 Dún Laoghaire public park, promoted by Fás, appearing with the actors of stage musical, Grease.
25.8.95 The Bridge, Belfast, promoted by University of Ulster.
9.94 Newtown Pery, Limerick, appearing with Slackjaw.
**PRIZES/AWARDS/APPOINTMENTS:**
1990, 1992, 1994 prize winner in the International Busking Competition, awarded by Limerick Paddy Expo.
**AVAILABILITY:**
General.

## Len McCarthy *Alto Saxophone*

**Contact:** Mr Len McCarthy
'Hillgrove'
Tramore Road, Cork
**Tel:** +353 21 965108
*See clarinet page 269.*

## Gerard McChrystal *Saxophone*

**Contact:** Mr Gerard McChrystal
24, Leas Close
Totterbridge
High Wycombe
Bucks HP13 7UW
England
**Tel/Fax:** +44 1494 464 831
**Email:** saxsaxsax@aol.com
*See saxophone page 52.*

## Rory McGuinness *Tenor Saxophone*

**Contact:** Mr Rory McGuinness
Rere Bungalow
Stradbook Park
Blackrock
Co Dublin
**Tel:** +353 1 2808330

**KEY IRISH PERFORMANCES** (since January 1994):
From 10.3.97 to 23.3.97, Tour of Ireland, promoted by Music Network, appearing with John Wadham (drums), Dave Fleming (bass guitar), and Myles Drennan (piano).
**ADDITIONAL INFORMATION:**
Started the first jazz club in Ireland called the 'Green Lounge'. Was Resident Musician with RTÉ's 'Late Late Show'. Has played with Ella Fitzgerald, Sarah Vaughan, Petual Clark, Diana Ross and the Supremes, Dick Haymes, Louis Armstrong, Warren Vache, Spike Robinson, Gerry Mulligan, Pepper Adams, Bobby Shew, Sonny Fortune, Maynard Ferguson, Ronnie Scott, and Johnny Dankworth, as well as leading Irish jazz musicians.

## Gay McIntyre *Saxophone*

**Contact:** Mr Gay McIntyre
6, Laurence Hill
Derry BT48 7NJ
Northern Ireland
**Tel:** +44 1504 271174

## Neil McMahon
### *Tenor and Soprano Saxophones*

**Contact:** Mr Neil McMahon
'Hazel Hatch'
Thormanby Road
Howth
Co Dublin
**Tel:** +353 1 8391174
**Other instruments:** Clarinet, flute.

**KEY IRISH PERFORMANCES** (since January 1994):
Regular performances in the Conrad Hotel, Dublin with Louis Stewart (guitar).
**REGULARLY PERFORMS WITH:**
Hugh Buckley (guitar), 'Prof' Peter O'Brien (piano).
**AVAILABILITY:**
General.

## Charles Meredith
### *Soprano, Alto and Baritone Saxophones*

**Contact:** Mr Charles Meredith
6 Cross Avenue
Blacrock
Co Dublin
**Tel:** +353 1 2885183
*See trumpet page 271.*

## Eamon Murray *Saxophone*

**Contact:** Eamon Murray
**Tel/Fax:** +353 404 46096
*See harmonica page 276.*

## Patrick G Rice
### *Baritone and Tenor Saxophone*

**Contact:** Patrick G Rice
10, Mountainvale Drive
Glengormley BT36 7AJ
Northern Ireland
**Tel:** +44 1232 840068
**Other instruments:** Bass clarinet, flute.

**KEY IRISH PERFORMANCES** (since January 1994):
1996 Belfast, appearing with Ulster Orchestra.
1997 Belfast Waterfront Hall, appearing with the orchestra accompanying singer Marti Webb.
**AVAILABILITY:**
General.
**ADDITIONAL INFORMATION:**
Experienced in big bands and pit orchestras. Has worked for UTV, BBC and RTÉ.

# TROMBONE

## Rodney Foster *Trombone*

**Contact:** Mr Rodney Foster
18, Cherry Hill Avenue
Belfast BT16 OJD
Northern Ireland
**Tel:** +44 1232 481784

## John Scott-Trotter *Trombone*

**Contact:** Mr John Scott-Trotter
1, Browning Drive
Londonderry, BT47 1HN
Northern Ireland
**Tel:** +44 1504 311119
**Other instruments:** Piano, accordion, violin, bagpipes.

**KEY IRISH PERFORMANCES** (since January 1994):
6/8.95 Belfast, promoted by Larry's piano bar, appearing with Roy Williams.
**KEY PERFORMANCES OUTSIDE IRELAND** (since January 1994):
3.96 White Mountain Motel, New Hampshire, U.S.A, appearing with Dan Delaney (piano).
8.96 Brecon Jazz Festival, appearing with Don Rendell.
**SELECTED BROADCASTS AND/OR RECORDED WORK:**
From 1980 to 1997, Many Irish and Scottish recordings, for Rego Records, New York, USA.
1996 With Susan Tomelty, independently recorded.
**REGULARLY PERFORMS WITH:**
Trevor England (bass), Ken Goodman (sousaphone), Linley Hamilton (trumpet), Jim McDermott (saxophone/clarinet), Gabriel McLaughlin (tenor saxophone/trumpet), Tommy Thomas (drums).

**AVAILABILITY:**
General.
**ADDITIONAL INFORMATION:**
Has taken part in fifteen all-state American tours. Apppeared at Guinness Cork International Jazz Festival with many world-class musicians, including Louis Stewart, Spike Robinson, Jim Doherty, Len McCarthy and Gay McIntyre. Also appeared at Brogans Pub, Dublin with own quintet.

# TRUMPET

## Charles Meredith *Trumpet*

**Contact:** Mr Charles Meredith
6, Cross Avenue
Blackrock
Co Dublin
**Tel:** +353 1 2885183
**Other instruments:** Soprano, alto and baritone saxophones, clarinet.

*"... Pleasure of Rock Fox's marvellous chameleon like ability ... as persuasive as ever ... we should hear him in public more often"*

6.5.93 Irish Times.

**KEY IRISH PERFORMANCES** (since January 1994):
Has performed at the Guinness Cork International Jazz Festival, the Howth Jazz Festival and the National Concert Hall, Dublin.
**SELECTED BROADCASTS AND/OR RECORDED WORK:**
1970 Radio recordings with Gerry Mulligan, for RTÉ.
1981 'Do You Do' album with Freddy White, for Mulligan records.
29.8.95 Recordings for Arts Council.
**SELECTED REVIEWS** (since January 1994):
11.7.85 Irish Times "10 names from jazz".
6.5.93 Irish Times.
28.7.93 Irish Times.
**PRIZES/AWARDS/APPOINTMENTS:**
From 1983 to 1985, Member of the Arts Council commitee for European Music year.
1985 Member of the steering commitee for the publication on musical education in Ireland - "Deaf Ears" published by the Arts Council.
From 1987 to 1993, member of the Board of Directors of the Contemporary Music Centre, Dublin.
**REGULARLY PERFORMS WITH:**
Jazz Coasters, Rory McGuinness, 'Prof' Peter O'Brien.
**AVAILABILITY:**
General.
**ADDITIONAL INFORMATION:**
Jazz historian, composer, arranger and musicologist. Collector of historic recordings. Has written articles and reviews in several journals. Regular broadcaster on RTÉ. Co-founder (1984) of Irish Youth Jazz Orchestra. Has played with Pepper Adams, Art Blakey, Sandy Brown, Danny Moss, Teddy Wilson, Sarah Vaughan, etc.

# SINGERS

## Charlie Burton *Singer*

**Contact:** Mr Charlie Burton
3, Knockdene
Bangor
Co Down, BT20 4UZ
Northern Ireland
**Tel:** +44 247 458141
*See percussion page 277.*

## Aidan Coleman *Singer*

**Contact:** Aidan Coleman
28, Lisalea
Frascati Park
Blackrock
Co Dublin
**Tel:** +353 1 2835117
**Other instruments:** Piano/keyboards, guitar, percussion.

**KEY IRISH PERFORMANCES** (since January 1994):
From 10.95 to 12.96 resident performer at the Earl of Desmond Hotel, Tralee.
**KEY PERFORMANCES OUTSIDE IRELAND** (since January 1994):
4.94 Hotel Atlas-Asni, Marrakech, appearing at GATT Conference.
From 10.94 to 6.95 Fontana de Oro Bar, Madrid, resident performer.
**REGULARLY PERFORMS WITH:**
Sons Gavan Coleman (drums), Kealan Coleman (guitar and bass).
**AVAILABILITY:**
General.
**ADDITIONAL INFORMATION:**
Writer, composer, performer, director, sound engineer and multitrack recording engineer. Repertoire of 1400 songs and knowledge of several languages. April 1991, Artist in residence at the Tyrone Guthrie Centre, Annaghmakerrig.
*See bass-baritone page 112.*

## Ursula Connolly *Singer*

**Contact:** Ms Ursula Connolly
9, Temple Court
Palatine Square
Arbour Hill
Dublin 7
**Tel:** +353 1 6717589
*See singers page 244.*

## Morgan Crowley *Singer*

**Contact:** Morgan Crowley
259, Howth Road
Dublin 5 (Home)
or
C/o Hilary Gagan Associates
Caprice House
3, New Brlington Street
London W1X 1FE (Agent)
**Tel:** +353 1 8335805
**Email:** morganstar@compuserve.com
*See baritone page 112.*

## Fionnuala Gill *Singer*

**Contact:** Ms Fionnuala Gill
151, Ard na Mara
Malahide
Co Dublin
**Tel:** +353 1 8450698
*See soprano page 88.*

## Honor Heffernan *Singer*

**Contact:** Honor Heffernan
**Tel:** +353 1 2844679

*"... She can with no apparent effort, even in repose, hold her audience completely ..."*

26.02.92 Irish Times (Gerald Davis).

**KEY IRISH PERFORMANCES** (since January 1994):
1995 Tour of Ireland: St John's Arts and Heritage Centre, Listowel, Cahir Castle, Abbey Hotel, Roscommon, Belturbet, Limerick. Drogheda, Carlingford, promoted by Music Network, appearing with Michael Nielsen, Andy Clyndert and Stephen Keogh.
26.8.95 Kilkenny Arts Festival, appearing with Louis Stewart.
**KEY PERFORMANCES OUTSIDE IRELAND** (since January 1994):
29.9.95 Sandvik, Oslo, appearing with Kurt Mikailsen Quintet.
1.10.95 Oslo, appearing with Kurt Mikailsen Quintet.
2.12.95 Sandila Theatre, Oslo, appearing with Sandila Big Band and Rob McConnell.
**SELECTED BROADCASTS AND/OR RECORDED WORK:**
1991 'Chasing The Moon', for Cargo Records.
'Late Late Show' and 'Live at 3' for RTÉ.
**REGULARLY PERFORMS WITH:**
Noel Kelehan (piano), Michael Nielsen (guitar), Louis Stewart (guitar).
**AVAILABILITY:**
General.
**ADDITIONAL INFORMATION:**
Has toured extensively. Large repertoire of songs.

## Liza Hingerty *Singer*

**Contact:** Ms Liza Hingerty
'Villette'
Corrig Avenue
Dún Laoghaire, Co Dublin
**Tel:** +353 1 2822273

**REGULARLY PERFORMS WITH:**
Nightbirds.

## Denise Long *Singer*

**Contact:** Denise Long
26/27, Drury Street
Dublin 2
**Mobile:** +353 87 2345736
*See soprano page 91.*

## Dorothy Murphy *Singer*

**Contact:** Dorothy Murphy
33, Celtic Park Avenue
Beaumont
Dublin 9
**Tel:** +353 1 8313004

*"Combines softness with strength ... her diction and timing are excellent"* 9.6.96 Irish Independent.

**KEY IRISH PERFORMANCES** (since January 1994):
4.5.96 'Paddy Expo', Castletroy Hotel, Limerick, appearing with Michael Buckley, Brian Connor, Ronan Guilfoyle, John Wadham.
1996 Brogan's, Dublin, appearing with Brian Connor, Niall O'Neill, Kieran Phillips, Hugh Buckley, Dave Fleming, Dave Mason and Bob Whelan.
1997 University of Limerick, appearing with Mike Nielson Duo.
28.4.97 Brogan's, Dublin, appearing with Mike Neilson and Michael Coady.
**KEY PERFORMANCES OUTSIDE IRELAND** (since January 1994):
6.96 Tivoli Gardens, Copenhagen, Denmark, promoted by International Association of Jazz Schools, appearing with a 30 piece big band under the direction of Jens Winther and Dave Liebman.
6.96 Klaipeda, Lithuania, Tallinn, Estonia and Kalingrad, Russia, promoted by International Association of Jazz Schools, appearing with Rolf Hansen, Sebastien Rather, Claudio Zarp and Érik Elderius.
**SELECTED BROADCASTS AND/OR RECORDED WORK:**
1994 'Kenny Live' for RTÉ.
1997 'Art Live' for Dublin Weekend Radio.
1997 'Cafe Live' for RTÉ radio.
**SELECTED REVIEWS** (since January 1994):
4.96 Sunday Times.
4.97 Evening Herald.
16-29.97 Dublin Event Guide.
**PRIZES/AWARDS/APPOINTMENTS:**
1996 Chosen to represent Ireland at International Association of Jazz Schools in the Baltic States.
**TRAINING AND/OR QUALIFICATIONS:**
From 1995 to 1997, Newpark Music Centre with Ronan Guilfoyle and Tommy Halferty.
8.95 Attended the International Jazz Summer School, University of Ulster, Jordanstown.
10.95 Masterclass with Norma Winstone.
1996 Masterclass with Dee Spencer (New York).
**REGULARLY PERFORMS WITH:**
Dorothy Murphy Quartet, duo with Hugh Buckley, duo with Mike Nielsen.
**AVAILABILITY:**
General.
**ADDITIONAL INFORMATION:**
Has been working in Dublin for several years including regular performances in Sach's Hotel and Jury's Hotel. Extensive repertoire of songs.

## Eamon Murray *Singer*

**Contact:** Eamon Murray
**Tel/Fax:** +353 404 46096
*See harmonica page 276.*

## Sylvia O'Regan *Singer*

**Contact:** Sylvia O'Regan
169, Glenageary Park
Dún Laoghaire
Co Dublin
**Tel:** +353 1 2854108
*See mezzo-soprano page 105.*

## Melanie O'Reilly *Singer*

**Contact:** Ms Melanie O'Reilly
45, Shanganagh Vale
Cabinteely
Co Dublin
**Tel/Fax:** +353 1 2823814

*"Undoubtedly one of the major talents to*

*emerge in recent times ... possesses a voice which is rich and resonant"* 1996 In Dublin.

**KEY IRISH PERFORMANCES** (since January 1994):
1995 Guinness Cork International Jazz Festival.
1995 Whelans, Dublin promoted by Derek Nally.
1996 Temple Bar Festival promoted by Carpe Deum.
1996 St Patrick's Cathedral Dublin, promoted by the Red Cross and the Humanitarian Commission, appearing with Phil McDermott and Anúna.
**KEY PERFORMANCES OUTSIDE IRELAND** (since January 1994):
1995 Hangesund, Norway promoted by the Silda Jazz Festival.
1996 Barbican Centre, London promoted by the Barbican.
1996 Rhythmic Centre, London, promoted by Assembly Direct.
1997 Edinburgh Festival, Scotland, promoted by the Festival.
**SELECTED BROADCASTS AND/OR RECORDED WORK:**
1995 'Tir na Mara' (The Sea Kingdom) for CBM.
1996 'Kenny Live' for RTÉ.
1997 Síbín for TnaG.
**SELECTED REVIEWS** (since January 1994):
1995 Irish Times.
1995 The Big Issue.
**PRIZES/AWARDS/APPOINTMENTS:**
1994 Scottish Arts Council, funding for masterclasses with Sheila Jordan, New York.
1996 The Scotsman Newspaper 'Voice of the Year' award.
**TRAINING AND/OR QUALIFICATIONS:**
From 1989 to 1990, Guildhall School of Music and Drama, London.
1996 Goldsmiths University of London (improvisation) LTCL credit.
1997 Masterclasses with Madeline Eastman (New York).
**AVAILABILITY:**
General.
**ADDITIONAL INFORMATION:**
Fusion of ancient and modern musical styles.

# Rod Patterson *Singer*

**Contact:** Mr Rod Patterson
47, Pommern Parade
Belfast BT6 9FY
Northern Ireland
**Tel/Fax:** +44 1232 705098 / +44 831 197600
*See guitar page 275.*

# Siobhán Pettit *Singer*

**Contact:** Siobhán Pettit
47, Pommern Parade
Belfast BT6 9FJ, Northern Ireland
**Tel/Fax:** +44 1232 705098 / +44 1232 705098

**KEY IRISH PERFORMANCES** (since January 1994):
5.96 Derry jazz and Blues Festival, appearing with the Siobhán Pettit Band.
7.96 John Field Room, National Concert Hall, Dublin, appearing with 'Prof' Peter O'Brien.
10.96 Guinness Cork International Jazz Festival, appearing with the Siobhán Pettit Band.
11.96 Brogan's, Dublin, appearing with the SPB.
**SELECTED BROADCASTS AND/OR RECORDED WORK:**
1995 'Kenny Live' for RTÉ.
11.95 President Clinton visit, City Hall Belfast for BBC and UTV.
11.96 'Gerry Ryan Tonight' for RTÉ.
**TRAINING AND/OR QUALIFICATIONS:**
From 4.90 to 4.91, Taught by Mike Mitchell in Carnegie Hall, New York.
Summer 1995, Attended the International Jazz Summer School, University of Ulster, Jordanstown.
**REGULARLY PERFORMS WITH:**
Brian Connor (piano), John Fitzpatrick (fiddle), 'Prof' Peter O'Brien, Rod Patterson (bass), Siobhán Pettit Trio (Foggy Lyttle (guitar) and John Wilson (drums).
**AVAILABILITY:**
General.

# Ray Preston *Singer*

**Contact:** Mr Ray Preston
6, Willbrook Lawn, Dublin 14
**Tel:** +353 1 4931916
*See harmonica page 276.*

# Christine Tobin *Singer*

**Contact:** Christine Tobin
Eccentric Management
18 West Hill Park
London, N6 6ND, England
**Tel/Fax:** +44 181 3488638 / +44 181 3477099
**Email:** able@easynet.co.uk

*"A rich, haunting voice and a growing reputation"* 11.9.94 The Observer (Dave Gally).

**KEY IRISH PERFORMANCES** (since January 1994):
3.96 Tour of Ireland, promoted by Music Network, appearing with Steve Watts, Paul Clarvis and Phil Robson.
1997 Crescent Arts Centre, Belfast.
**KEY PERFORMANCES OUTSIDE IRELAND** (since January 1994):
1995 Wiesen Festival, Austria.
1995 Sopron Festival, Hungary.
1997 Frankfurt and Varna Jazz Festivals.
**SELECTED BROADCASTS AND/OR RECORDED WORK:**
5.5.95 'Aililiu', recorded by Babel Records.
1996 'Yell of the Gazel'.
**SELECTED REVIEWS** (since January 1994):
The Times (Chris Parker).
John Fordham (The Guardian).
**ADDITIONAL INFORMATION:**
Has recorded with Tim Garland, Pete Fairclough, Hugh Warren and Django Bates. Mixes a blend of African-American, Celtic and Latin-American in repertoire.

# Bob Whelan *Singer*

**Contact:** Bob Whelan
45, Woodlands Avenue
Dún Laoghaire, Co Dublin
**Tel/Mobile:** +353 1 2852250 / +353 87 631424

**KEY IRISH PERFORMANCES** (since January 1994):
7.94 National Concert Hall, Dublin, in 'A Few Words with Monk', appearing with Richie Buckley, Myles Drennan, Dave Fleming and Noel Kelehan.
**SELECTED BROADCASTS AND/OR RECORDED WORK:**
1987 'Late Late Show' for RTÉ.
1994/5 Brian Day's jazz programme for RTÉ.
1996 Jazz programme for Anna Livia FM Radio.
**REGULARLY PERFORMS WITH:**
Myles Drennan (piano), Dave Fleming (double bass), John Wadham (drums).
**AVAILABILITY:**
General.
**ADDITIONAL INFORMATION:**
Repertoire ranges from standards to bebop classics and contemporary pieces. Has lyricised many compositions by Monk, Parker, Gillespie, and has recently written some original compositions.

# JAZZ GROUPS

## All-Ireland Big Band

**Contact:** Mr Dave Gold
43, Garden Village Avenue
Kilpedder
Co Wicklow
**Tel/Fax:** +353 1 2819743

*"The Big Band, boasting Ireland's best, are dab hands at doing justice to Dave's gilt-edged arrangements"* 1996 Sunday Times.

**FORMED:** 1990.
**NUMBER IN GROUP:** 18.
**KEY IRISH PERFORMANCES** (since January 1994):
1993/1994/1995 Metropole Hotel, Cork, promoted by Guinness Cork International Jazz Festival.
1995 Howth Lodge Hotel, promoted by Howth Jazz Festival.
**SELECTED REVIEWS** (since January 1994):
1990 Irish Times.
1995 Sunday Times.
1995 Jazz News.
**PRIZES/AWARDS/APPOINTMENTS:**
1986 Dave Gold won Best Arranger (Big Band), awarded by BBC.
**ADDITIONAL INFORMATION:**
Emphasis is on original material by Dave Gold, but also combines other numbers.

## Blow by Blow

**Contact:** Mr Gerry Godley
20, Crostwaitte Park South
Dún Laoghaire
Co Dublin
**Tel/Fax:** +353 1 2805245

**FORMED:** 1995.
**GROUP MEMBERS:**
Michael Buckley (tenor saxophone), Brendan Doyle (alto/soprano saxophone), Gerry Godley (baritone saxophone), David Maine (alto saxophone).
**AVAILABILITY:**
General.
*See Michael Buckley page 282, Brendan Doyle page 283.*

## Justin Carroll Trio

**Contact:** Mr Justin Carroll
16, Westbrook Road
Dundrum
Dublin 14
**Tel:** +353 1 2984638

**FORMED:** 1996.
**GROUP MEMBERS:**
Justin Carroll (piano), Michael Coady (double bass), Ray McCann (drums).
**KEY IRISH PERFORMANCES** (since January 1994):
13.4.97 Brogan's, Dublin.
13.4.97 Waterford.
**AVAILABILITY:**
General.
**ADDITIONAL INFORMATION:**
A mixture between standards and contemporary music.
*See Michael Coady page 269.*

## Ellen Cranitch and Anne-Marie O'Farrell

**Contact:** Ms Ellen Cranitch
33, Westfield Road
Harolds Cross
Dublin 6
**Tel/Fax:** +353 1 4923486
*See Ellen Cranitch, flute page 271, Anne-Marie O'Farrell, harp page 8.*

## Dev Sirme

**Contact:** Mr Ronan Guilfoyle
10, O'Rourke Park
Sallynoggin
Co Dublin
**Tel:** +353 1 2853497
*See Ronan Guilfoyle page 273.*

## Jim Doherty Trio

**Contact:** Mr Jim Doherty
125, Tritonville Road
Sandymount
Dublin 4
**Tel:** +353 1 6684532

*"This most versatile trio has performed in so many styles with so many leading jazz soloists ....one of the best in Europe"* 6.95 Irish Times.

**FORMED:** 1980.
**GROUP MEMBERS:**
Jim Doherty (piano), Dave Fleming (double bass), John Wadham (drums).
**KEY IRISH PERFORMANCES** (since January 1994):
Various tours during 1994 and 1995 promoted by Music Network, Dublin Jazz Society, Limerick Jazz Society and Guinness Cork International Jazz Festival, appearing with Len McCarthy, Spike Robinson, Teddy Edwards, Bobby Shaw and Charles Mc Pherson.
**KEY PERFORMANCES OUTSIDE IRELAND** (since January 1994):
1994 Helsinki, Finland, promoted by Teravainer, appearing with various artists.
**SELECTED BROADCASTS AND/OR RECORDED WORK:**
1989 'Spondance' (a jazz ballet) for Livia records.
1993 'One Man in his Time' Spike Robinson with The Jim Doherty Trio, for Cargo Records.
*See Dave Fleming page 269, John Wadham page 279.*

## Brendan Doyle Quartet

**Contact:** Mr Brendan Doyle
**Tel:** +353 1 4517742

**FORMED:** 1996.
**GROUP MEMBERS:**
Michael Coady (double bass), Myles Drennan (drums), Brendan Doyle (saxophone/clarinet), Mike Nielsen, (guitar).

**KEY IRISH PERFORMANCES** (since January 1994):
10.96 Castletroy Park Hotel, Limerick, promoted by Limerick Jazz Society.
16.5.97 Siamsa Tíre, Tralee, Co Kerry, promoted by Music Network.
Regular performances at the Pendulum Jazz Club, Dublin.
**AVAILABILITY:**
General.
**ADDITIONAL INFORMATION:**
Large and varied repertoire including standards and originals as well the music of artists such as AC Jobim, Jim Hall, Sonny Rollins, Duke Ellington and Miles Davis.
*See Brendan Doyle page 283, Michael Coady page 269, Myles Drennan page 277, Mike Nielsen page 274.*

# 'Big' Jim Farrelly Group

**Contact:** Mr Jim Farrelly
70, Palmerstown Road
Rathmines
Dublin 6
**Tel/Fax:** +353 1 4960090 / +353 1 8333969

**FORMED:**
1991 (11-piece), 1991 (5-piece).
**GROUP MEMBERS:**
Jim Farrelly (alto saxophone, clarinet, soprano saxophone, tenor saxophone) and (5-piece band) keyboards, drums, bass, singer, saxophone or (11-piece band) 3 saxophones (alto, tenor, baritone), 2 trumpets, trombone, keyboards/piano, bass guitar, drums, singer(s).
**AVAILABILITY:**
General.

# Tommy Halferty Quartet

**Contact:** Mr Tommy Halferty
**Tel:** +353 1 2856883

*"... The tight bond ... allowed for fat-free jazz ..."* 7.5.97 Sunday Times.

**FORMED:** 1990.
**MEMBERS IN GROUP:**
Myles Drennan (piano), Dave Fleming (double bass), Tommy Halferty (guitar), John Wadham (drums).
**KEY IRISH PERFORMANCES** (since January 1994):
1994 Irish tour, promoted by Music Network, appearing with Martin Nolan and Ellen Cranitch.
1996 Played for President Clinton's Irish visit, appearing with Ronan and Conor Guilfoyle.
**KEY PERFORMANCES OUTSIDE IRELAND** (since January 1994):
1991 German television ('Ethnology'), appearing with Tommy Hayes and Ronan Brown.
1992 Parthenay Jazz Festival, France, appearing with Oregan Trio.
1994 Tel-Aviv International Guitar Festival, Israel.
**SELECTED BROADCASTS AND/OR RECORDED WORK:**
1995 'Anda', recorded by IMC Records.
1996 'Irish Connection', recorded by Steeplechase Records, Denmark.
**PRIZES/AWARDS/APPOINTMENTS:**
1991 Tutor at the University of Ulster, Jordanstown.
1994 Critics choice at the Tel-Aviv International Guitar Festival.
**TRAINING AND/OR QUALIFICATIONS:**
From 1992 to 1996, BA in Education.
From 1992 to 1996, Grade 8 (theory of music), Grade 6 (practical music).
**AVAILABILITY:**
General.
**ADDITIONAL INFORMATION:**
Promotes an indigeneous style in a world-wide setting. Jazz standards and original music, mostly in the style of the late Miles Davis Group.
*See Tommy Halferty page 273, Myles Drennan page 277, Dave Fleming page 269, John Wadham page 279.*

# Hammond Orgasm

**Contact:** Mr Nigel Mooney
4, Sylvan Lawns
Kilcoole
Co Wicklow
**Tel/Fax:** +353 1 2873533

*"The gig was an abject lesson in organ trioism ... rattled off with vigour and panache"*
16.4.97 Dublin Event Guide.

**FORMED:** 1996.
**GROUP MEMBERS:**
Justin Carroll (Hammond C3 organ), Myles Drennan (drums) and Nigel Mooney (guitar).
**KEY IRISH PERFORMANCES** (since January 1994):
10.96 Metropole, Cork, promoted by the Guinness Cork International Jazz Festival, appearing with Richie Buckley, Georgie Fame and others.
4.97 Brogan's, Dublin.
Plus regular concerts in the Thomas Read Lounge, Dublin (residency group).
1997 Kilkenny Arts Festival.
**TRAINING AND/OR QUALIFICATIONS:**
Members have attended the Newpark Music Centre Jazz Courses/ Jordanstown Jazz Course.
Banff Centre, Canada.
**AVAILABILITY:**
General.
**ADDITIONAL INFORMATION:**
Classic 50's and 60's organ trio which performs blues and hard bop.
*See Myles Drennan page 277, Justin Carroll page 288.*

# Harry and Friends

**Contact:** Mr Harry A Connolly
Liscahane House
Woodside
Kerry Pike
Co Cork
**Tel/Fax:** +353 21 271605 / +353 21 272839

**FORMED:** 1976.
**GROUP MEMBERS:**
Harry A Connolly (vocals, saxophone, flute), Brian Hyland (bass), Eamon Keane (piano, keyboard, vocals), Derry O' Flynn (drums), Steven O'Keeffe (guitar).
**KEY IRISH PERFORMANCES** (since January 1994):
1994, 1995 Guinness Cork International Jazz Festival.
1996 Guinness CJF appearing with Derrick O'Connor.
**SELECTED BROADCASTS AND/OR RECORDED WORK:**
1995 'Late Late Show' for RTÉ.
1995 Cork Opera House.
**AVAILABILITY:**
General.

# Irish Jazz Orchestra

**Contact:** Mr Brian Carson
Moving on Music
15, Knockbreda Road
Belfast BT6 0JA
Northern Ireland
**Tel/Fax:** +44 1232 643753
**Email:** Movingltd@oal.com

*"... Without exaggeration they were awesome ... red blooded and thrilling"* 29.10.96 Irish Times.

**FORMED:** 1995.
**NUMBER IN GROUP:** 20.
**MUSICAL/ARTISTIC DIRECTOR:** Hugh Fraser.
**KEY IRISH PERFORMANCES** (since January 1994):
3.95 Crescent Arts Centre, Belfast, promoted by Project Jazz.
3.95 Killiney Court Hotel, Dublin, promoted by Dún Laoghaire/Rathdown County Council.
9.96 Metropole Hotel, and the Opera House Cork, promoted by Guinness Cork International Jazz Festival.
**SELECTED BROADCASTS AND/OR RECORDED WORK:**
11.95 'Gravity Still Works' for Coyote records.
**SELECTED REVIEWS** (since January 1994):
3.95 Belfast Telegraph.
3.95 Irish News.
**AVAILABILITY:**
General.

# Jazz Action

**Contact:** Mr Frank Sherry
31, Kinvara Avenue
Navan Road
Dublin 7
**Tel:** +353 1 8384611

**FORMED:** 1981.
**GROUP MEMBERS:**
Johnny Butler (drums), Eugene Macari (guitar), Ed McCrudden (piano, alto saxophone, clarinet), Johnny McGuinness (tenor saxophone), Mike Nolan (trumpet, flugelhorn), Frank Sherry (vibraphone, drums), Paul Tobin (double bass, bass guitar).
**KEY IRISH PERFORMANCES** (since January 1994):
1994 Portlaoise Jazz Festival.
1995 Imperial Hotel, Cork, promoted by the Guinness Cork International Jazz Festival.
Since 5.95 Sunday night performances at Handel's Pub, Capel Street, Dublin.
1996 Silver Spring Hotel, Cork, promoted by Guinness Cork International Jazz Festival.
**SELECTED BROADCASTS AND/OR RECORDED WORK:**
5.94 'Ronan Collins Show' for RTÉ.
5.94 'Bryan Day Jazz Show' for RTÉ.
**PRIZES/AWARDS/APPOINTMENTS:**
1981 1st Prize winner, International Festival of Music, presented by Bord Failte.
**AVAILABILITY:**
General.
**ADDITIONAL INFORMATION:**
Mainstream/bop group. Both Johnny McGuinness and Johnny Butler, lived and worked in New York for many years and have experience with New York Jazz Groups. Have been promoted by Dublin Jazz Society at the Guinness Cork Jazz Festival, the Portlaoise Jazz Festival and by various jazz venues around the country.
*See Eugene Macari page 273.*

# Kaluarachchi & Co

**Contact:** Mr Tony Kaluarachchi
162, Cliftonville Road
Belfast BT14 6LA
Northern Ireland
**Tel:** +44 1232 741942

**GROUP MEMBERS:**
Sumi Kal (bass), Tony Kaluarachchi (vocals, guitars), Mark Gerry Lisk (drums, percussion) Mark Moore (flute, tenor saxophone).
**KEY IRISH PERFORMANCES** (since January 1994):
1994 Monaghan Festival, promoted by Monaghan County Council.
1995 Guinness Cork International Jazz Festival, appearing with John McLaughlin.
1996 West Belfast Festival.
1996 Belfast City Carnival, promoted by the Arts Guild of Ulster.
**KEY PERFORMANCES OUTSIDE IRELAND** (since January 1994):
1994 Glasgow May Festival, appearing with the Hump Family.
1995 Coventry St Patrick's Day Festival, promoted by BBC, appearing with Mary Coughlan.
**SELECTED BROADCASTS AND/OR RECORDED WORK:**
1994 'In This City' for BBC.
1994 'Stay With Me' for UTV.
1995 'Death has no Mercy' for BBC.
**AVAILABILITY:**
General.
**ADDITIONAL INFORMATION:**
Perform original music, sound tracks, blues, soul, jazz rock and classic rock.

# Anthony Kerr Group

**Contact:** Mr Anthony Kerr
3, Priory Walk
St Albans, AL1 2JA
England
**Tel:** +44 1 727 859400

**FORMED:** 1988.
**GROUP MEMBERS:**
Albert Bover (piano), Stephen Keogh (drums), Anthony Kerr (vibraphone), Matt Miles (double bass).
**KEY IRISH PERFORMANCES** (since January 1994):
1993 Belfast Festival at Queen's, appearing with Louis Stewart.
1996 Guinness Cork International Jazz Festival, appearing with Grant Stewart.
**KEY PERFORMANCES OUTSIDE IRELAND** (since January 1994):
1992 Royal Albert Hall, part of the Proms, appearing with the Mike Westbrook Orchestra.
1997 Ronnie Scotts.
**AVAILABILITY:**
General.
*See Anthony Kerr page 278, Stephen Keogh page 278.*

# Khanda

**Contact:** Mr Martin Nolan
34, St Marys Drive
Drimnagh
Dublin 12
**Tel:** +353 1 4563144
*See other groups page 302.*

# Dorothy Murphy Quartet

**Contact:** Dorothy Murphy
33, Celtic Park Avenue
Beaumont, Dublin 9
**Tel:** +353 1 8313004
*See singers page 286.*

# Nightbirds

**Contact:** Ms Liza Hingerty
'Villette'
Corrig Avenue
Dún Laoghaire
Co Dublin
**Tel:** +353 1 2828273

**GROUP MEMBERS:**
Richie Buckley (saxophone), Myles Drennan (drums), Dave Fleming (double bass), Mike Neilsen/Hugh Buckley (guitar).
**KEY IRISH PERFORMANCES** (since January 1994):
31.12.94 Dalkey, Co Dublin, appearing with Richie Buckley and Anto Drennan.
12.95 Dalkey, Co Dublin.
7.96 Donnybrook tennis club, promoted by Aoife McHale.
1.97/2.97 Blanchardstown, Co Dublin, appearing with Hugh Buckley and Dick Buckley.
**KEY PERFORMANCES OUTSIDE IRELAND** (since January 1994):
2.94 El Gringo, St Agata, Sorrento, Italy, promoted by De Rosa, appearing with Antonio De Rosa.
11.94 Circolo Dei Forestieri, Italy, promoted by Rafaele, appearing with De Roas and Ionazio.
7.95/7.96 il Mulino, Sorento, Italy, by Serfio Vettore, appearing with Sergio Vettore.
**SELECTED BROADCASTS AND/OR RECORDED WORK:**
1989 'Bibi' for RTÉ.
From 1992 to 1994, studio recordings for East Coast Radio, Italy.
1994 Live recordings for East Coast Radio, Italy.
**PRIZES/AWARDS/APPOINTMENTS:**
1993 and 1994, Arts Council flight.
**TRAINING AND/OR QUALIFICATIONS:**
From 1973 to 1986, ALCM, from London College of Music and GNEIM, from National Institute of Music Education.
From 1986 - 1987 (teacher Cyntia Ryrne).
From 1991 to 1992, (teacher Nancy Beavan).
**REGULARLY PERFORMS WITH:**
Michael Buckley/Dick Buckley (saxophone), Bob Diebold (piano).
**AVAILABILITY:**
General.
**ADDITIONAL INFORMATION:**
Have a repertoire of Italian and continental flavoured songs, as well as over 150 jazz standards.
*See Myles Drennan page 277, Dave Fleming page 269, Hugh Buckley page 272, Mike Nielsen page 274.*

# Nightswing

**Contact:** Mr Rod Patterson
47, Pommern Parade
Belfast BT6 9FY
Northern Ireland
**Tel/Mobile/Fax:** +44 1232 705098 or +44 831 197600 /
+44 1232 705098

**FORMED:** 1993.
**NUMBER IN GROUP:** 9.
**KEY PERFORMANCES OUTSIDE IRELAND** (since January 1994):
9.96 Scarborough, Scotland, promoted by Haven Holidays.
12.96 Worthing, England, promoted by Hammond Productions.
**SELECTED BROADCASTS AND/OR RECORDED WORK:**
14.2.97 'Kelly', recorded by UTV.
**AVAILABILITY:**
General.
**ADDITIONAL INFORMATION:**
Music played by a range of musicians covering jazz, swing and popular music.

# Otis and the Elevators

**Contact:** David Taylor
22, Ward Avenue
Bangor
Co Down BT20 5HW
Northern Ireland
**Tel/Fax:** +44 1247 472754

*"So forget about the quickstep and the oldtime waltz - but come prepared to bop till you drop"*
10.96 Belfast Festival at Queen's programme.

**FORMED:** 1982.
**NUMBER IN GROUP:** 6.
**GROUP MEMBERS:**
David Galloway (bass), Bob Hunt (tenor/alto/baritone saxophones), Gerald McClurg (trumpet), Billy McCoy (guitar) Eddie McKee (drums), David Taylor (harmonica and guitar).
**KEY IRISH PERFORMANCES** (since January 1994):
5.9.94 Monaghan Hillgrove Jazz and Blues Festival, main act.
3.9.96 Coleraine University Biko Hall promoted by the First Trust Bank, main act.
16.10.96 Belfast Whitla Hall promoted by Belfast Queen's Festival Ball, main act.
29.6.97 Belfast Waterfront Hall promoted by David Hull promotions, main act.
**KEY PERFORMANCES OUTSIDE IRELAND** (since January 1994):
9.10.95 Forté Village Sardinia, Otis Elevator World Convention.
1996 Rally Optic 2000, Sahara Desert, Tunisia appearing with Eurosport.
19.4.96 Maiden voyage of the Napolean Bonapart Liner, France appearing with Eurosport.
**SELECTED BROADCASTS AND/OR RECORDED WORK:**
'Totally out of Order' live CD, recorded at the the Errigle in Belfast.
21.3.96 Performance of 'Julian gets cool' for Ulster Television.
15.10.96 Live at the Festival Club for BBC Radio 4.
**AVAILABILITY:**
General.
**ADDITIONAL INFORMATION:**
Play their own arrangements of jazz, soul and rhythm 'n blues classics.

# Ozone

**Contact:** Keith Donald
Boathouse
Rockbrook, Dublin 16
**Tel:** +353 1 4934499
*See Keith Donald, saxophone, page 269.*

# Siobhán Pettit Trio

**Contact:** Siobhán Pettit
47, Pommern Parade
Belfast BT6 9FJ, Northern Ireland
**Tel/Fax:** +44 1232 705098
*See singers page 287.*

# The Fallen Angels

**Contact:** The Fallen Angels
c/o MBE
6 Seafield Crescent
Blackrock
Co Dublin
**Tel/Fax:** +353 1 269 3821 / +353 1 269 3777
**Email:** mbe@indigo.ie
*See groups page 265.*

# TIME *(The Improvised Music Ensemble)*

**Contact:** Mr Ronan Guilfoyle
10, O'Rourke Park
Sallynoggin
Co Dublin
**Tel:** +353 1 2853497
*See Ronan Guilfoyle page 273.*

# Ulster Orchestra Jazz Ensemble

**Contact:** Mr Hugh Carslaw
13, Sycamore Park
Jordanstown
Co Antrim, BT37 ONR
Northern Ireland
**Tel:** +44 1232 867980

**FORMED:** 1980.
**GROUP MEMBERS:**
S Barnett (trombone/piano), Hugh Carslaw (trumpet), H Hamilton (bass/piano/vocals), G Hopkins (bass/guitar), M Neale (kit/piano), P Schuman (clarinet/sax).
**ADDITIONAL INFORMATION:**
All members are players with the Ulster Orchestra and are specialists in the classical as well as the jazz field. Perform regularly throughout Northern Ireland, and have performed abroad (Birmingham and Zimbabwe). Repertoire includes a large selection from early dixieland to mainstream.

# Ulster Youth Jazz Orchestra

**Contact:** Mr Ken Jordan
29, Glendarragh
Knocknagoney Road
Belfast BT4 2WB
Northern Ireland
**Tel:** +44 1232 760403

**FORMED:** 1993.
**NUMBER IN GROUP:** 28.
**MUSICAL/ARTISTIC DIRECTOR:**
Ken Jordan.
**KEY IRISH PERFORMANCES** (since January 1994):
1.97 Open day at the Belfast Waterfront Hall.
**KEY PERFORMANCES OUTSIDE IRELAND** (since January 1994):
7.96 National Festival of Music for Youth, London.
**SELECTED BROADCASTS AND/OR RECORDED WORK:**
27.6.97 for Radio Ulster.
**AVAILABILITY:**
General.

# Wednesday Night Prayer Meeting

**Contact:** Mr Gerry Godley
20, Crostwaithe Park South
Dún Laoghaire
Co Dublin
**Tel/Fax:** +353 1 2805245

**FORMED:** 1996.
**GROUP MEMBERS:**
Michael Buckley (tenor saxophone/flute), Justin Carroll (piano), Michael Coady (bass), Brendan Doyle (alto saxophone/clarinet), Gerry Godley (baritone saxophone), Barry McBrian (trombone), Kieran Phillips (drums), Karl Ronan (trombone).
**AVAILABILITY:**
General.
*See Michael Buckley page 282, Justin Carroll page 288, Michael Coady page 269, Brendan Doyle page 283, Kieran Phillips page 279.*

# Section eleven

## Other Music

The musicians in this section either:

1. Perform music which does not fall 'neatly' under the categories of classical, traditional and jazz.

2. Perform classical, traditional and jazz music but may also perform a fusion of all three, or other music such as world, contemporary, folk, modern, experimental etc

# INSTRUMENTALISTS AND SINGERS

## David Agnew *Oboe*

**Contact:** Mr David Agnew
Beaufort House
Butterfield Avenue
Rathfarnham
Dublin 14
**Tel/Fax:** +353 1 4945939
**Email:** oboeking@iol.ie

**OTHER MUSIC TYPE:**
Classical/traditional/pop.
*See oboe page 24.*

## Michael Buckley *Saxophone*

**Contact:** Mr Michael Buckley
17, St Peter's Drive
Walkinstown, Dublin 12
**Mobile:** +353 87 415580

**OTHER MUSIC TYPE:**
Session/film.
*See Jazz Saxophone page 282.*

## Dermot Byrne *Guitar*

**Contact:** Dermot Byrne
79, Fairyhill Estate
Bray, Co Wicklow
**Tel:** +353 1 2863234
**Other instruments:** Harmonica, mandoline, banjo

*"This guy is just great"* 2FM (Mike Moloney)

**KEY IRISH PERFORMANCES** (since January 1994):
9.96 Clifton Blues Festival, promoted by Ronan Wilmot, appearing with Ed O'Callaghan.
2/5.5.97 Carling Blues Festival, Cork, promoted by Larry Ruddy, appearing with Ed O'Callaghan and Dave Ross.
**REGULARLY PERFORMS WITH:**
Dermot Byrne Band.
**AVAILABILITY:**
General.
**ADDITIONAL INFORMATION:**
Blues performer and songwriter. Plays semi-acoustic bottleneck, fingerstyle and boogie.

## Lloyd Byrne *Percussion*

**Contact:** Mr Lloyd Byrne
c/o 46, Loreto Avenue
Rathfarnham
Dublin 14
**Tel/Mobile:** +353 1 4950103 / +353 87 2390961

**OTHER MUSIC TYPE:**
Combination of classical/jazz/session.

## Leslie Cassidy *Guitar*

**Contact:** Mr Leslie Cassidy
38, Thatch Road
Whitehall, Dublin 9
**Tel:** +353 1 8377076

**OTHER MUSIC TYPE:**
Classical/combination.
*See Classical Guitar page 19.*

## Rita Connolly *Singer*

**Contact:** Ms Rita Connolly
c/o MBE Artist Management and Agent
6, Seafield Crescent
Blackrock, Co Dublin
**Tel:** +353 1 2693821 / +353 1 2693777

**OTHER MUSIC TYPE:**
Contemporary folk.

## Christopher Cronin *Guitar*

**Contact:** Mr Christopher Cronin
Killyfad
Aughamore
Carrick-on-Shannon
Co Leitrim
**Tel:** +353 78 24685

**OTHER MUSIC TYPE:**
Folk/country/pop.
*See Traditional Guitar page 222.*

## Donald Cullington *Piano*

**Contact:** Dr Donald Cullington
113, Station Road
Greenisland
Carrickfergus
Co Antrim
Northern Ireland BT38 8UW
**Tel:** +44 1232 863852

**OTHER MUSIC TYPE:**
Classical/jazz.
*See Classical Piano page 35.*

## Róisín Dempsey *Soprano*

**Contact:** Róisín Dempsey
Apt 2, 130 Sandford Road
Ranelagh, Dublin 6
or
Greenville
Enniscorthy, Co Wexford
**Tel:** +353 1 4973873 / +353 54 33241

**OTHER MUSIC TYPE:**
Traditional/classical/liturgical.
*See Singers page 87.*

## Violet Dunne *Singer*

**Contact:** Ms Violet Dunne
PO Box 4640
Rathfarnham
Dublin 16
**Tel/Mobile/Fax:** +353 1 4932676 or +353 88 510299 / +353 1 4932676

**KEY IRISH PERFORMANCES** (since January 1994):
Corporate functions, festivals and events all over Ireland.
**ADDITIONAL INFORMATION:**
A professional performer since 1986, with full actor's equity. Repertoire includes traditional (unaccompanied singing), jazz (fronting band), opera (DGOS, RTÉ choir, feis) and studio work. Has also performed as a live act comedy character performer at events throughout the country and as a professional actor in music and theatre.

## Patrick Fitzpatrick *Piano*

**Contact:** Patrick Fitzpatrick
c/o IFSC (Irish Financial Services Centre)
96, Custom House Harbour
Dublin 1
**Tel:** +353 1 6701949 / +353 1 8326172 (a)
**Other instruments:** Keyboards

**KEY IRISH PERFORMANCES** (since January 1994):
10.95 City Hall, Belfast, for President Bill Clintons visit to Northern Ireland, appearing with Van Morrison.
**KEY PERFORMANCES OUTSIDE IRELAND** (since January 1994):
Tour of North America, appearing with Warren Zevon.
**SELECTED BROADCASTS AND/OR RECORDED WORK:**
During 1996 and 1997, session work for RTÉ.
During 1996 and 1997, session work with 'Kelly Show' for UTV.
**REGULARLY PERFORMS WITH:**
Something Happens, Jeannette Byrne.
**AVAILABILITY:**
General.
**ADDITIONAL INFORMATION:**
Session keyboards/pianist working in Ireland. Has worked with Van Morrison, Mary Coughlan, Something Happens, The Chieftains and on film and television productions. Registered with the agency Moon Note Productions.

## Jackie Flavelle *Bass Guitar*

**Contact:** Mr Jackie Flavelle
61, Millisle Road
Donaghadee
Co Down BT 21 OHZ
Northern Ireland
**Tel/Fax:** +44 1247 882351 / +44 1247 815252

*"Northern Ireland's Mr Blues"* British Blues Review

**SELECTED BROADCASTS AND/OR RECORDED WORK:**
1972 'Admission Free' for York Records
**SELECTED REVIEWS** (since January 1994):
1995 Impartial Reporter
**REGULARLY PERFORMS WITH:**
Chris Barber Band, Rod Stewart, Don Ewell Quintet
**AVAILABILITY:**
General.

## Nigel Flegg *Percussion*

**Contact:** Mr Nigel Flegg
Saint Nicholas House
Rostrevor Road
Rathgar
Dublin 6
**Tel/Mobile:** +353 1 4961369 / +353 87 2365112

**OTHER MUSIC TYPE:**
Blues/Latin/pop/world.
*See Jazz Drums page 277.*

## James Galway *Flute*

**Contact:** Mr James Galway
c/o Kathryn Enticott
IMG Artists
Media House
3, Burlington Lane
Chiswick
London W4 2TH
England
**Tel/Fax:** +44 181 233 5800 / +44 181 233 5801

**OTHER MUSIC TYPE:**
Folk/popular songs.
*See Classical Flute page 14.*

## Deirdre Gilsenan *Singer*

**Contact:** Ms Deirdre Gilsenan
Loughan
Kells
Co Meath
**Mobile:** +353 88 2756326

**OTHER MUSIC TYPE:**
Traditional/madrigals.
*See Singers page 88.*

## Barry Guy *Double bass*

**Contact:** Mr Barry Guy
Carrickmourne
Thomastown
Co Kilkenny
**Tel/Fax:** +353 56 58708 / +353 56 58709
**Email:** maya@tinet.ie

*"Barry Guy has given us one of the most fascinating improvised bass recordings in recent memory"* 1993 Cadence

**KEY IRISH PERFORMANCES** (since January 1994):
4.97 Waterford Institute of Technology.
7.97 Wexford Festival Opera, appearing with Maya Homburger.
**KEY PERFORMANCES OUTSIDE IRELAND** (since January 1994):
1995 Zürich, Switzerland, promoted by Red Factory with London Jazz Composers' Orchestra.
1996 Mulhouse, France, promoted by Jazz Festival, appearing with Maya Homburger.

1996 Barbican, London, première of 'Falling Water' for Orchestra (own composition).
**SELECTED BROADCASTS AND/OR RECORDED WORK:**
1993 'Fizzles' (solo album) for Maya Recordings.
1993 'After the Rain' (own composition for orchcestra), for NMC (GB).
1994 'Witch Gong Game' (own composition), a Maya recording for the Now Ensemble (Canada).
**PRIZES/AWARDS/APPOINTMENTS:**
1992 Awarded Composition Prize for Chamber Music by the Royal Philharmonic Society.
1994 Joint winner of the Hilliard Composition Prize.
**TRAINING AND/OR QUALIFICATIONS:**
1960's Guildhall School of Music and Drama, London, qualified in composition and double bass.
**REGULARLY PERFORMS WITH:**
Maya Homburger (violin), Evan Parker and Paul Lytton Trio.
**AVAILABILITY:**
General.
**ADDITIONAL INFORMATION:**
Improviser, composer and double bass soloist.

# John Hogan
***Alto and soprano saxophones***

Contact: Mr John Hogan
47, Hermitage Drive
Rathfarnham
Dublin 16
Tel: +353 1 4947412

*"An impressive display of youthful flair ... imaginative and wide-ranging expression"*
21.9.95 Irish Times

**KEY IRISH PERFORMANCES** (since January 1994):
9.95 John Field Room, National Concert Hall, Dublin appearing with Ioana Pectu-Colan and Dearbhla Collins.
8.96 John Field Room, National Concert Hall, promoted by the National Concert Hall Young Platform series, accompanied by Dearbhla Collins.
**KEY PERFORMANCES OUTSIDE IRELAND** (since January 1994):
10.95 Luxembourg, European Music for Youth Competition.
Since 1996, UK and USA, appearing with the 'Riverdance' Orchestra in 'Riverdance the Show'.
**SELECTED BROADCASTS AND/OR RECORDED WORK:**
9.95 Recital from the John Field Room, National Concert Hall live for RTÉ.
1997 'Two Saxophones' (duos with Kenneth Edge) for RTÉ.
Also various film soundtracks.
**SELECTED REVIEWS** (since January 1994):
27.8.96 Irish Times.
**PRIZES/AWARDS/APPOINTMENTS:**
1995 Winner of the McCullough Cup for Woodwind Concerto at the Feis Ceoil, Dublin.
9.96 Appointed saxophonist for the 'Riverdance the Show' Orchestra.
**ADDITIONAL INFORMATION:**
Studio musician.

# Edward Holly *Piano*

**Contact:** Mr Edward Holly
40, Glenmore Drive
Drogheda, Co. Louth
**Tel:** +353 41 38000

**OTHER MUSIC TYPE:**
Pop/musicals/swing.
*See Classical Piano page 39.*

# Philip Horan *Shakuhachi (flute)*

**Contact:** Mr Philip Horan
17, Elm Mount Park
Beaumont, Dublin 9
**Tel:** +353 1 8316096

**OTHER MUSIC TYPE:**
Classical/jazz/world.
*See Classical Flute page 15.*

# Dawn Kenny *Piano*

**Contact:** Dawn Kenny
49, Great Southern
Newbridge, Co Kildare
**Tel:** +353 45 434163
**Other instruments:** Voice.

*"Dawn Kenny is a serious musician"*
16.8.96 Irish Times

**KEY IRISH PERFORMANCES** (since January 1994):
1993 - 97 Various venues: National Concert Hall, DIT Conservatory of Music and Drama, Wexford Arts Centre.
Temple Bar Music Centre, Dublin.
Eamonn Doran's Pub, Temple Bar, Dublin.
**SELECTED BROADCASTS AND/OR RECORDED WORK:**
1994 Radio 1, Morning Ireland.
94/95 'Cursaí', for RTÉ.
**PRIZES/AWARDS/APPOINTMENTS:**
1994 Songwriting Prize awarded by Bord na Gaeilge.
94/95 Songwriting Prize awarded by An tOireachtas.
1995 Composition Scholarship, awarded by DIT CMD.
**TRAINING AND/OR QUALIFICATIONS:**
From 1989 to 1993, BMusEd, DipMusEd, Trinity College, Dublin and DIT CMD.
1994 LTCL Piano, Trinity College, London.
From 1995 to 97, MA in Composition, University College, Dublin and DIT CMD.
**REGULARLY PERFORMS WITH:**
Cathal Coughlan.
**AVAILABILITY:**
General.
**ADDITIONAL INFORMATION:**
Has composed music ranging in style from contemporary to rock including music for the film 'Refusal to Mourn'.

# Andrew Lavery *Drums*

**Contact:** Mr Andrew Lavery
37, Glengoland Gardens
Dunmurry, Belfast BT17 0JE
Northern Ireland
**Tel:** +44 1232 621505

*"Andrew has talent and a sheer passion for music"* 6.94 Ulster Star

**KEY IRISH PERFORMANCES** (since January 1994):
3.95 Grand Opera House, Belfast, appearing with the Ulster Orchestra, in 'The Barber of Seville'.
5.95 Bangor Festival of Light Opera, appearing with amateur operatic societies.

9-10.95 Tour of Northern Ireland, appearing with Peter Corry.
11.95 Belfast Festival at Queen's University, appearing with Papo Furado.
**KEY PERFORMANCES OUTSIDE IRELAND** (since January 1994):
7.95 Hard Rock Cafe, Singapore, appearing with house band.
**SELECTED BROADCASTS AND/OR RECORDED WORK:**
26.2.93 'Anderson On The Box' (Roy Walker), for BBC Northern Ireland.
22.10.93 'Anderson On The Box' (Ulster Operatic Society), for BBC Northern Ireland.
29.10.93 'Kelly Show' (with Blues Experience), for UTV.
**SELECTED REVIEWS** (since January 1994):
6.94 Sunday World.
**PRIZES/AWARDS/APPOINTMENTS:**
1994 Berklee College of Music Summer School, (scholarship awarded by the Arts Council of Northern Ireland).
**TRAINING AND/OR QUALIFICATIONS:**
From 1984 to 1991, Guildhall Grade 8 percussion, from City of Belfast School of Music.
**REGULARLY PERFORMS WITH:**
Papo Furado (5-piece, classical 70's soul and funk).
**AVAILABILITY:**
General.
**ADDITIONAL INFORMATION:**
Teaches at City of Belfast School of Music and other Belfast secondary schools. Has performed with artists including Jackie Flavelle and Peter Corry. Makes regular appearances with the Ulster Orchestra. Enjoys playing for theatre and pantomime.

## Órna Loughnane *Violin*

**Contact:** Órna Loughnane
Brockmanngasse 114/9
A-8010
Graz
Austria
**Tel:** +43 316 842344
**Other instruments:** Singer (traditional), mandolin (traditional), piano (classical).

**KEY IRISH PERFORMANCES** (since January 1994):
1994 Royal Dublin Society, Dublin promoted by DIT Conservatory of Music and Drama, Dublin.
1995 National Concert Hall, Dublin, promoted by the DIT CMD Music String Society, solo recital.
1996 Tour of Ireland (Dublin and Cork main venues), promoted by Opera Theatre Company, appearing with London Baroque Sinfonia.
**KEY PERFORMANCES OUTSIDE IRELAND** (since January 1994):
1995 Graz, Austria, promoted by Graz Chamber Musicians, appearing with Herz Jesu Kirche Orchestra.
1996 Edinburgh and London (Convent Garden), promoted by Opera Theatre Company, Dublin, appearing with London Baroque Sinfonia.
1996 Graz Music Academy.
1997 Concert Hall, Graz appearing with St. Petersburg Chamber Orchestra.
**SELECTED BROADCASTS AND/OR RECORDED WORK:**
1993 'Míle Dath' with Eilín Begley for Clór Iar Chonnachta, Galway.
1994 'Dance of the Honey Bees' with Charlie Lennon and the Lennon Family for RTÉ.
1995 'Shenanigans' for independent label, Shenanigans.
**PRIZES/AWARDS/APPOINTMENTS:**
1995/96, Arts Department Scholarship from the Austrian Government.
1996/97, Awarded study scholarship for Talented Students by the Music Academy, Graz.
**TRAINING AND/OR QUALIFICATIONS:**
From 1991 to 1995, B Mus from DIT CMD, Dublin.
From 1995 to 1996, masterclasses with Boris Belkin at the Music Academy, Siena, Italy and with Yair Kless at Mozarteum Salzburg, Austria.
Since 1995 to 1999, Master of Music, Arts and violin studies at Academy of Music, Graz, Austria.
**REGULARLY PERFORMS WITH:**
Stacey Bartsh (piano), Ogygia, Graz Academy Orchestra.
**AVAILABILITY:**
Subject to arrangement.
**ADDITIONAL INFORMATION:**
Comes from a traditional music background and is a trained classical musician.

## Carla Maney *Soprano*

**Contact:** Ms Carla Maney
57, Arran Street
Roath
Cardiff CF2 3HT
Wales
**Mobile/Tel:** +44 467 623329 / +44 1222 493301
+44 1693 69292 (Northern Ireland)

**OTHER MUSIC TYPE:**
Popular songs/musicals.
*See Singers page 92.*

## Gerard McChrystal *Saxophone*

**Contact:** Mr Gerard McChrystal
24, Leas Close
Totteridge
High Wycombe
Bucks HP13 7UW
England
**Tel/Fax:** +44 1494 464831

**OTHER MUSIC TYPE:**
Jazz/folk.
*See Classical Saxophone page 52.*

## Mel Mercier *Percussion*

**Contact:** Mr Mel Mercier
Music Department
University College Cork
Cork
**Tel/Fax:** +353 21 902271 / +353 21 271595

**OTHER MUSIC TYPE:**
Experimental/world.
*See Traditional Bodhrán and Bones page 198.*

## Sandi Miller *Fiddle*

**Contact:** c/o Mr Bill Whelan
39, Fairview Gardens
Dublin 3
**Tel:** +353 1 8331920
**Other instruments:** Acoustic guitar, mandolin, tenor banjo, vocals.

*"Stringband music with rock and roll firepower just about says it for me"*

'Moloney after Midnight' RTÉ (Mike Moloney)

**KEY IRISH PERFORMANCES** (since January 1994):
From 28.4.95 to 30.4.95, Galway Rythm and Roots Festival, promoted by MCD, appearing with The Slightly Bewildered String Band.
From 5.5.95 to 7.5.95, Paddy Expo Limerick, promoted by Irish Distillers Ltd, appearing with The SBSB.
From 2.6.95 to 4.6.95, Castlebar Blues Festival, promoted by Larry Roddy, appearing with The SBSB.
Feakle Festival of Traditional Music, promoted by Gary Peter, appearing with The SBSB.
**KEY PERFORMANCES OUTSIDE IRELAND** (since January 1994):
From 3.3.95 to 5.3.95, Hobart Oyster Festival, promoted by T.Whelan, appearing with The SBSB.
From 10.3.95 to 12.3.95, Portfairy Festival, promoted by T.Whelan, appearing with The SBSB.
17.3.95 Snake Wake Festival, promoted by T.Whelan, appearing with The SBSB.
18.3.95 Port Elliot, promoted by T. Whelan, appearing with The SBSB.
**SELECTED BROADCASTS AND/OR RECORDED WORK:**
10.3.95 'Music Deli', for Australian Broadcasting Co.
20.5.95, 'Kenny Live', for RTÉ.
9.9.95 'The Slightly Bewildered String Band' CD for Starc Records, Ireland.
**PRIZES/AWARDS/APPOINTMENTS:**
7.75 1st All-Ireland winner (mandolin), awarded by CCÉ.
**TRAINING AND/OR QUALIFICATIONS:**
From 9.81 to 7.84, studied classical Indian music, at the Conservatory of Music, Basel, Switzerland.
**REGULARLY PERFORMS WITH:**
Rick Epping (guitar, mandolin, vocals), Ennis Mor (guitar, mandolin, vocals, banjo).
**AVAILABILITY:**
General.
**ADDITIONAL INFORMATION:**
Has a solo CD of original songs and tunes with the Starc label. Influences range from American blues, traditional Irish and Indian classical music.

## Louise Muckell *Mezzo-Soprano*

**Contact:** Louise Muckell
17, Roches Road
Rathkeale
Co Limerick
**Tel:** +353 69 64033

**OTHER MUSIC TYPE:**
Popular songs/cabaret.
*See Singers page 104.*

## Eamon Murray *Harmonica*

**Contact:** Eamon Murray
**Tel/Fax:** +353 404 46096

**OTHER MUSIC TYPE:**
Rhythm/blues/country/rock.
*See page 263.*

## Niamh Ní Bheoláin *Fiddle*

**Contact:** Ms Niamh Ní Bheoláin
104, Captains Rd
Crumlin
Dublin 12
**Tel:** +353 1 4903378

**OTHER MUSIC TYPE:**
Folk/bluegrass/jazz.
*See Traditional Fiddle page 210.*

## Tom O'Farrell *Guitar*

**Contact:** Mr Tom O'Farrell
12, Restelouet
22340 Plévin
France
**Tel:** +33 2 962 96792

**OTHER MUSIC TYPE:**
Contemporary/latin American.
*See Traditional Guitar page 224.*

## Sylvia O'Regan *Mezzo-Soprano*

**Contact:** Sylvia O'Regan
169, Glenageary Park
Dún Laoghaire
Co Dublin
**Tel:** +353 1 2854108

**OTHER MUSIC TYPE:**
Jazz/comedy style.
*See Singers page 105.*

## Mícheál Ó Súilleabháin *Piano*

**Contact:** Prof Mícheál Ó Súilleabháin
Irish World Music Centre
University of Limerick
Co Limerick
**Tel:** +353 61 202065

**OTHER MUSIC TYPE:**
Classical/jazz/traditional/world.
*See Traditional Piano page 234.*

## Rod Patterson *Guitar*

**Contact:** Mr Rod Patterson
47, Pommern Parade
Belfast BT6 9FY
Northern Ireland
**Tel/Fax/Mobile:** +44 1232 705098 / +44 831 197600

**OTHER MUSIC TYPE:**
Musicals/country/gospel/blues.
*See Jazz Guitar page 275.*

# Sebastien Petiet *Violin*

**Contact:** c/o Marie Petiet
23, Park Crescent House
Blackhorse Avenue
Dublin 7
**Tel:** +353 1 8681210
**Other instruments:** Guitar

**KEY IRISH PERFORMANCES** (since January 1994):
8.95 Hillgrove Hotel, Dingle appearing with Padraig Ó Sé and Tommy Sullivan.
28.9.95 Old Moran's Hotel, Dublin appearing with Ned Ó Sé.
30.9.95 The Merchant, Dublin appearing with Ned Ó Sé.
18.10.95 Waterford, Poleberry Centre, promoted by Camelot.
**KEY PERFORMANCES OUTSIDE IRELAND** (since January 1994):
19.8.95 Big Sky Country Festival, Crans Montana, USA, appearing with Blue Highway, promoted by Christian Hager.
**SELECTED BROADCASTS AND/OR RECORDED WORK:**
Between 1988 and 1992, 'Trotwood' (four albums) for Presence Production.
1994 'Aifreann Chéiliúradh' for Raidió na Gaeltachta. Demo tape available on request.
**SELECTED REVIEWS** (since January 1994):
9.95 Country News, USA.
**REGULARLY PERFORMS WITH:**
Mazurka (violin, guitar, 'cello, doublebass), Pádraig Ó Sé agus lé Cairde, (fiddle, guitar, accordions, banjo, tin whistle, vocals and step dance).
**AVAILABILITY:**
General.
**ADDITIONAL INFORMATION:**
Composer, arranger and multi-instrumentalist performer in a variety of authentic styles including traditional Irish, gypsy, classical and ballroom.
*See also page 65.*

# Andrew Rowan *Flute*

**Contact:** Mr Andrew Rowan
10, Galbraith Gdns.
Waringstown BT66 7QN
Northern Ireland
**Tel:** +44 1762 881097

**OTHER MUSIC TYPE:**
Folk.
*See Classical Flute page 19.*

# Tommy Sands *Singer*

**Contact:** Mr Tommy Sands
Northern Ireland
**Tel/Fax:** +44 16937 38577 / +44 16937 38750
**Other instruments:** Guitar, mandolin, banjo and bodhrán.

*"Sheer power and poetry"*
European Art Foundation (Richard Di Marco)

**SELECTED BROADCASTS AND/OR RECORDED WORK:**
1985 'Singing of Times' album. 'Down by Bendy's Lane' album.
1992 'Beyond the Shadows' album.
1995 'The Heart's a Wonder' album.
1.97 Recorded title track for the album 'Where have all the Flowers gone?' for the tribute to Pete Seeger with Dolores Keane, Liam O'Flynn and others.
**SELECTED REVIEWS** (since January 1994):
Boston Globe.
Radio Leipzig.
Belfast Telegraph.
Irish Times.
**REGULARLY PERFORMS WITH:**
The Sands Family.
**ADDITIONAL INFORMATION:**
Has worked with Bob Dylan, Bruce Springstein and Nancy Griffith. Has performed in the Olympic Stadium in Moscow and the Carnegie Hall in New York. Has written the 'The Shadow of O'Casey' the title song from a stage musical written by Sands and Playwrite, Sean O'Casey's daughter Shivaun. Has worked with Sarajevo cellist Vedran Smailovic and Kathy Matthea from Nashville. Since 1977 presenter of weekly 'Country Céili' programme on Downtown Radio, Belfast.

# Eleanor Shanley *Singer*

**Contact:** Ms Eleanor Shanley
c/o MBE Artist Management and Agency
6, Seafield Crescent
Blackrock
Co Dublin
**Tel/Fax:** +353 1 2693821 / +353 1 2693777

**OTHER MUSIC TYPE:**
Contemporary folk.

# Olive Simpson *Soprano*

**Contact:** Miss Olive Simpson
7, Emperor's Gate
London SW7 4HH
England
**Tel:** +44 171 3734453

**OTHER MUSIC TYPE:**
Studio.
*See Singers page 97.*

# Peadar Townsend *Percussion*

**Contact:** Mr Peadar Townsend
Flat 2
8, Mayfield Road
Whalley Range
Manchester M16 8FT
England
**Tel/Mobile:** +44 161 232 9315 / +44 421 366 376

**OTHER MUSIC TYPE:**
Salsa/Latin/Cuban dance.
*See Classical Percussion page 31.*

# Tanya Vassilevich *tSimbali*

**Contact:** Ms Tanya Vassilevich
2, Dominic Street Court
Dominic Street
Cork
**Tel/Fax:** +353 21 398475 / +353 1 272103
**Other instruments:** Bayan (accordion).

*"... Tanya Vassilevich, opened a challenging curtain on the Eastern European landscape, in the magic garden of exotic sound"* 11.9.95 Irish Times.

**KEY IRISH PERFORMANCES** (since January 1994):
18.11.94 Lismore, Co Waterford, promoted by Lismore Festival of Early Music, appearing with the Lismore Choir.
31.4.95 City Hall, Cork, promoted by Cork Choral Festival, appearing with Cork School of Music.
**SELECTED BROADCASTS AND/OR RECORDED WORK:**
26.11.91 Choral programme, for Republic Television Company, Minsk, Belarus.
**ADDITIONAL INFORMATION:**
tSimbali (dulcimer) is a national Byellorussian chromatic stringed instrument.
*See Bayan (accordion) page 195.*

## John Walsh *Trumpet*

**Contact:** John Walsh
27, Ardmore Drive
Artane
Dublin 5
**Tel:** +353 1 8472294
**Email:** jaw_s@hotmail.com

**KEY IRISH PERFORMANCES** (since January 1994):
11.4.97 John Field Room, National Concert Hall Dublin, promoted by DIT Conservatory of Music and Drama, appearing with Peter Dains (piano).
1997 John Field Room, NCH, Dublin, appearing with Dublin Boy Singers.
**SELECTED BROADCASTS AND/OR RECORDED WORK:**
11.96 Church music competition for RTÉ.
**PRIZES/AWARDS/APPOINTMENTS:**
1994 Gold Medal winner at Feis Ceoil.
**TRAINING AND/OR QUALIFICATIONS:**
From 1992 to 1997, Bachelor of Music Performance at DIT Conservatory with Graham Hastings.
1993 Studied with John Wallace at the Royal Irish Academy of Music, Dublin.
1994 Studied with David Mason at Royal College of Music, London.
**REGULARLY PERFORMS WITH:**
Peter Dains (piano), brass quintets.
**AVAILABILITY:**
General.
**ADDITIONAL INFORMATION:**
Performs with the National Symphony Orchestra of Ireland, RTÉ Concert Orchestra, Irish Chamber Orchestra, Pit orchestras for shows, and enjoys playing all styles of music from baroque to jazz.

## John White *Singer*

**Contact:** Mr John White
**Tel/Fax:** +353 1 2802682
**Other instruments:** Flat top acoustic guitar, resonator guitar

*"... White's bottleneck guitar playing on [his song] 'End My Misery' featured on the Irish Blues Club CD '40 Shades of Blue' reminds me of Bob Brozman"*

4.97 Anna Livia FM (Charlie Hussey on 'The Blues Train Show')

**KEY IRISH PERFORMANCES** (since January 1994):
7.95 to 1997 Temple Bar Blues Festival.
6.97 Castlebar Blues Festival, promoted by Larry Roddy, appearing with Pat Martin.
7.97 Dublin Blues Festival, appearing with Pat Martin.
**SELECTED BROADCASTS AND/OR RECORDED WORK:**
1997 'And God Created Slide', with Pat Martin, (own cassette).
16.4.97 'Live at 3' for RTÉ.
7.7.97 'Moloney after Midnight' for RTÉ.
**SELECTED REVIEWS** (since January 1994):
7.94 Ray Stubbs.
5.97 Pigmeat Pete Smith.
**REGULARLY PERFORMS WITH:**
Pat Martin.
**AVAILABILITY:**
General.

## Stephen Wickham *Violin*

**Contact:** Stephen Wickham
P.O. Box 282, Sligo
**Tel:** +353 1 4966341
**Other instruments:** Electric violin, violin, mandolin, traditional singer, jazz and classical guitar

**KEY IRISH PERFORMANCES** (since January 1994):
12.95 Olympia Theatre Dublin, promoted by Denis Desmond, appearing with Mike Scott.
1.96 Droichead Arts Centre, promoted by the Centre and Colin Blakey, appearing with Connacht Ramblers.
1996 Lobby, Cork, promoted by Pat Conway, appearing with Connacht Ramblers.
1997 Punchbag Theatre Galway, appearing with Connacht Ramblers.
**KEY PERFORMANCES OUTSIDE IRELAND** (since January 1994):
5.96 Scarborough Folk Club, promoted by Traci Gordon, appearing with Connacht Ramblers.
11.96 Hammersmith Irish Centre, London, promoted by Traci Gordon, appearing with Connacht Ramblers.
11.96 Weaver's Pub, London, promoted by Traci Gordon, appearing with Connacht Ramblers.
5.97 Molly Malone's Pub Helsinki, promoted by John Higgins, appearing with Deirdre Cunningham Band.
**SELECTED BROADCASTS AND/OR RECORDED WORK:**
9.86 'Fisherman's Blues' for Chrysalis Records.
9.94 'The Connacht Ramblers' for Ramblin Records.
4.96 'Stop! Connacht Ramblers' for Ramblin Records.
**PRIZES/AWARDS/APPOINTMENTS:**
1986 Musician of the Year, awarded by Stag and Hot Press.
**REGULARLY PERFORMS WITH:**
Connacht Ramblers, Deirdre Cunningham Band, Sligo Strings.
**AVAILABILITY:**
General.
**ADDITIONAL INFORMATION:**
Has recorded with over 45 international recording artists, including U2, Sinéad O' Connor, Bob Dylan, The Waterboys, Karl Wallinger and World Party, Elis Costello, Hot House Flowers, Maria McKee, Sharon Shannon, In Tua Nua, Anthony Thistlethwaite, Light A Big Fire. Music has been used in several films ie. 'Some Mother's Son' and 'This is the Sea'.

## Thomas Wiegandt *Percussion*

**Contact:** Mr Thomas Wiegandt
Nature Art Centre, Ballybane
Ballydehob, Co Cork
**Tel:** +353 28 37323

**OTHER MUSIC TYPE:**
Latin percussion/Irish traditional/jazz.
*See Djembe-Drums page 279.*

## GROUPS

# Athem Brass

**Contact:** Athem Brass
3, Butterfield Grove
Rathfarnham, Dublin 14
**Tel:** +353 87 2330228 or +353 88 2715534 or
+353 88 2726421

**FORMED:** 1997
**MEMBERS OF GROUP:**
Colm Byrne (trumpet), Helen Mackle (trumpet), Shane O'Neil (french-horn), Conor O'Riordan (tuba), Gavin Roche (trombone).
**AVAILABILITY:**
General.
**ADDITIONAL INFORMATION:**
Music to suit all occasions, from Renaissance to new commissions, classical to light Jazz arrangements.
*See Conor O'Riordan page 55.*

# Blues Experience

**Contact:** Mr Jackie Flavelle
61, Millisle Road
Donaghadee
Co Down BT21 0HZ
Northern Ireland
**Tel/Fax:** +44 1247 882351 / +44 1247 815252

*"This band caused communal ecstasy"*

1995 Irish News

**FORMED:** 1992
**GROUP MEMBERS:**
Colm Fitzpatrick (drums), Jackie Flavelle (bass, vocals), Ronnie Greer (guitar, vocals), Paul McIntyre (keyboards).
**KEY IRISH PERFORMANCES** (since January 1994):
9.94 - 97 Monaghan Blues Festival, promoted by Somhairle MacConghail.
10.94/95/96 Cork Guinness International Jazz Festival.
6.94/96 Castlebar Blues Festival, promoted by Larry Roddy.
7.95/96 Temple Bar Blues Festival, promoted by Temple Bar Properties.
**KEY PERFORMANCES OUTSIDE IRELAND** (since January 1994):
7.95/96 Edinburgh Festival.
**SELECTED BROADCASTS AND/OR RECORDED WORK:**
1993 'Gerry Andersen Show' for BBC Northern Ireland.
1994 'The Kelly Show' for UTV.
**SELECTED REVIEWS** (since January 1994):
1996 Irish News.
1996 Irish Times.
1996 British Blues Magazine.
**AVAILABILITY:**
General.
*See Jackie Flavelle page 295.*

# Classical Fusion

**Contact:** Bernard and Denise Traynor
26-27, Drury Street
Dublin 2
**Tel/Mobile:** +353 1 4518527 / +353 87 2345736
*See Small Groups page 74.*

# Dermot Byrne Band

**Contact:** Mr Dermot Byrne
79, Fairyhill Estate
Bray
Co Wicklow
**Tel:** +353 1 2863234

*"As good as, if not better than hot international competition"* 7.95 Hot Press

**FORMED:** 1993
**GROUP MEMBERS:**
Dermot Byrne (guitars, harmonica, mandoline), Ed O'Callaghan (percussion), Dave Ross (bass guitar).
**KEY IRISH PERFORMANCES** (since January 1994):
6.96 Temple Bar Blues Festival, promoted by Úna Johnston.
23.12.96 Whelan's, Dublin, 'Moloney after Midnight Christmas Special' for 2FM radio.
**SELECTED BROADCASTS AND/OR RECORDED WORK:**
10.95 'Blues for your Pocket' (own cassette).
1.96 '40 Shades of Blue' for Gael Linn.
1.97 'Live at 3' for RTÉ.
**SELECTED REVIEWS** (since January 1994):
9.96 Irish Times.
1.97 In Dublin.
**AVAILABILITY:**
General.
**ADDITIONAL INFORMATION:**
Plays delta/folk blues and composes songs, (based on this tradition) uses acoustic and electric instruments.
*See Dermot Byrne page 294.*

# Dordán

**Contact:** Martina Goggin
Bothúna
An Spideál
Co Galway
**Tel/Fax:** +353 91 553255

**OTHER MUSIC TYPE:**
Combination of baroque and Irish traditional.
*See Traditional Groups page 260.*

# Fattenin' Frogs for Snakes

**Contact:** Mr Eamon Murray
**Tel/Fax:** +353 404 46096

*"... The accent on generating a big exciting rocking sound ..."* 11.96 Irish Times

**FORMED:** 1995
**GROUP MEMBERS:**
Noel Barrett (bass), John McLoughlin (guitar), Eamon Murray (vocal, saxophone, harmonica), Gavin Povey (piano), Rod Quinn (drums).
**AVAILABILITY:**
General.
*See Eamon Murray page 276.*

# Jasid Orchestra

**Contact:** Mr Ross Rooney
Victoria House
Eyre Square
Galway
**Mobile/Fax:** +353 87 519913 / +353 91 567394

**FORMED:** 1994
**GROUP MEMBERS:**
Seamus Boland (trumpet), Mark Conlon (percussion), Daniel Healey (trumpet), John McGrath (drums), Donna Nedrick (singer), John O'Dee (keyboards/piano), Aidan Reade (guitar), Ross Rooney (bass guitar), Evin Ryder (trombone).
**KEY IRISH PERFORMANCES** (since January 1994):
6.96 Point Depot, Dublin, appearing with M People.
7.96 Olympia Theatre, Dublin, promoted by MCD.
10.96 Queen's University, Belfast, promoted by Queen's University Student's Union.
**SELECTED BROADCASTS AND/OR RECORDED WORK:**
28.6.96 'Good Grief Moncrieff' for RTÉ.
2.97 'Gerry Ryan Tonight' for RTÉ.
**AVAILABILITY:**
Prepared to travel any distance.

# Kaluarachchi & Co

**Contact:** Mr Tony Kaluarachchi
162, Cliftonville Road
Belfast BT14 6LA
Northern Ireland
**Tel:** +44 1232 741942
*See Jazz Groups page 290.*

# Khanda

**Contact:** Mr Martin Nolan
34, St Marys Drive
Drimnagh
Dublin 12
**Tel:** +353 1 4563144

**GROUP MEMBERS:**
Ellen Cranitch (concert alto and Irish flutes), Conor Guilfoyle (tablas, mridagan and drumbeck), Ronan Guilfoyle (acoustic bass guitar), Tommy Halferty (guitar), Martin Nolan (uilleann pipes).
**SELECTED BROADCASTS AND/OR RECORDED WORK:**
1997 CD 'Khanda' for IMC.
**AVAILABILITY:**
General.
**ADDITIONAL INFORMATION:**
Brings together the rhythm and mystique of four continents with Indian, Middle Eastern, and Irish influences. Music reflects the diversity of backgrounds each member brings to the group. Blend jazz, classical and traditional music from around the world to create cohesive sound.
*See Martin Nolan page 237, Ellen Cranitch page 271, Conor Guilfoyle page 278, Ronan Guilfoyle page 273, Tommy Halferty page 273.*

# Mazurka

**Contact:** Marie Petiet
23, Park Cresent House
Blackhorse Avenue, Dublin 7
**Tel:** +353 1 8681210

**FORMED:** 1995
**GROUP MEMBERS:**
John O'Mahony-Adams (violin), Sebastien Petiet (violin, guitar), Simon Webb (cello), Waldemar Kozak (double bass).
**KEY IRISH PERFORMANCES** (since January 1994):
9.7.95 Polish Cultural Association, Dublin, promoted by Maciej Smolénski.
**AVAILABILITY:**
General.
**ADDITIONAL INFORMATION:**
A new and innovative four-piece String Ensemble. Repertoire is entirely composed of original arrangements, including traditional Irish, light classical, jazz, cabaret, gypsy, folk and dance music.
*See Sebastien Petiet page 299.*

# Parchman Farm

**Contact:** Mr Peter McGowan
**Tel:** +353 1 4965572

*"... Do not compromise to commercialism but play authentic Chicago blues, occasionally betraying the Texas influence of Leadbelly ... "*

7.95 Galway Magazine, The Edge

**KEY IRISH PERFORMANCES** (since January 1994):
8.95 Warehouse, Belfast, promoted by Paul Darby.
9.95 Monaghan Jazz and Blues Festival, promoted by Heineken.
9.95 Wexford Blues Festival.
10.95 Cork Jazz Festival, promoted by Guinness.
**KEY PERFORMANCES OUTSIDE IRELAND** (since January 1994):
8.95 British Rhythm and Blues Festival, Colne, Britain, promoted by Gary Hood.
**SELECTED BROADCASTS AND/OR RECORDED WORK:**
6.93 'Just the Blues' cassette.
'All that Jazz and Blues' with Bryan Day for RTÉ.
'Bluestime' with Marcus Connaughton for RTÉ.
'Bluestrain' with Charley Hussey for Annalivia FM.
**SELECTED REVIEWS** (since January 1994):
6.95 Blues and Boogie Club (Dino McGartland).
7.95 Galway Events Guide.
19.9.95 Irish Times (Justin Comiskey).
**AVAILABILITY:**
General.
**ADDITIONAL INFORMATION:**
Uses original material.

# Salsa Brava

**Contact:** Mr Martin O'Reilly
38, The Crescent
Binn Eadair View
Sutton
Dublin 13
**Tel:** +353 1 8393899

**FORMED:** 1995
**GROUP MEMBERS:**
Mark Adams (trumpet, Ronan Dooney (trumpet), Nigel Flegg (congas), David Hillary (bass), Danilo Karell (piano), Jim McGill (drums), Barry McGrien (trombone), Tony Oscar (timbales, vocals), Monica Vazquez (vocals).
**KEY IRISH PERFORMANCES** (since January 1994):
9.2.96 Gaiety Theatre, Dublin, promoted by Colm Walsh.
2.3.96 Andrews Lane Theatre, Dublin, promoted by Conor Larkin.
22.3.96 Gaiety Theatre, Dublin, promoted by Colm Walsh.
23.3.96 Andrew's Lane Theatre, Dublin, promoted by Conor Larkin.

**SELECTED REVIEWS** (since Janaury 1994):
21.2.96 Dublin Event Guide.
**AVAILABILITY:**
General.
**ADDITIONAL INFORMATION:**
Nine piece Latin-Salsa band made up of Irish and Cuban musicians. Formed by Monica Vazguez from Galicia, North Spain.
*See Nigel Flegg page 277.*

# The Ben Prevo Band

**Contact:** Mr Benjamin Prevo
9, Ross Street
Dublin 7
**Tel:** +353 1 8681551

*"Prevo's ability to draw effortlessly from so many sources constantly proved to be the strength behind his set"* 21.8.96 Irish Times

**FORMED:** 1991
**MUSICAL/ARTISTIC DIRECTOR:**
Benjamin Prevo.
**GROUP MEMBERS:**
(Pool) Leo Barnes (alto saxophone), Rob Coleman (bass guitar), John Earle (tenor and soprano saxophone), Ken Matthews (bass guitar), Carl O'Byrne (trumpet), Vincent O'Connor (keyboards), Kieran Phillips (drums), Benjamin Prevo (guitar, voice).
**SELECTED BROADCASTS AND/OR RECORDED WORK:**
5.97 'Live at 3' for RTÉ.
1.97 'Síbín' for TnaG.
'Moloney after Midnight' for RTÉ.
**AVAILABILITY:**
General.
**ADDTIONAL INFORMATION:**
Willing to share their brand of music with as many people as possible either as a full group or with other musicians. Can adapt their performance to suit event type, ie stage presentation to quiet background performances.

# The Dave McHugh Band

**Contact:** Mr Dave McHugh
58, Carnlough Road
Cabra West, Dublin 7
**Tel/Fax:** +353 1 8380275

*"A talent as red raw as anything you're likely to witness outside of an operating theatre..."*

8.96 Hot Press

**FORMED:** 1996
**GROUP MEMBERS:**
Robbie Brennan (drums), John Earle (saxophone), Anth Kacey (piano), Dave McHugh (electric, acoustic guitars, vocals), Alan Murray (bass guitar), Steve O'Brien (bass guitar), Alan Thunder (drums).
**PRIZES/AWARDS/APPOINTMENTS:**
7.96 Awarded Best Blues Newcomer at the Guinness Temple Bar Blues Festival.
**KEY IRISH PERFORMANCES** (since January 1994):
6.97 Elmwood University, Belfast, promoted by the Friends of Rory Gallagher Society, appearing with Gerry McAvoy (bass).
**SELECTED BROADCASTS AND/OR RECORDED WORK:**
1.97 'Cúrsaí Ealaíne' for RTÉ.
5.97 'Another Time, Another Space' for RTÉ.
6.97 'UTV Live at Six' for UTV.

**SELECTED REVIEWS** (since January 1994):
2.96 and 5.97 'Radio Review', Sunday Tribune (Tom Widger).
**AVAILABILITY:**
General.

# The Deirdre Cunningham Band

**Contact:** Deirdre Cunningham
Lake Recording Studio
Cootehall
Boyle
Co Roscommon
**Tel:** +353 79 67055

**FORMED:** 1995
**GROUP MEMBERS:**
Colin Blakey (congas, didgeridoo and flute), Deirdre Cunningham (vocals, accousic guitar), Liam Cunningham (accordion, synthesizer), Glen Garrett (bass), Steve Wickham (fiddle, mandolin, vocals).
**KEY IRISH PERFORMANCES** (since January 1994):
25.11.95 Eamon Dorans Pub, Dublin, promoted by Tracy Gordon.
7.1.96 Eamon Dorans Pub, Dublin, promoted by Tracy Gordon.
25.1.96 Drogheda Arts Centre, promoted by Tommy Hodgins.
8.2.96 The Barge Pub, Leitrim, promoted by Dave Knight.
**SELECTED BROADCASTS AND/OR RECORDED WORK:**
1995 'City Of The Tribes' album, recorded by Lake Records.
1995 'Lost River', recorded by Lake Records.
1995 'It Won't Be Back Again' recorded by Lake Records.
13.2.95 Gerry Ryan television show.
**SELECTED REVIEWS** (since January 1994):
1.96 In Dublin.
1.96 Hot Press.
1.2.96 Roscommon Herald.
**ADDITIONAL INFORMATION:**
Interested in traditional Irish songs, slow airs and ballads.
*See Steve Wickham page 300.*

# The Fallen Angels

**Contact:** The Fallen Angels
c/o MBE
6, Seafield Crescent
Blackrock
Co Dublin
**Tel/Fax:** +353 1 2693821 / +353 1 2693777
**Email:** mbe@indigo.ie
*See page 265.*

# The Mandies

**Contact:** Ms Niamh Ní Bheoláin
The Music Lab
Tymon Bawn Community Centre
Aylesbury
Tallaght
Dublin 24
**Tel/Fax:** +353 1 4520611 or +353 1 4621029 / +353 1 4520611
*See page 266.*

# The Mary Stokes Band

**Contact:** Ms Mary Stokes
33, Dunville Ave
Ranelagh
Dublin 6
**Tel:** +353 1 2088551

**FORMED:** 1987
**GROUP MEMBERS:**
Gary (Wolfie) Eglinton (bass guitar, mandolin), Ciaran (Foxy) Murphy (electric and slide guitar), Eoin O'Doherty (drums), Brian Palm (harmonica), Mary Stokes (vocals).
**KEY IRISH PERFORMANCES** (since January 1994):
6.6.94 Ulster Hall, Belfast, appearing with Fats Domino.
6.94 The Stadium, Dublin, appearing with Fats Domino.
7.95 Central Bank Plaza, promoted by the Temple Bar Blues Festival.
10.95 Cork Guinness International Jazz Festival.
**SELECTED BROADCASTS AND/OR RECORDED WORK:**
6.95 'Live in Dublin '95' (Independent recording).
8.96 'Through With You' (Irish Blues Club CD) for Gael-Linn.
4.97 'Live at 3' ('Comfort') for RTÉ.
**PRIZES/AWARDS/APPOINTMENTS:**
1990 Best Unsigned Act from Smithwicks and Hot Press.
**AVAILABILITY:**
General.
**ADDITIONAL INFORMATION:**
Have performed extensively throughout Ireland, the USA and Europe, playing support to BB King, John Lee Hooker, Bo Diddley, Fats Domino. Performs regularly on radio and television.

# The Tolka Delta Boys

**Contact:** Mr Bill Whelan
39, Fairview Green
Dublin 3
**Tel/Fax:** +353 1 8331920

**FORMED:** 1996
**GROUP MEMBERS:**
Damien Gallagher (bottleneck slide guitar), Randall Lee Rainwater (LAP steel and dobro guitars), Tim Rodgers (mandolin, fiddle), Bill Whelan (5 string banjo, electric bass guitar, percussion).
**KEY IRISH PERFORMANCES** (since January 1994):
From 2.5.97 to 4.5.97, Cork Blues 'n' Roots Festival.
30.5.97 Castlebar Blues Festival.
19.7.97 Guinness Blues Festival.
5.9.97 Cork Folk Festival.
**SELECTED BROADCASTS AND/OR RECORDED WORK:**
1.97 'The Tolka Delta Boys' (cass 001) for 'Home for the Bewildered String Band Company'.
**AVAILABILITY:**
General.
**ADDITIONAL INFORMATION:**
Life long interest in American traditional music and have attended stringband workshops in Elkins College, West Virginia. Have also undertaken research into the Irish traditional music connections in Virginia's surrounding counties.

# Appendix one

# APPENDIX ONE

## Individuals consulted about the initial design stages of the Directory of Musicians in Ireland

Jody Ackland, Project Arts Centre
David Agnew, Londonderry Féis
Robert Agnew, Belfast Festival at Queen's
Brian C Agus, South Eastern Education and Library Board Music Service
Chris Ahern, Cork City VEC
Fergus Ahern, Boyle Arts Fesival
Maureen Ahern, Cahir Castle Arts Society
Rod Alston, Sligo Early Music Festival
Andersonstown Traditional Music School
Maureen Armstrong, Clotworthy House Arts Centre
Chris Bailey, Belfast City Council
Dr Ita Beausang, DIT Conservatory of Music and Drama
Daphne Bell, Ulster College of Music
S Bell, Limavady Borough Council
Dr Peter Bennett, Dublin Jazz Society
Sheila Benny, Suzuki Education Institute of Ireland
Eithne Benson, South Eastern Education and Library Board Music Service
Robert Bible, Robert Bible School
James Bloe, Feile Pobal Loch an Luir
Kate Bond, Armagh City and District Arts Committee
Eric Boyd, North Eastern Education and Library Board Music Service
H. M. Bracefield, University of Ulster
Jean Brennan, Omagh District Council
Shane Brennan, Schola Cantorum
Alma Brown, Newry Musical Feis
John Buckley
Séamus Burke, Clifden Blues Festival
John Butler, Armagh City Folk Club
Nora Butler, Bray Music Centre
Philomena Byrne, Irish Museum of Modern Art
Tom Byrne, The Songwriter's Workshop
Stephen Cairns, British Trombone Society
Mary Callan, Leeson Park School of Music
Kate Campbell, Northern Ireland Voluntary Trust
Philip Campbell, Newry and Mourne District Council
Yvette Campos, Ballina Arts Events
Jarlath Canney, Mall Theatre and Cinema
Mahon Carmody, Early Music Organisation of Ireland
Una Carmody, Temple Bar Blues Festival
Nicholas Carolan, Irish Traditional Music Archive/Taisce Cheol Dúchais Éireann
Laura Carr McKee, National Operatic and Dramatic Association (NODA)
Brian Carson, Moving on Music Services
Josephine Carter, Coleraine Music Festival
Ian Cartwright, Ards Arts Centre
Dr Anthony Carver, Queen's University School of Music
Rory Casey, Fleadh Nua
Phil Cassidy, Cassidy's Music and Sport
Paul Clamp, North Down Borough Council
Annette Clancy, Garter Lane Arts Centre
Eileen Clandillon, Arklow Music Festival
James Clarke, Sonorities Festival of Contemporary Music
William Clements, North of Ireland Bands Association
Patrick Clerkin, Féis na nGleann
John Cloke Music School
Cathy Cole, Newtownabbey Borough Council
Joan Coleman, Danfay Limited
Michael Colgan, The Schubert Institute
John Coll, Mayo County Council
Mary Coll, Belltable Arts Centre
Denis Collins, Wexford Arts Centre
David Collopy, Dublin Grand Opera Society
Lorraine Comer, Wexford County Counil
Enid Conaghan, British Kodaly Academy
Miriam Connor, Opera Theatre Company
Tony Convey, County Antrim Fleadh Ceoil
Séan Corcoran, Féile na Boinne/Dúchas
Sharon Corcoran, Tinahely Courthouse Centre
Antonio Cosenza, Istituto Italiano di Cultura
Margaret Cosgrave, Kilkenny County Council
Prof David Harold Cox, University College, Cork
Dr Gareth Cox, Mary Immaculate College of Education
Matt Cranitch
Séamus Crimmins, RTÉ
Colm Croffy, Mary from Dungloe Festival
Joanna Crooks, Jeunesses Musicales Ireland
Ed Cunningham, Offaly Community Arts Group
Michael D' Arcy
Deirdre Davitt, Bord na Gaelige
Padráig de Buis, Éigse na Brideoige
Sheila Deegan, Limerick Corporation
Noel Delaney, Department of Arts, Culture and the Gaeltacht
Dr Idé Delargy, Performing Arts Medicine Trust
Donal Doherty, Two Cathedrals Festival
Keith Donald
Liz Donnan, Crescent Arts Centre
Fidelis Doran, The Classical Music Society
Naomi Doran, Dungannon Music and Drama Festival
Angela Dorgan, Federation of Music Collectives
Séan Dower, Waterford International Festival of Early Music
Dick Doyle, Phonographic Performance Ireland Ltd
Martin Drury, The Ark
Kieran Dunlop, Galway Music Cooperative
Veronica Dunne
Paddy Dunning, Temple Bar Music Centre
Maura Eaton, Association of Irish Composers
Angela Eborall, St Barrahane's Festival of Church Music
Eigse Carlow Arts Festival
Colin Ellis, Carrickfergus Borough Council
Niamh Fawl, Very Special Arts Ireland
Dr Michéal Fanning, Féile na Bealtaine
Donal Farrell, Dún Laoghaire Festival
Marie Farrell, Linenhall Arts Centre
Anne Farrelly, Music Hibernia
Bairbre Ferguson, Sligo Arts Festival
Victor Finn, Mechanical Copyright Protection Society
Ann Finnegan, O' Carolan Harp and Cultural Weekend
Harold Fish, British Council, Dublin
John Fitzpatrick, Cork International Choral Festival
Maggie Fitzsimons, Samhlaíocht Chiarrai - Kerry Arts Festival
RE. Flaherty, Ulster Hall
John Flanagan, Scoraiocht Lann Léire
Madeleine Flanagan, Music for Galway
P Flanagan, Irish Branch Society of Recorder Players
Colin Fleming, Flutewise
Margaret Fleming, Waterford County Council
Brendan Flynn, Clifden Community Arts Group
John Foley, Féile na nDéise
John Forde, Top Twenty Music School
Frank Fox, Michael Shanley Traditional Weekend
Mary Fox, Belfast City and District Set Dancing Society
H Francis, Larne Borough Council

Hugh Frazer, Combat Poverty Agency
Aideen Friel, Co - Operation North
Ann Fuller, Guardian Dublin International Piano Competition
Kieran Gallagher, Drogheda Samba Festival
Eoin Garrett, Dublin International Organ and Choral Festival
Liam Garrett, Music Matters
Raymond Gaughan, Ballyshannon Folk and Traditional Music Festival
Adrian Gebruers, 69th Season of St Colman's Cathedral Carillon
Maureen Gibbons, Letterkenny International Festival
Jack Gilligan, Dublin County Council
Paddy Glackin
Janice Gordon, Best Cellars Music Collective
Philip Gray, Galway Arts Centre
Bernadette Greevy
Kieran Griffin, Arts Festival 1996
Alan Grundy, Dublin School of Guitar
Ronan Guilfoyle, Improvised Music Company
Stuart Haigh, Castlederg School of Music
Kevin Hall, Dundalk International Maytime Festival
Harry Hamilton, Northern Ireland Musicians' Association
William Hammond, Cork Folk Festival
James Harrold, Galway County Council
Brian Harten, Dundalk UDC Arts Office
Lorna Hastings, Live Music Now
Bernadette Hayden, Kildare School of Excellence for Young Musicians
Frank Hayes, Bray Organ Festival
Máire Hearty, Tig an Tobair
Barbara Heas, Cumann Naisiúnta na gCór
Michael Heffernan, Melody School of Music
Michael Henson, Ulster Orchestra
Ollie Hennessy, Hennessy Music
Eileen Herlihy, Wexford School of Music
Robin Hewitt, City of Belfast School of Music
Albert Higgins, Midlands Arts Resource Centre
Margaret Higgins, Ballymoney Borough Arts Committee
Charles Holmes, Carrickfergus Music Festival Association
Jill Holmes, Down Arts Centre
Hannah Horowitz, Visting Arts Office of Great Britian and Northern Ireland
Joan Houston, Bangor Choral Festival
Liam Howard, Village Arts Centre
Francis Humphrys, West Cork Music
Fionnuala Hunt
Séamus Hunt, St David's Pipe Band School
Christine Hunter, Association of Medical Advisors to the British Orchestras - Northern Ireland
Jerome Hynes, Wexford Festival Opera
Kate Ingram, Open Arts
David Irwin, Savins School of Music
H Jamison, Whiteabbey Music Club
Rodger Jarvis, Department of Education - Northern Ireland
Peter Jeffers Music School
G Johnston
Una Johnton
Rev Patrick Jones, Advisory Committee on Church Music
Catherine Jordan, Crafts Council of Ireland
D K Kapur, Causeway Coast Arts Committee
Cathleen Kavanagh, St Mary's College, Belfast
Ger Keane's Limerick Yamaha School
Fergal Kearney, Magherafelt Autumn Festival
Jim Kearns, Athlone River Festival
Maria Keleman, Young European String School of Music
Deirdre Kelleher, Feis Ceoil Association
Sheila Kelleher, Cork International Choral Festival
Anne Kelly, Arts Administration Studies, UCD
Gerard Kelly, Cork Pops Orchestra
Gina Kelly, South Dublin County Council
Joe Kelly, Sligo International Choral Festival
John Kelly, Irish Chamber Orchestra
Henry Kennedy Music School
Celine Kennelly, Triskel Arts Centre
James Kenny, Paddy Music Expo Limerick
Aileen Keogh, Westport Arts Festival
Jim Kerr, Ulster Canal Stores
Kerry County Council
Caroline Kieran, Association for Business Sponsorship of the Arts (ABSA)
R Kirk, Strabane Arts Advisory Committee
Pat Lalor, National Musical Instrument Museum
Margaret Langhammer, Belfast Music Society
Johnny Lapin, Irish Music Copyright Reform Group
Mark Larmour, Summer Recital Series at Belfast Cathedral
Joe Leake, City Music College
Emer Leavy, Roscommon County Council
Tommy Leddy, Boyne School of Music
Mary Lenihan, Kildare County Council
James Liddane, International Songwriter Association
Bernie Lloyd, Music for Wexford
Hilda Logan, Castleward Opera
Denise Long, Dublin School of Music
Pat Long, Music for Monaghan
Aidan Lynch, Killarney School of Music
Peter Lyner, British Council in Northern Ireland
Bernard Lyons, Project Jazz
Caoimhín Mac Aoidh, Donegal Fiddlers' Weekend
Mary McAuliffe, Waterford Corporation
Jimmy McBride, Inishowen Traditional Singers' Circle
Áine McCann, Heineken Green Energy Weekend
Cormac McCann, Belfast Civic Festival
Kate McCarthy, Sligo Arts Festival
Maureen McCarthy, Portaferry Gala Week
Michael McCarthy, Arklow Music Festival
Timothy McCarthy, Feis Maitiú
Valerie McCarthy, EPTA Ireland
Aubrey McClintock, Charles Wood Summer School
Somhairke MacConghail, Monaghan County Council
Maeve McCormack, Hawk's Well Theatre
Michelle McCormack, Drake Music Project
Aibhlín McCrann, Cáirde na Cruite
Mary McDermott, Feile Séamus Ennis
Paula McDermott, Irish Music Rights Organisation (IMRO)
Jack McGouran, Guinness Jazz Festival
Helen McGovern, Meath Arts Group
Joe McGowan, Céilidh on the Green
Feargal McGrath, Galway Arts Fetsival
Joan McKernan, Limerick County Council
Dermot McLaughlin, The Arts Council
Grainne McLoughlin, Greystones Summer Festival
Marie McMahon, Woodford Mummers Festival
Rosaleen McMullan, Pinebank House Arts Centre
Therese McNicholl, Dungannon District Council
Liam McNulty, Na Píobairí Uilleann
Grainne McShane, Carlingford Liugh Heritage Trust
Deirdre McSherry, Aonach Paddy O' Brien Traditional Music Festival
Catherine Madden, Dún Laoghaire Music Centre
Anthony Madigan, Royal Irish Academy of Music
Joan Maguire, Oifig an Cheoil
Joe Mahon, Arts Administration Studies, University College, Galway

Joe Mallon, Garage Theatre, Monaghan
Tommy Mangan, Tommy Mangan Keyboards
John Mardiosian, Waltons New School of Music
Fr Eamonn Martin, Féis Dhoire Cholm Cille
Christopher Marwood
Ronald Masin, ESTA Ireland
Debbie Metrustry, Assocation of Music Typesetters in Ireland
Baz Millar, Limerick International Band Festival
Hilda Milner, Newpark Music Centre
Model Arts Centre, Sligo
Colette Moloney, Charlesville School of Music
Mary Mooney, Kilkenny Arts Week
Michael Moore, Moore Music School
Evan Morrissey, Limerick Jazz Society
Jerome Morrissey, Senior College, Ballyfermot
Liam Morrissey, Alternative Entertainments
Mary Mullen, Association of Irish Musical Societies (AIMS)
Mary Mulligan, Michael Van Dessel Memorial Dundalk Choral Festival
Tom Munnelly, Clare Festival of Traditional Singing
Malcolm Murchison, Flowerfield Arts Centre
Marion Murnane, The Thomas Moore Society
Anne Murphy, Mater Dei Institute
Joe Murphy, St John's Arts and Heritage Centre, Listowel
Michael Murphy, University of Limerick Concert Hall
Sheila Murphy, Leinster School of Music
Mary Nesbitt, Joint Committee for Church Music in Ireland
Muireann Ní Chonaill, Laois County Council
Pádraigín Ní Uallacháin, O Bhéal go Béal
Marion Nolan, Newcastle West School of Music
Padraic Noone, O'Carolan Harp and Traditional Music Festival
Colin North, Performing Rights Society
Josephine Nugent, Contemporary Music Making for Amateurs (COMA)
Rosemary O'Brien, Froebel College of Education
Rory O'Byrne, Fingal County Council
Aidan O'Carroll, Kerry School of Music
Padraig Ó Cearbhaill, Sean Nós Cois Life
Brian O'Connor, Tralee Regional Technical College
John O'Conor, Royal Irish Academy of Music
Michéal Ó Cuaig, Féile Chomhartha Joe Einiú
Finola O'Doherty, Derry City Council
Rory O'Donnell, Mick Carr Memorial Traditional Weekend
Dan O'Donoghue, Professional Music Education Company
Sinéad Ó Duinnín, Royal Dublin Society
Traolach Ó Fionnáin, Donegal County Council
Liam O'Flynn
Gerry O'Hanlon, Slieve Gullion Festival of Traditional Singing
Paul O'Hanrahan, Droichead Arts Centre
Oilibhéar Ó hÉidhín, Department of Education
Agnes O'Kane, Irish Associationof Youth Orchestras
Eamonn O'Keefe, Metropolitan School of Music
Barry O'Kelly, Bank of Ireland Arts Centre
Eve O'Kelly, Contemporary Music Centre
Liam Ó Maoladha, An t - Oireachtas
Labhras Ó Murchú, Comhaltas Ceoiltoirí Eireann
Gladys O'Neill, Percy French Society
Vincent O'Neill, Dublin Philharmonic Society
Catriona O'Reilly, Cavan County Council
Paul O'Reilly, Limerick City Gallery of Art
Séan O'Reilly, Carrickmacross Choral Festival
Evelyn O'Riordan, Waterford Music Club
Michéal Ó Súilleabhain, Irish World Music Centre
Javier Odriozola, Instituto Cervantes
Ashley Pringle, International Concert Management
Peter Pringle, Irish Federation of Musicians
Marie Queenan, Coleman Country Traditional Festival
Fergus Quinlivan, Limerick Civic Week Festival
Donal Quinn, Coalisland Folk Club
Angela Reid, Ulster Museum
M Reith, Banbridge District Council
Andrew Robinson, Maoin Cheoil an Chláir
James Rose, Castlereagh Borough Council
John Ruddock, Limerick Music Association
Pauline Russell, Northern Lights Festival
Victor Ryan, Assocation of Irish Festivals and Events (AOIFE)
Fionnuala Salmon, Essaness Music
Pamela Scrayfield, Ardhowen Theatre
Michael Scott, Humewood Opera Festival
Cliodhna Shaffrey, Dún Laoghaire - Rathdown County Council
Randall Shannon, Opera Northern Ireland
John Sherlock, Classical Guitar Society of Northern Ireland
Alan Smale
Allen Smith, Improvised Music Company
Ann Smith, Galway Early Music Festival
Pamela Smith, Arts Council of Northern Ireland
Simeon Smith, Creative Activity for Everyone (CAFE)
Thérèse Smith, Cumann Cheol Tire Éireann
Geoffrey Spratt, Cork Orchestral Society
Tom Staunton, Staunton's Music and Sport
Bob Stewart, Cork Musicians' Project
Louis Stewart
Reinhard Schmidt Supprian, Goethe Institut
Magella Swan, Carlow College of Music
Connie Tantrum, Music for New Ross
David Taylor, Derravaragh Music Association
Simon Taylor, RTÉ
The Secretary, Cookstown District Arts Committee
Tim Thurston, Early Music Festival
Dr Marian Tierney, Duiske Concerts
Hugh Tinney
Crawford Tipping, AIB Festival of Music in Great Irish Houses
Joe Thoma, CIBEAL / Kenmare Folk Club
Rev P Rhys Thomas, Youghal Festival of the Arts
Sighle Tobin, Kilkenny Arts Week
Simon Trezise, Trinity College, Dublin
Ann Tully, Cootehill Arts Festival
Jacqueline Turley, Newry and Mourne Arts Centre
Alice Turner, Ballyclare Music Festival Association
University Arts Administrator, Riverside Theatre
Jan Van Putten, West Waterford Music
Fintan Vallely
Tom Wallace, Monastic City Trust
Paddy Ward
Gerard Watson, Cothú
Martin Whelan, Siamsa Tíre
Harry White, University College, Dublin
Siobhán White, Lisburn Arts Advisory Council
Ken Willie, Stranmillis College
M Wilkinson
Joseph Woods, Ulster Arts Club
Judith Woodworth, National Concert Hall

# Index

# INDEX